Examination of
Water for Pollution Control

A REFERENCE HANDBOOK

IN THREE VOLUMES

Other Pergamon Titles of Interest

ALBAIGES
Analytical Techniques in Environmental Chemistry

CURI
Treatment and Disposal of Liquid and Solid Industrial Wastes

HUTZINGER *et al*
Aquatic Pollutants—Transformation and Biological Effects

KUCHARSKI *et al*
Industrial Waste Water Treatment and Disposal

MOO-YOUNG
Waste Treatment and Utilization—Theory and Practice of Waste Management

OUANO *et al*
Water Pollution Control in Developing Countries

PAWLOWSKI
Physicochemical Methods for Water and Wastewater Treatment

TEBUTT
Principles of Water Quality Control, 2nd Edition

WORLD HEALTH ORGANIZATION
Waste Discharge into the Marine Environment

ZOETEMAN
Sensory Assessment of Water Quality

Related Pergamon Journals

Conservation and Recycling

Talanta

Water Pollution Research in Canada

Water Research

Water Science and Technology

Water Supply and Management

Full details on any of the above titles and a free specimen copy of any journal are available on request from your nearest Pergamon office.

Examination of
Water for Pollution Control

A REFERENCE HANDBOOK

IN THREE VOLUMES

VOLUME 3
Biological, Bacteriological and
Virological Examination

Edited by

MICHAEL J. SUESS
World Health Organization
Regional Office for Europe, Copenhagen, Denmark

Published on behalf of the

WORLD HEALTH ORGANIZATION
REGIONAL OFFICE FOR EUROPE

PERGAMON PRESS
OXFORD · NEW YORK · TORONTO · SYDNEY · PARIS · FRANKFURT

UK	Pergamon Press Ltd., Headington Hill Hall, Oxford OX3 0BW, England
USA	Pergamon Press Inc., Maxwell House, Fairview Park, Elmsford, New York 10523, USA
CANADA	Pergamon Press Canada Ltd., Suite 104, 150 Consumers Road, Willowdale, Ontario M2J 1P9, Canada
AUSTRALIA	Pergamon Press (Aust.) Pty. Ltd., PO Box 544, Potts Point, NSW 2011, Australia
FRANCE	Pergamon Press SARL, 24 rue des Ecoles, 75240 Paris, Cedex 05, France
FEDERAL REPUBLIC OF GERMANY	Pergamon Press GmbH, 6242 Kronberg-Taunus, Hammerweg 6, Federal Republic of Germany

First edition 1982

British Library Cataloguing in Publication Data
Examination of water for pollution control
1. Water – Pollution
1. Suess, Michael J
628.1'68   TD420   80-41459
ISBN 0-08-025255-9

The views expressed in this book are those of the authors and do not necessarily represent the decisions or the stated policy of the World Health Organization

Cover: Biological sampling (photo WHO/M. Jacot). Colonies of faecal streptococci (courtesy of Karin Ormerod, Norwegian Institute of Water Research, Oslo); human adenovirus (courtesy of Robert W. Horne, John Innes Institute, Norwich, U.K.)

Printed in Great Britain by A. Wheaton & Co. Ltd., Exeter

CONTENTS

PREFACE

The older industrialized countries experienced gross pollution of water, air and soil for many years before either the political will or the technical means existed for effective control. Nevertheless, in some of these countries, substantial steps were being taken to carry out improvements as early as the beginning of the century and in the field of water pollution, for example, many biological treatment plants still in operation were constructed over half a century ago.

Countries which have experienced rapid industrialization more recently have had more technical experience to draw on, but have often had to face pressures to maintain or improve the quality of the environment in a much shorter time.

During the last few years, there has been an increasing realization that water resources are limited and must be conserved, leading to the necessity for stringent quality control.

Many of the communicable diseases having the greatest impact on mankind are waterborne, and a permanent reduction in morbidity and mortality can most effectively be achieved by providing safe drinking-water and satisfactory sanitation. It is the ambitious target of the International Drinking-Water Supply and Sanitation Decade that such facilities will be available for all communities in the world by 1990. This programme fits well into the World Health Organization's increased emphasis on the preventative approach to health care. The investment will be largely wasted unless it embodies the development of systematic water quality surveillance.

In addition to the long-standing problem of microbiological pollution, the introduction to the environment of an increasing range of chemicals has led to the need for ever more complex technologies for surveillance and control.

Effective water quality management involves systematic programmes of sampling and analysis of rivers, lakes and groundwater and all stages of waste treatment. Proven and harmonized procedures must be adopted if results are to be reliable, reproducible and comparable.

The present Handbook has been developed by the WHO Regional Office for Europe with these objectives in mind. It has involved the active cooperation of many institutions and over 250 scientists in 31 countries, over a period of 10 years. It is primarily intended for routine use in relation to process control and surveillance programmes, but it is hoped that it will also be useful both for research and in training laboratories.

Many countries share common water resources and an increasing number of countries are now adopting similar systems of pollution monitoring and control, through various forms of international agreements. It has been the intention of all concerned in the development of the Handbook that its adoption should help such cooperation by facilitating the harmonization of sampling and analytical procedures throughout the world.

On behalf of WHO, I should like to thank all concerned in its production.

J. Ian Waddington
Director, Promotion of Environmental Health,
WHO Regional Office for Europe

CONTENTS OF OTHER VOLUMES

ix

Contents of Other Volumes

NOTE ON TERMINOLOGY

WHO policy in respect of terminology is to follow the official recommendations of authoritative international bodies such as the International Union of Pure and Applied Chemistry (IUPAC) and the International Organization for Standardization (ISO). Every effort has been made in this publication to comply with such recommendations.

Nearly all international scientific bodies have now recommended the use of the SI units (*Système international d'Unités*) developed by the Conférence générale des Poids et Mesures (CGPM),[a] and the use of these units was endorsed by the Thirtieth World Health Assembly in 1977. In almost all cases, only SI units are used in this publication. However, the use of the curie (Ci) instead of the becquerel (Bq) has been retained in radiological texts (1 mCi = 37 MBq).

As the base unit "amount of substance", the CGPM has adopted the mole. As a result, the variable units "equivalent" and "normality" are inconsistent with the international system. Confronted with this problem, the 29th IUPAC General Assembly in 1977 officially abandoned the use of " equivalent " and " normality " and approved a new terminology to replace them. Subsequently a joint IUPAC–ISO *ad hoc* group made detailed recommendations for implementing this new terminology. A new physical quantity named " equivalent entity " has been defined, and since it is a physical quantity and not a unit, the fact that it may vary according to the particular reaction in which an acid, a base, or an oxidizing or reducing agent participates is of no consequence.

The unit in which equivalent entity is expressed is the mole, or an appropriate multiple or submultiple. Concentrations of acids, bases, and oxidizing or reducing agents are therefore expressed in $mol \cdot m^{-3}$ or an appropriate multiple or submultiple, such as $mol \cdot l^{-1}$ or $mmol \cdot l^{-1}$. These units replace " normality " as well as such units as $mEq \cdot l^{-1}$.

---

[a] An authoritative account of the SI system entitled "The SI for the Health Professions" has been prepared by the World Health Organization and is available, through booksellers, from WHO sales agents, or direct from Distribution and Sales Service, World Health Organization, 1211 Geneva 27, Switzerland.

EXAMPLES

1. Acid–base reaction

In the reaction

$$H_2SO_4 + 2NaOH = Na_2SO_4 + 2H_2O$$

$\frac{1}{2}$ mole of H_2SO_4 is equivalent to 1 mole of NaOH, i.e., the equivalent entities are ($\frac{1}{2}$ H_2SO_4) and (NaOH). The substance concentration of sulfuric acid is written as $c(\frac{1}{2}$ $H_2SO_4)$, e.g. $c(\frac{1}{2}$ $H_2SO_4) = 0.1$ mol$\cdot$l^{-1}, instead of H_2SO_4, 0.1N solution.

2. Redox reaction

In the reaction

$$5FeSO_4 + KMnO_4 + 4H_2SO_4 = \tfrac{1}{2}K_2SO_4 + MnSO_4 + 5/2Fe_2(SO_4)_3 + 4H_2O$$

each reacting entity of ($5FeSO_4$) is equivalent to one of $KMnO_4$ at the equivalence point. Five electrons are transferred in the reaction:

$$MnO_4^- + 8H^+ + 5e^- = Mn^{2+} + 4H_2O$$

$$5Fe^{2+} = 5Fe^{3+} + 5e^-$$

and the equivalent entities of iron(II) sulfate and potassium permanganate are ($FeSO_4$) and ($1/5$ $KMnO_4$). The substance concentration of potassium permanganate is therefore written as $c(1/5$ $KMnO_4)$, e.g. $c(1/5$ $KMnO_4) = 0.1$ mol$\cdot$l^{-1}, instead of $KMnO_4$, 0.1N solution.

It should also be noted that all substance concentrations are expressed in the form mol$\cdot$l^{-1}, g$\cdot$l^{-1}, mg$\cdot$kg^{-1}, etc., the denominator being always the litre or the kilogram. Such expressions as p.p.m., %(w/v), and g% are no longer in conformity with the recommendations of international scientific organizations.

It will be noted that when the new definition of equivalent entity as a quantity (rather than unit) is used, there is no change in the numerical values traditionally associated with the concept of " normality ".

INTRODUCTION

Pollution of water affects the lives of a great many people throughout the world, especially those living in industrialized areas. Moreover, the organic and inorganic pollution load in natural waters continues to increase. Among the causes are the large volumes of wastewater—often subject to little or no control—originating from highly populated cities, the discharge of untreated effluents by industrial complexes, and the use of a wide variety of chemical fertilizers and pesticides in agriculture. Its results include harm to humans and to animal and plant life, unpleasant odours, reduced water clarity, damage to property, and a reduction in the recreational quality of coastal and inland water and beaches.

Many people are willing to accept some environmental deterioration in exchange for a higher standard of living and a greater abundance of consumer goods but, as living standards rise, man-made water pollution is seen first as a major irritation and then as a threat to this very goal of an improved quality of life. Excessive pollution can jeopardize health, while certain types of pollution may even render some areas unfit for normal habitation and, therefore, constitute a serious obstacle to socioeconomic development. Hence many national, regional and city administrators are now faced with public demands for stricter control over water pollution.

All programmes to reduce pollution or to improve the quality of water used for human consumption depend on reliable analytical measurements. A large variety of analytical methods has been developed to determine important chemical and microbial determinands, and some biological survey methods have evolved to estimate the quality of surface water. Several of the analytical methods used in the assessment of pollution are not concerned with the concentration of specific substances but measure a general property of the water. These methods, of which the measurement of biochemical oxygen demand is an example, are empirical, but are carried out under carefully standardized conditions. The results obtained will depend on which conditions are employed for a given test. However, even when determinations are made of specific constituents, results may vary according to the particular analytical method used. It is therefore important to agree on a limited set of well-tested methods when undertaking any study that involves more than one analytical laboratory.

The number of published methods and variants of methods for any one determinand is often so large that different methods are apt to be used in different countries. In many countries there exists some form of agreement on the analytical methods to be employed in order that the results obtained in different laboratories may be comparable. Internationally, however, there are at present only limited agreements among countries, and strong opinion has been expressed that uniformity of analytical methods throughout the European Region is necessary.

Even when the same method is being used, the results from different laboratories do not always agree, and there is sometimes disagreement even between results obtained by workers in the same laboratory. In some places it is the practice to send out samples of known composition for analysis to laboratories to ascertain their levels of accuracy. This practice is valuable and could usefully be extended, both nationally and internationally.

Also, sampling is a vital link in the chain of information. Unless the sampling procedure is clearly defined, the analytical results can be misleading and a proper comparison of analytical data may not be possible. There are, sometimes among laboratories but more often among countries, differences in the terms in which results are expressed, and there is a need to promote uniformity in this matter also.

Although the WHO Regional Office for Europe had been implementing individual projects on water pollution for over 20 years, it was not until 1969 that, conscious of the seriousness of the problem, the WHO Regional Committee for Europe decided to adopt a comprehensive long-term programme on environmental health, including water quality and pollution control. The main aim of the programme was to develop management guides and decision aids for use by government administrations, executive agencies and scientific institutions concerned with the quality of the environment and the protection of public health.

Following the introduction of the long-term programme, a Working Group on Trends and Developments in Water Pollution Control in Europe was convened in Copenhagen in September 1969 to review the European situation. The recommendations of this Group formed the basis for programme activities in the water pollution sector. On the basis of its evaluation, the Group recommended that "a preliminary study should first be made comparing the analytical methods and the sampling procedures employed in water pollution control throughout the European Region. The project should culminate in the production of a European Manual of Methods of Analysis for Use in the Control of Water Pollution. " Work began in 1970, when Professor V. Maděra was invited to undertake a limited comparative study of the more important analytical methods for the examination of water.

At the beginning of 1972, when the editor took over the responsibility for this project, a re-evaluation was made of its scope and purpose. It was soon recognized that a text of limited scope could not be justified, and the conclusion was reached that the involvement of the Regional Office in such a task could be justified only if three principles were accepted. First, the new text should cover the whole range of water analysis, starting with the planning of a sampling programme, sampling itself, evaluation of results, etc., and ending with the compilation of a laboratory manual. The aim was to provide a method for every analysis that might be required, including not only physical and chemical but also radiological, biological and microbiological examination. Second, it was felt that the average water laboratory in Europe, which is the first concern of the Regional Office, should be encouraged as far as possible to use a *single* method of analysis that had proved itself over the years to be reliable and workable, and which could be agreed on by experts from many countries in Europe and elsewhere. Third, once such an elaborate text had been completed, it could well serve as a standard work for the development of water sampling and analysis in any country in the world. Consequently, it was decided to enlarge the scope, and Professor Mancy and Dr. Suess prepared a detailed outline for consideration by a gathering of experts on water analysis and pollution control, which was convened specially for this purpose during the Sixth International Conference on Water Pollution Research, held in Jerusalem in June 1972. This group recognized the urgent need for such a comprehensive text and warmly endorsed the proposals for its new and enlarged structure.

The present 3-volume Handbook is the culmination of a decade of concerted effort by some 250 scientists from 31 countries in 5 continents (see Annex 1 of each volume). Eight scientific working groups, each addressing the subject matter of one or more chapters, met at various times to review the material and to recommend methods, terminology and additional requirements. Among the participants in these groups were representatives of four intergovernmental and five nongovernmental organizations. The working group meetings and their participants are listed in Annex 2 of each respective volume. Drafts underwent several reviews before and after the working group meetings, to ensure a reasonable uniformity of presentation and style.

The book is intended to provide information and recommendations which will assist in setting up water pollution control programmes and in establishing a unified system for analysing fresh and waste waters and recording the results. It is also designed to serve as a technical and laboratory guide for scientists, engineers and laboratory technicians active in the fields of water quality, pollution control and analysis.

The wide activities began in 1972, with emphasis on preparing a text that would not only concentrate on the presentation of standard methods but exhibit the unique feature of bringing together and treating all aspects of the entire process of water examination for pollution control, of which water analysis is just one.

When planning a water examination exercise, it is important to determine from the very beginning its objectives and, accordingly, develop an appropriate measurement programme. Often, water samples are taken without sufficient consideration of location, time and climate, and the sampling system within a whole catchment area is not always well coordinated. The need for and use of routine monitoring—be it automated or not—of specific determinands in the field and the advantages of automated techniques in the laboratory, imply strong cost–benefit characteristics in any modern water pollution control project. It is also useful to be well informed about recent developments in instrumental analysis, and their applications to water examination, even if such techniques are not essential for the routine work. The execution of any water pollution control and abatement programme at both the national and the international level is, from the scientific point of view, heavily based on the validity and availability of the data generated. To this end, it is important to understand the methods and to use proper techniques for the processing and storage of data for their retrieval when needed. Statistical treatment and error determination are essential for establishing the validity of data when these serve as a basis for decision making on technical, economic or political levels. Moreover, to ensure compatibility and comparability of data among different water laboratories, intercalibration and intercomparison exercises have to be developed and maintained.

Finally, not forgetting the human element involved, it is important to provide laboratory staff with properly structured premises. This includes well designed working spaces, correct placing of precious and sensitive instruments, adequate storage of materials, and appropriate service rooms and emergency facilities.

The first volume covers sampling, data analysis and laboratory equipment, and its seven chapters are the result of elaborate reviews and lengthy deliberations. The views and knowledge of water specialists from different professional disciplines were sought, considered, and generally amalgamated into the text, thus setting out the present international state of the art and a good projection of the needs for the future. It is hoped, therefore, that these chapters will provide water managers with a useful tool for their planning process and decision making.

The second and third volumes are solely and wholly devoted to the detailed description of analytical procedures. They provide concise and systematic descriptions of each method, including sampling, storage, standardization, precise operating instructions, and calculation of results for routine work, together with a single set of methods suitable for measuring all the determinands that may be important in the control of water pollution. In each case, an attempt has been made to describe the best method available for use in the average laboratory.

More specifically, the second volume deals with physical, chemical and radiological methods for the analysis of substances found in water. The methods have usually been classed as "reference" or "secondary", and these terms relate to the amount of experience available for a given method. A reference method is one that has been sufficiently well tested and proved to permit its unqualified recommendation, subject to any restrictions stated in the method itself. This is not to say, however, that the reference method is the most advanced or a highly instrumental one. When a reference method could not be identified, one or more secondary methods were selected. By implication, these are methods where, at present, WHO cannot provide an unconditional recommendation, either because of insufficient experience in its application or because doubts arise as to the accuracy of the results obtained. The latter class of method may, of course, be perfectly adequate for many purposes.

The method to be used for a particular determinand should be selected for its ability to provide the information required. This means, in particular, that the method should allow satisfactory levels of detection and accuracy to be achieved. When choosing a particular method, the presence of agents in the sample capable of causing interference must be recognized, and careful reading of instructions for analysis is therefore essential. When a method has been selected, the prescribed procedure should be closely followed, otherwise small changes of procedural detail may cause unexpectedly large errors. In applying these methods, the importance of proper control of any hazards (e.g. toxic chemicals, explosions, fires) cannot be overemphasized, and each laboratory should take all necessary precautions to ensure adequately safe working conditions. (Refer also to vol. 1, chapter 7.)

It is worth emphasizing that the use of these methods alone will not necessarily ensure accurate results. Many sources of error are usually present during sample collection and handling before analysis, and steps must be taken to control such errors (see vol. 1, chapter 2 and the relevant sections in individual methods). In addition, analytical errors have occasionally been found to be much larger than anticipated, even when standard methods were used. This is not surprising when one considers how many factors affecting accuracy cannot be controlled, even when the written description of the method is scrupulously followed. Accordingly, the provision of these methods does not in any way decrease the importance of each laboratory maintaining a continuously self-critical approach to the reliability of its results. As an aid to this, the techniques and tests for experimental estimation of accuracy, intercalibration and interlaboratory comparison exercises (see vol. 1, chapter 6) are strongly recommended as an integral part of the application of any analytical method.

An average laboratory could be expected to undertake routinely some radiological examination of water. In some countries, only one or just a few laboratories are assigned by the authorities to develop and maintain competence in the radiological examination of the environment, and they are then expected to possess the more sophisticated instrumentation and undertake the more complicated analyses. However, at least routine monitoring of gross radioactivity could and should be performed by the average water laboratory, even with relatively simple equipment and a properly trained laboratory technician. The more sophisticated analysis of individual nuclides and perhaps the interpretation of results should then be left to better-equipped laboratories and more highly qualified personnel.

The third volume deals with the sampling, identification and examination of organisms that may be found in water, from fish to viruses. Special attention is given to bacteriological assays, which are so important to the investigation of public health problems. Methods are presented for evaluating the quality of water based on an examination of the organisms living in it. Indices based on such analyses are capable of providing much information but have been relatively neglected in many countries.

The purpose of the chapter on virological examination is to encourage those working in the average water laboratory to become more aware of and interested in viruses, by providing them with some guidance and orientation, as well as some detailed concentration procedures. Hence, a collaboration can be envisaged between two types of laboratory, one being concerned with the sampling and concentration and the other—the more specialized—being responsible for the cultivation, enumeration and identification of the viruses. Under such circumstances transportation problems gain in importance, and the chapter deals with this subject too.

The list of references following each chapter reflects the completion date of that chapter. For this reason they are not completely up to date. However, the objective of this work was not to present the reader with a critical review of current literature. What is important is that the fundamental information contained in this publication is sound and will remain valid for many years. The only exception perhaps applies to the chapter on virological examination, a subject which at present is dynamic and in which new knowledge is accumulating rapidly. The updating of the material and references will be given consideration in a future revision.

By the very nature of works such as this, many subjects are handled in more than one place, and the reader is therefore encouraged to examine all three volumes. A great effort has been made to present a uniform text as regards style and terminology. Moreover, the general rule of the World Health Organization in its publications is to follow authoritative, internationally approved scientific terms and units, some of which are rather new. The reader is is therefore advised to study carefully the Note on Terminology which precedes this Introduction. While in general the mention of manufacturers' products and trade marks has been avoided, in a few cases it was necessary to use these in order to simplify the description of an analytical procedure. Such mention does not imply endorsement or recommendation in preference to others of a similar nature.

A number of sets of standard methods for the analysis of water and wastewater already exist and are in widespread use. Many of the methods in this book are based on one or more of these compilations, whereas others are based on later modifications, or on original methods reported in the literature, when no suitable standard method was available. Compilations of standard methods from various countries have all been reviewed in choosing the methods in vols. 2 and 3. Where the method is well established, liberal use has been made of these sources, which are widely used in European and other countries. The sources are as follows:

AMERICAN PUBLIC HEALTH ASSOCIATION, AMERICAN WATER WORKS ASSOCIATION & WATER POLLUTION CONTROL FEDERATION. Standard methods for the examination of water and wastewater, 13th & 14th ed., American Public Health Association, 1015 Eighteenth Street, NW, Washington, DC 20036, 1971 & 1976.

CANADA, INLAND WATERS DIRECTORATE, WATER QUALITY BRANCH. Analytical methods manual, Ottawa, 1974.

COUNCIL FOR MUTUAL ECONOMIC ASSISTANCE. Standard methods for water quality examination. Part I. Methods of chemical analysis of water, 2nd ed., Moscow, 1974.

GESELLSCHAFT DEUTSCHER CHEMIKER, FACHGRUPPE WASSERCHEMIE. Deutsche Einheitsverfahren zur Wasser-, Abwasser- und Schlammuntersuchung: physikalische, chemische und bakteriologische Verfahren, 3rd rev. ed., Weinheim, Verlag Chemie, 1975.

INTERNATIONAL BIOLOGICAL PROGRAMME (IBP) HANDBOOKS. Oxford, Blackwell Scientific Publications, 1969–1974.

UNITED KINGDOM, DEPARTMENT OF THE ENVIRONMENT. Analysis of raw, potable and waste waters, London, HM Stationery Office, 1972.

UNITED STATES, ENVIRONMENTAL PROTECTION AGENCY, METHODS DEVELOPMENT AND QUALITY ASSURANCE RESEARCH LABORATORY. Methods for chemical analysis of water and wastes, Washington DC, Office of Technology Transfer, 1974.

Some of the figures and tables are reproduced from other published works. In all cases, this has been indicated by a suitable acknowledgement immediately below the figure caption or table. The authors and WHO wish to thank the publishers concerned for granting permission to reproduce figures and to quote or adapt portions of copyright material.

In addition to its use for routine analysis at the national level, this Handbook has also been designed to serve international programmes such as interlaboratory calibration and comparative studies and transfrontier regional and river basin programmes. The United Nations Environment Programme (UNEP), the World Health Organization, The United Nations Educational, Scientific and Cultural Organization, and The World Meteorological Organization have already used parts of vol. 2 for the preparation of an operational guide for the cooperative water programme under the UNEP Global Environmental Monitoring System (known as GEMS).

Although the book was originally planned by WHO for use in European countries, in its present form it should be of equal value to countries all over the world, and to other international organizations which develop programmes aimed at the control of noxious effluents and the protection of natural water bodies. Moreover, it should provide water pollution control specialists everywhere with helpful information based on international practice.

The World Health Organization is grateful to the Governments of Austria, Belgium, Czechoslovakia, the Federal Republic of Germany and Hungary for their support in agreeing to host working group meetings, and to Belgium and the Federal Republic of Germany for special financial contributions which made the convening of some of the meetings possible.

Pergamon Press, the publishers of this work, are to be complimented for their cooperation in producing this scientific text in their best book publishing tradition.

I should like to record my personal indebtedness to all the colleagues, reviewers, and participants in the meetings who have contributed in many ways and at various stages. All of these are listed in Annex 1, acknowledging their contribution to the volume in question, and I offer my sincere apologies to anyone who may have been unintentionally excluded. The very close collaboration with the authors of the chapters and other particularly active contributors among the working group participants, many of whom have become personal friends in the course of the work, and their painstaking efforts to upgrade and update the material, are warmly acknowledged.

The friendly assistance and goodwill of various members of the Regional Office staff on different occasions is greatly appreciated. They include secretaries, draftsmen, publications and reproduction staff, registry and mailing personnel, and the administration. Though too numerous to mention individually, all have contributed toward the successful implementation of this project. I am also grateful to Mr J. Kumpf and Mr J. I. Waddington, former Chief and present Director, respectively, of the environmental health team in the Regional Office, for their continuous support during the implementation and completion of this mammoth work. Their far-sightedness and recognition of the potential value of this text in harmonizing water analysis methodology in many countries was a great help and encouragement. The long-time leadership of Dr Leo A. Kaprio, WHO Regional Director for Europe, has provided the necessary and continuous administrative and financial support for the programme under which this work was executed; for his patience and understanding, many thanks.

Finally, particular recognition, acknowledgement and thanks should go to Dr A. M. Woolman for his demonstration of vast experience, competence and linguistic knowledge in preparing the manuscript for typesetting; to Mr A. L. Wilson for his careful and systematic examination of the physical and chemical methods (vol. 2, chapters 1–4) for accuracy of procedure and terminology, and for his advice on useful corrections and additions; to Dr R. B. Dean for his thorough examination and proofreading of many of the chapters, and his assistance in ensuring uniformity of presentation; and to Christiane Sørensen who, as my secretary from 1974 to 1978, spared no time and effort on behalf of this project and helped in so many ways to initiate, implement and follow up the various activities which led to the eventual completion of this work.

A revised and updated edition is already being planned and readers are invited to submit comments, corrections and observations as well as suggestions for additional material to the World Health Organization, Regional Office for Europe, 8 Scherfigsvej, 2100 Copenhagen Ø, Denmark.

In this work, when it shall be found that much is omitted, let it not be forgotten that much likewise is performed. (Samuel Johnson)

MICHAEL J. SUESS
Regional Officer for Environmental Hazards,
WHO Regional Office for Europe

BIOLOGICAL EXAMINATION

V. Sládeček,[a] H. A. Hawkes,[b] J. S. Alabaster,[c] I. Daubner,[d]
I. Nöthlich,[e] J. F. de L. G. Solbé[f] & D. Uhlmann[g]

CONTENTS

[a] Associate Professor in Hydrobiology, Department of Water and Environmental Technology, Prague, Czechoslovakia.
[b] Reader, Applied Hydrobiology Section, Department of Biological Sciences, University of Aston, Birmingham, England.
[c] Head, Pollution Division, Stevenage Laboratory, Water Research Centre, Stevenage, Herts, England.
[d] Chief, Limnology Section, Institute of Experimental Biology and Ecology, Bratislava, Czechoslovakia.
[e] Biologist, Federal Institute of Hydrology, Koblenz, Federal Republic of Germany.
[f] Manager, Fish, Toxicity and Biodegradability, Environmental Protection, Stevenage Laboratory, Water Research Centre, Stevenage, Herts, England.
[g] Professor and Head, Chair of Hydrobiology, Water Section, Technical University, Dresden, German Democratic Republic.

1

4　　*Biological, Bacteriological and Virological Examination*

INTRODUCTION

Biological studies are an essential part of water pollution control programmes and are designed to provide information for a variety of water management functions:

1. In non-polluted aquatic ecosystems typical biocoenoses are associated with different natural biotopes. Biological surveillance provides information of value in the environmental protection of the natural aquatic biota by detecting detrimental changes and it permits assessment of the effectiveness of remedial actions taken to restore the balance of a disturbed ecosystem.

2. Changes in water quality are reflected by changes in the biota. The community structure in a given aquatic habitat can therefore be used as an indicator of water quality, and changes in community structures, detected by biological surveillance, may be used to detect short-term and long-term trends in water quality.

3. The trophic and saprobic state of water, which is of significance in water management, can only be established by biological studies, although some evidence may be obtained from certain physical and chemical determinands.

4. Biological studies enable the effects of specific pollutants on the species composition, abundance, and metabolic activities of aquatic communities to be determined.

5. Biological studies are essential to determine the effects of specific pollutants or complex mixtures of chemical and/or physical pollutants on specific aquatic organisms.

6. Bioaccumulation and biomagnification of toxicants taken up from the aquatic environment into food-chains leading to man can be detected only by ecological studies.

7. In the management of water supplies, in treatment processes, and in fisheries, direct information is provided by biological surveillance.

8. Biological studies enable the biological status of an aquatic ecosystem to be established. This is of value in predicting the likely consequences resulting from changes in the regime, e.g., flow regulation or water abstraction schemes, and in the subsequent monitoring of such changes.

9. Sources of pollution can often be detected and sometimes identified by biological surveys.

10. Biological data are often acceptable as crucial evidence in legal actions and public enquiries.

To provide data for these different uses a range of biological methods has been developed. Unlike physical, chemical, and even bacteriological methods, which over the years have become standardized, biological methodology is, at present, less systematic, each worker or team developing methods independently. This chapter describes the better developed and more generally accepted methods and it is hoped that its publication will assist in standardizing biological methodology so that biological data from different regions may be more reliably compared.

The methods are described under two main headings—" Field surveys " and " Biological tests ", most of the latter being carried out in the laboratory. The different methods applicable to the sampling of the different biotopes are described separately, followed by sections describing data processing methods.

Within these different biotopes the sampling of different taxa is dealt with. The aquatic bacteria are included here in as much as they form an essential part of the aquatic ecosystem. The bacteria of more direct public health interest are dealt with in chapter 2 of this volume.

Most of the methods should be within the capabilities of the average biological laboratory in Europe. More advanced methods, required for specific research investigations, such as scuba diving, are not included but can be found in limnological textbooks.

Although most of the methods can be carried out by trained technicians, an experienced hydrobiologist is required for the correct interpretation of the data collected. A rule-of-thumb processing of the data can often lead to misleading conclusions.

A. BIOLOGICAL SURVEYS

In water bodies different communities exist depending on their association with the water and with the air-water and solid-water interfaces. Of these, two different habitats and their associated communities are of importance in water pollution control surveys: (1) the free-water, and (2) the banks and bottom.

1. The free-water comprises the pelagic zone of the lakes and other lentic water in which the PLANKTON and NEKTON are the dominant communities, while the NEUSTON and PLEUSTON are either secondary communities or absent.

The term "seston", introduced by Kolkwitz (*1*) is very often used instead of plankton. It means all material that can be removed from the free-water by means of filtration, centrifugation, and other similar procedures. It consists of a living part called bioseston, which is a synonym of plankton and nekton, and of a non-living part called abioseston or tripton.

It is the aim of the hydrobiologist to identify as many as possible of the living organisms and also to determine the nature of the non-living material present in the water samples under examination. In lotic waters, e.g., rivers, the free-water is represented by the main body of water flowing down the river as opposed to the " dead water " associated with the banks and bottom. The communities found in the free-flowing water depend upon the current. In rapidly flowing rivers, only nekton is represented; any plankton cannot be regarded as a self-maintaining community but is merely " drift ". In slow-flowing rivers a planktonic community similar to that in lentic waters may become established.

2. Associated with the banks and bottom other communities exist. In both lentic and lotic waters BENTHOS and PERIPHYTON are of importance as well as the special associations on the mud-water interface and in the interstitial dead water.

The different methods of sampling these several communities are described below. The different communities are of relevance in respect of different management requirements. The plankton is of relevance in waters to be used as a source for drinking water, bathing, and other recreations and for industrial supply. The benthic communities, including periphyton, are of special value in monitoring water quality in rivers since they remain fixed in relation to the water flow and consequently respond to the range of water qualities flowing over them.

1. PLANKTON

Plankton is the community of small organisms floating or swimming in the free-water (pelagic zone) of lakes, impoundments, fish ponds, other standing water bodies, and slow-flowing rivers.

Depending on body size, the plankton is divided into the following groups:

(*a*) ultraplankton (less than 5 μm),

(*b*) nanoplankton (5 to 50 μm),

(*c*) microplankton (50 to 500 μm),

(*d*) mesoplankton (0.5 to 1 mm),

(*e*) macroplankton (more than 1 mm).

Often a practical division into only two groups is used: small plankton, up to 60 μm, and net plankton, caught by plankton net or screen, more than 60 μm. The size of net plankton depends on the mesh size of the silk bolting cloth or other material used for filtration (see Table 1).

From the taxonomic point of view, plankton is divided into microbial plankton (i.e. bacterioplankton), phytoplankton, and zooplankton.

Table 1. Mesh sizes of different plankton filtering materials
according to Schwoerbel (2)

No.	Silk bolting cloth xxx (µm)	Monodur Perlon (µm)	Monofilament Nylon (µm)	Pore area (%)
0	490	500	500	54
3	490	280	300	50–54
8	195	200	180	44–47
12	106	112	112	34
16	74	71	87	22
20	63	63	75	20
25	55	56	65	20
20 GG	1000	1000	—	66
30 GG	670	670	—	62
54 GG	328	334	—	45

1.1   Microbial plankton

1.1.1   *Scope*

In water, microorganisms form an important and specific community, the biotope being in most cases free water. No study of water quality would be complete or exact without the determination of microbes, which are present in various amounts in all waters. The aim is not only to estimate the actual number of organisms present in the water but also to facilitate the evaluation of water quality from the limnological and sanitary standpoint.

This section includes the microscopic determination of microbial plankton as a whole; and specifically some of its substantial parts, namely: heterotrophic bacteria, iron bacteria, sulfur bacteria, etc., as they are not dealt with in chapter 2 on bacteriological examination.

1.1.2   *Field of application*

The plate method permits the detection of only a small percentage of the organisms present in the examined water. A considerable part of the water community is represented by specific microflora participating in the turnover of elements, such as ammonifying, nitrifying, denitrifying, iron, sulfur and other bacteria, yeasts, viruses, etc. There are also waters in which, especially under the influence of wastewaters from chemical, pharmaceutical and other factories, a special microflora has developed. The detection of all these microbial groups and species is of great importance for the evaluation of water quality.

Microscopic counts permit not only the determination of the number of microbial plankton present in the water but also their morphological differentiation. By the use of special stain procedures and chemical reactions, some groups, such as Gram-positive and Gram-negative bacteria, iron bacteria, and spore-bearing bacteria can be differentiated. The ratio of rods to cocci, or of sporulating to nonsporulating organisms, for example, can be used for the evaluation of water quality, trophic conditions, etc. In polluted waters and during the early stages of self-purification, the rods predominate; in waters rich in food, the vegetative forms are more frequent.

Data on the number of microbial plankton may be used for estimating the microorganisms participating in biochemical processes characterizing the water community, e.g., in the self-purification process. From the microscopic count of microorganisms their mass and trophic value can be estimated.

1.1.3 *Definition*

Microbial plankton represent the microbial water community (i.e., microscopic organisms), the biotope of which is the free water. Like other parts of the biocoenosis, the microbial plankton is also subject to changes caused by the environment. At the same time, it affects the biotope and changes it to a certain degree.

Cholodny suggested in 1928–1929 the term "bacterial plankton" for the microbial water community. However, this term is not quite exact. Under the term "bacteria" only schizomycetes are considered in the true sense. Other microbial groups, e.g., yeasts, actinomycetes, fungi, are not included. Pelsh in 1933 therefore suggested the term " ultrananoplankton ", but this is not clearly understandable. Razumov (3) suggested the name " microbial plankton " and this term seems to be the best (4).

Microbial plankton can be divided into *autochthonous* and *allochthonous* organisms. The former consist of those organisms that have found all the suitable conditions for their existence in the water and have become a natural part of the biocoenosis, while allochthonous flora comprise microorganisms that have found their way into the water from various sources in the environment. A great many of them die within a short time because the conditions are unsuitable for their development.

1.1.4 *Principles*

The term " total bacterial count " at present refers only to saprophytic bacteria able to grow under artificial conditions at temperatures between 18 and 37°C, during a cultivation time of 24–72 hours, and at a given pH. It is not, therefore, quite correct. The bacteria mentioned represent only a small percentage of the total microbial water community. In chlorinated drinking water, they comprise 0.1–0.01% and in clean natural waters only 0.00001%. None of the media used up to now can ensure the growth of all species of microorganism present in water. The most accurate method for the determination of the total microbial count in a certain volume of water is direct microscopic count on membrane filters. A certain disadvantage is that both living and dead cells are counted together. However, the error thus introduced is not very great: it has been proved that dead bacteria constitute not more than 10–20% of the total.

1.1.5 *Sample collection and preservation*

The first and basic requirement for microbiological analysis of water is to collect and process a representative sample that is not influenced by transport or contaminated as a result of improper collection. In general, if samples are to be collected for other examinations, sampling for microbiological analysis should be done first.

1.1.5.1 *Frequency*

The number of samples to be processed is dependent on whether the objectives of the survey are to evaluate cycles of immediate pollution, the duration of peak pollution, or the probable average pollution. Because microbiological data reflect only the instantaneous state, monthly or more frequent sampling is desirable. Only by taking the average of many analyses it is possible to obtain an acceptable result. In many instances, the number of sampling sites may represent a compromise based on the physical limitations of the laboratory and the possible frequency of collection.

1.1.5.2 *Location*

The samples should be representative of the water being tested and protected from any external contamination from the hands, soil, animals, waste, etc. at the time of collection and in the period prior to examination. Samples from surface waters should not be taken immediately below the outlet of wastewaters, near the bank, or under a bridge, unless it is intended to study these localities.

Samples may be collected at points distant from the shore one-quarter, one-half, or one-third the width of the source or at other distances, depending on the objectives of the survey. Samples of bathing beach water should be collected when and where the bathing load is highest. Samples of wastewater are collected from the sewer immediately above the point of discharge.

1.1.5.3 *Depth*

Water samples for microbiological analysis are usually taken from a depth of 0.3–0.5 m below the surface and not less than 0.5 m from the bottom.

1.1.5.4 *Equipment*

Sterile bottles of 100 ml capacity and with ground-in stoppers are used for sampling. They are prepared as follows:

The thoroughly washed bottle is stoppered and the stopper and neck are wrapped in aluminium foil or parchment paper and tied (Fig. 1). It is sterilized by heating at 160°C for 1 hour.

When sampling surface waters, either tongs or sampling rods are useful (Fig. 1). There are various special sampling devices for taking samples from greater depths; two such simple devices are shown in Fig. 2. If the sample is to be taken by hand, special care is needed to prevent contamination, particularly in the case of stagnant waters; when streams are to be sampled the mouth of the bottle should be directed against the stream. During sampling of wastewaters, the hands should be protected by rubber gloves and rods or tongs should be used.

The bottle should be opened just before sample collection. A gap of 1–2 cm must be kept between the surface of the sample and the stopper to facilitate mixing of the sample by shaking, preparatory to examination.

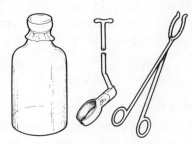

Fig. 1. Devices for surface sampling

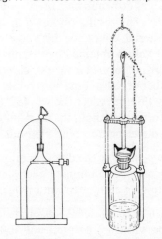

Fig. 2. Devices for depth sampling

1.1.5.5 *Volume*

To obtain a representative sample 100 ml are sufficient.

1.1.5.6 *Transport and preservation*

Samples for microbiological analysis should be examined as soon as possible, preferably immediately after sampling without any transport or storage. When this requirement cannot be met, the sample should be transported or stored at the temperature of 1–5°C for not longer than 24 hours. If determination of the microbial plankton is to be performed only by direct microscopic count, the microorganisms can be fixed by 40% formaldehyde (1 ml per 50 ml of the sample). In this case, the sample must not be chilled.

1.1.5.7 *Labelling*

All samples should be appropriately labelled (or marked with numbers) immediately after collection to avoid any mistakes. The descriptive data should include: name of the locality, day and hour of sampling, number of the sample and, if appropriate, any unusual phenomena or deviations.

1.1.6 *Sample analysis*

1.1.6.1 *Total number of microorganisms*

The total microbe count in a given volume of water still cannot be exactly determined. In the majority of cases, the number of microbes is determined from the number of colonies grown from a certain quantity of water, usually 1 ml, on standard media. The results obtained in this way are universally known as the total bacterial count, or by some other similarly inexact term. Not only are false values obtained by this method—owing to the fact that microbial colonies are not formed from a single cell but often from groups containing a larger number of cells—but these values are also lower than the true values because they do not reflect the whole bacterial community.

No doubt the best information about the total number of microbes present in water is obtained by direct microscopic methods.

(*a*) *Equipment and reagents.* For the determination of microbial plankton the method of direct microscopic counting of microbes on membrane filters is recommended. The following equipment and reagents are necessary:

Membrane filters with pore size of 0.3–0.5 µm
Binocular microscope, with 10 × eyepiece and 100 × immersion objective
Filtration equipment with an effective filtration diameter of 10 mm

Formaldehyde
Erythrosine
Phenol solution, 50 g·l^{-1} in water
Acid fuchsin
Methylene blue
Nitric acid

(*b*) *Filtration.* First, it is necessary to prepare filter membranes of a small diameter (12–15 mm, depending on the filter equipment); the pore size should be 0.3–0.5 µm. No residual substances must be present in the pores and the membranes must be sterilized. Membranes are placed in a 100–150-ml glass beaker containing distilled water and carefully heated to 80°C. The water is gradually changed 2–3 times. After that the membranes are boiled for 20 minutes over a moderate flame.

A sterile membrane filter is put into the filtration apparatus with flamed forceps, closed, and fixed on a vacuum flask (Fig. 3). The use of a syringe fitted with a filter holder is also advantageous (Fig. 4).

The sample is filtered using a water pump or other type of vacuum pump. A hand pump or microsyringe with filter holder may be used in the field.

For the microscopic analysis of clear waters, 10–50 ml are required, for polluted waters 0.1–1 ml, depending on the degree of pollution. For details of filtration and membrane filters, see (5).

(*c*) *Staining.* After filtration is finished, the membrane is taken out and placed on a marked slide where it is allowed to dry, under either a glass bell jar or a Petri dish. The dry filter is then placed on a filter paper saturated with a 30 g·l^{-1} solution of erythrosine in a 50 g·l^{-1} solution of phenol in water.

Not all brands of erythrosine are of high enough quality for this purpose and because the powder is light sensitive a highly stable product has to be selected (5). After staining for 30–60 minutes, the membrane is placed on

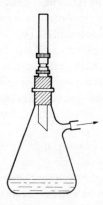

Fig. 3. Membrane filtration apparatus for direct microscopic counts

Fig. 4.   Microsyringe adapted for membrane filtration

another filter paper saturated with distilled water in order to remove surplus dye. This is repeated until only a slight pink stain remains on the filter paper.

To make the differential diagnosis of microbes and artefacts easier, combined staining procedures have been developed. The membrane filter with the microbes is placed for 2 minutes on a pad saturated with a 10% solution of nitric acid. It is then placed on another pad saturated with a $1 \text{ g} \cdot \text{l}^{-1}$ solution of acid fuchsin for 3 minutes, and finally, on a pad saturated with $0.2 \text{ g} \cdot \text{l}^{-1}$ solution of methylene blue at pH 6–6.5 for 2 minutes (6).

(*d*) *Microscopic counting.* After staining and decolorization, the membrane filter is allowed to dry out. Then, a microscopic preparation is made: a drop of cedar wood oil or Canada balsam is put on a slide and the membrane filter is placed on it, so that it becomes transparent. A further 1–2 drops of cedar wood oil are added and the preparation is covered with a cover glass, which must be as thin as possible. Thicker glass would cause difficulty in focusing perfectly.

The microorganisms are counted at 1000-fold magnification (immersion objective 100 × and eyepiece 10 ×). At least 10–15 fields of view should be enumerated in different parts of the preparation, starting from the bottom left-hand corner and finishing in the upper right-hand corner.

To facilitate counting and to prevent errors due to counting cells twice, it is recommended that a ruled grid subdivided into 10 × 10 areas be inserted in the eyepiece of the microscope.

Depending on the number of organisms per field of view, 4, 8, 16, 20 or 25 squares are counted; the lower the number of microorganisms, the more squares should be counted.

Microscopic counting can be performed by the use of phase contrast. The advantage of this method is that staining is not necessary and, according to some authors, it is easier to distinguish microbes from artefacts. However, greater accuracy is not secured by any special procedure; it is necessary only to be familiar with the microscopic technique and to have enough practice.

(*e*) *Expression of results.* The total count of microbes in a given volume of water, usually in 1 ml, is calculated from the following formula:

$$x = K\frac{N}{V}$$

where

x = the total number of microbes;

K = the coefficient of the microscope, i.e., the ratio of the size of the field of view or area of the squares of the eyepiece grid in which the microbes were counted to the area of the membrane filter;

V = the volume of water examined;

N = the average number of microorganisms in one field of view. The more cells enumerated, the greater statistical significance of the results.

1.1.6.2 *Heterotrophic bacteria*

This group of microorganisms is fully described in chapter 2 of this volume (" Bacteriological examination "), sections 5.1 and 5.5.

1.1.6.3 *Sulfur bacteria*

A treatise on this group of microorganisms has been prepared by Fjerdingstad (7). For detailed information see also (4) and (8).

1.1.6.4 *Iron bacteria*

In water containing iron (surface water, groundwater), bacteria taking part in the iron cycle develop. Often they achieve massive growth and their presence is made evident by the yellowish-brown colour of the water and the formation of rusty pellicles, especially on the bottom of shallow places. Iron bacteria play an important role in the formation of iron-manganese nodules in lakes and oceans, and also in wells and some hydraulic structures.

The iron bacteria include species that behave differently towards organic substrates. Some are autotrophs and live in water containing dissolved ferrous bicarbonate. Others are mixotrophs and a third group is heterotrophic and dwells on the surface of aquatic plants and algae in water containing significant amounts of organic substances.

Some iron bacteria require a low pH for growth. Others, which use the organic part of iron humates, are encountered in more alkaline waters.

There are no general methods for culturing iron bacteria, and a number of forms have not yet been obtained in pure culture. The taxonomy of iron bacteria demands further accumulation of data, special studies of individual species, and more exact descriptions of them. Therefore, a variety of nutrient media must be used to study the iron bacteria in a water body.

The simplest method of determining the presence of iron bacteria in water is the direct microscopic examination of submerged slides or of membrane filters through which a specific volume of water has been filtered. The specimens are treated with a 2–5% solution of potassium ferrocyanide for 2–3 minutes, and then with 5% hydrochloric acid for 1–2 minutes. They are then stained with erythrosine (a $50 \text{ g} \cdot \text{l}^{-1}$ in solution in $50 \text{ g} \cdot \text{l}^{-1}$ aqueous phenol). Thus the cells of ferrobacteria, which stain red, are distinguished from their iron sheaths and small stalks, which stain blue. When submerged slides are examined under a microscope, the iron bacteria can be readily identified.

(*a*) *Equipment and reagents*

Membrane filters with pore diameter 0.3–0.5 μm
Binocular microscope with 10 × eyepiece and 100 × immersion objective
Filtration equipment for direct microscopic count of bacteria as described in section 1.1.6.1(*b*)
Erythrosine
Aqueous phenol solution, $50 \text{ g} \cdot \text{l}^{-1}$
Potassium ferrocyanide
Hydrochloric acid
Phenol
Cover slides
Microscopic slides
Petri dishes
Erlenmeyer flasks
Koch steam sterilizer

(*b*) *Culture media*

Winogradsky Medium

Distilled water	1000 ml
NH_4NO_3	0.5 g
$NaNO_3$	0.5 g
K_2HPO_4	0.5 g
$MgSO_4 \cdot 7H_2O$	0.5 g
$CaCl_2 \cdot 6H_2O$	0.2 g
Ferric ammonium citrate	10 g

This medium may be used as a solid medium if $15 \text{ g} \cdot \text{l}^{-1}$ agar is added.

Iron Bacteria Medium

Distilled water	1000 ml
$(NH_4)_2SO_4$	1.5 g
KCl	0.05 g
$MgSO_4 \cdot 7H_2O$	0.5 g
K_2HPO_4	0.05 g
$Ca(NO_3)_2 \cdot 4H_2O$	0.01 g
$NaHCO_3$	0.03 g
Solution of trace elements (see below)	1 ml

The medium is poured in 100-ml amounts into 250-ml conical flasks and sterilized in an autoclave. Iron solution (10 ml) is poured aseptically into each of the flasks. The iron solution is prepared as follows:

$FeSO_4 \cdot 7H_2O$	10 g
Distilled water	100 ml

The solution is sterilized by filtration through an ultra-filter. The solution is slightly opalescent and has a pH of about 6.5.

Solution of Trace Elements

Sodium ethylenediaminetetraacetate	50 g
$ZnSO_4 \cdot 7H_2O$	22 g
$CaCl_2 \cdot 6H_2O$	5.54 g
$MnCl_2 \cdot 4H_2O$	5.06 g
$FeSO_4 \cdot 7H_2O$	4.99 g
$(NH_4)_6 \, Mo_7O_2 \cdot 4H_2O$	1.1 g
$CaSO_4 \cdot 2H_2O$	1.57 g
$CoCl_2 \cdot 6H_2O$	1.61 g
Distilled water	1000 ml

Leptothrix Medium

The following solutions are prepared and sterilized: (1) $0.25 \text{ g} \cdot \text{l}^{-1}$ peptone solution; (2) $0.05 \text{ g} \cdot \text{l}^{-1}$ solution of $Mn(CH_3COO)_2$ manganese acetate; and (3) willow leaf broth.

The willow leaf broth is prepared as follows: 12–15 g of leaves are covered with 1 litre of water, steamed for 15 minutes in a Koch steam sterilizer, filtered, poured into test tubes, and sterilized with flowing steam. The medium must contain:

Willow leaf broth	1 ml
Solution of $Mn(CH_3COO)_2$, $0.005 \text{ g} \cdot \text{l}^{-1}$	1 ml
Peptone solution, $0.25 \text{ g} \cdot \text{l}^{-1}$	1 ml
Distilled water	8 ml

This medium, which has a pH of 5.8–6.8, yields optimal conditions for the growth of species of the genus *Leptothrix*. Pure cultures are obtained by serial transfer in the described medium with the addition of 10 g·l^{-1} of agar.

Growth of organisms belonging to the genus *Leptothrix* can be obtained in other solid media, particularly in a medium containing ferric ammonium citrate.

Ferric Ammonium Citrate Medium

Water sample	1000 ml
$Mn(CH_3COO)_2$	0.75 g
Ferric ammonium citrate	0.75 g
Peptone	0.25 g
Agar	10 g

Lieske Medium (for *Gallionella ferruginea*)

Distilled water	1000 ml
$(NH_4)_2SO_4$	1.5 g
KCl	0.05 g
$MgSO_4 \cdot 7H_2O$	0.05 g
K_2HPO_4	0.05 g
$Ca(NO_3)_2 \cdot 4H_2O$	0.01 g

To prepare this medium, salts of a high degree of purity must be used. When culturing autotrophs, glassware should be washed with an acid dichromate cleaning solution.

The medium is poured in 30-ml amounts into tall straight bottles. After sterilization, the bottles are left to stand until a gaseous equilibrium with the atmosphere develops. Before inoculation, iron in the form of iron filings or flat pieces (3% according to weight), or freshly precipitated ferrous sulfide, is added to each vessel. FeS is precipitated from a solution of $FeSO_4$ with Na_2S. The precipitate is centrifuged with glass-distilled water that has been freshly boiled to remove the air.

Lieske medium may be used for other species of iron bacteria if leaf extract is added. Leaf extract is prepared by heating in an autoclave fresh leaves of table lettuce (*Lactuca sativa*) in tap water for 20 minutes. The liquid contains Fe^{2+} ions and has a pH of about 6.6. The pH is adjusted to 7.4, when the liquid changes to a reddish colour. The liquid is poured into small bottles and again sterilized.

Silverman and Lundgren Medium (for *Ferrobacillus ferrooxidans*)

Distilled water	700 ml
$(NH_4)_2SO_4$	3 g
KCl	0.1 g
K_2HPO_4	0.5 g

$MgSO_4 \cdot 7H_2O$ 0.5 g
$Ca(NO_3)_2 \cdot 4H_2O$ 0.01 g
$0.05 \ mol \cdot l^{-1}$ Solution of H_2SO_4 1 ml
$147.4 \ g \cdot l^{-1}$ Solution of $FeSO_4 \cdot 7H_2O$ 300 ml

(c) *Inoculation.* An appropriate amount of the water sample (1–10 ml) is poured into the Erlenmeyer flasks with the medium and thoroughly mixed. If the pour-plate method for colony count is used, the water sample is poured into the Petri dish and covered with an appropriate medium. For detailed information see chapter 2 of this volume (" Bacteriological examination "), section 3.6.

(d) *Cultivation.* The cultivation temperature for iron bacteria is 10–20°C; the culture should be held at this temperature for several days until the growth has appeared.

(e) *Counting.* For colony counting see chapter 2 of this volume, sections 3.6–3.8.

(f) *Identification.* In a liquid medium iron bacteria appear in the form of clumps or fine clusters. Microscopically, typical threads or other forms of iron bacteria are recognizable. On solid media, iron bacteria form brown colonies.

(g) *Expression of results.* Results of iron bacteria detection are expressed either as positive findings or as a number of colonies in the water volume examined. For further information see also chapter 2 of this volume, section 3, as well as references (4) & (8).

1.1.6.5 *Nitrogen cycle bacteria*

There are four main groups of microorganisms that take part in the nitrogen cycle in water. These are ammonifying, nitrifying and denitrifying bacteria as well as nitrogen fixing bacteria. The process of nitrification that leads to the formation of nitrogen compounds has tremendous significance in the overall biology of water masses. The recycling of nitrogen compounds within the nitrogen cycle after ammonification has taken place, i.e., the oxidation of ammonia into nitrites and then into nitrates, is an important step. The nitrates are further converted to organic nitrogen compounds in the microbial cells.

1.1.6.5.1 *Nitrifying bacteria*

The presence and number of nitrifying bacteria in the water and sediments of water masses is determined by dilution (transferring various quantities of inoculum into liquid media) and by counting colonies that appear on silicic acid plates treated with a selective medium.

An analysis is run separately for phase I nitrifying bacteria, i.e., those forms that oxidize ammonium salts to nitrites, and for phase II nitrifying bacteria, which oxidize nitrites to nitrates.

(a) *Equipment*

Binocular microscope with 10 × eyepiece and 100 × immersion objective
Petri dishes
Erlenmeyer flasks
Reagent tubes

(b) *Culture media*

Winogradsky Medium (for detecting the presence of phase I nitrifying bacteria)

$(NH_4)_2SO_4$	2 g
K_2HPO_4	1 g
$MgSO_4 \cdot 7H_2O$	0.5 g
NaCl	2 g
$FeSO_4 \cdot 7H_2O$	0.4 g
Distilled water	1000 ml
Chalk, precipated	

A very small amount of chalk is added separately to each flask. The medium is sterilized in an autoclave for 10 minutes. When preparing a medium for nitrifying bacteria, great attention must be paid to the chemical purity of the reagents used: each of the necessary reagents must be checked for nitrite and nitrate impurities. Only a medium that is completely free of nitrites and nitrates can be used for inoculations.

The medium must be poured in a thin layer (no more than 1.5–2 cm) into Winogradsky flasks or small Erlenmeyer flasks. All glassware must be treated with a dichromate cleaning solution and thoroughly flushed out with distilled water before use.

For the cultivation of nitrifying bacteria in the form of colonies, silicate gel medium saturated with either 2 ml of the above described Winogradsky medium or 10 ml of a $5 \text{ g} \cdot \text{l}^{-1}$ solution of NH_4MgPO_4 is used. These solutions are spread on the surface of the medium and allowed to evaporate. The preparation of silicate gels is described by Daubner (*4*, pp. 351–352).

Winogradsky Medium (for detecting the presence of phase II nitrifying bacteria)

Distilled water	1000 ml
$NaNO_2$	1 g

Na_2CO_3	1 g
NaCl	0.5 g
K_2HPO_4	0.5 g
$MgSO_4 \cdot 7H_2O$	0.3 g
$FeSO_4 \cdot 7H_2O$	0.4 g

When preparing the medium, great attention must be paid to the chemical purity of the reagents used. If contamination of a salt by nitrates occurs, it must be recrystallized. To purify a commerical product (96–97%), 500 g of the salt are dissolved in about 750 ml of water by heating. The salt solution is filtered; the filtrate is concentrated until crystals (a layer on the surface) begin to form, and is then cooled. Crystals of the pure preparation are suction filtered with paper filters in a Büchner funnel and the filtrates are in turn evaporated 1 to 2 times until crystallization begins. The yield of a pure (100%) preparation is approximately 400 g. Recrystallization must be repeated until an acceptable degree of purity is achieved. The purified liquid must be kept in a dry place and checked from time to time for the presence of nitrate.

The prepared nutrient medium is poured in 50-ml amounts into Winogradsky flasks or small Erlenmeyer flasks previously washed with dichromate cleaning solution and rinsed with distilled water. The medium is sterilized in an autoclave at 120°C for 15 minutes.

A quantitative determination of the numbers of *Nitrobacter* may be made by dilution or by counting colonies that develop on gel plates. Two solutions are prepared:

1. Distilled water	200 ml
K_2HPO_4	0.5 g
$MgSO_4 \cdot 7H_2O$	0.3 g
NaCl	0.3 g
$FeSO_4 \cdot 7H_2O$	0.02 g
$MnSO_4 \cdot 5H_2O$	0.02 g
A salt of one of the following: zinc, titanium, molybdenum, or aluminium	trace
2. Distilled water	200 ml
KNO_2	6 g

The solutions are sterilized. Well-ground kaolin (0.5 g) is sterilized separately. Two millilitres of the first solution and 1 ml of the second are placed in a small sterile flask together with the kaolin, mixed well, heated, and poured, while hot, on the surface of a gel prepared as described above. The kaolin is added to provide a flat smooth surface on which the growth of colonies of Nitrobacter is more easily observed. The mixture is distributed uniformly over the surface of the gel by rotating and swirling the dish in a figure of eight. The Petri dishes are then partially dried.

(c) *Inoculation.* The procedure is performed as described in section 1.1.6.4(c).

(d) *Cultivation.* The nitrifying as well as the denitrifying and the nitrogen-fixing bacteria are generally cultivated for 2–4 days at 25–28°C, if using an incubator, or for at least 6 days at room temperature.

(e) *Counting.* For colony counting see chapter 2 of this volume, section 3.

(f) *Identification:*
Nitrifying bacteria, phase I. Beginning with the fourth day after inoculation, chemical reactions for the presence of ammonia and nitrite are regularly conducted on alternate days and when a positive reaction for nitrite is recorded, the developed microflora are examined under the microscope.

For detecting nitrite, Griess reagent is used. When a red or purple colour appears after adding a few drops of the reagent, the reaction is considered positive. For detecting ammonia in the culture, Nessler reagent is used. On reaction with ammonia, a yellow-orange-brown colour develops, depending on the concentration of ammonia. The disappearance of ammonia in cultures indicates its oxidation by bacteria only if nitrite appears simultaneously and a microscopic investigation indicates the presence of nitrifying bacteria. The most important genus is *Nitrosomonas.*

Nitrifying bacteria, phase II. The presence of phase II nitrification is detected by the disappearance of nitrite, the appearance of nitrate, and the presence of the causative agent or agents. The reagents listed above are used for detecting nitrites; dimethoxystrychnine or diphenylamine are usually used for detecting nitrates. Dimethoxystrychnine is used as a $0.2 \ g \cdot l^{-1}$ solution in sulfuric acid containing no nitrates. If nitrates are present, a rose or cherry-red coloration appears, depending on the concentration of nitrite in the medium. For the determination of *Nitrobacter* see p. 21.

(g) *Expression of results.* The results of nitrogen bacteria detection are expressed as described in section 1.1.6.4(g).

1.1.6.5.2   *Denitrifying bacteria*

The process of denitrification, or reduction of nitrates via nitrites, to molecular nitrogen, is brought about by a variety of bacteria widely distributed in water. Bacteria of this group vary in their morphological and biochemical features. When a mass development of denitrifying bacteria occurs in a body of water and when their activity is high, nitrate ions dissolved in water and vital to the development of phytoplankton may be totally destroyed, i.e., converted to molecular nitrogen, which is inaccessible to the vast majority of algae.

The presence of denitrifying bacteria in water is determined either by dilution, i.e., inoculation in a liquid enrichment medium, or by a plate count when a solid medium is used.

(a) *Equipment.* As for nitrifying bacteria, see section 1.1.6.5.1(a).

(b) *Culture media.* Giltay medium is often used for denitrifying bacteria.

Giltay Medium (for denitrifying bacteria)

Two solutions are prepared:

1.	Distilled water	500 ml
	Asparagine	0.5 g
	Glucose	10 g
	KNO_3	2 g
2.	Distilled water	500 ml
	Sodium citrate	2.5 g
	KH_2PO_4	2 g
	$MgSO_4 \cdot 7H_2O$	2 g
	$CaCl_2 \cdot 6H_2O$	0.2 g
	$FeCl_2 \cdot 4H_2O$	trace

The solutions are mixed and the pH is adjusted to 7.0 by adding a saturated solution of sodium bicarbonate. Several millilitres of the indicator bromothymol blue should be added to the medium so that the progress of the reaction may be observed by following changes in the pH (when denitrifying bacteria are present, the medium becomes strongly alkaline). Tall columns of medium are prepared in test tubes and the tubes are sterilized with flowing steam for 30 minutes on 3 successive days.

In order to grow denitrifying bacteria in the form of colonies, the following medium is recommended:

Tap water	1000 ml
$NaNO_3$	2 g
K_2HPO_4	1 g
$MgSO_4 \cdot 7H_2O$	0.5 g
KCl	0.5 g
$FeSO_4 \cdot 7H_2O$	trace
Saccharose	30.0 g
Agar	15.0 g

Dissolve the ingredients in water, adjust the pH to 7.0 and sterilize in an autoclave at 100 kPa (1 atm) pressure.

(c) *Inoculation.* The procedure is performed as described for iron bacteria, see section 1 . 1 . 6 . 4(c).

(d) *Cultivation.* Denitrifying bacteria are generally cultured at 25–28°C for 2–4 days, if using an incubator, or for at least 6 days at room temperature.

(e) *Counting.* For colony counting see chapter 2 of this volume, section 3.

(f) *Identification.* Denitrification is detected by the liberation of gas, which forms bubbles or foam on the surface of the medium, according to whether there is partial or complete disappearance of nitrates, and by the appearance of nitrites and ammonia in the medium. The same reagents as used for nitrifying bacteria are used for the nitrate, nitrite, and ammonia reactions.

If denitrifying bacteria are cultivated on membrane filters, after incubation the membrane is placed on a pad saturated with Griess reagent. The colonies of denitrifying bacteria become red in colour within 1–2 minutes. For details see (5).

(g) *Expression of results.* The results are expressed as described in section 1 . 1 . 6 . 4(g).

1.1.6.5.3 *Nitrogen-fixing bacteria*

Nitrogen fixation in water is carried out by various species of bacteria belonging to several families and genera: nitrogen-fixing *Azotobacter*; aerobic rod-shaped bacteria; Spirillaceae; sulfur bacteria; anaerobic bacilli, i.e., *Clostridium pasteurianum,* and by yeasts. The number of nitrogen-fixing bacteria is determined by dilution (inoculating liquid media with various amounts of water and sediment from the water mass) or by counting colonies on silica gel plates treated with a suitable medium.

(a) *Equipment.* As for nitrifying bacteria, see section 1 . 1 . 6 . 5 . 1(a).

(b) *Culture media*

Medium for *Azotobacter* (aerobic nitrogen fixation)

Distilled water	1000 ml
Mannitol	20 g
K_2HPO_4	0.3 g
$CaHPO_4$	0.2 g
$MgSO_4 \cdot 7H_2O$	0.3 g
K_2SO_4	0.2 g
NaCl	0.5 g
$FeCl_3 \cdot 6H_2O$	0.1 g
$CaCO_3$	5 g
Trace elements	1 ml

Trace Elements Solution

Distilled water	1000 ml
H_3BO_3	5 g
$(NH_4)_2MoO_4$	5 g
KI	0.5 g
NaBr	0.5 g
$ZnSO_4 \cdot 7H_2O$	0.2 g
$Al_2(SO_4)_3 \cdot 18H_2O$	0.3 g

The mixture of trace elements is prepared separately. Concentrated solutions of trace elements are sterilized in an autoclave and used as needed; the necessary amount is withdrawn aseptically with a sterile pipette.

Winogradsky Medium (anaerobic nitrogen fixation)

Distilled water	1000 ml
Glucose	20 g
K_2HPO_4	1 g
$MgSO_4 \cdot 7H_2O$	0.5 g
NaCl	trace
$MnSO_4 \cdot 5H_2O$	trace
$FeSO_4 \cdot 7H_2O$	trace
$CaCO_3$	40 g

For the aquatic forms of *C. pasteurianum* this medium is optimal when the following are added: a mixture of trace elements (1 ml), ascorbic acid (1 g), and yeast autolysate (1 ml). These ingredients are added aseptically to the prepared medium.

Winogradsky medium is poured into test tubes in 15-ml amounts and sterilized in an autoclave at 100°C for 20 minutes.

(c) *Inoculation.* The procedure is performed as described for iron bacteria, see section 1.1.6.4(c).

(d) *Cultivation.* Nitrogen-fixing bacteria are generally cultured at 25–28°C for 2–4 days if using an incubator, or for at least 6 days at room temperature.

(e) *Counting.* For colony counts, see chapter 2 of this volume, section 3.

(f) *Identification:*

Aerobic nitrogen fixation. Growth of *Azotobacter* is confirmed by microscopic examination. Observations are made starting 3–4 days after inoculation. When *Azotobacter* are present, a thin oily film develops on the surface of the medium. The presence of spirilla is suspected when the medium becomes very turbid. Typical large *Azotobacter* cells are easily recognized when examined under the microscope.

Anaerobic nitrogen fixation. The beginning of the nitrogen fixation process is measured by the liberation of gas bubbles at the bottom of the test tube. Gas formation increases gradually and a luxurious foam appears on the surface of the medium. The precipitate is examined under a microscope for the presence of *C. pasteurianum.* The cells of this species have a characteristic spindle-shaped form and contain oblong spores. A granulose reaction with iodine is used in identifying the species. A drop of the culture taken from the precipitate is placed on a slide and covered with a cover glass. A drop of a solution of iodine in potassium iodide is placed under the cover glass, and the surplus iodine is removed with a small piece of filter paper. The cytoplasm of *C. pasteurianum* turns blue from the iodine; the spores do not stain and are therefore visible against the blue background.

(g) Expression of results. The results are expressed as described in section 1.1.6.4(*g*).

1.1.6.6 *Fungi*

This group of microorganisms is briefly described in chapter 2 of this volume, sections 5.1.2 and 5.1.3.

1.1.6.7 *Actinomycetes*

This group of microorganisms is also briefly described in chapter 2 of this volume, section 5.1.3.

1.2 Phytoplankton

1.2.1 *Scope*

Phytoplankton is present in all types of standing water bodies as well as in the middle and lower reaches of rivers. It is responsible for the primary production of the biomass in the free-water zones and for the biogenic oxygenation of the water during the daytime. The species composition of phytoplankton communities is dependent on the water quality, especially on the content of putrescible organic matter; the quantitative development is dependent on the content of inorganic nutrients, and in polluted waters also on organic nutrients. Phytoplankton organisms serve as basic indicators of the water quality of surface water bodies.

1.2.2 *Field of application*

Phytoplankton is a substantial part of the pelagic community. It inhabits the lakes, artificial impoundments, fishponds, pools, different small water bodies, and slowly flowing rivers. It is absent in underground waters, wastewaters, and quickly flowing upper reaches of rivers.

1.2.3 *Definitions*

Phytoplankton is formed by chlorophyll-bearing organisms. These are blue-green algae, other algae, and coloured flagellates. Algae float in the water, coloured flagellates swim and show migrations. Phytoplankton depends on light and shows a stratification in the vertical sense. In deep standing water bodies, this vertical stratification is abolished only during the short periods of vernal and autumnal turnover. A horizontal zoning is apparent especially in long artificial reservoirs.

1.2.4 *Principles*

The species composition and quantity of the phytoplankton show changes below pollution sources in the course of eutrophication and self-purification. A comparison of samples from different localities reflects the changes in the water quality. As the generation time of the majority of phytoplankton organisms is about one day, the changes can be retarded in time and in flowing waters also in space.

During the year the composition of the phytoplankton undergoes changes and shows a natural succession of species even if the water quality is unchanged.

A part of the phytoplankton consists of small coloured flagellates, e.g., *Cryptomonas, Chlamydomonas, and Chromulina*, which must be determined and counted in the living state because they are destroyed by preservation. On the other hand, diatoms and chlorococcal green algae can be determined in the preserved state.

1.2.5 *Sampling*

There are two different approaches to phytoplankton sampling: (*a*) plankton caught with a plankton net; (*b*) sampling of water and subsequent direct examination or concentration and examination.

The first procedure does not secure quantitative data and is recommended only for species determination. In many cases this simple procedure is sufficient.

The second procedure is necessary if quantitative data are needed.

1.2.5.1 *Frequency*

A year-round study of phytoplankton consists of 12 regular samplings in the middle of each month and 1 or more additional samplings per month when there is apparent danger to the water quality, as indicated by water-blooming (i.e., algae collecting at the surface), vegetative colouring of water of the euphotic zone, secondary pollution, or seasonal pollution caused by the beet sugar, potato, and other seasonal industries.

The experience gained in the first year will be a guide to the frequency of sampling in the following years.

1.2.5.2 *Location*

Sampling sites must be located in the free-water, i.e., outside the littoral zone, e.g., in the centre of a river or near the deepest point of an impounding reservoir or fishpond.

1.2.5.3 *Depth*

In flowing water 1 sample 100–200 mm below the water surface may be sufficient. In standing water bodies the vertical distribution within the epilimnion or euphotic zone should be examined at depths of 1, 2, 3 m and more. The density of samples can be reduced in very clean waters.

1.2.5.4 *Sampling equipment*

Surface samples can be taken in a convenient bottle, preferably that used for transport and storage.

Samples from the depth must be taken by special equipment, the most simple being Mayer's bottle (Fig. 5). This is a home-made water-sampling

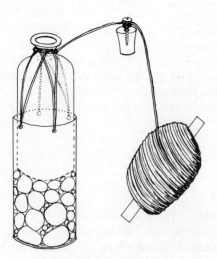

Fig. 5.   Mayer's water bottle

bottle, capable of being operated at depths of up to 20–25 m. It is lowered close to the desired depth from a boat or from a bridge, dam, etc., then opened by jerking the thin rope.

More complicated samplers, such as the Kemmerer sampler and the Friedinger water bottle for zooplankton are described in section 1.3.5.4.

1.2.5.5 *Volume*

Generally, 100 ml of water are sufficient for a phytoplankton analysis. Larger quantities (1 or more litres) are needed only in very clean waters, e.g, ultra-oligotrophic lakes.

1.2.5.6 *Preservation*

Qualitative analysis (i.e., species composition) of the phytoplankton must always start with the living organisms for determination of the delicate flagellates (Chrysomonads, green flagellates, *Cryptomonas*, *Euglena*, etc.) and end with the analysis of the preserved diatoms, peridineans and green chlorococcal algae. For this reason, it is recommended that 2 parallel samples be taken, one without preservation and the other preserved immediately.

The most common preservative is commercial formalin. Add 1 ml of it to 100 ml of water.

A better preservative is Lugol's solution (a saturated aqueous iodine-potassium iodide solution prepared by dissolving 60 g of potassium iodide and 40 g of iodine crystals in 1 litre of distilled water). Lugol's solution stains parts of the algal cells, making identification easier. It also aids in settling, since the iodine causes some plankters to lose gas and therefore buoyancy. This preservative is effective for at least 1 year. Lugol's solution is added in such an amount that the preserved sample is coloured wine-yellow (about 4 ml to 100 ml of water).

The third preservative is thiomersal. This is prepared by dissolving 1.0 g of thiomersal and 1.5 g of sodium borate in 1 litre of distilled water and adding 1.0 ml of Lugol's solution. About 3.6 ml of thiomersal preservative are added to 1 litre of sample.

1.2.5.7 *Labelling*

The bottles for transport and storage of phytoplankton samples must be labelled either with the serial number of the sample or in advance with the abbreviation of the locality and the depth of sampling.

1.2.6   *Sample analysis*

A sample is analysed qualitatively in order to determine the species composition as well as quantitatively to determine the number of organisms per unit volume.   Analysis is done mainly with living material.

A good knowledge of the phytoplankton organisms is necessary. Unknown species are designated provisionally, e.g., x_1, x_2, x_3 etc., and figured or photographed for later identification.   Some representatives of the most common phytoplankton organisms are shown in Fig. 6.

1.2.6.1   *Direct examination*

Direct examination of the phytoplankton can be made only if large numbers of organisms are present, so that no concentration of the material is

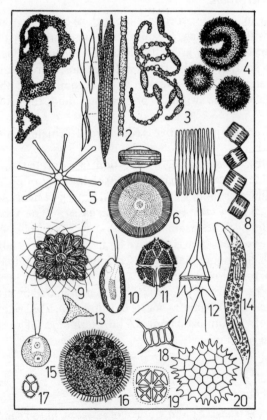

Fig. 6.   Some common phytoplankton organisms (for key see facing page)

Adapted from Sládeček (*9*)

necessary. This is the case with eutrophied waters (algal blooms) as well as with stabilization ponds for wastewater treatment. Direct examination is unsuitable for underground or for clean oligotrophic surface waters. Generally speaking, at least 100 organisms per 1 ml must be present. Plankton cells (i.e., chambers) of various types can be used.

Sedgwick-Rafter cell

The Sedgwick-Rafter (S-R) cell is the most commonly employed device for plankton counting because it is easily manipulated and provides reasonably reproducible information when used with a calibrated microscope equipped with an eyepiece measuring device such as the Whipple micrometer. The Sedgwick-Rafter cell is 50 mm long by 20 mm wide by 1 mm deep. The total

---

Key to Figure 6

Taxon[a]	Characteristics[b]						S_i	Remarks
	x	o	β	α	p	l		
1. Microcystis aeruginosa (Kützing)	—	3	6	1	—	3	1.75	Blooms
2. Aphanizomenon flos-aquae (Ralfs ex Born. et Flah.)	—	1	6	3	—	3	2.25	Blooms
3. Anabaena flos-aquae (Bréb. ex Born. et Flah.)	—	1	8	1	—	4	2.0	Blooms
4. Gloeotrichia echinulata (Smith et Richt)	—	5	5	—	—	3	1.5	
5. Asterionella formosa (Hassall)	—	6	4	—	—	3	1.4	
6. Cyclotella bodanica (Eulenst.)	—	10	—	—	—	5	1.0	
7. Fragilaria crotonensis (Kitton)	—	6	4	—	—	3	1.4	
8. Tabellaria flocculosa ((Roth) Kütz.)	4	6	+	—	—	3	0.6	
9. Synura petersenii (Korshikov)	—	1	6	3	—	3	2.25	
10. Cryptomonas ovata (Ehrenberg)	—	—	1	8	1	4	3.0	pH 5-7
11. Peridinium bipes (Stein)	—	10	—	—	—	5	1.0	
12. Ceratium hirundinella ((Müll.) Schrank)	1	7	2	—	—	3	1.15	
13. Goniochloris cochleata (Pascher)	—	10	—	—	—	5	1.0	pH <6
14. Euglena spirogyra (Ehrenberg)	—	3	5	2	—	2	1.95	
15. Chlamydomonas simplex (Pascher)	—	—	7	3	—	4	2.3	
16. Volvox aureus (Ehrenberg)	—	5	5	—	—	3	1.5	
17. Tetrastrum staurogeniaeforme ((Schröd.) Lemm.)	—	—	8	2	—	4	2.2	
18. Scenedesmus quadricauda ((Turp.) Bréb.)	—	2	6	2	—	3	2.0	
19. Crucigenia tetrapedia ((Kirchn.) W. et G. S. West)	—	4	4	2	—	2	2.75	
20. Pediastrum boryanum ((Turp.) Menegh.)	—	2	7	1	—	3	1.85	

[a] No. 1–4 = blue-greens (Cyanophyta), 5–8 = diatoms (Bacillariophyceae), 9 – Chrysophyceae, 10 = Cryptophyceae, 11–12 Peridinians (Dinophyceae), 13 = Xanthophyceae, 14 = Euglenophyta, 15–20 green algae (Chlorophyta).

[b] x = xenosaprobity, o = oligosaprobity, β = beta-mesosaprobity, α = alpha-mesosaprobity, p = polysaprobity, l = indicative weight of species, S_i = individual saprobic index of the species.

area is 1000 mm² and the total volume is 1 ml. The greatest disadvantage of the cell is that high magnification cannot be used unless the microscope is equipped with special devices, such as adjustable zoom or objective lenses that provide sufficient magnification and clearance between objective lenses and the S-R cell.

(*a*) *Filling the cell.* Before filling the S-R cell with the sample to be counted, the cover glass is placed diagonally across the cell and the sample transferred with a large-bore pipette (Fig. 7).

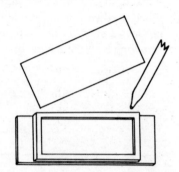

Fig. 7.   Sedgwick-Rafter counting cell

Reproduced from US Standard Methods (*158*)

Placing the cover slip in this manner will prevent formation of air bubbles in the cell and eliminate errors. The cover slip will often rotate slowly and cover the inner portion of the S-R cell during filling, but it should not be allowed to float high on an overfilled cell, since this would yield a depth greater than 1 mm and an invalid count would result.

Before proceeding with the count, allow the S-R cell to stand for at least 15 min to permit settling of the plankton. Counts are made of the plankton on the bottom of the S-R cell. Some phytoplankton, notably some blue-green algae, may not settle but instead may rise to the underside of the cover slip. When this occurs, separate counts must be made of such organisms and these totals are added to the total of those counted on the bottom of the cell, to derive the total number of organisms in the sample. The units to be counted are each isolated cell and each natural colony (clump) of cells. One colony—like an isolated cell—is counted as one unit, and the total count is the summation of all units in the sample.

(*b*) *Strip counting.* A " strip " the length of the cell constitutes a volume 50 mm long, 1 mm deep, and the width of the total Whipple field. When 10 × eyepieces and 20 × objectives are used and the width of the total Whipple field is calibrated to be 0.5 mm (500 μ), the volume of one strip is 25 mm³, or 2.5%

of the total volume of the cell. The total number of plankters in the S-R cell is calculated by multiplying the actual content of plankton in the " strip " by the number (enumeration factor) representing the portion of the S-R cell counted.

Usually 2 or 4 strips are counted, depending on the density of the plankters; the fewer the plankton, the greater the number of strips to be counted. When $10 \times$ eyepieces and a $20 \times$ objective are used, the enumeration factor for plankton counted along two strips would be approximately 20; for 4 strips it would be approximately 10, depending on the calibration. The arithmetic expression used to derive the number of plankton in the S-R cell is:

$$\text{Enumeration factor} = \frac{1000 \text{ mm}^3}{\text{volume of "strips" counted, in mm}^3}$$

$$\text{No. per ml} = \text{Actual count} \times \text{enumeration factor}$$

(c) *Field counting.* As an alternative method, field counts rather than strip counts may be made. Field counts of plankton in the S-R cell are made by using the entire Whipple grid (outermost dimensions) on samples containing many plankton. Plankters should be counted in 10 or more random fields of the Whipple grid. The total area of the combined fields is multiplied by the enumeration factor to derive the total number of algae in the sample.

Other counting cells

A variety of different flat counting cells and haemacytometers can be used for direct counts, if there are enough small-sized organisms, e.g., µ-algae, aquatic bacteria, colourless flagellates. The biological material is examined in the living state. Table 2 lists counting cells applicable to different purposes.

1.2.6.2 *Membrane filter concentration technique*

Application of the membrane filter method of plankton counting requires a vacuum source, filtering membranes, and experience in determining the proper amount of sample to be filtered. Plankton in samples from waters containing substantial quantities of suspended matter such as silt may be difficult to enumerate by this method, since, in the process of filtering, the suspended matter tends to crush the plankton or otherwise obscure them from view. However, the method has certain features that make it especially suitable for use on waters with a low phytoplankton and silt content. In particular, the method permits the use of high magnification for enumeration of small plankters, provides relatively rapid processing of samples if the investigator is familiar with the procedure and the plankton, does not require counting of individual plankters to assemble enumeration data, and increases the probability of observing the less abundant forms.

Table 2. Different flat counting cells

Type	Volume (ml)	Depth (mm)	Area (mm²)
Kolkwitz	1	2.63	380
Kolkwitz, large	15	8	1900
Kolkwitz, drop-cell	0.05	0.25	200
Naumann, small	0.38	1	380
Naumann, large	19	10	1900
Birge and Juday	1	2	500
Utermöhl, medium	4	5	800
Utermöhl, 3 ml	3	8	380
Utermöhl, 2.5 ml	2.5	10	250
Utermöhl, ultra a	2.8	4	700
Utermöhl, ultra b	1.4	2.	700
Utermöhl, ultra c	0.7	1	700
Thoma (haemacytometer)	0.0001	0.1	1
Frantzev, No. 1	0.9	0.1	?
Frantzev, No. 2	5	0.2	?
Frantzev, No. 3	50	0.5	?
Frantzev, No. 4	1	0.1	1
Nageotte	0.05	0.5	100
Bürker (haemacytometer)	0.001	0.1	1
Vošahlík	0.0001	0.01	1
Cyrus I	0.1	0.1	100
Cyrus II	0.05	0.05	100
Palmer	0.1	0.4	250
Lund	various	?	various
Lund-Sládeček	various	0.2	various
Spencer-Neubauer	0.1	0.1	1
Sedgwick-Rafter	1	1	1000

Filter the sample through a membrane filter 25 mm in diameter (with a pore size depending on its purpose). Allow the filter to dry for 5 min, remove, and place on top of 2 drops of immersion oil on a microscope slide. Add 2 drops of immersion oil on top of the filter. Dry until clear (10–15 min in a low-temperature oven, up to 48 h at room temperature); cover the filter with a cover slip prior to examination.

During microscopic examination the magnification and sampling field or quadrat must be of such a size that the most abundant species will appear in at least 70% but not more than 90% of the microscopic quadrats examined (80% is optimum). Otherwise, the field size or the amount of sample concentrated must be altered. The occurrence of each species in 30 random microscopic fields is recorded. The results are reported as organisms per millilitre, calculated as follows:

$$\text{No. of organisms per ml} = \frac{d \times Q}{V \times K}$$

where

d = density (organisms/field) as obtained from Table 3

Table 3. Conversion table for membrane filter technique (based on 30 scored fields)

Total occurrence	F%	d
1	3.3	0.03
2	6.7	0.07
3	10.0	0.10
4	13.3	0.14
5	16.7	0.18
6	20.0	0.22
7	23.3	0.26
8	26.7	0.31
9	30.0	0.35
10	33.3	0.40
11	36.7	0.45
12	40.0	0.51
13	43.3	0.57
14	46.7	0.63
15	50.0	0.69
16	53.3	0.76
17	56.7	0.83
18	60.0	0.91
19	63.3	1.00
20	66.7	1.10
21	70.0	1.20
22	73.3	1.32
23	76.7	1.47
24	80.0	1.61
25	83.3	1.79
26	86.7	2.02
27	90.0	2.30
28	93.3	2.71
29	96.7	3.42
30	100.0	?

Where $F = \dfrac{\text{total number of species occurrences} \times 100}{\text{total number of quadrats examined}}$

Q = number of quadrats per filter
V = volume filtered (ml)
K = dilution factor (0.96 for 4% formalin preservative).

Results are expressed in numbers of organisms per 1 ml and the pore size of the membrane filter used must be indicated.

1.2.6.3 *Drop sedimentation method*

Apparatus: centrifuge, centrifuge tubes, pipettes (5, 10, 50 and 100 ml), counting cells (either haemacytometer or a flat cell), micropipettes, needles.
An electric clinical centrifuge is necessary, equipped with a head that takes

4 tubes of 100 ml capacity and can also carry tubes of 10 and 50 ml volume. The tubes are long-cone point centrifuge tubes, which can be obtained as a regular stock item or made by the laboratory glassblower. The tubes must be tapered and must be calibrated in the tapered portion at 0.1 and 0.2 ml and in bigger tubes also at 0.5 and 1.0 ml.

After centrifugation of the samples at 10 000 × g for 5 minutes, the supernatant is decanted and the sample centrifuged again for 1 minute.

The final concentrate in the tapered portion is adjusted to the desired volume by addition or removal (after again centrifuging) of water. The sample is concentrated in this manner so that there are approximately 30 organisms in one eyepiece field. Afterwards the plankton is mixed either by air bubbling or by stirring with a needle, transferred into a counting cell (haemacytometer) and counted.

The counting of organisms is done immediately. At least 400 individuals have to be counted for the error to be less than 10%.

The total water volume treated by centrifugation is 100–300 ml (in extremely clean waters up to 1000 ml), using 2, 4, or 8 equal portions (e.g., 2 × 100 ml) for each run.

The counting can be made either per eyepiece field or in squares on a firm grid of the cell.

The presence of abioseston will interfere.

Some delicate species, mainly flagellates, can be damaged or even destroyed by centrifuging.

The results are expressed in number of organisms per ml.

The procedure is applicable to fresh samples only.

1.2.6.4 *Sedimentation concentration technique*

Plankton samples may be concentrated by settling with the aid of a liquid detergent. To concentrate the phytoplankton, place 500 ml of a sample in a 1-litre glass cylinder and add 20 ml of commercial formalin or 18 ml of thiomersal preservative and 10 ml of a liquid household detergent. Sedimentation of the plankton is essentially complete within 24 h. Carefully siphon the supernatant from the cylinder and wash the concentrate into 100-ml centrifuge tubes. Centrifuge at 10 000 × g for 5 min.

Decant the supernatant from the tubes, wash the concentrate into vials with 4% formalin or 3.6% thiomersal preservative, and adjust the volume to the nearest 5 ml by adding preservative.

The results are expressed in number per ml for the phytoplankton and number per litre for the zooplankton.

Some delicate flagellates can be damaged or destroyed during the process of preservation. Lugol's solution is less damaging.

Large volumes of samples (up to 10 litres) should be taken when examining very clean water.

1.2.7 *Expression of results*

Numbers of individuals are usually expressed per ml. The values most often found range between a few hundred and a few thousand. Coenobia, colonies, filaments, etc. are counted as single units. For scientific purposes either the number of individual cells or the biomass in μm^3 must be calculated. The cell volumes calculated by the first method do not agree with those calculated by the second one.

1.3 Zooplankton

1.3.1 *Scope*

Zooplankton is generally present in all types of surface waters. Although there is an inapparent transition between the phytoplankton and the zooplankton, especially within the phylum Euglenophyta, the zooplankton can be classified by the absence of chlorophyll, by heterotrophic nutrition, and by active movements. Zooplankton is dependent mainly on the phytoplankton, but also on bacteria, fungi, dead suspended material, and colloidal organic matter.

1.3.2 *Field of application*

Water quality of lakes, impoundments, fishponds, small water bodies, slowly flowing rivers and some underground waters can be estimated according to the species composition of the zooplankton. It occurs also in stabilization ponds treating sewage and some kinds of industrial wastewaters.

1.3.3 *Definitions*

Zooplankton is the animal part of the total plankton. It consists of Protozoa (e.g., colourless flagellates, rhizopods, ciliates), Vermes (e.g., rotifers), Crustacea (e.g., cladocerans, copepods) and a few other invertebrates (e.g., larvae of the dipteran *Chaoborus*). Zooplankton is distributed irregularly, shows a distinct vertical and horizontal stratification, and exhibits vertical diurnal migrations. Swarms of zooplankton occur in both large and small water bodies.

1.3.4 *Principles*

Zooplankton species reflect the conditions of the water quality much more slowly than do the phytoplankton species. Zooplankton has a longer individual life span and is more resistant to changes within the water quality. On the average, a protozoan lives 1 to a few days, a rotifer 1 week, a cladoceran 1 month, and a copepod about 2 months. The saprobial index has a wider spread, the indicative weights of species are lower, and the tolerance to short-termed adverse effects is greater than for phytoplankton.

Planktonic protozoans and some rotifers (e.g., *Amphileptus, Collotheca*) must be examined and determined only in the living state. After preservation they are destroyed or badly damaged. Fortunately, they are not present in large numbers in the zooplankton.

1.3.5 *Sampling*

As for phytoplankton, there are two approaches to zooplankton sampling: (*a*) plankton catch with a plankton net; (*b*) sampling of water and subsequent concentration of the zooplankton.

The first procedure is suitable for qualitative analysis only, although catches made by means of the Clarke-Bumpus plankton sampler can be considered quantitative. The second procedure is generally needed if quantitative data have to be provided.

1.3.5.1 *Frequency*

A year-round study consists of 12 regular samplings in the middle of each month. As far as circumstances permit, the sampling is made more frequently at peak periods.

1.3.5.2 *Location*

Sampling sites may be identical with those for phytoplankton.

1.3.5.3 *Depth*

The samples may be the same as those of phytoplankton, but the vertical and horizontal distribution of the zooplankters must be taken into account. Several species prefer the metalimnion or hypolimnion. The situation is complicated by vertical migrations. For this reason the exact time of sampling of each vertical stratum must be noted.

1.3.5.4 *Sampling equipment*

Water samples for plankton examination are taken in much the same fashion as samples for chemical analyses. In most cases, a 1-litre volume of water is sufficient. The modified Kemmerer water sampler (Fig. 8) is widely used in the USA for limnological investigations, but there is some flow inhibition leading to inaccuracies in depth sampling. In special studies it may

Fig. 8. Kemmerer sampler

Reproduced from US Standard Methods (*158*)

be advantageous to use one of the specialized plankton samplers such as the Clarke-Bumpus sampler (*11*) or a Van Dorn-type sampler. Care should be taken to obtain samples containing a typical dispersion of aquatic organisms free only of floating debris, mud, or other extraneous materials.

In Europe a common water sampler is that manufactured by the firm of Friedinger, Switzerland (Fig. 9). In shallow water bodies (up to about 20 m in depth) a wide-mouthed Mayer's water bottle (Fig. 5) can be employed. In oligotrophic water plankton traps, such as devised by Juday, or a Patalas sampler are more useful.

The plankton population in many rivers can be ascertained by examining periodic samples collected at midstream 30–60 cm beneath the surface. Depending on the velocity of the water mass, the plankton in the sample is the resultant of factors affecting water quality at some point upstream rather than at the sampling site.

The sampling frequency will depend on objectives, facilities, weather conditions and personnel available. In special studies, samples are often collected daily or even periodically during a day. To measure plankton populations that may change rapidly, daily collections are desirable throughout the season of active biological growth. Where this is not possible, weekly, biweekly or monthly collections may still be useful to determine major population changes.

Live samples should occupy no more than one-half the volume of the container and should be examined within 2 or 3 h after collection. For

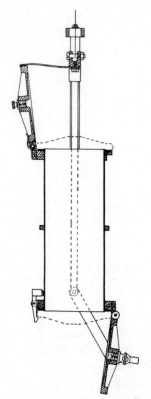

Fig. 9.   Friedinger water sample

extended storage, the sample must be preserved and the container may be filled. Because colours fade rapidly, the preserved plankton must be stored in the dark. Under favourable conditions, although carotenes and xanthophyll are said to break down, chlorophyll retains its colour rather well; it has been found that an expert can identify most organisms in a preserved sample even after several years of storage. For practical purposes a preserved sample has many advantages, but it should be remembered that the plankton organisms in a preserved concentrate have been subjected to sudden immersion in a fluid which often produces severe contraction, distortion of body form, or destruction. No ideal preservative has yet been found. The microscopist, therefore, must always be on the alert for misleading effects produced by the preservative. Comparison with an occasional live sample from the same source will help the investigator to recognize forms that may be distorted in routine preserved samples.

Preservation can be accomplished by the immediate addition of 40 ml of formalin (a 37–42% aqueous solution of formaldehyde) per litre of sample. Alternatively, the 1-litre sample is mixed with 36 ml of thiomersal preservative.

1.3.5.5 *Volume*

Quantitative data on the zooplankton can be obtained by filtering known volumes of water: 0.5 litre for very eutrophic water bodies, 1.0 litre for eutrophic, 5 or 10 litres for oligotrophic ones.

1.3.5.6 *Preservatives*

The basic preservative is commercial formalin, which is added in the proportion 10 ml to 1 litre of sample. Other preservatives are described in section 1.2.5.6.

1.3.5.7 *Labelling*

As fixed samples of zooplankton can be stored for many years and examined after a considerable lapse of time, samples must be labelled in such way that other investigators can recognize them easily. A duplicate small label is placed inside the bottle.

1.3.6 *Sample analysis*

For qualitative analysis, a living sample is analysed as quickly as possible after sampling. A good knowledge of the species is necessary. Some representatives are shown in Fig. 10. Unknown species are designated provisionally, e.g., *Daphnia* sp. 1, *Daphnia* sp. 2, etc. and figured as well as photographed for later identification.

Quantitative zooplankton analysis is made with a preserved sample.

1.3.6.1 *Total counting*

If the zooplankton in the sample is not too dense, the whole content of a quantitative sample can be enumerated.

The preserved sample is allowed to stand for about 1 h. The majority of the supernatant water is removed very carefully with a pipette, so that the sedimented plankton is not disturbed. The plankton is then transferred, a portion at a time, into a counting cell of the Sedgwick-Rafter type (Fig. 7) and counted under the microscope. After all material has been examined and counted the sample is either thrown away or put into the bottle again and kept for possible re-examination, mainly from the taxonomical point of view.

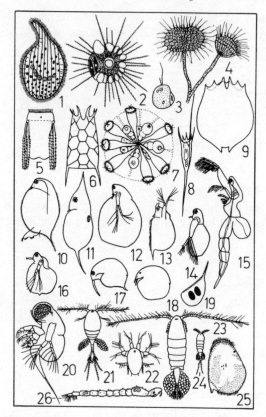

Fig. 10.   Some common zooplankton organisms (for key see facing page)

Adapted from Sládeček (*9*)

1.3.6.2   *Subsampling*

If the zooplankton is too dense, it is hardly possible to enumerate all the individuals in a reasonable time.

The sample must be perfectly mixed in order to withdraw a representative part of it with a special pipette. The piston pipette devised by Hensen (Fig. 11) may be used with advantage.

1.3.6.3   *Filtration*

In clean waters, larger volumes of water must be filtered in order to obtain a suitable sample for quantitative analysis. Five or ten litres of water taken by a sampler from the desired depths are filtered either through a silk

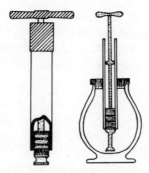

Fig. 11. Hensen piston pipette

Key to Figure 10

Taxon[a]	Characteristics[b]							Remarks
	x	o	α	β	p	l	S_i	
1. *Amphileptus trachelioides* (Zach.)	—	7	3	—	—	4	1.3	
2. *Actinophrys sol* Ehrenberg	—	—	4	6	—	3	2.6	
3. *Monas vulgaris* (Cienk.) Senn	—	—	—	—	10	5	4.0	E, H_2S
4. *Anthophysa vegetans* (Ehr.) Stein	—	—	+	8	2	4	3.2	Fe
5. *Polyarthra vulgaris* Carlin	+	3	5	2	—	2	1.85	
6. *Keratella quadrata* (O. F. Müller)	2	3	5	—	—	2	1.55	
7. *Conochilus unicornis* Rousselet	—	7	3	—	—	4	1.3	
8. *Kellicottia longispina* (Kellicott)	1	6	3	—	—	3	1.25	
9. *Brachionus urceus* Linné	—	—	8	2	—	4	2.2	
10. *Daphnia magna* Straus	—	—	—	6	4	3	3.4	
11. *Daphnia cucullata* (Sars) m. kahlbergensis (Schoedler)	+	4	5	1	—	2	1.75	
12. *Simocephalus vetulus* (O. F. Müller)	—	5	5	—	—	3	1.5	Littoral
13. *Scapholeberis mucronata* (O. F. Müller)	+	2	6	2	—	3	2.0	Littoral
14. *Diaphanosoma brachyurum* (Lievin)	+	6	4	+	—	3	1.4	
15. *Leptodora kindtii* (Focke)	—	4	5	1	—	2	1.65	
16. *Moina rectirostris* (Leydig)	—	—	+	6	4	3	3.4	Pools
17. *Bosmina longirostris* (O. F. Müller)	1	4	4	1	—	1	1.55	
18. *Chydorus sphaericus* O. F. Müller	1	3	4	2	—	1	1.75	Littoral
19. Winter egg of *Daphnia*								
20. *Polyphemus pediculus* (Linné)	—	7	3	—	—	4	1.3	
21. *Cyclops* sp.	—	+	+	+	—		2.0	
22. *Cyclops* sp., nauplius	—	+	+	+	—		2.0	
23. *Diaptomus* sp.	—	+	+	—	—		1.5	
24. *Canthocamptus staphylinus* Jurine	—	7	3	—	—	4	1.3	Littoral
25. *Notrodromas monache* (O. F. Müller)	—	7	3	—	—	4	1.3	Littoral
26. *Chaoborus* sp. (larva)	—	+	+	+	—		2.0	Migrations

[a] No. 1–4 = Protozoa, 5–9 = Rotatoria, 10–20 = Cladocera, 21–24 = Copepoda, 25 = Ostracoda, 26 = Diptera.
[b] x = xenosaprobity, o = oligosaprobity, β = beta-mesosaprobity, α = alpha-mesosaprobity, p = polysaprobity, l = indicative weight of species, S_i – individual saprobic index of the species, E = species occurring also in eusaprobic conditions in the total absence of dissolved oxygen.

plankton net (see Table 1) or through a screen made from phosphor-bronze. The mesh size should be 60 or 80 μm approximately and should be noted in the record. The material obtained is preserved immediately and handled as described in sections 1.3.6.1 or 1.3.6.2.

1.3.7 *Interference*

When sampling zooplankton, larger phytoplankton (e.g., *Ceratium, Asterionella, Fragilaria, Volvox, Dinobryon, Synura,* etc.) and, in polluted waters, filaments of sewage fungi may also be taken.

Errors may occur in sampling because the very good swimmers like *Diaptomus* or *Chaoborus* may escape before the sampler is closed. Allowance must be made for the vertical migrations of the zooplankton.

1.3.8 *Expression of results*

The results of zooplankton counts are usually expressed in individuals per litre, but in the case of ultra-oligotrophic lakes in individuals per 10 litres. Individuals forming colonies of *Carchesium, Zoothamnium, Epistylis, Conochilus,* and *Conochiloides* are counted separately. Biomass in $μm^3$ is calculated only for research purposes.

2. NEKTON

2.1 Scope

As many fish are much more sensitive to pollutants than are protozoa or algae, the condition of the fish stock of a water body can be a meaningful index of water quality. Load surges of toxic material may cause massive and complete kills of fish. At a lower level of concentration toxicants cause a reduction in reproductive capacity, growth, or resistance to disease and parasites. On the other hand, biochemically degradable organic wastes increase both the nutrient supply in the water and the standing crop of fish, to the extent that atmospheric aeration is sufficient to maintain the necessary oxygen concentration. Only by using fish to monitor water on a long-term basis is it possible to ensure that the quality of the water is adequate for fisheries.

2.2 Definition

Nekton are motile aquatic organisms living in the pelagic zones of lakes and the free-flowing water of rivers and able to swim against the current. In inland waters, the nekton are mainly represented by fish species, although there are also a few insect representatives.

2.3 Field of application

The pollutional state of water may be reflected by the following features related to its fish population:

—degree of reduction in the number of fish species in comparison with unpolluted reaches of similar physical structure;*
—abundance, both relative and absolute, of each fish species;*
—size/age distribution,* which is primarily related to the time necessary for complete repopulation;
—growth rate of the fish;*
—condition of the fish;
—rate of accumulation of substances potentially hazardous to man;
—success of reproduction of the fish;
—incidence of disease and parasites;
—fish productivity;*
—palatibility.

Fisheries data are useful in both short-term and long-term water quality monitoring. Fish are the only biological indicators that are able to provide a sufficiently clear indication of shock loads of low frequency (1 or 2 pulses per year).

Fish kills can result both from primary toxic effects and from secondary action, such as an increase in non-dissociated ammonia resulting from a rise in pH as induced by very intensive photosynthesis. One of the most frequent causes of fish kills is oxygen depletion, which may also result from natural causes, such as extended periods of ice cover.

The following data must be obtained with all possible speed: location; time of the observed kills; number and weight of dead fish; other kinds of organism affected. In addition, specimens of dead fish must be collected for autopsy and samples must be taken for chemical analysis.

On the other hand, there are a number of limitations on the correct interpretation of fisheries data as related to pollution. First, without a profound knowledge of the life histories of the species involved, the presence or absence of fish can be correlated with water quality only with difficulty. Secondly, fish surveys need a great expenditure of time and effort. Thirdly, unlike benthos, nekton are able to move out of polluted zones or avoid them completely.

Fish are usually studied by hydrobiologists in connexion with fisheries management rather than as indicators of water quality. For the latter purpose observations should be made on the number of species taken and

---

* The components marked with an asterisk also depend largely on the kind and intensity of fisheries management, such as overexploitation or an excessively high stock of the main carnivores.

their relative abundance and condition. For special studies more detailed work on growth and pollutant contamination can be carried out. Further details of ichthyobiological methods may be found (*13, 14*).

2.4 Sampling and preservation

2.4.1 *Active sampling techniques*

(*a*) *Hawl seine.* A hawl seine is a strip of a strong netting hung between a stout lock or float line at the top and a strong, heavily weighted lead line at the bottom. Seining is not effective in deep waters because the fish can escape. The method is not quantitative in most cases and is more useful in determining the variety of fishes.

(*b*) *Trawls.* Trawls are specialized, completely submerged seines used in large open water areas. Different types are used depending on whether the aim is to capture primarily bottom fish or schooling fish. Data are expressed in weight per unit of time. The use of trawls requires experienced personnel.

(*c*) *Electrofishing.* In this method an electric current is applied to the water causing the fish to be oriented to and attracted by the positive electrode. This method is more successful in shallow waters, including the littoral region of lakes, and more effective by night than by day.

(*d*) *Chemical fishing.* Of the chemicals suited for fish sampling rotenone is the most acceptable because of its high degradability. At the concentrations used for fish eradication (0.025–0.050 mg·l^{-1} active ingredient) rotenone is not considered to be hazardous to man and warm-blooded animals. Sampling is usually employed on a short reach of a river or a small bay of a lake, taking into consideration the corresponding area and volume.

2.4.2 *Passive sampling*

(*a*) *Entangelement nets.* Gill and trammel nets are suited for sampling fish populations in estuaries, lakes, reservoirs, and larger rivers. The results are expressed as number or weight of fish taken per length of net per day.

(*b*) *Entrapment devices.* These cause the fish to enter an enclosed area through a series of funnels from which it cannot escape. Both hoop and trap nets can be operated from small open boats.

2.4.3 *Preservation of samples*

To preserve fish in the field 10% formalin and a solution containing 3 g of sodium borate and 50 ml of glycerol per litre is used. Specimens longer than

7.5 cm should be slit to allow the preservative to penetrate into the internal organs. After fixation the fish are exposed to repeated washing and placed in diluted isopropanol (400 ml·l⁻¹) with one change of the alcohol.

3. TRIPTON (ABIOSESTON)

Although abiotic, this portion of the seston is likely to be observed by the biologist only while making microscopic examination of the plankton and should therefore be recorded at the same time.

The water samples for tripton determination—if necessary—are taken directly into containers of arbitrary volume and are centrifuged without preservation. 10 ml of sample are centrifuged at $10\,000 \times g$ for 5 minutes. The water is then decanted off so that only a small amount remains in the tip of the tube. After careful mixing, the material is transferred quantitatively, by a micropipette to a microscopic slide and covered with a cover glass measuring 20×20 mm.

The approximate amount of tripton is expressed in terms of the following scale, according to the area of an eyepiece field covered by the particles at $100 \times$ magnification:

1—less than 1%,
2—1-3%,
3—3-10%,
4—10-20%,
5—20-40%,
6—40-100%.

It is necessary to differentiate (1) detritus, i.e., remains of bodies of plants and animals, which may be fine or coarse; (2) inorganic particles, classed according to their size as clayey, loamy, dusty, and sandy particles; (3) remains recognizable as cellulose fibres, artificial and natural fibres, starch grains, fat droplets, faecal pellets (of zooplankton), etc. Such material helps to identify the source of pollution.

A photographic record, e.g., a colour film of a whole microscope field, can be kept for future comparisons.

Some common representatives of the tripton are shown in Fig. 12.

4. BENTHOS

4.1 Scope

Benthic communities in lotic waters are affected by the nature of the water flowing over them. The nature and therefore the quality of the water is a major factor determining the composition of the benthic community. The benthic community therefore reflects or monitors the general conditions over a period of time rather than the quality of that body of water passing at the time of sampling. Benthic communities are therefore very useful as indicators in lotic waters. They are most readily sampled in the upper (rhithron) zone of rivers. In the slower flowing lower reaches (the potamon), other communities such as the seston, which is more readily sampled in such zones, may prove more useful.

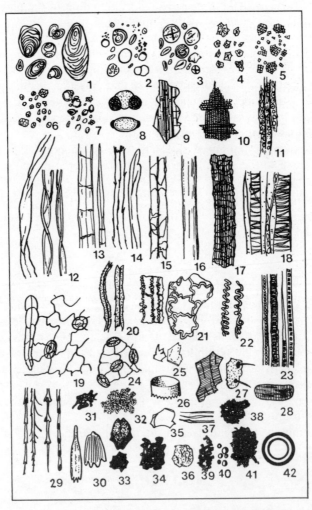

Fig. 12. Some common representatives of tripton (abioseston) (for key see facing page)

Adapted from Sládeček (*9*)

Like all indicator systems for monitoring water quality, benthic communities indicate the general ecological conditions. Although directly applicable to fishery requirements, they do not always measure all water-quality parameters. Although water shown by biological indicators to be of poor quality is suspect for most uses, water shown to be of good quality ecologically, although acceptable for most uses, may not necessarily always be free from pathogens or harmful chemical compounds, such as trace organics. To detect these, specific microbiological and chemical tests are necessary. Nevertheless, for most water uses biological indicator systems using benthic communities are valuable guides to water quality.

4.2 Field of application

Benthic communities in streams and rivers may be examined with different objectives in mind. The objective of such surveys should be clearly identified at the outset as this may affect the method of sampling, the processing of the catch, and the method of data processing.

The following are possible applications of the method:

(*a*) A general survey of a specific river or stretch of river to ascertain its resource potential, e.g., for fisheries, amenities, public supply.

(*b*) To monitor the effect on a river of a known discharge, as in the case of an industrial or sewage treatment plant effluent.

Key to Figure 12

1.	Potato starch	21.	Remains of surface tissue of grass (hay or straw)
2.	Wheat starch		
3.	Rye starch	22.	Spiral fibre from a plant tissue
4.	Maize (corn) starch	23.	Rat hairs
5.	Rice starch	24.	Lower side of a leaf with stomata
6.	Oats starch	25.	Flakes of a rock
7.	Barley starch	26.	Chitin segment of an insect
8.	Pine pollen	27.	Chitin remains of an insect
9.	Remains of a plant tissue (rootlet or stalk)	28.	Muscule fibre
		29.	Bird's feathers
10.	Remains of a tissue of a coniferous tree	30.	Butterfly's scale
		31.	Rust
11.	Remains of the wood of a coniferous tree	32.	Iron (III) hydroxide ($Fe(OH)_3$)
		33.	Coal dust
12.	Cotton fibre	34.	Lignite
13.	Flax fibre	35.	Glass splinter
14.	Hemp fibre	36.	Sand grain
15.	Raw silk fibre	37.	Oligochaete hairs (worms)
16.	Rayon fibre	38.	Iron (mono)sulfide (FeS)
17.	Wool fibre	39.	Carbon black
18.	Tissue of a broad-leaved tree	40.	Oil drops
19.	Surface tissue of lettuce with stomata	41.	Organic detritus (remains of unknown origin)
20.	Paper fibre		
		42.	Air bubble

(c) To assess the self-purification of a river following pollution. This may be related to the distance downstream of a known polluting discharge or to the time after an isolated accidental pollution. Self-purification may also occur following the elimination of a discharge or a change in its character affecting the pollution load.

(d) To monitor the quality of water at a point of intake for specific uses, e.g., public supply.

(e) To monitor the ecological consequences of management policies, e.g., flow regulation, water transfer, flood control, weed control.

(f) As part of a routine national or regional classification programme for river water quality.

Although most commonly used to monitor organic pollution, changes in benthic communities reflect other types of pollution, such as toxicity and physical pollution, that are more difficult to monitor by physicochemical methods, especially when the source is not known.

4.3   Definition

Benthos is that community inhabiting the bottom deposits of bodies of water such as rivers and lakes. It is sometimes separated into the *eubenthos*—those organisms living down in the substratum, in the mud or between stones—and the *epibenthos*—those organisms associated with the upper surfaces of the substratum. Many organisms found in the benthos are also found living associated with submerged solid surfaces; these constitute the *periphyton*. Literally periphyton means " around plants ", but by common usage it has come to mean the community growing on the surface of submerged solid surfaces. The German term *Aufwuchs*, which has no English equivalent, best describes this community. Depending on the nature of the substratum the organisms may be:

> epiphytic—on plants
> epizooic—on animals
> epilithic—on rock
> epidendritic—on wood.

Ecologically such communities are similar to the benthic community in lotic waters in that they remain fixed. Their composition is determined by the nature of the water flowing over them and hence they monitor the general water quality. Since they react in a similar way to the benthos they are here considered together under the one general heading. The methods of sampling are different, however, and are dealt with in different subsections.

The benthos may also be classified by size into microbenthos, including periphyton (*Aufwuchs*) and macrobenthos, which comprises macrophytes and macro-fauna. The benthos is greatly influenced by the nature of the substratum. In the interpretation of the data in relation to water quality it is essential to take into account the nature of the substratum sampled.

4.4 Microbenthos—mud-water interface community

Most of the surveillance work on lotic waters using benthos to assess water quality concentrates on the macro-fauna, dealt with below. One benthic habitat sometimes sampled, however, is that of the mud-water interface. The microbenthic community living in the contact zone of mud and water has been found useful in indicating water quality. This community may include organotrophic, chemotrophic, and phototrophic bacteria, colourless flagellates, rhizopods, and ciliates.

4.4.1 *Sample collection and preservation*

The samples are taken by means of a siphon consisting of a glass tube having an inner diameter of about 6 mm, bent at right angles and fitted with a strong rubber bulb. The arm of the siphon must be applied horizontally to the surface of the mud, so that the material is sucked off from the mud-water interface only. If deeper layers of the mud are sampled a wholly different community, mostly anaerobic, is obtained. There are some devices that also permit samples to be taken from deeper water bodies.

The material should be analysed on site immediately after sampling, since delay results in changes in the biocoenosis. If necessary, the material can be stored for a few hours at a lowered temperature (5–10°C). Preservation destroys the majority of organisms present.

100-ml sampling bottles should be two-thirds filled if aerobic material is present, and fully filled without air-bubbles if the material is anaerobic.

For examination, the mud sample is diluted to 4 times its volume with water and 10 ml of the mixture are poured into a 10-ml diameter Petri dish. For smaller species, preparations are made on a slide with a larger cover glass, e.g., 24 × 24 mm. Usually, at least 3 preparations are examined, each of them being subdivided into about 50 fields of view, and the results are related to 100 fields of view.

The abundance (*h*) is then expressed on a relative scale 1-2-3-5-7-9 according to the numbers per field of view, taking into account the size class of the species, as for periphyton (Table 4).

Using an appropriate counting cell (see section 1.2.6.1) the procedure can be made quantitative.

4.5 Periphyton

4.5.1 *Field of application*

Periphyton is a part of the littoral community. As the attached organisms also have free-moving or free-floating stages, the periphyton can develop on artificial substrata even at large distances from the shore, e.g., in streams, lakes, and man-made lakes. They occur naturally in brooks, rivers, fishponds, pools, ditches, and other small water bodies. Periphyton develops also in underground water wells, pipes, and in the drinking water mains.

4.5.2 *Definitions*

All attached organisms and their communities are called periphyton whether they are plants, animals, or bacteria and whether the substratum is a plant, an animal, or non-living material. The attached organisms are immobile, are adjusted to the sessile life by means of various rhizoids, gelatinous capsules, stalks, etc., and are termed true periphyton, whereas the dependent organisms (the pseudo-periphyton) are free-moving, creeping and grazing among the true periphyton.

4.5.3 *Principles*

In rivers, the periphyton shows abrupt changes in its species composition as well as in amount, immediately below pollution sources. A comparison of a station above with one below the source is the minimum requirement for proving the site and degree of pollution.

The periphyton needs a definite time to appear and develop. This time interval is a few hours to a few days for bacteria and fungi, a few days for algae and protozoa, and several days for Rotifera. The more the water is organically polluted, the more rapid is the colonization of bare areas. A climax periphyton community needs approximately 2–4 weeks to develop.

The composition of periphyton shows a natural seasonal succession of species even in cases where the water quality is unchanged. Many of the sessile organisms must be observed and determined while living, because after preservation they fall off the substratum or become damaged or destroyed. However the diatoms, testacea, and several other organisms can be easily determined in the preserved state.

4.5.4 *Sampling*

4.5.4.1 *Natural substrata*

It is difficult to obtain a quantitative sample from natural substrata. Only samples for qualitative analysis (species composition) may be taken by scraping submerged stones, sticks, piles, piers of bridges, dams, submerged roots of trees, macro-vegetation, etc. The fine periphyton on thin-layered and transparent leaves can be observed directly under the microscope. Epidermis can be cut or stripped from big leaves. The quantitative scraping and transfer of periphyton from a definite area on to a glass slide or into a counting cell is very difficult, but is possible under some circumstances.

Sample collection does not require any special or complicated equipment. A sharp knife, a spoon with sharpened edge, or other simple device is adequate for scraping periphyton samples from any submerged object in shallow water. In deep water, or at a distance from the shore or from a boat, the sampling can be carried out by means of a special scraper on a folding rod. For larger sessile animals, such as sponges and ectoprocta, some types of dredges may be useful. In any case, the samples must be scraped off large areas in order to include such types of growth forms as cushions, bush, crusts, etc., which are usually visible to the naked eye.

The scraped periphyton, little stones, parts of macrophytes are then transported in wide-mouthed bottles. To prevent death and decomposition, it is necessary to put a small amount of periphyton into a large bottle with an adequate amount of air, e.g., about 3 ml of periphyton with about 10 ml of water into a 100-ml bottle.

It is convenient to estimate immediately the degree of development of individual types of periphyton according to an abundance scale (Table 4) e.g.,

Table 4. Estimation of abundance of the periphyton

Number of organisms in 100 fields of view	Number of individuals in 1 or more field of view	Abundance (h)
First class: up to 50 μm diameter		
1–50	a maximum of 1 individual in every second field of view	1
50–200	a maximum of 2 individuals per field	2
200–1000	less than 10 individuals per field	3
1000–5000	less than 50 individuals per field	5
5000–25 000	less than 250 individuals per field	7
more than 25 000	more than 250 individuals per field	9
Second class: 50–200 μm diameter		
1–5	up to 1 individual per 20 fields	1
6–20	up to 1 individual per 5 fields	2
21–100	a maximum of 1 individual per field	3
100–500	less than 5 individuals per field	3
500–2500	less than 25 individuals per field	7
more than 2500	more than 25 individuals per field	9
Third class: 200–2500 μm diameter		
1	1 individual per 100 fields of view	1
2	1 individual per 50 fields	2
3–10	a maximum of 1 individual per 10 fields	3
11–50	less than 1 individual in every second field	5
50–200	less than 2 individuals per field	7
more than 200	more than 2 individuals per field	9

1, 2, 3, 5, 7, 9. The samples are kept alive until submitted to microscopic examination.

A duplicate sample can be preserved with formalin, in a final concentration of about 3%, for a detailed determination of diatoms, desmids, filamentoids, and other resistant organisms. Preserved samples can be stored for extended periods before examination or given to specialists for an exact determination. All living periphyton must be examined immediately— at the latest within approximately 6 hours of sampling—and should preferably be kept at 5–10°C to avoid appreciable changes.

4.5.4.2 *Artificial substrata*

Transparent artificial substrata such as glass, Perspex (Plexiglass), or celluloid are exposed in water to allow the periphyton to colonize them. The most widely used are the standard plain glass microscopic slides $76 \times 25 \times 1$ mm. If larger areas are needed, photographic plates or Perspex panels can be used. If panels made of opaque materials are used the periphyton have to be scraped off for examination, which may be damaging to soft organisms. In practice, therefore, the only suitable panels are those made of glass or transparent plastics.

In shallow streams and in the littoral region of standing water bodies, slides may be attached to bricks or stones with adhesive or placed in frames anchored to the bottom. In large, deep streams or lakes and ponds the slides are best placed in a floating rack or they can be inserted in corks (or rubber bands). These are threaded on a cable at appropriate intervals and kept at the desired level by knots in the cable just above and below them. The whole device is fastened to a buoy and anchored to the bottom.

The slides can be inserted in the corks in a vertical or a horizontal position. Where siltation or plankton sedimentation is a problem, the slides should be always placed vertically.

The duration of exposure depends upon the water temperature, the trophic state of the water body, and pollution, but is generally about 2–4 weeks. In beta-mesosaprobic waters, the most convenient exposure time is about 2 weeks; in oligosaprobic waters it is longer and in alpha-mesosaprobic and polysaprobic ones shorter. Short exposures—several hours up to 1–2 days—are used for bacteria only.

4.5.4.2.1 *Bacterial growth on slides (microbial periphyton, Aufwuchs)*

Artificial substrata may be used to give a rough estimation of the character of the bacterial periphyton or *Aufwuchs* in a given water. The colonies developing on a given area of slide are identified and the numbers of cells within individual colonies are enumerated to provide information on their growth rates.

Procedure: Pairs of microslides are placed, fixed back-to-back, on a supporting rod (Fig. 13), weighted at the lower end. The rod with the attached slides is immersed in the water for 2–3 days after which time it is removed, the slides detached and dried out. The attached microbes are fixed either with absolute methanol or formalin vapour. Staining is carried out as described for microbial plankton (section 1.1.3.1(*c*)). A solution of carbol erythrosin (30–50 g·l^{-1}) is most commonly used. After washing off the surplus stain the slide is dried out and the numbers of bacteria estimated by direct microscopic examination.

When more detailed study involving isolation of the different organisms is required, the slides are not fixed. Instead, the slides are placed in separate sterile Petri dishes and a thin layer of medium poured over them. Depending on the study, one slide may be used for cultivating and the other for differential diagnostic tests by adding the appropriate media.

4.5.5 *Analysis*

The periphyton can be analysed with varying degrees of precision, microscopically or by a mass analysis. The selection of an appropriate method depends on the purpose for which the analysis is needed.

4.5.5.1 *Macroscopic analysis*

A simple macroscopic analysis can be made with the naked eye at the time of sampling. The colour, density, and consistency of the sample are estimated and the periphyton classified accordingly:

Brown compact layers	= diatoms
Light green discs	= filamentous green algae
Slimy whitish mats	= *Sphaerotilus* (and *Cladothrix*)
Rusty precipitations	= ferric hydroxide and iron bacteria
Dark brown precipitations	= compounds of manganese and manganese bacteria
Wholly transparent slide	= no periphyton.

Several macroscopic organisms can be also recognized according to their shape, e.g., larvae of chironomids, caddis-flies, mayflies, hydras, colonies of *Carchesium* and *Zoothamnium*. It may be noted that hydras and stalked colonial ciliates prefer the lower side of slides in the hanging position. The macroscopic observations are noted and compared with the state after transportation and storage, because several organisms may drop off the slides.

4.5.5.2 *Microscopic qualitative analysis*

(*a*) A small part of the scraped preserved or living periphyton is examined under the microscope and the species found are identified. Unknown species are designated provisionally, e.g., x_1, x_2, etc. and numbered for a later identification. It is preferable to use a counting cell, e.g., the Sedgwick-Rafter cell (see section 1.2.6.1). The abundance of individual species is estimated according to a subjective scale, e.g., 1, 2, 3, 5, 7, 9, or using the criteria indicated in Table 4.

(b) Select one side of the slide with well-grown periphyton, clean and dry the other side and examine under the microscope. The upper side with periphyton must be wet during the whole analysis. The slide can be also laid in a Petri dish and covered with water. The whole area of the slide is examined for larger but scarcer organisms, but only a few fields of view or strips are examined for the small and common organisms. The magnification is changed according to the need, always starting with about 100 ×. Identify the organisms and estimate the abundance.

4.5.5.3 *Microscopic quantitative analysis*

Enumerate the numbers of the individual species in an area comprising a certain number of fields of view or transects. For delimiting the fields to be counted and for measurement of the organisms the Whipple ocular micrometer or an auxiliary slide with a grid can be used (*15*).

The size of the periphytic organisms plays an important role in the choice of a convenient counting area and an adequate magnification. For each size class of organisms a different area must be chosen, e.g., several fields of view at a high level of magnification for the smallest algae, protozoa and bacteria, one or few cm^2 for the majority of diatoms and protozoa, and the whole area of the slide for Rotifera and other larger invertebrates.

4.5.5.4 *Gravimetric analysis*

When sampling natural substrata, the periphyton is separated and an amount related to the area is sampled. Artificial substrata, such as glass slides, are more convenient since the area can be determined more accurately.

The wet and dry weight of periphyton on glass slides can be determined by weighing the slides before and after exposure. It is very convenient to mark the slides with numbers using a diamond pencil before exposure and to note the weights of the clean slides.

Equipment

Analytical balance with sensitivity of 0.1 mg.
Drying oven, double-walled, thermostatically controlled to within ±1°C.
Electric muffle furnace with automatic temperature control.

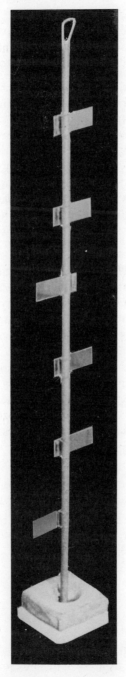

Fig. 13. Device for determining microbial growth on slides

Procedure

1. Determine the wet weight. This is an approximation because the moment when the excess moisture has been removed cannot be determined precisely.

2. Dry the material to constant weight at 105°C in a drying oven. Under field conditions, the weight of the air-dried material can be substituted.

3. Ignite the material for 1 hour at 500°C in the electric muffle furnace and weight subsequently.

4. Wet the ash again with distilled water and dry to constant weight at 105°C. This step is taken to reintroduce the water of hydration of the clay and other minerals, which is not driven off at 105°C but is lost during ashing. If not corrected for, this water loss will be recorded as volatile organic matter.

5. Calculate the ash-free dry weight (mean value for several parallel determinations) and report as grams per square metre of exposed surface. If standard glass slides are used, then the dry weight of periphyton in

$$g \cdot m^{-2} = \frac{\text{mean weight per slide } (g)}{0.00375}.$$

4.5.5.5   *Chlorophyll*

The chlorophyll content of attached communities is a useful index of the biomass of the phytoperiphyton. Because quantitative chlorophyll determinations require the collection of periphyton from a known surface area, artificial substrata are well suited for this purpose. Details are given in section 5.4.4.1.

Plexiglass (Perspex) is soluble in acetone and if used as the substratum the periphyton must be scraped from it before solvent extraction.

When the concentrations of pigments in the extract have been determined as described in section 5.4.4, the amount of pigment per unit surface area of substratum is calculated as follows:

$$Q = \frac{C \times V}{A}$$

where

Q = weight (mg) of chlorophyll a per m^2
C = weight (mg) of chlorophyll a per litre of extract
V = volume of extract in litres
A = area of substratum sampled in m^2.

4.5.5.6   *Periphyton productivity measured by biomass accumulation*

The rate of accumulation of organic matter on artificial substrata by the attachment, growth, and reproduction of colonizing organisms has been widely used to estimate the productivity of streams and reservoirs. In the application of this method, several replicate clean substrates are exposed for a predetermined period and the accumulated material is scraped from the slides and ashed as described previously. The productivity (P) in mg per square metre per day is given by the formula:

$$P = \frac{W}{T \cdot A}$$

where W is the ash-free weight (mg) per slide, T is the exposure time in days and A is the area of a slide in square metres.

Estimates of the seasonal changes in the standing crop of established communities are obtained by placing many replicate substrata at a sampling point and then retrieving a few at a time at regular intervals, such as every 2 weeks or every month, over the period of a year or longer. The gain in ash-free weight per unit area from one collection period to the next is a measure of net production.

4.5.6   *Special cases*

4.5.6.1   *Diatom species proportional counts*

The preparation of permanent diatom mounts from periphyton samples usually requires somewhat different treatment from mounts prepared from plankton samples because of the presence of large amounts of extracellular organic matter (such as the gelatinous attachment materials and formalin) which, if not removed, will lay down a thick brown or black carbonaceous deposit on the cover glass when the sample is incinerated. The organic substances can be decomposed by oxidation with ammonium persulfate before mounting the sample. Oxidation and clean-up are carried out as follows:

Place approximately 5 ml of sample in a disposable 10-ml vial. Allow to stand for 24 hours, withdraw the supernatant liquid by aspiration, replace with a 50 mg·l^{-1} solution of ammonium persulfate, and mix thoroughly. A total volume of 8 ml should not be exceeded. Heat the vial to approximately 90°C for 30 min. Allow to stand for 24 hours, withdraw the supernatant liquid, and replace with distilled water. After 3 changes of distilled water, transfer a drop of the diatom suspension to a cover glass with a disposable pipette, evaporate the water by heating, and prepare and count a mount as described for plankton diatoms, except that separated individual valves are counted as such and the count divided by 2.

4.5.6.2   *Glass slide method in man-made lakes*

In man-made lakes and reservoirs, a vertically arranged series of glass slides makes it possible to follow the water quality in the whole column. A cable, such as an electric cable, is fastened to a buoy and anchored in the bottom. Attached to the cable are corks with microscope slides, spaced approximately 1 m apart, from the surface down to the bottom. The first slide is directly on the water surface, the last one may be in contact with the mud. An analysis generally reveals 5 zones:

(1) Surface zone
(2) Zone of producers (trophogenic layer)
(3) Transition zones (compensation layer)
(4) Zone of consumers (aphotic layer)
(5) Benthic zone (with possible formation of H_2S).

The most suitable water quality for drinking water intake lies in the zone of consumers, i.e., in the upper layers of the hypolimnion during the summer stagnant period.

4.6 Benthic macroinvertebrates

4.6.1   *Scope*

Generally, the benthic invertebrate communities of the riffle reaches, where the water flows rapidly over a stony eroding substratum, are more sensitive to change in water quality than the communities in the muddy depositing substrata of the slow-flowing deep rivers. Thus, methods of using benthic invertebrates are most useful in the upper reaches of rivers—the rhithron—which have at least some riffle zones to serve as sampling stations. It may well be that in the slower flowing lower reaches—the potamon—other communities, periphyton or seston, are more suitable indicators. However mud-dwelling invertebrate communities have proved useful in the biological surveillance of water quality in lowland streams in the Netherlands (16). The use of artificial substrata could also be useful in these rivers.

In continental Europe, the Saprobic System has been commonly developed as a biological system of measuring water quality. This system is described fully in section 6.2. Originally the system was based largely on microorganisms, but as it was developed other taxa including macroinvertebrates were included. In other countries, such the United Kingdom and the USA, probably because of early scientific insulation and language barriers, adoption of the Saprobic System, with the associated classification of zones, was delayed. Instead there was an independent development of several systems using different taxa; the most popular organisms being macro-invertebrates.

The advantages of benthic macro-invertebrates as indicator organisms are:

(1) They are readily sampled qualitatively.

(2) Most are readily identifiable by the use of standard taxonomic keys.

(3) The reaction of most species to different types of pollution is well established.

(4) The specific ecological requirements of many invertebrates are known.

The disadvantages and other factors that need to be taken into account are:

(1) Because of their non-random distribution in the river bed they are difficult to sample quantitatively.

(2) Their distribution is also affected by factors other than water quality, such as current velocity and the nature of the substratum.

(3) Many, especially the insecta, have a well-defined seasonal incidence and may therefore not be found at some times of the year.

An appreciation of these difficulties, however, makes it possible to plan sampling programmes that take them into account.

4.6.2 *Definition*

Benthic macro-invertebrates are animals without backbones that are sufficiently large (> 0.5 mm) to make them clearly observable without the aid of a microscope, although for specific identification it may be necessary to examine parts of them microscopically. They live for at least part of their life-cycle associated with the substratum of the river bed. The following invertebrate taxa are usually included in the macrobenthos:

Porifera (sponges)

Platyhelminthes
 Turbellaria (flatworms)

Aschelminthes
 Ectoprocta (moss-animals)

Annelida
 Oligochaeta (true worms)
 Hirudinea (leeches)

Arthropoda
 Crustacea
 Insecta
 Arachnida (Hydracarina—water mites)

Mollusca
   Pelecypoda (bivalves—cockles and mussels)
   Gastropoda (snails and limpets).

4.6.3 *Principles*

For the successful application of biological monitoring methods in assessing water quality it is essential to have some understanding of the principles upon which they are based. In the past, misapplication of such methods, in ignorance of the principles involved, has led to misleading results and consequent mistrust of biological methods. In this section therefore, the principles are outlined in some detail.

The nature of benthic communities in lotic waters is largely determined by the following interrelated factors:

(*a*) current velocity;
(*b*) nature of the substratum;
(*c*) chemical nature of water-dissolved gases and salts;
(*d*) physical nature of water-temperature, colour, turbidity;
(*e*) zoogeographical region.

Changes in water quality that affect the chemical or physical character of the water or the nature of the substratum induce detectable changes in the benthic biota reflecting changes in ecological conditions. Whether such ecological changes constitute pollution will depend upon their magnitude in relation to water use. Some changes in the biota may reflect ecological changes involving slight changes in the nature of the water that do not, in themselves, affect the several legitimate uses of the water and do not, therefore, constitute pollution in a practical sense. Nevertheless, such changes do indicate a deterioration in conditions that, if continued, could result in pollution; they are therefore of value in pollution-preventing work in signalling potential or incipient pollution. It has been established that many of the changes in water quality that adversely affect the use of the water and amenity of the river, such as toxicity, deoxygenation, changes in acidity, salinity, organic and mineral salt concentrations, and changes in such physical factors as temperature, turbidity and suspended solid content, are all associated with observable changes in the benthic biota.

The general premise upon which biological monitoring systems are based is that by examining the benthic communities in rivers the general quality of the water flowing over them can be assessed. To derive maximum indicator information from the results of examinations of the benthic communities, an appreciation of the ecological changes induced by changes in different parameters of water quality is necessary. Although these ecological changes are most complex in detail, some generalizations are helpful. These will be considered in relation to different types of change in water quality, arbitrarily classified as:

(1) Trophic—changes in the concentration of nutrients (organic and inorganic).

(2) Chemical—e.g., toxicity, salinity hardness.

(3) Physical—e.g., temperature, suspended solids, turbidity, siltation.

4.6.3.1 *Trophic changes*

These affect the trophic structure of the benthic communities by causing an imbalance between the autotrophic and heterotrophic components. This imbalance is reflected by changes in the structure of the invertebrate riffle community, involving three major trends (Fig. 14) associated with increasing organic concentration:

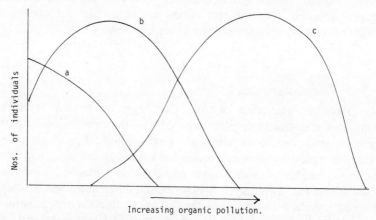

Fig. 14. Three trends exhibited by different taxa associated with increasing organic enrichment of a riffle biotope

(*a*) The progressive reduction in numbers and eventual elimination of non-tolerant species according to their degree of tolerance. These correspond to the *saprophobic* phytomicroorganisms (*17*).

(*b*) The initial increase in numbers of those species that at first tolerate the induced ecological changes and are able to benefit from the increased food available and reduced competition. As the degree of pollution increases these too are successively reduced in numbers and eventually eliminated according to their degree of tolerance. (These correspond to the *saproxenic* phytomicroorganisms.)

(c) The invasion of the habitat by species that under natural conditions are not members of the riffle community; such species are naturally found in the depositing substratum of the pool reaches or in lentic waters. As the degree of pollution further increases even these species are successively eliminated.

In the pool reaches of upland rivers and in lowland rivers with depositing substrate, the changes in benthic communities usually involves trends (a) and (b) above, although different species are involved. Since the natural community of such reaches is primarily a decomposer one involved in the breakdown of deposited natural organic materials, it is less sensitive to nutrient enrichment than the riffle community. Riffle communities are therefore more sensitive as indicators of nutrient enrichment.

Thus, with increasing nutrient enrichment, as a result of the three trends outlined above, the structure of the benthic riffle community changes, in terms both of species present and of percentage species composition. There is also a general trend for the number of species to decline while the number of individuals of the tolerant species increases. The diversity of the community is thereby reduced. The different effects are made use of by the several methods of data processing outlined in section 6.4.

4.6.3.2   Chemical changes

(a) *Toxicity*. The effect of toxic discharges on benthic invertebrate communities is relatively simple compared with the complexities of nutrient enrichment described above, although the physiological processes involved are more complex. The overall ecological consequences of toxicity are the reduction in number of species and in number of individuals, i.e., a reduction in populations and in diversity. Species exhibit different degrees of tolerance to different specific poisons. Thus, the degree of reduction in population and the number of species depends both on the specific poison and on its concentration. The selective elimination of the less tolerant species and the resultant reduction in interspecific competition or predation may, in some circumstances, result in an increase in population of the more tolerant species.

(b) *Salinity and pH*. Besides having toxic effects at extreme levels that cause similar ecological changes to those described above, less extreme conditions result in a change in species composition in which the tolerant forms and those requiring high salinity or extreme pH values become established. Such replacement communities, however, only become established when discharges are continuous, producing fairly uniform conditions; intermittent discharges may create unstable conditions in which neither the normal benthic community nor the replacement community would exist.

4.6.3.3 *Physical changes*

(*a*) *Temperature.* The indirect effects of temperature on benthic communities, which are brought about by influencing the effect of other factors, are probably more significant than the direct effects. Thermal discharges usually occur to lowland rivers where the benthic communities are naturally eurythermal and therefore relatively insensitive to temperature changes. Certain benthic invertebrate species have been associated with the warm waters below thermal discharge, including *Physa acuta* and *Branchiura sowerbyi*. These may be considered as indicators of elevated temperatures. In upland rivers where water temperatures are raised by activities such as deforestation, the oligothermal invertebrates may be adversely affected. Although the temperatures are more readily measured directly, the ecological consequences of raised temperatures are best measured by direct examination of the benthic communities.

(*b*) *Turbidity and suspended solids.* These affect the light penetration, suppressing plant life and dependent invertebrate food chains. This results in a reduction in the number of individuals of benthic invertebrates. The deposition of the solids on the river bed in a riffle zone causes siltation and this directly affects the community, a silt-loving fauna replacing the normal lithophilus one. Again, although the suspended solid concentration in the water can be readily measured, the ecological consequences are measured by direct examination of the benthic community.

4.6.4 *Sampling*

The sampling method adopted will depend upon the data processing to be used as determined by the objectives of the survey (see section 4.2).

The different methods may be considered as:

(*a*) Qualitative—when only a species list is required.

(*b*) Semiquantitative—when, in addition to a species list, some idea of the abundance of the different species in the community is required, or when the relative abundance at different sites, or at different times, needs to be compared.

(*c*) Quantitative—when the number of individuals of the different species is required; the number may be per unit of river bed, or per sample to determine the percentage species composition.

Different methods are also required for the sampling of eroding substratum typical of the upper fast-flowing reaches of rivers (rhithron) and the depositing substratum of the deeper slow-flowing stretches (potamon). Appropriate methods for these different biotopes are therefore dealt with separately. A bibliography of methods for sampling benthic invertebrates has recently been prepared (*18*).

Because the benthic communities of eroding substrate are more readily sampled and are more sensitive indicators of changes in water quality, where available in the rhithron zones of rivers, they should be selected as sampling sites. In the potamon, however, such riffles may not be available and it is then necessary to sample the depositing substrata. In interpreting the data, however, it is important to take into account the type of substratum sampled.

4.6.4.1   *Sampling of eroding substrata (riffles)*

4.6.4.1.1   *Qualitative methods*

(*a*) *Hand sampling* (Fig. 15a). The riffle communities are most readily sampled qualitatively using a hand-net having a straight lower edge (Fig. 16). Two important criteria are the mesh size and the depth of the net. The finer the mesh, the deeper should be the net bag to prevent the organisms flowing round the net opening; too deep a net, however, is inconvenient in use. For routine work 12 threads per cm with a net depth of 50 cm is recommended. The net is held against the stream bed whilst the stones immediately upstream of it are turned over in the flowing water in which the dislodged animals are carried into the net. The stones are examined and attached or clinging species are removed and added to the sample. In this way the substratum is worked over and the finer lower deposits are stirred to a depth of 10 cm to dislodge any further organisms in the depth of the river bed. This process is repeated at several places across the river to include the different biotopes within the riffles. The removal of the catch can be facilitated by washing it to one corner of the net using the flowing water and gently shaking the upper corner of the net whilst withdrawing it from the water. The net is then everted to remove the sample; and any animals clinging to the net are removed and transferred to the sample.

(*b*) *Kick sampling* (Fig. 15b). Where the fauna is sparse, owing to toxic or physical pollution for example, or where the water is too deep or cold for hand-sampling, " kick-sampling " may be useful. This is carried out using the same type of net as for hand-sampling but the sample is taken by disturbing the substratum with the heels of the boots whilst working backwards upstream and keeping the net with the straight edge on the river bed in front of the toes. By working diagonally upstream across the river different biotopes are sampled. This method is somewhat selective in that fewer of the attached animals may be taken. Where practicable therefore, some stones should be lifted and examined for these. When a comprehensive species list is required for a site it is necessary to explore thoroughly all the

(a) Hand sampling   (b) Kick sampling

(c) Quantitative sampling using cylinder sampler

Fig. 15. Methods of sampling benthic macroinvertebrates in riffles

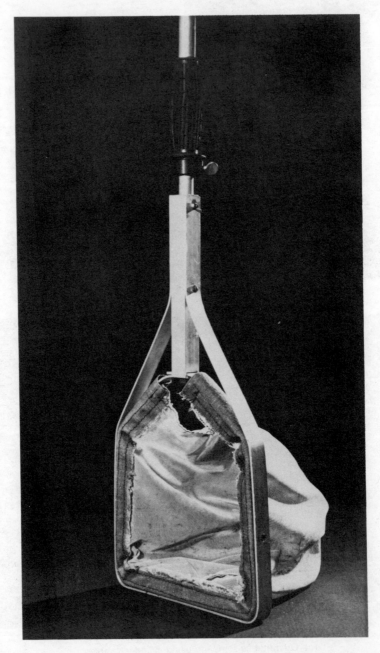

Fig. 16.   Hand-net for sampling benthic invertebrates in shallow flowing waters
(× 0.25)

biotopes, using both hand- and kick-sampling, including sweeps through weed beds and between the roots of overhanging trees.

4.6.4.1.2 *Semi-quantitative methods*

Some indication of the abundance of organisms in a clearly defined biotope may be obtained by either of the qualitative methods, described above, if sampling is continued for a timed period. With hand-sampling a period of up to 10 minutes is required, with kick-sampling a shorter period— up to 2 minutes is sufficient. Longer periods of kick-sampling in a river with a rich benthic fauna result in an unnecessary large catch to process. Excessive and frequent kick-sampling carried out at a station can also adversely affect the community one is studying. Kick-sampling should therefore be of restricted duration and reserved for situations where hand-sampling is not suitable.

To ensure comparable results, the sampling effort over the timed period should be similar. For this reason only one operator is best involved. Even then, different conditions, such as current velocity, depth, temperature (with hand-sampling), and nature of the substratum, may affect the sampling efficiency achieved for the same effort.

4.6.4.1.3 *Quantitative methods*

Basically these involve the collection of all the animals inhabiting a known area of the river bed. With the different quadrat samplers available, a given area of the river bed is partially or totally enclosed and this is hand-sampled, the dislodged animals being swept back by the current and collected in the net.

(*a*) *Surber-type sampler.* The original Surber sampler (*19*) was designed to sample an area of one-square foot of river bed (929 cm^2) and this has been modified by various workers to meet their specific needs. It consists essentially of a net (16 mesh/cm) having a square, metal-framed mouth, hinged on the lower edge to a similar sized frame (Fig. 17). In use the net is placed facing upstream with the mouth vertical and the hinged frame locked at right angles so as to delineate a known area to be sampled. Triangular cloth wings connecting the sides of the two frames partially enclose the sampling area laterally. The delineated area is then hand-sampled, the catch being carried backwards with the current to be collected in the net.

(*b*) *Cylinder sampler* (Fig. 18). Again modifications of a basic principle may be used. In general, a known area (0.05 or 0.1 m^2) of the river bed is totally enclosed by the cylinder, which is some 50 cm high. The lower edge of the cylinder may be serrated to facilitate it being pushed into the river bed. Water flows into the cylinder through a perforated plate facing

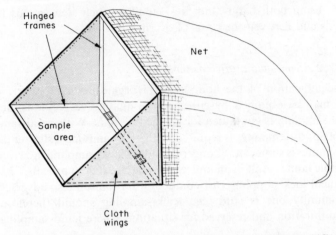

Fig. 17. Surber-type sampler for benthic macroinvertebrates (*19*)

upstream and passes out through a port downstream to which is attached the stainless steel sampling net (16 mesh per cm). The area enclosed is hand-sampled and the catch is carried backwards by the current to be collected in the detachable net. Three samples are usually taken (Fig. 15c).

4.6.4.2 *Depositing substrata sampling*

4.6.4.2.1 *Qualitative sampling*

This is usually performed for the purpose of producing a species list for the station being sampled. The effectiveness of the sampling depends, more than in other habitats, on the expertise of the sampler and his recognition of the different microhabitats available at the station. Because in such river zones the presence or absence of species is naturally affected by several factors other than water quality, species lists from different stations need to be carefully interpreted in light of the natural conditions of the sampling site; these should therefore be carefully recorded at the time of sampling. A variety of techniques are available for qualitative sampling and none may be regarded as standard, different samplers preferring different methods. The choice of method will also depend upon the nature of the river and substratum and whether macrovegetation is present. In deeper waters, dredges or trawls are used and some of these are provided with means of closing the net as it is lowered or raised through the overlying water. Such devices are discussed in *12, 20 & 21*. In the shallower littoral zone, hand nets or screens on poles can be used to collect from macrophytes and other substrata. Grabs, described in the next section for quantitative sampling can, of course also be used for qualitative sampling.

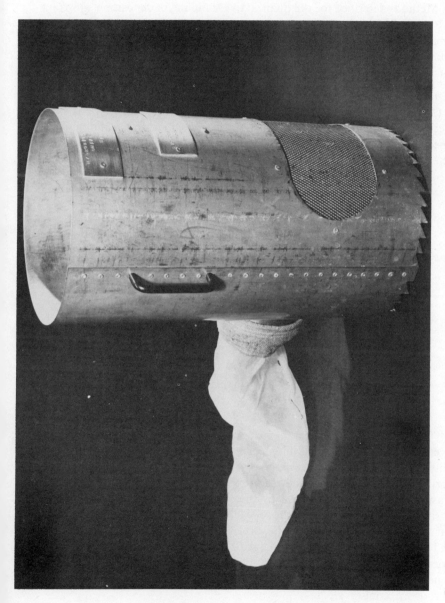

Fig. 18. The Aston cylinder sampler for quantitative sampling of benthic invertebrates in shallow flowing waters (× 0.36)

4.6.4.2.2   *Quantitative sampling*

Methods described for the quantitative sampling of depositing substrata give imprecise estimates of the populations and, at best, should be regarded as semi-quantitative. In water quality control work however, where the relative abundance of species is important, and knowledge of precise populations is not necessary, such methods are useful.

(*a*) Grabs. Several types of grab are available and are described in detail in (*10*) & (*12*). The nature of the substrata determines which type is most effective. For hard substrata, such as clay, coarse sands, and gravels, especially in swift currents and deep waters, the heavier grabs such as the Petersen and the Ponar, which is a modification of the former, are most useful. This type of grab (Fig. 19) is activated by the joint effect of gravity and

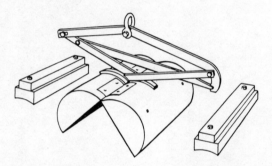

Fig. 19.   The Petersen grab for sampling hard substrata

Reproduced from US Standard Methods (*158*)

levers. As the grab, which is in the form of two hinged halves of a cylinder, is gently lowered through the water the jaws are kept open by means of a horizontal bar, which is positioned across the levers and is locked by the tension on the levers produced by the weight of the grab. With the grab positioned on the substratum, the rope tension is eased causing the horizontal bar to disengage and allow the jars to close under the joint forces of gravity and leverage as the grab is raised. Auxiliary weights may be bolted on the sides of the grab; these help to stabilize the grab in strong currents, aid penetration of hard substrata, and enhance the cutting force through hard or fibrous materials.

For sampling soft bottom deposits, such as light silt, mud and fine sand, the Ekman grab (Fig. 20) is most suitable. This grab is light, the jaws being closed by strong springs activated by a messenger-type tripping device. The springed jaws are manually cocked and care must be exercised in handling this

(a)

Fig. 20. The Ekman grab fitted on a pole for sampling benthic invertebrates in depositing substratum (× 0.33). (a) Set with jaws open for sampling, (b) Jaws closed retaining sample.

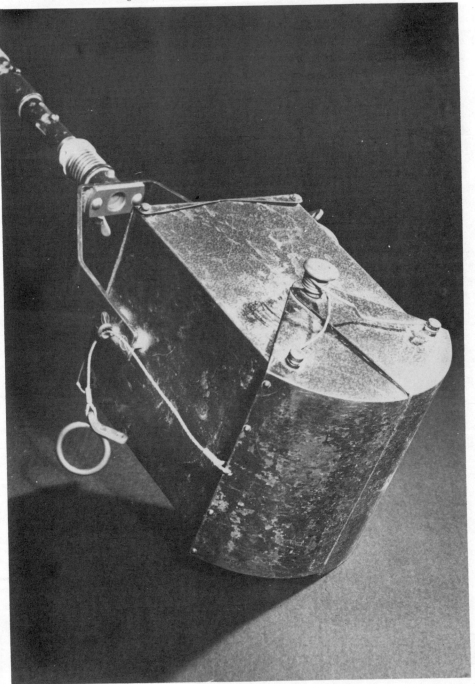

(b)

type of grab as it can cause injury if accidentally released. The grab is essentially a square box closed at the bottom by the spring-operated jaws and at the top by two thin, hinged, overlapping lids. During descent through the water with the jaws locked open, the upper hinged lids open to allow the free passage of water through them, thus minimizing disturbance and shock waves. On raising the sampler, the upper lids close, entrapping the sample. The upper lids also permit the examination and possible subsampling of the surface layers of the sampler after retrieval.

The imprecision of the grab sample is due to several factors and an appreciation of these enables them to be minimized. Although the surface area of substratum sampled can be determined, the volume of the sample depends upon the depth of penetration and angle of closure of the jaws; these factors, which are inherent in the design of the grab, also affect the proportion of substratum sampled at different depths within the sample. In this respect, the Ekman grab, with its rectangular box shape, deep penetration in soft substrata, and the sharp angle of closure of the jaws is probably superior.

In very light deposits, care must be taken to prevent the Ekman sampler sinking too deeply into the deposit before closure, otherwise the epibenthic invertebrates, such as *Asellus*, some chironomid larvae and *Sialis* and those in the upper layers of the deposit, may be lost. It is recommended that the grab should not be filled to within 5 cm of the top and that on retrieval the upper layers should be undisturbed.

In rivers less than 2 m deep, it is possible to use the Ekman grab on a pole, thus providing greater control over the positioning of the sampler on the bottom.

All grabs suffer from a tendency for the jaws to fail to close completely when they become fouled by large objects—stones, twigs, etc. If this occurs, the samples should not be used for quantitative analysis.

Interference is also caused by the shock wave produced as the sampler approaches the bottom, as this disturbs the epibenthic invertebrates. In the Ekman sampler described above and in the Ponar modification of the Petersen grab, this interference is minimized by the fitting of side curtains and by the screen on top through which the water flows thus reducing the shock wave.

In deep, rapid-flowing rivers, benthic grab sampling is most difficult and for water quality control work sampling is best done towards the banks where the fauna is naturally richer and more abundant. The sampler should of course be taken in the main river flow so that it is representative of the water quality of the river. Alternatively, below a discharge into a large river, samples can be taken on the two banks of the river for comparison. On very large impounded rivers where lentic conditions exist, the plankton could prove a more useful indication of water quality.

(*b*) *Core samplers.* Several coring devices are available for taking core samples of relatively homogeneous soft sediments sufficiently compacted to ensure retention of the sampler on retrieval. However, because the area sampled by most such core samplers is small (25 cm²) they are not useful for sampling most macroinvertebrate communities other than oligochaetes.

(*c*) *Cylinder samplers.* For sampling sluggish streams less than 60 cm deep, large diameter cylinder samplers of the stovepipe type (Wilding sampler) may be used (Fig. 21). These are particularly useful for sampling

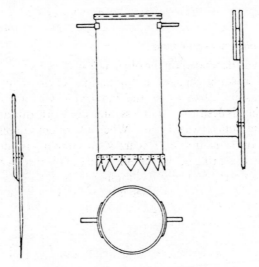

Fig. 21.   Wilding stovepipe sampler

Reproduced from US Standard Methods (*158*)

weed beds. They consist essentially of a strong metal cylinder some 30 cm in diameter and 75 cm long, provided with teeth on the lower edge and handles near the upper end. The cylinder is pushed, if necessary by a rotary cutting action, into the substratum. This encloses the invertebrates among the vegetation and in the bottom deposits. The enclosed vegetation and coarser substrate material is collected by hand and the invertebrates are then removed from this. The remaining material is repeatedly stirred, the suspension poured off, and the invertebrates removed by sieving. Although the process is laborious and time consuming, in difficult habitats in slow moving waters it is probably the only method of obtaining a reliable quantitative sample of benthic invertebrates.

4.6.4.3   *Number of samples needed*

To determine populations of benthic organisms in a riffle, it is necessary to take large numbers of samples to achieve statistically acceptable results (22). The number of samples required would be impracticable in routine work. Fortunately, fewer samples suffice for comparative studies or where the relative abundance of a species in a population is needed to determine community structure as indicative of water quality. Three to five samples are usually sufficient for such studies. Because of the contagious distribution of invertebrates in the benthic biotopes, it is preferable to take a number of smaller samples rather than one large sample.

4.6.4.4 *Frequency of sampling*

This again will depend upon the objectives of the survey. Ideally, because of the natural seasonal changes in populations of many invertebrates and because of seasonal changes in the induced environmental conditions, monthly sampling is desirable. For less intensive work, quarterly sampling is adequate; a minimum is twice a year. When infrequent sampling is practised, it should be at the same time each year; when sampling is done twice a year, this should be in the spring before the emergence of the insects and again in the autumn. In contrast to chemical sampling, it is not necessary for all the stations in a river stretch to be sampled in a single day, but sampling should be completed within a few days—say one week. High flows caused by the occasional storm can scour out the river bed and cause a marked reduction in the population of some species. Conversely, after a prolonged period of low flow, large populations of some species become established. It is therefore advisable to record any abnormal flow conditions in the period preceding the day of sampling.

4.6.4.5 *Other methods*

4.6.4.5.1 *Artificial substratum samplers*

Since the nature of the substratum is an important determinant of benthic community structure, standardized substratum samplers are sometimes used. These may consist of trays, cages, or net bags fitted with natural river bed stones. Others are artificial structures designed to present a large surface for colonization, e.g., the multiple-plate sampler (Fig. 22) and the standard *Aufwuchs* unit (S.AUF.U.) being developed for the Water Data Unit (Department of the Environment) for use in British rivers (Fig. 23). In shallower waters—less than 1 m deep—the samplers are secured to the bottom by pegging or weighting. In deeper waters, the sampler is suspended from anchored floats so that it lies in the euphotic zone within 1.2 m of the surface.

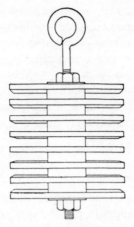

Fig. 22.   Multiple-plate or Hester-Dendy sampler

Reproduced from US Standard Methods (*158*)

In natural riffle zones of rivers, the artificial substrate sampler will be colonized by members of the local riffle benthic community.   In deeper waters with a depositing substratum, the artificial substrate sampler is colonized both from the local epibenthic invertebrates and the drift organisms, possibly from an upstream riffle.   Thus, whereas in a riffle zone the community developing on an artificial substrate sampler is representative of the local riffle community, 70–80% of the species colonizing it within 14 days, the community developed on an artificial substratum positioned in a depositing substratum zone of a river is not representative of the local benthic community but is a typical *Aufwuchs* community containing species not present in the local benthic community.   Artificial substrata do not therefore sample, even qualitatively, the natural depositing substratum community; nevertheless, the *Aufwuchs* community colonizing them may be of use in monitoring river water quality.   Such communities take longer to become established than those in the riffle zones.   Unless it can be established that the community is fully established earlier, a period of 6 weeks' exposure should be allowed before removal.   When the samplers are retrieved, they should be lifted in a dip net to prevent the escape of animals.

Difficulties experienced with the use of artificial substrata include: positioning of the sampler so as not to be a hazard to navigation or a nuisance to anglers, loss by vandalism, and the fouling of the sampler by detached algal mats and other floating materials.

4.6.4.5.2   *Drift samplers*

Many benthic invertebrates migrate or are washed from the river bed and

Fig. 23. Standard *Aufwuchs* unit (S.AUF.U.)—an artificial substratum for use in biological surveillance of deep rivers using macroinvertebrates (× 1)

are carried downstream in the flow. This drift fauna can be sampled by placing suitable nets across the flow of the river as described in detail in *23*. After a few hours, large numbers of different invertebrate species and insect exuviae will usually be taken, and since the drift occurs over relatively short distances these may be taken as representative of the immediate upstream fauna.

4.6.4.5.3 *Electrofishing*

Electrofishing techniques have been used to study benthic invertebrate communities but such methods are very selective; some species react more strongly than others.

4.6.5 *Sample processing*

Individual workers prefer different methods of processing benthic samples, which mostly involves the separation of the animals from other materials taken in the sample, and the subsequent sorting, identification and counting, as required. The method of processing will also be determined by the nature of the sample—whether it is a riffle sample or a grab sample from a depositing substratum.

The degree of sample processing will be determined by the requirements of the data processing technique adopted, as discussed in section 6.4. The different degrees of processing are the following:

(*a*) full identification and counting of the species and individuals in each species determined;

(*b*) determination of the number of species present (without necessarily identifying them) and the number of individuals of each species;

(*c*) identification of all species present without counting them;

(*d*) identification of all species present and an estimation of their frequency;

(*e*) identification of key taxonomic groups only;

(*f*) identification of key taxonomic groups and an estimation of their frequency.

Whatever the subsequent processing used, immediate examination on site in the field is recommended. Some delicate organisms, such as Turbellaria may be destroyed beyond recognition when transported in a bulk sample. Preliminary examination of the sample on a white tray may be carried out in the field when general observations on the fauna can be recorded; a pocket type tape recorder is most useful for this purpose. For some requirements, when only taxa lists are needed, many taxa, depending upon the degree of taxonomic penetration, can be identified in the field and returned to the river. Identification to species level usually requires examination in the laboratory and for this purpose the sample should be transported to the laboratory in specimen tubes preserved in formalin, where appropriate. Semiquantitative sampling may also be carried out in the field and even though only taxa lists are required it is useful to record the relative abundance of the different species, using the following abbreviations: r—rare; o—occasional; f—frequent; a—abundant.

The absence of any species from a habitat where it would normally be expected to be present is also worth noting, as the absence of such species may be of greater significance than the presence of others. Noting the absence of a species provides a more positive record than its omission from a species list, which may be accidental or an oversight.

Quantitative samples are best processed in the laboratory. Care should be taken in the transport of the sample for this purpose. Large stones and sticks, etc. may be removed in the field after carefully removing from them any attached invertebrates. The sample is then transferred to a numbered wide-mouthed plastic jar or bag. The specimens are most easily sorted and identified alive, but this must be done soon after sampling. Where that is possible, the water is allowed to drain from the catch before transferring to a plastic bag; in the absence of free water, predation and asphyxiation are prevented. In most cases there is a delay between sampling and processing, in which case the sample should be preserved in the field to prevent specimens being eaten and to stop decay. The sample may be preserved by the addition of formalin to the sample in water (50 ml of formalin to 1 litre of sample). Some workers find the subsequent processing of such samples objectionable, even after they have been washed in water; others consider the use of formalin a health hazard and prefer to add methanol to produce a 700 ml·l^{-1} solution. In either case, to ensure adequate preservation the bulk sample should not occupy more than half the container to leave room for the preservative. The samples should be kept as cool as possible and once they reach the laboratory they should be placed in a cold room to await further processing, which should be carried out as early as possible.

In the field, the sample should be adequately labelled using water-resistant paper and a soft lead pencil, the label being placed inside the jar with the sample. As a precaution, a note may be made of the reference number of the sample jar along with other necessary notes on the nature of the river bed, flow, etc. Any small specimens occurring infrequently in the sample that are spotted in the preliminary field examination are best removed and put in a small sealed plastic vial, which is then placed in the larger bulk sample container.

4.6.5.1   *Quantitative analysis*

4.6.5.1.1   *Eroding substratum samples*

Riffle benthic samples, however taken, are likely to contain extraneous matter in the form of stones, fine silt, and vegetable matter, both living and dead. Although laborious, the most effective way of recovering all the invertebrates is by picking over the sample by hand. The heavier stones and silt can best be separated by placing the sample in water in a long trough through which water is flowing at such a velocity that the heavier particles settle and the lighter ones, including the animals, are carried forward to be recovered from the wash water by passing through a sieve (mesh size 0.5 mm). The deposited stones are examined for attached animals before they are discarded. The larger vegetable material—leaves and twigs in the sample—are removed from the sieve and again examined for attached invertebrates; the remainder of the sample is then distributed evenly in a thin layer over a shallow white tray from which all animals visible to the naked eye are removed by forceps or a metal spatula. The earlier addition of a dye to the sample when preserving it enables the smaller organisms to be more readily detected in the debris. On removal, the animals are sorted into major taxa for subsequent identification. If this is delayed, they should be preserved in 90% methanol (900 ml $\cdot$ l^{-1}) in sealed labelled containers. To estimate the number of very abundant organisms, such as chironomid larva or tubifucid worms, a subsample is taken. This can be achieved by using a white tray that has previously been marked off in areas of approximately 5 cm^2; to avoid large errors, the area counted should be not less than one quarter of the whole. The provision of marked subareas also facilitates the counting of the whole of the tray. Some workers use flotation techniques, involving the use of sugar or saline solutions or air bubbling, to separate the invertebrates from the debris. Although a high proportion are removed in this manner, thus reducing the need for hand-sorting, recovery is not 100% and the debris should still be examined by hand-sorting for the remaining specimens, some of which may be attached to the heavier debris.

4.6.5.1.2   *Depositing substratum samples*

Because of the large amount of extraneous material involved, many workers prefer to carry out the initial stages of processing in the field so as to reduce the bulk of sample to be carried and preserved. Living animals are less damaged in the process of sieving than when dead. The sample is suspended in screened water in a bucket by stirring, and the suspension is then strained through a sieve of mesh 0.5 mm. Any large pieces of debris should be removed before stirring and where necessary the suspensions may be passed through coarser sieves (1–0.5 cm mesh). The sieved material is washed and then transferred to preservative in vials for transport to the laboratory where it is sorted on trays, as described for riffle samples. Artificial substratum samplers are most readily processed, since they usually contain a minimum amount of extraneous matter. The sampler and any animals recovered in the net used in retrieving the sampler are transferred to a plastic bag for transport to the laboratory. The medium and the contents of the bag are washed into a volume of water, care being taken to remove attached animals. The animals are then collected on a sieve and sorted as above.

Using a stereoscopic microscope (up to 40 × magnification) most species can be identified, although for examination of the finer detail necessary for some species determination, a compound microscope (up to 100 × magnification) is necessary. The taxonomic level to which the specimens are identified will be determined by the requirements of the system used (Fig. 40, section 6.4.2). Because of differences in the geographic distribution of invertebrates throughout Europe, individual workers must use the appropriate taxonomic keys for their areas. The different possible methods by which invertebrate data may be processed in connexion with water quality surveillance are outlined in section 6.4.

4.7 Macrophytes

4.7.1 *Scope*

Although in aquatic ecosystems macrophytes do not assume the role of major primary producers, as they do in terrestrial ecosystems, the algae usually being more important, they are nevertheless conspicuous members of most freshwater ecosystems. Their presence is of significance to man, being beneficial in some respects (they provide shelter for fish and fish food organisms and substratum for periphyton and they have aesthetic value), but in others they are detrimental, especially when in profuse amounts, because they impede navigation, interfere with angling, impair drainage, and affect the oxygen balance. Conversely, man's activities, such as flow regulation and discharge of effluents, affect the distribution and abundance of macrophytes.

Although some macrophytes were listed as indicators of water quality by Kolkwitz & Marsson (*24*) in their earlier work on the saprobic system, they have in the past not been a popular taxa in biological water quality classification systems. It is true that they cannot be recommended for use on their own as a basis for a water quality classification system; nevertheless, because they are so conspicuous and readily sampled, at least qualitatively, and because they are intrinsically of applied significance, it would seem reasonable to include them in any biological water quality survey.

4.7.2   *Definition*

The term macrophytes includes all higher plants living in freshwaters having cells differentiated into tissues, including the mosses, liverworts, ferns, and flowering plants. The following groups are recognized:

Floating—free-floating or anchored plants with most of their leaf-stem tissue at or above the water surface, rising and falling with the water level, e.g., *Lemna, Nuphar.*

Submerged—plants with most or all of their vegetative tissue beneath the water surface, only the reproductive structures being sometimes aerial, e.g., *Ceratophyllum.*

Emergent—rooted or anchored plants with most of their leaf-stem tissue above the water surface, the height being unaffected by the water level, e.g., *Sparganium.*

Although not strictly macrophytes, as defined above, filamentous algae that produce macroscopic growths, e.g., *Cladophora,* are sometimes considered as macrophytes.

4.7.3   *Principles*

The distribution of macrophytes is influenced by several natural factors including:

- the current, depth and nature of the substratum;
- the availability of nutrients and dissolved gases;
- light.

Different plant communities have become established on different rock types, e.g., soft rocks and hard rocks. For rooted emergent plants there is evidence that the nutrients are supplied mainly or entirely from the soil. The trophic status of the stream for macrophytes therefore depends on the amount of silt and its nutrient content. Floating and submerged plants are thought to derive their nutrients directly from the water; when roots are present they act only as anchors. Different plant communities are therefore to be found in different freshwater biotopes because of natural causes. Some river zones, e.g., trout becks, are characteristically sparse in rooted plants.

Changes in water quality may affect macrophytes in the following ways:

(1) An increase in nutrient status causes a change in the plant community and increased growth (eutrophication).

(2) Decrease in species diversity.

(3) Decrease in sensitive species.

(4) Increase in the most tolerant species with severe pollution, when all are eliminated, e.g., *Potamogeton pectinatus, P. crispus, Schoenoplectus lacustris, Sparganium emersum, and S. erectum.*

(5) Herbicides cause a drastic decrease in most species at concentrations not apparently affecting other organisms in the biocoenose.

(6) Single toxic discharges may kill part or all of the plants present but have no permanent effect, the vegetation recovering rapidly after the event.

(7) Low level chronic toxic pollution is more damaging to plant communities. When such pollution ceases, because its effects are not quickly lost from the substratum, the vegetation may not recover for up to 2–4 years (25).

The use of macrophytes as indicators of water quality therefore requires even more careful interpretation of the data than the use of other taxa.

4.7.4 *Sampling methods*

4.7.4.1 *Qualitative sampling*

This involves the identification of all the macrophytes species present. Some can be identified *in situ*. To collect specimens different methods are available, depending upon the depth of the water. In shallow waters, wading and collection by hand or garden rake is most appropriate, in deeper waters a grapnel or weighted hook on the end of a rope is useful for collecting submerged plants, while a hook on a pole is useful for collecting leaf bases from roots. Grabs may also be used and skin-diving techniques may also be employed by suitably experienced workers.

When it is necessary to obtain specimens for subsequent identification in the laboratory, it is essential that appropriate material be collected. Since aquatic macrophytes have often to be identified from vegetative parts, only the necessary parts must be included and these must be of sufficient length to show the branching pattern. With emergent plants, aquatic and aerial parts must be included. The specimens should be transported in sealed, watertight, plastic bags within a rigid container. They should be kept in the shade and as cool as possible. For examination in the field or the laboratory, they are best floated out in water in a wide, shallow, white dish.

When reproductive parts are available, identification may be achieved by the use of an appropriate flora for the region. Some keys are also available for identification from vegetative parts only (26).

4.7.4.2 *Semi-quantitative sampling*

Even in qualitative sampling, most workers record the dominance and relative abundance of the species present. Although this is necessarily a subjective assessment, it adds much to a mere species list for little extra effort involved. A somewhat more objective assessment may be made by dividing the river into a series of transects in which the percentage cover and percentage species composition of successive 0.5-m widths of river bed are estimated. It is also useful at the same time to record the depth of water at each 0.5-m point and the depth of the vegetation. All of these data can then be presented diagrammatically as a transverse vertical section across the river.

4.7.4.3 *Quantitative sampling*

Although this will not be required in routine biological surveillance for water quality monitoring, it could be useful in special investigations on eutrophication, thermal enrichment, and toxic discharges. It usually involves the measurement of the biomass of plants (standing crop) per unit area of bed. The total plant material or that of individual species is collected from within small areas (quadrats) marked by a floating wooden framework of predetermined area anchored to the bottom. In shallow waters, a large-diameter cylinder or core sampler, as described for use in sampling benthic invertebrates (see Fig. 21) may be used.

The wet weight of the whole sample is determined after draining under standard conditions for a predetermined time. The dry weight is determined by taking a subsample of known wet weight and reweighing after drying at 105°C for 24 hours. The dry weight biomass of the plant material per unit area can then be calculated.

By determining the standing crop at predetermined intervals a measure of productivity can be obtained.

5. COMMUNITY METABOLISM

5.1 Scope

All organisms linked to metabolic processes in the environment have a specific function in energy transfer. Phototrophs use part of the incident solar energy to synthesize organic substances and thus store up potential energy. This is the basis of the system of heterotrophic consumers and decomposers (bacteria, fungi) where the gradual degradation of organic matter is associated with a loss in potential energy.

If the process leads to closer food relationships between the organisms, food chains develop. Frequently, however, much more complex connexions (food webs) result (*27, 28*). This gives rise to a specific community structure with gradual energy (food) transfer from the basis (level of primary production) to the consumer and decomposer level. These relationships, termed " trophic structures " in American literature, can be represented in various ways (*28*). For example, beginning with the lowest level (primary producers), a pyramid of numbers (trophic pyramid) is built up for the following consumer levels on the basis of individual counts (*29*). The biomass of the organisms, measured as dry weight and expressed in calorific values or as cell volume or individual volume, is better suited for the purpose than the abundance of organisms. The production of organic matter and its degradation by organisms are a component of the total metabolic activity and related to the structure of the biocoenosis. Biocoenoses may thus be considered as indicators of the metabolic activity in a water (*30*). The structure of the biocoenosis, i.e., the pattern of its component functional units and the way they are supplied with oxygen (producers/consumers), is of fundamental importance. The trophic level—primary producers, herbivores, decomposers, carnivores—on which the energy transfer takes place is a decisive factor (*29, 31–41*).

5.2 Field of application

Community metabolism in streams, rivers, lakes, reservoirs, or any kind of waterway may be examined with different objectives in mind. The objective of such surveys should be clearly identified as this may affect the method of sampling, the analytical procedure, and the method of data processing. In most cases, however, the main objective will be to examine, how organic pollution, such as domestic sewage, or toxic effluents, affects the community structure or the metabolic activity (bioactivity) of the organisms involved. For practical purposes, analyses of metabolic activity are often linked to oxygen balance measurements of polluted aquatic system.

5.3 Definition

Community metabolism may be defined as a complex process, involving the import, export, and storage of energy or organic matter within the community. The efficiency of each transfer is linked to the metabolic activity of the various types of organism involved. Heterotrophic microorganisms play key roles at each stage in the decomposition of dead organisms and of their excretory products. The energy that is not stored or exported from the community system is ultimately degraded as heat and is lost. Important information about energy flow (or transformation of organic matter) can be gained from (*a*) the determination of primary productivity and (*b*) the evaluation of community respiration.

5.4   Methods for determining primary productivity

5.4.1   *Scope*

Primary production is the basis of the entire biogenous cycle in aquatic environments, the organic substance being produced by photo-autotrophic organisms (plants, algae, bacteria with assimilation pigments). The basic process involved is photosynthesis, which can be represented by the general equation:

$$6CO_2 + 6H_2O \xrightarrow[\text{light}]{282\,kJ} C_6H_{12}O_6 + 6O_2$$

According to Van-Niel (*42*), the photosynthetic reaction can also be understood as a redox process:

$$CO_2 + 2AH_2 \xrightarrow[\text{energy}]{h \cdot v} (HCOH) + 2A + H_2O$$

where AH_2 stands for the H_2-donator, e.g., water (H_2O), hydrogen sulfide (H_2S), or reduced organic hydrocarbon compounds.

The reaction equation shows which parameters are of decisive importance for the measurement of the primary production rate: O_2-production, the formation of organic substance, and hydrocarbon assimilation. For the analysis of these parameters, various methods have been developed which are based either on *in situ* measurements or on *in vitro* tests, all of which attempt to determine the intensity of primary production from the biomass formed.

In situ measurements can be performed in two ways: parameters such as O_2 present and pH may be measured directly in the water, or samples may be taken and exposed *in situ* for a certain test period. During exposure *in situ*, local conditions such as light, temperature, and nutrients remain essentially the same; tests under laboratory conditions can only be complementary. Frequently, however, the conditions are merely kept constant, taking into account the physiological tolerance of the primary producers, so as to facilitate intercomparison of different series of measurements.

5.4.2   *Oxygen light and dark bottle technique*

This simple and widely used method has the advantage that every average laboratory is equipped for the determination of oxygen, either titrimetrically by the Winkler technique or electrometrically by means of membrane electrodes. It was used first by Gaarder & Gran (*43*) and is generally known as the light-dark-bottle method.

5.4.2.1   *Principles*

Under the influence of solar energy, the phytoplankton present in all surface waters, at least during the summer months, produces glucose by assimilation of carbon dioxide. In the course of this photochemical synthesis, oxygen is set free (gross production). At the same time, the phyto-organisms consume oxygen for the katabolic process (respiration). The quantitative difference between the formation of oxygen in the course of gross photosynthetic production and the consumption of oxygen during respiration is called the net production. Normally, the amount is positive in the daytime and negative at night, when respiration predominates. As long as organic substances are synthesized in the surface water (" primary production " during the growing period), net production is positive, even when considered over 24-hour periods (day-and-night periods). During that time, " biogenous aeration " takes place in the surface water.

5.4.2.2   *Interferences*

Interferences by oxidizable substances are possible if the BOD_1 of the water to be analysed exceeds its oxygen content. On the other hand, the presence of pollutants, e.g., industrial wastewater, should not be considered as an interference with the measuring procedure as they affect the water uniformly.

5.4.2.3   *Instruments and chemicals*

All instruments and all chemicals are needed for the usual oxygen measurement. The oxygen bottles used should be of colourless glass and be fitted with reliable suspension devices that will not darken the bottles (steel, brass, or Perlon wire loops with eye rings).

Also required are water-resistance covers of plastic foil that are impervious to light and shaped to fit the oxygen bottles, as well as a measuring tape or chain that can be kept afloat by buoys and held in a stretched vertical position by suspended weights; this measuring tape should be provided with pairs of snap hooks spaced at 20-cm intervals for holding the eye rings of the bottles.

5.4.2.4   *Procedure*

The number and location of points in the vertical section of the surface water at which primary production is to be measured should be determined before the start of the test. For each measuring point, two oxygen bottles fitted with a suspension device should be filled with water drawn by a scoop or pump from the depth at which this pair of samples is to be held for measurement, and all gas bubbles should be excluded. One sample from each pair should be darkened by means of a cover that is impervious to light. After all the samples have been prepared in this way and hooked up at the corresponding points of the measuring chain, the latter is lowered into the water at the sampling point. Care should be taken to make sure that the arrangement is kept in the vertical position by sufficiently heavy weights and is not shadowed by, for example, buoys or watercraft. The uppermost pair of samples should hang just below the water surface. At the conclusion of the test period (which may be 1 to 3 or 24 hours, depending on the purpose of the measurement), the oxygen in all the samples should be fixed without delay, and its concentration measured.

Provided that there is no stratification, in particular no stratification of the phytoplankton at the measuring site (as is usually the case in running waters), the complicated and time-consuming sampling at specified depths can be dispensed with in favour of samples taken from the water surface.

The determination of the oxygen content of the water at the start of the test, while not absolutely necessary, is recommended. If stratification exists, the oxygen content must be determined at all depths of the vertical section at which pairs of samples are to be suspended.

The duration of the exposure depends on the specific purpose of the test. In most cases, interest is focused on the 24-hour balance of the biogenus aeration. This can be determined by means of long-duration tests (24 hours) or a series of short-duration tests. Experience gained in limnology shows that the values obtained from the long-duration tests are, generally, rather low.

This method serves to determine the gross production (photosynthesis, including algal respiration). As algal respiration cannot be determined separately from bacterial respiration, net production (photosynthesis less algal respiration) cannot be measured. However, net production can be estimated if respiration in the dark bottle is taken into account and if it is assumed that algal respiration accounts for 50% of this oxygen consumption. The net production is then given by subtracting this amount from the gross production.

5.4.2.5 *Calculation*

The primary production can be calculated according to the following formulae:

$$\text{gross production} = \frac{(HF - DF) \times 0.375 \times 10^3}{PQ} \ (\text{mg of C per m}^3)$$

$$\text{respiration} = (AF - DF) \times 0.375 \times RQ \times 10^3 \ (\text{mg of C per m}^3)$$

where

$$PQ \text{ is the photosynthesis quotient} = \frac{+ \Delta O_2}{- \Delta CO_2}$$

RQ is the respiration quotient $= \dfrac{+\Delta CO_2}{-\Delta O_2}$

10^3 = conversion factor from litres to cubic metres
0.375 = conversion factor from mg of O_2 to mg of C
AF = oxygen content of the water at the start of the test in mg per litre
HF = oxygen content of the light bottles in mg per litre
DF = oxygen content of the dark bottles in mg per litre.

For normal phytoplankton populations a PQ of 1.25 and an RQ of 0.8 can be recommended. If the production rate in a measuring series is simultaneously determined as a function of depth in the water body, the results should be tabulated or, even better, represented graphically with the production rates (mg of C per m^3) on the x-axis and the depth of exposure below the water surface, in metres, on the y-axis. The quantity of carbon assimilated under $1\ m^2$ of surface is calculated by means of graphic integration or with the aid of a planimeter.

5.4.3   *Carbon-14 light and dark bottle technique*

The ^{14}C-method is, without doubt, a very sensitive method for the determination of primary production. Since its introduction into hydrobiology by Steemann-Nielsen (*44*), it has been amended and complemented in a variety of ways. At an IBP (International Biological Programme) Symposium on Primary Productivity held in 1965 at Pallanza, Italy, experts discussed the ^{14}C-method thoroughly with a view to giving a clear picture of its practicability and to preparing recommendations for its application and standardization.

The procedures described below are based on the instructions given by Vollenweider (*45*) and by Sorokin & Kadota (*50*).

5.4.3.1   *Preparation of ^{14}C working solutions*

The "working solution" or "stock solution" is the solution that is ultimately used in ^{14}C productivity assays; its preparation is not dependent on the kind of counting equipment used. Labelled carbon compounds are now available in a large variety of forms, either directly from radioisotope production centres or through national agencies and representatives. In some countries special licences are need to obtain radioisotopes.

The normal form in which radiocarbon is used in productivity studies is a dilute $Na_2{}^{14}CO_3$ solution. Such a solution can be prepared either by dilution of a commercial solution of high specific concentration (1–5 mCi in 0.5–2 ml), or from solid $Ba^{14}CO_3$.

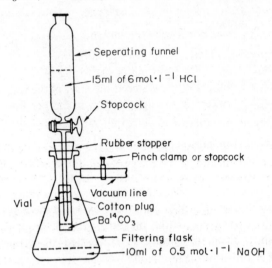

Fig. 24.   One-vessel device for preparing ^{14}C working solutions from solid $Ba^{14}CO_3$

Reproduced from IBP Handbook (50) after Doty & Oguri (46)

In the latter case, the radioactive barium carbonate must be transformed to sodium carbonate in a closed evacuated system by acidification of the barium carbonate and absorption of the evolved $^{14}CO_2$ in a sodium hydroxide solution. A simple one-chamber apparatus for this purpose has first been described by Steemen-Nielsen (44) and is shown in Fig. 24.

For the preparation of 400 ml of working solution proceed as follows:

(1) Prepare a 0.5 NaOH solution. Weigh a slightly larger amount of NaOH than is needed for 100 ml of solution (about 2.1 g), wash the surface rapidly with double-distilled water and dissolve the rest in 100 ml of double-distilled, boiled water. This solution has to be freshly prepared every time a working solution is made up.

(2) 10 ml of this solution are poured into the vacuum flask (Fig. 24).

(3) Bring the radioactive barium carbonate + carrier[a] into the vial, and fix this vial to the rubber stopper so that it hangs inside the flask with the mouth of the separating funnel about 1 cm above the barium carbonate. Close the upper part of the vial loosely with cotton wool as indicated in the figure. Close the vacuum flask and pour into the separating funnel 15 ml of $6 \text{ mol} \cdot \text{l}^{-1}$ HCl.

---

[a] The total weight of high activity $Ba^{14}CO_3$ may be too low to be measured with a normal analytical balance, and furthermore the amount of CO_2 evolved may be insufficient for complete transfer to the alkaline solution. For this reason, a certain amount of carrier, i.e., non-labelled barium carbonate, is added to the labelled portion. The amount added depends on the alkalinity of the water to be assayed.

(4) Evacuate and check for leaks; then close the pinch clamp or stopcock.

(5) Add acid in *small* portions to the vial until no further evolution of CO_2 occurs. Close the stopcock of the separating funnel and wait at least one hour. To ensure complete absorption of the evolved CO_2 in the NaOH solution, place the vacuum flask on a magnetic stirrer at a low speed.

(6) Slowly open the pinch clamp or stopcock and remove the separating funnel + vial, being careful not to spill any of the contents.

(7) Dilute the contents of the vacuum flask with double-distilled, boiled water to about 350 ml, and adjust the pH by adding portions of $0.1 \ mol \cdot l^{-1}$ HCl, checking frequently, to about 9.5 (but not lower). Fill up to 400 ml with distilled water.

The simple system described above has the disadvantage that careless handling of the apparatus may spoil the working solution. Therefore, a two-chamber system, in which the gaseous $^{14}CO_2$ is carried from the acid chamber to the alkaline chamber by means of a slow N_2 gas stream, is preferable. Like the one-chamber system, such a two-chamber system can easily be built with standard laboratory glassware.

In practice, direct dilution of a commercial high activity $Na^{14}CO_3$ solution is now the more common procedure. A certain amount of carrier (Na_2CO_3) is added to the labelled solution, dilution is made with a freshly prepared 0.01 or $0.005 \ mol \cdot l^{-1}$ NaOH solution, and the pH is adjusted as above.

If the working solution is to be used for determinations of brackish or sea water, then a certain amount of NaCl (according to the salinity of the water to be assayed) must be added (*46*).

It is recommended that all manipulations be practised first without labelled carbonate to become perfectly acquainted with the technique and to avoid the unhappy experience of losing costly ^{14}C. Further, it should be borne in mind that only high grade chemicals and distilled water (preferably distilled from quartz) must be used for preparations. Utmost cleanliness in all manipulations is imperative.

Activity of the working solution. The activity needed per millilitre of the working solution in individual experiments, and hence the total activity to be dissolved, depends on several conditions: production rates expected, duration of the exposure, bottle size, etc. Some authors prefer adding standard amounts of 1 ml of working solution per bottle, other workers use only fractions of millilitres (e.g., 0.2 ml) per bottle. In the latter case, the specific activity of the working solution should be correspondingly higher, and the solution is injected into the water assayed by means of a calibrated syringe. As a general rule, however, 1 µCi per 100 ml of a moderately productive water gives a sufficient number of counts after an exposure time of 4–6 hours at light optimum, provided that the counting efficiency of the GM equipment used is not too low (i.e., not lower than 10%).

Preparation of ampoules. The working solution can be stored in a clean stoppered Pyrex glass bottle, but it is preferable to distribute it into ampoules in portions of 1, 2, 5, 10 or 20 ml according to the needs of later experiments. The working solution, or the sealed ampoules, should be autoclaved to prevent growth of bacteria.

5.4.3.2   *Standardization of working solutions*

The specific activity of working solutions is known only approximately. Although the original activity of the labelled compound is determined by the manufacturer, and hence the final activity of the working solution could be found by calculation, a certain amount of activity may be lost during subsequent manipulations. It is therefore necessary to determine the final activity individually for any newly prepared working solution.

The standardization procedures for GM (Geiger-Müller) counting and liquid scintillation counting are essentially different. Many pitfalls in GM standardization have been encountered giving rise to a considerable amount of discussion. A critical review of various techniques used in the past has recently been made by Wood (47, 48). Scintillation techniques, too, are still undergoing development. It appears, however, that these techniques are more reliable than GM techniques, although a number of problems still need solving.

Since different principles are involved in the two techniques the basic procedures are treated separately in the following. As already mentioned, the biological material, after exposure, has to be separated from the liquid phase for counting. In GM counting, filters are normally mounted on planchettes and dried in a desiccator prior to counting, keeping counting geometry as close as possible to that adopted for standardization of the working solution. In scintillation counting, the filters may either be dried prior to immersion in the scintillation fluor or they may be dissolved directly in the fluor. Different types of fluor are used, depending on which of these methods is adopted (see section 5.4.3.2.3).

5.4.3.2.1   *GM techniques*

(*a*) *Chemical precipitation of* $Na_2{}^{14}CO_3$ *as* $Ba^{14}CO_3$

Chemical precipitation of an aliquot (0.2–1 ml) of the working solution, according to the equation:

$$Na_2{}^{14}CO_3 + BaCl_2 \text{ or } Ba(OH)_2) = Ba^{14}CO_3 + 2NaCl \text{ (or } 2NaOH)$$

is performed in an alkaline medium having a pH of at least 10. The precipitated $Ba^{14}CO_3$ is filtered off from the solution by means of membrane filters, and the activity is measured after desiccation.

A serious problem in this procedure arises from self-absorption of the weak β-radiation with increasing amounts (or thickness) of barium carbonate per unit filter area. To overcome this difficulty, two modifications of the procedure outlined are commonly used in radioisotope laboratories. In the first, *constant amounts of activity* are precipitated in a series of test tubes, the amount of Na_2CO_3 added per tube being increased each time, so that the total amount of barium carbonate precipitated progressively increases in the series. From each tube, the whole amount of precipitate is filtered off.

Theoretically, therefore, each filter should have the same number of decays per second, but the measured specific activity (^{14}C per mg $BaCO_3$) decreases with increasing sample thickness. The (crude) relationship that governs the measured (relative) activities (a, in counts per second) in relation to sample thickness (t, in mg $BaCO_3$ per cm^2) and self-absorption (μ = self-absorption coefficient), is given by

$$a = a_0 \cdot \frac{1}{\mu \cdot t}(1 - e^{-\mu \cdot t})$$

The activity at zero thickness, a_0 (which is of interest in this connexion) cannot be determined directly but must be estimated by extrapolation from a linear or semi-log plot, or by calculation.

This procedure, proposed by Steeman-Nielsen (*44*) has been used by many workers in the determination of primary productivity. However, serious criticism can be raised against its further application. Primarily, $BaCO_3$ is insufficiently precipitated at very low concentrations; hence, zero thickness activity will be underestimated. Secondly, as was demonstrated by Hendler (*49*) the above formulation—although theoretically founded—does not hold over a large range of $BaCO_3$ precipitates. A hyperbolic function was found to be in better agreement with experimental data. Thirdly, under certain conditions of counting (thick window counter, large source-counter distance) selective and scattering effects were observed, as a result of which the maximum counting does not occur at the (theoretical) zero thickness but at a thickness of 1–2 mg $BaCO_3$ per cm^2. In this case, zero activity would be over-estimated by extrapolation from a data plot. Contrarily, Wood (*47, 48*) concludes that the phenomena observed are due to selective absorption. To minimize this he recommends that detection be done with a thin-end window detector so that the total thickness of the system (including window and thickness due to air gap) is at least 2 mg $\cdot$ cm^{-2}. In this case, extrapolation to zero thickness from a semilogarithmic plot would be acceptable.

In the second modification of the precipitation technique, the ^{14}C activity is precipitated at a *constant level of $BaCO_3$*; the amount selected was determined experimentally in order to balance completeness of precipitation with minimal self-absorption. After precipitation and remixing of the precipitate, increasing portions of the same solution (1, 2, 3 ml) i.e., increasing amounts of activity, are filtered off, and the best straight line through a linear plot of activity counted against weight (mg) filtered is extrapolated to the activity of the total precipitate.

This technique has been widely used by Vollenweider (see below), and (allowing for counter efficiency) gives only slight underestimates in comparison to gas-phase checks.

(b) Standardization procedure used by Sorokin (52)

Self-absorption correction factors for $Ba^{14}CO_3$ precipitates can be calculated by constructing an empirical curve based upon the known zero thickness activity of a ^{14}C sample of labelled algae or bacteria.

In practice, the self-absorption curve is obtained as follows: an aliquot of the labelled algal material is filtered off through a Millipore molecular filter as a thin layer and its activity is measured under the same conditions as subsequent measurements are done; the filter is then combusted by the van Slyke procedure in a closed system in which the evolved $^{14}CO_2$ is transferred quantitatively into a dilute NaOH solution. Brought up to a mark (e.g., 100 ml), this solution of known activity at zero thickness is distributed, in portions of 5 ml, to test tubes. To each portion is added a certain amount (the value of which is increased from tube to tube) of non-active carbonate, and $BaCO_3$ is precipitated by a standard procedure. After filtration the activity of each sample is measured, and the corresponding values are plotted against their weights per cm^2 (Fig. 25). The activity of a 5-ml portion of the original solution is taken as 1, and relative corrections

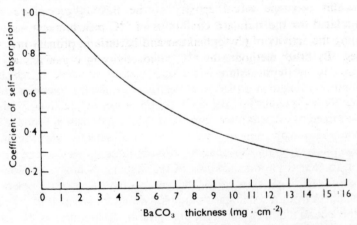

Fig. 25.   Curve of self-absorption of ^{14}C radiation in $BaCO_3$ precipitates (50)

Table 5. Correction coefficient (K) for self-absorption

BaCO$_3$ thickness (mg·cm^{-2})	K	BaCO$_3$ thickness (mg·cm^{-2})	K
0.0	1.0	3.6	1.415
0.4	1.012	4.0	1.495
0.8	1.032	4.4	1.581
1.2	1.065	4.8	1.664
1.6	1.111	5.2	1.733
2.0	1.161	5.6	1.810
2.4	1.213	6.0	1.902
2.8	1.272	6.4	2.086
3.2	1.342	6.8	2.170

factors are calculated for each individual subsample. In this manner, a set of factors are obtained as a function of the weight of BaCO$_3$ per cm^2 (cf. Table 5), which are later used for the correct standardization of the working solutions.

For the standardization of the working solution proceed as follows: place in a test tube, 2 ml of 0.4 mol·l^{-1} KOH, 3–4 ml of tap water, and 1–2 ml of the solution to be tested and mix (the activity should be in the range of 1–5×10^3 counts per minutes; if stronger, the solution must be diluted with 0.001 mol·l^{-1} KOH + 100 mg·l^{-1} Na$_2$CO$_3$). Then 1 ml of 100 g·l^{-1} BaCl$_2$ solution is added, and the stoppered test-tube is heated at 80°C for 10 minutes. After cooling, the BaCO$_3$ precipitate formed is filtered on a previously weighed membrane filter; the filter is dried, counted under the counter, and again weighed. Using the table, the self-absorption correction coefficient can be found from the weight of precipitate per cm^2 of filter surface, and the zero thickness activity is calculated from the actual activity of the precipitate multiplied by the corresponding correction coefficient.

In this way the actual activity of the BaCO$_3$ precipitate can be extrapolated for the standard conditions of ^{14}C measurement, as used in counting the activity of phytoplankton and bacteria in primary production studies. By other methods, the ^{14}C radioactivity in organisms would be measured in one physical state, and the radioactivity of the hydrocarbonate in quite another, and hence the values obtained would not be comparable; cf. Jitts & Scott (51) and Sorokin (52). However, Sorokin's method has been challenged by Wood (48).

(c) Standardization procedure used by Vollenweider (45)

Reagents

1.   Sodium carbonate solution, 0.1 mol·l^{-1} (1.06 g of Na$_2$CO$_3$ dissolved in 100 ml of distilled water).

2.   Buffer solution: 25 ml of 1 mol·l^{-1} NH$_4$NO$_3$ and 25 ml of 1 mol·l^{-1}

NaOH mixed with CO_2-free distilled water to 500 ml (0.05 mol·l^{-1} NaOH + NH_4NO_3).

3. $BaCl_2$, solid.

Procedure

To a 100-ml measuring flask, containing about 50 ml of CO_2-free distilled water, 10 ml of solution (2) and 3 ml of solution (1) are added. The mixture should have a pH of 10–11.

1 ml, or an aliquot containing about 0.5–1 μCi, of the ^{14}C solution to be tested is carefully measured with a calibrated syringe and mixed with the above solution. Then an excess of $BaCl_2$ is added and the solution in the measuring flask brought up to the mark with distilled water. It is allowed to precipitate for several hours.

After thorough mixing, 1, 2, and 3 ml are filtered through millipore filters, distributing the $BaCO_3$ precipitate homogeneously on the filter area. To avoid creeping of the $BaCO_3$, the filters are pressed on the filter plug by means of a ring-like holder having practically no walls (Fig. 26). Prepare at least two replicates.

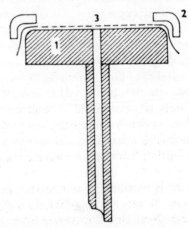

Fig. 26. Filtration apparatus used by Vollenweider (*45*) for ^{14}C standardization. 1—metallic filter plate; 2—ring-like filter holder; 3—membrane filter.

After drying, the ^{14}C activity of the filters is counted on the GM equipment. The values obtained, appropriately corrected for background counts and coincidence losses, are then plotted on millimetre paper, and the total activity of the solution to be calibrated is determined by extrapolating the straight line that best fits the 1-ml and 2-ml counts starting from zero. The 3-ml counts are used as a check, and should be somewhat below the corresponding value of the interpolation line as predicted by self-absorption.

Precision

With repeated duplicates, the statistical error was found to be about $\pm 2\%$.

Accuracy

Compared with gas phase countings (appropriately correcting the GM countings for counter efficiency), the above procedure was found to give estimates about 4–5% below the theoretical values.

(d) Standardization procedure used by Wood (48)

Wood (1971) proposes a simple procedure in which $BaCO_3$ is precipitated directly on planchettes made from aluminium foil by injecting an aliquot of the $Na^{14}CO_3$ stock solution (e.g., 50 µl from a microsyringe) into a drop of $Ba(OH)_2$ placed on the planchette.

Planchettes are prepared from common household aluminium foil by folding small squares over a suitable form. These planchettes are weighed accurately before carrying out the above reaction.

The thickness of the $BaCO_3$ film is controlled by varying the amount of $Ba(OH)_2$ solution placed on planchettes. After injection of the $Na^{14}CO_3$ solution, the excess of $Ba(OH)_2$ is allowed to react with atmospheric CO_2 (distributing the solution as evenly as possible over the whole planchette surface); then the solution is slowly evaporated to dryness under an infrared lamp. After GM counting the planchettes are weighed again to determine the $BaCO_3$ thickness.

The activity measured is plotted on semilogarithmic paper against the $BaCO_3$ thickness ($mg \cdot cm^{-2}$) (range covered 0.5–10 mg) and linearly extrapolated to zero thickness. Note that thicknesses lower than 0.5 $mg \cdot cm^{-2}$ are unreliable. An acceptable set of values should yield a negative slope between 0.125 and 0.135 (activity expressed in natural logarithms).

In order to avoid any uncertainty regarding the actual standard of the working solution employed, standardization can be carried out directly from the experimental bottle after injection and mixing of the ^{14}C solution. Replicate aliquots (0.5 ml) are withdrawn from the bottle by a syringe and injected into a $Ba(OH)_2$ drop and treated as above. The $Ba(OH)_2$ used should be sufficient to give at least 2 mg of $BaCO_3$ per cm^2. The zero activity is calculated from the exact weight of the $BaCO_3$ and a standard diagram prepared previously as above.

This technique is comparable to that proposed by Schindler for liquid scintillation counting but obviously can be applied as a routine only under appropriate conditions (e.g., in laboratory studies).

(e) Standardization by means of algae[a]

In this procedure the ^{14}C activity of an adequate subsample of the working solution is entirely absorbed, by processes of photosynthesis, and assimilated by an algal culture.   Zero thickness activity is determined from an aliquot of the labelled algal material filtered off.   The principal advantage of this procedure lies in the fact that the zero activity is measured almost under the same conditions as, later on, the activity of the experimental natural phytoplankton.

The whole procedure appears to be relatively simple.   However, as there is still little experience with it, the results should be checked against other independent methods.

It has always been assumed that the determination of ^{14}C in an ampoule by means of a $BaCO_3$-self-absorption correction curve is only an approximation.   Observations have shown that the errors are worse than expected, particularly if GM tubes with thick mica windows are used.   Other techniques have therefore been suggested.   One technique is to transfer all $^{14}CO_2$ from an ampoule into the organic matter of small plankton algae and determine the radioactivity of these algae in exactly the same way as when measuring the activity of the algae from ordinary experiments (53).

As first shown by Egle & Schenk (54), the carbon dioxide compensation point in *Chlorella* is found below 0.001 % (volume) CO_2.   By working at a pH of about 4.0, where all CO_2 is in the form of free CO_2, and by starting at a CO_2-concentration of about 0.5%, it is thus possible to let *Chlorella* assimilate practically the total amount of CO_2.

In practice, the work has been done in the following way: In a separating funnel containing 1339 ml of a culture solution (CO_2 concentration 0.5% by volume, reduced tension of O_2 and N_2), an amount of centrifuged *Chlorella pyrenoidosa* and the content of a ^{14}C-ampoule were introduced.   The final pH was 4.2.   Twelve clear-stoppered 15-ml bottles were filled and placed on a rotating wheel in a water-thermostat illuminated at 10 lux.   Every 30 minutes a bottle was removed, and 2 samples of 5 ml each were filtered by membrane filters.   One of the filters was quickly dried and counted by means of an end-window tube.

When 3 consecutive filters had given the same counts, it was assumed that all CO_3 had been assimilated.   As a control, 30 ml from 2 other bottles were mixed in a separating funnel (130 ml) with fresh culture medium, the

---

[a] This method has been severely questioned recently by Wood (48).

concentration of free CO_2 being 0.25%. Six 15-ml bottles were filled and placed on a rotating wheel. When, according to the first part of the experiment, all free CO_2 should have been assimilated, the first bottle was removed and 15 ml filtered. After a further 30 minutes the same was done with the next bottle, and so on. As was to be expected, all $^{14}CO_2$ was already assimilated during the first part of the experiment. The weight of algae per cm^2 on the filter was kept far below 0.1 mg, preventing almost any influence of self-absorption.

In special experiments, the fraction of extracellular assimilates has to be measured. It is about one per cent of the total assimilates.

When using the equipment at the International Agency, Denmark (mica-window $= 1.3$ mg cm^{-2}, efficiency about 7%), the biological ^{14}C technique gives results that are about 31% lower than the values obtained by the original $BaCO_3$ technique. However, they agree with measurements by means of scintillation counting (personal communication by Dr P. V. Ramachandran Nair).

5.4.3.2.2 *Absolute activity determination*

The problems encountered in determining relative activity by GM procedures make it imperative to check specific procedures by occasional determinations of the absolute activity of inorganic or biological ^{14}C sources, using the same samples for both relative and absolute activity determination. For this purpose, filters containing either $Ba^{14}CO_3$ or labelled biological material are first counted with the GM system, then transferred to a closed system, acidified or chemically oxidized by van Slyke procedures to carbon dioxide and then measured with a gas-phase or ionization counter. By this means, absolute decays per second are obtained, and the efficiency of the GM system employed is calculated from the corresponding relative counts (55).

If no gas-phase counter is available, then GM efficiency may also be obtained from the comparison of a ^{14}C source counted with the GM system and the same source counted with a scintillation system as discussed in section 5.4.3.2.3. Procedures of this kind have been described in *51, 56 & 57*.

In the procedure of Findenegg, replicates of water samples containing plankton to which equal aliquots of a ^{14}C stock solution have been added are exposed for some hours to light, filtered and dried on planchets and then counted with the GM counter. After this the filters are burned by van Slyke procedures (100 ml of H_3PO_4, 150 ml of concentrated H_2SO_4, 35 g of chrome oxide) and the CO_2 evolved is absorbed in ethanolamine (6 ml). 5 ml of this is mixed with the scintillation fluors and counted by scintillation techniques. From this a GM efficiency factor is found which is applied to the stock solution; the absolute activity of the latter is measured directly by scintillation techniques.

Sample preparation as well as selection of the counting equipment must be done in accordance with the basic characteristics of the weak β-emitters. Absolute values of disintegration rates for ^{14}C samples may be obtained using appropriate techniques, but relative values are usually sufficiently adequate for the purpose of primary production measurements.

5.4.3.2.3 *Liquid scintillation techniques*

Liquid scintillation counting offers several advantages over the widely used GM techniques. Stock ^{14}C solutions, membrane filters, and filtrates may all be rapidly and conveniently assayed, using the same preparation and counting procedure for all. The need for preparation of ^{14}C by $BaCO_3$ slurries and drying of filtrates on planchets for assay is therefore eliminated. A counting efficiency is determined for each sample assayed and, at least on modern machines, this efficiency is determined within a few seconds of when the sample is counted. Filters may be taken directly from filter funnels and put into counting vials, eliminating the need for cementing filters to planchets, saving time and eliminating the possibility of contamination or loss of radioactive material. Finally, counting efficiencies are usually higher than with normal Geiger-Müller counters of either the thin window or windowless type. The exact efficiency will depend on the type and age of the counter, the type and purity of the fluor, and the properties of the algae or other material counted (usual range = 50–80%).

(a) *Fluors*. Membrane filters and other radioactive sources for counting have to be immersed in organic mixtures (fluors) consisting essentially of two kinds of ingredient, the *solvent* (e.g., toluene, dioxane, xylene) and the actual *scintillator(s)* (PPO, POPOP, dimethyl POPOP, etc.).[a] A few of such mixtures will be mentioned in the text. In addition, certain solubilizers, such as NCS, Soluene, or Biosolv, and other ingredients may also be required for dissolution of organic matter and bleaching. Fluors and filters are placed in special vials of glass or plastic, which are then tightly closed with appropriate caps.

(b) *Counting of intact dried filters*. An adaptation of the method of Lind & Campbell (58) is used. After filtration of the contents of experimental bottles, the membrane filters are transferred to plastic scintillation vials where they are placed unfolded along the wall of the vial with the residue to the inside. The vials are kept in a desiccator over silica gel until the filters are thoroughly dry

---

[a] PPO = 2,5-diphenyloxazole; POPOP = 1,4-bis[2-(5-phenyloxazolyl)]benzene.

and then filled for counting with a toluene-based scintillation fluid consisting of 6 g of PPO and 0.075 g of POPOP per litre of toluene. The membrane filters are rendered transparent by the toluene.

The activity of the working solution (pH 10.4) is determined by first placing about 2 mg of $Ba(OH)_2$ crystals in the corner at the bottom of a scintillation vial and pipetting onto the crystals 100 µl of the $Na_2{}^{14}CO_3$ solution using an Eppendorf micropipette or similar device. After the crystals have dissolved, one millilitre of NCS solubilizer (Nuclear-Chicago Corp) is added and allowed to take up the water, after which the vial is filled and counted, using the scintillator described above.

(c) *Counting of wet filters: dissolution of filters.* If loss of activity on storage of filters in the dry state is considered important (221) then the wet filters may be counted in toluene-based scintillators, replacing about 10% of the volume of toluene with dioxane to take up the water (59) or with the addition of cellulose materials (60). Otherwise, to obviate this problem and problems involving counting geometry and self-absorption, which may result from counting intact filters (61), it may be necessary to dissolve the filters in the scintillator immediately after filtration. Toluene-based scintillators may be employed if digests of the filters are made with solubilizers such as NCS, but such digests may be very dark coloured and require bleaching. Care must be taken to allow for the possibility of chemiluminescence resulting from such treatment. Xylene-based scintillators are also available, which will dissolve membrane filters. However, the most frequently used scintillation fluids for this application are dioxane-based solutions, such as that used by Schindler (62).

All of these approaches have disadvantages, however. If samples containing toluene-based fluids must be stored for any length of time, the more expensive and fragile glass vials must be used to prevent loss of solvent. The vapours are also moderately toxic and extremely inflammable.

With approaches involving dissolution of the filter undissolved particles in high concentrations may still present a problem of self-absorption and may also require the addition of a thixotropic agent (62) to prevent settling of the particles. Finally, dioxane-based fluids may be chemically unstable, making it difficult (if not impossible) to keep reliable standards around and sometimes giving rise to erratic counting efficiencies. Also dioxane is dangerously toxic, producing corrosive fumes and dissolving rubber and many plastics, so that its use should be avoided unless the surroundings are very well ventilated.

A versatile fluor for routine assays of ${}^{14}C$-labelled organic material consists of 60 g of naphthalene, 4 g of PPO, and 0.2 g of dimethyl POPOP in one litre of dioxane (slightly modified from the proportions recommended by Schindler, 62). This fluor will dissolve up to 30% of water without significant reduction of counting efficiency, and in most modern counters efficiencies of 50–75% are possible using relatively inexpensive reagent-quality naphthalene and dioxane. If the purer and therefore more costly scintillator grades of these chemicals are used, efficiencies as high as 75–80% are possible. The fluor completely dissolves cellulose ester, cellulose acetate, or cellulose nitrate membrane filters and most algal cells in a matter of minutes.

Bray's fluor (*222*) consisting of 60 g of naphthalene, 4 g of PPO, 200 mg of POPOP, 100 ml of methanol, 20 ml of ethylene glycol and sufficient dioxane to make up to 1 litre, is also satisfactory, but is more complicated to prepare.

Other fluors have some advantages that are worth mentioning. Aquasol, a ready-mixed xylene-based fluor marketed by New England Nuclear Corp., gives slightly higher counting efficiencies than the fluor described above, but is much more costly. Millipore filters dissolve in the fluor overnight, with some assistance from a tube buzzer or sonifier. Several solubilizers, including NCS (Amersham-Searle), Soluene (Parkard Instrument Co.) and Biosolv (Beckman Instrument Co.), will dissolve membrane filters and most other wet organic material, after which a toluene fluor may be used for assay. All of the above colour strongly, causing reduced counting efficiency when a membrane is dissolved, or require heating to dissolve the membranes. Colouring problems may be partially overcome by suspending the samples in quartz tubes in strong ultraviolet light and adding a few drops of strong hydrogen peroxide, as is done for total dissolved nitrogen in water analyses (*63*). All will dissolve enough water to assay most standards and filtrates without excessive quenching, and are excellent CO_2 absorbants.

Standardization of the working solution may be done as described above, or by directly dispensing a quantitative subsample of the $Na^{14}CO_3$ solution (using a calibrated microlitre pipette) from an incubation bottle into counting vials containing fluor. This is convenient when containers of unknown volume are used. If the vials are to be stored for several days before radio-assay, adding 0.5 ml of any of the above-mentioned solubilizers or $0.1 \ mol \cdot l^{-1}$ NaOH will prevent loss of CO_2. If vials containing solubilizers are to be left standing for any length of time, they should be fitted with Teflon cap liners or nylon or polyethylene caps, since the usual foil-covered cork cap liners, dissolve, causing unnecessary quenching.

(*d*) *Determination of counting efficiency.* The calibration and use of all techniques for determining counting efficiency are fully described in the manuals on liquid scintillation counting supplied by most manufacturers of radioassay equipment. Efficiency is determined either by re-counting after a measured amount of ^{14}C-labelled hexadecane of known activity has been added to each vial, or by the channels-ratio or external standard channels-ratio techniques, if the available counting equipment has two counting channels and/or an external radioactive standard of known properties. If the channels-ratio or external standard channels-ratio method is employed, a set of quenched standards of known activity will be required. These are available commercially for simple dioxane and toluene-base fluors, or they may be prepared directly from the exact counting fluor to be used by adding known activities of labelled hexadecane and minute quantities of CCl_4, saturated alcoholic picric acid, or some other chemical quenching agent.

One disadvantage of all calibration techniques is that ideally they are really accurate only for homogeneous samples such as are not likely to occur in primary production work. This is especially true with the external standard channels-ratio and channels-ratio techniques where reference is made to standard solutions, comparison with which may not satisfactorily account for differences in efficiency caused by heterogeneity of the sample, particularly when filters are heavily laden with material. One approach to this problem in connexion with the counting of intact filters have been given by Pugh (61) who suggests calibration by means of standard ^{14}C-sucrose incorporated into membrane filters.

(*e*) *Calculation.* Count filtered activity and correct counts for background. Determine counting efficiency according to one of the above-mentioned techniques as described in user manuals, and recalculate the total decays of each filter; than apply the formula given in section 5.4.3.4.4.

5.4.3.3 *Apparatus*

(*a*) *Instrumentation for β-counting*

Two types of apparatus, based on essentially different principles, have now come into common use:

- Gas counters (and ionization chambers) where use is made of ionized particles produced in the counting gas. These charged particles are collected at appropriate electrodes giving rise to an electric current or voltage variations, which may be recorded after suitable amplification. The classical GM counters are of this type.

- Scintillation counters in which atoms, molecules or crystal structures absorb energy from the atomic decay process and convert it into light. Such light impulses are amplified by photomultipliers and recorded in the usual way.

Each of these systems has its basic characteristics that impose certain rules to be followed in actual measurements. In particular, it has to be remembered that sample preparation and routine operations for the two systems are different but that in both systems there are limitations in counting efficiency, two of which need particular attention, i.e., self-absorption in GM counting and quenching in scintillation counting.

It is self evident that the specific instructions supplied by the manufacturers for each particular instrumentation have to be carefully observed.

Any one of a great variety of GM detectors may be used for counting the rather weak beta radiation of ^{14}C-labelled algae. Three types of GM counters are in general use: these are windowless, thin-window, and thick-window, in order of their relative efficiency of detection. The higher efficiency of windowless GM counters is offset to some degree by complications (64). Thin-window gas-flow detectors with an efficiency of about 25% and high reproducibility are probably the best compromise (48). Thick-window counters with counting efficiencies below 10% often require an excessively long counting time to achieve a statistically reliable total count and are not recommended if the thin-window counting equipment is available.

The scaling equipment that records the total number of counts per unit time may be of the "preset count" or "preset time" variety. Preset counting has the advantage of counting all samples to the same total count and hence the same statistical accuracy. Many units are now available that automatically change the samples and usually record for each sample the time to reach a preset count.

During recent years, a great variety of reliable scintillation counters for weak β-counting have also come on to the market. Such instruments are furnished with one or more channels, with or without external standards, calculation units, and automatic sampler changers. Special additional units that are available make such instruments particularly versatile for radioisotope work other than ^{14}C counting.

(b) Accessory equipment for preparation of ^{14}C samples

- The ^{14}C samples to be counted may be prepared using suitable metallic cuvettes (cylinders), metallic discs, or planchettes. The choice depends on the nature of the original ^{14}C sample and on the particular scope of the experiment. Although filters fixed on planchettes are most commonly used, ^{14}C-labelled liquids can also be dried on discs or absorbed on activated carbon, which is then transferred to metallic cuvettes. In the latter case, counting is done at the so-called saturation height (65).

  For liquid scintillation counting special plastic or glass vials are used. Plastic vials are somewhat cheaper but cannot be used for all fluors.

- In most productivity work, however, the labelled material (phytoplankton, or other biological material; also $Ba^{14}CO_3$ for standardization procedures) must be separated from the liquid phase. For this purpose various kinds of filter apparatus are used, some of which are ordinary laboratory devices, others are specifically adapted to primary productivity studies and may also be used in the field (46, 66, & 67). The most commonly used filters are membrane filters having a pore size of 0.5 μm.

A specific filter device is described below. Other systems may be devised as well but it should be borne in mind that, once a system has been adopted, no change in the filter should be made when using GM techniques; otherwise all previous standardizations will have to be repeated.

• The special filtration device shown in Fig. 27 has 3 funnels for the filtration of samples through Millipore filters (68). The device has been used on shipboard for productivity work in reservoirs and at sea.

Before filtration, the stopper of the bottle containing the sample is replaced by a rubber bung carrying a tube (B), the end of which is cut at a slant and fitted with a clamp. The bottle is inverted and placed in the support so that the end of the tube passes into the upper part of the funnel (A). Then, by opening the clamp and the stopcocks (C) and (D), the contents of the bottle are automatically emptied through the filter. While one funnel is in use, another can be prepared for the next filtration. When the container (E) is full, its contents are emptied into a special disposal vessel.

A compact filtration unit has also been described (46) and is similar in principle to that of Sorokin. For field study purposes a small one-chamber filtration unit, constructed by Steeman-Nielsen (223), has proved to be very useful.

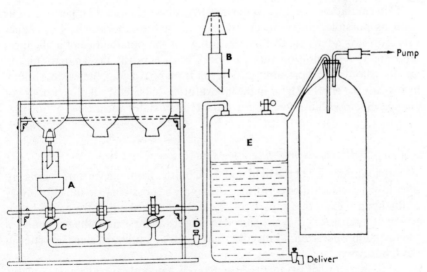

Fig. 27.   Filtration device used by Sorokin (68)

Reproduced from IBP Handbook (50)

E WPC3 - I

5.4.3.4   *Determination of primary productivity*

5.4.3.4.1 *Preparation of light and dark bottles*

It is recommended that water should first be collected from all the various depths to be sampled and that the light and dark bottles should be filled immediately after collection and stored in a dark box. At least one light and one dark bottle should be prepared for each depth sampled. If the water column is reasonably well mixed, fewer dark bottles are needed.

The ^{14}C working solutions, prepared as described in section 5.4.3.1, are best added to the samples by means of a graduated hypodermic syringe having a needle not shorter than 5 cm. Injection of the ^{14}C working solutions into the various bottles is done rapidly and, after thorough shaking, the bottles are lowered at once to the preselected depths of exposure.

Experience will tell the analyst how much ^{14}C activity it is necessary to add to the bottles in order to produce a moderately radioactive plankton sample for assay. The resultant activity at the end of the exposure is dependent on numerous variables, including growth rates, plankton density, length of incubation, and amount filtered. For many lakes of moderate productivity, an addition of 1–3 µCi for 125 ml of sample, with a 4-hour incubation period and filtration of a 50-ml subsample, yields a moderately " hot " sample without excessive layering of plankton on the filter.

5.4.3.4.2 *Alkalinity and pH determinations*

Determinations for each water sample collected should be performed as soon as possible, either on board ship or in the laboratory. For higher precision it is advisable to take advantage of the possibilities of a chemical laboratory, on condition that this does not delay the determinations too much. Should the determinations be made on board ship, the values should, in any case, be checked later in the laboratory. In general, alkalinity does not change much within a few hours, but pH may suffer variations.

5.4.3.4.3 *Preparation of filters for counting*

After withdrawal of the light and dark bottles from the various depths (an operation that should be performed as rapidly as possible to avoid light injury or further photosynthesis, particularly of those samples that were exposed at low light intensities), they are stored in a light-free case until the beginning of the filtration operation. Filtration may be done on board ship, or better in the laboratory.

The amount of water to be filtered depends very much on the phytoplankton density. In oligotrophic waters the whole contents of the bottle may be filtered, whereas in very eutrophic situations 10 ml or less may be sufficient; in mesotrophic waters filtration of 50 ml may be adequate. The accumulation of several layers of phytoplankton on the filter should be avoided to reduce self-absorption.

Aliquots to be filtered are transferred as rapidly as possible to a suitable filtration apparatus with membrane filters of about 0.5 μm porosity (e.g., Millipore HA, or Membrane No. 2). If the funnels are kept clean and coated with a silicone film, the necessity of rinsing the walls of the funnel is eliminated. The vacuum applied to the filtration system should be below 5×10^4 Pa (0.5 atmospheres), to reduce the possibility of rupturing more fragile cells (*69*). The vacuum should be released immediately after liquid has passed to avoid rapid air desiccation. The filtration operation should be done in a semi-darkened area.

After removal of the filters from the filtration unit, they are placed on planchettes for GM counting, avoiding any contact with the plankton on the filter surface, and then placed in a desiccator containing a suitable desiccant (e.g., silica gel). If carbonate precipitates are to be expected (e.g., in samples from waters of high alkalinity), it is advisable to expose the dried filters to fumes of HCl for 10 minutes to remove possible ^{14}C precipitates extracellularly; these filters are again desiccated before counting.

Counting of the " hot " samples is done to about 5000 counts at a " count preset " unit. Samples from dark bottles are relatively inactive, and sometimes require separation from the light bottle samples for counting, which is then done to about 500 or 1000 counts only.

For liquid scintillation counting the procedures discussed in section 5.4.3.2.3 should be followed.

5.4.3.4.4 *Calculation*

Activities are expressed as counts per second or counts per minute, and the rate of ^{12}C assimilation in $\mu g \cdot l^{-1} \cdot h^{-1}$ or $mg \cdot m^{-3} \cdot h^{-1}$ is calculated from the following formula:

$$\text{Rate of } {}^{12}\text{C assimilation} = \frac{c}{b} \times a \times k_1 \times k_2 \times k_3$$

where

$a = {}^{12}$C available = alkalinity in mol $\cdot l^{-1} \times pH_T$ factor $\times 12 \times 100$ ($= \mu g$ of ^{12}C available per litre)

$b = {}^{14}$C available = ^{14}C activity added (e.g., expressed as relative " zero thickness " activity, if only relative measurements are made, or as μCi $\times$ counter efficiency at the given counter geometry)

$c = {}^{14}$C assimilated = (filter counts − background) $\times$ 1.06 (1.06 is a factor to allow for the isotropic effect).

The corrections factors k_1, k_2 and k_3 have the following meanings:

k_1 = a correction for the aliquot factors. For example, if 50 ml from a bottle containing 133 ml were filtered, and 1 ml of working solution was added, then this factor is $132/50 = 2.64$.

k_2 = a time factor to reduce the measured rate of photosynthesis over the effective exposure time to a standard exposure, e.g., 1 hour. For example, if the effective exposure time was 2.5 hours, then this factor is $1/2.5 = 0.4$.

k_3 = a dimension factor, e.g., to convert $mg \cdot l^{-1}$ to $mg \cdot m^{-3}$.

An example will demonstrate the various calculation steps:

Alkalinity	$0.67 \text{ mmol} \cdot l^{-1}$
pH	7.8
Temperature	15°C
factor (from graph, Fig. 28)	1.04

^{12}C available
$= 0.67 \times 1.04 \times 12 \times 100 = 8320 \ \mu g \cdot l^{-1} \ (= a)$

Total activity added in portions of 1 ml/127 ml	100 000 counts per minute ($= b$)
Activity counted on filter (minus background)	500 counts per minute
^{14}C assimilated	500×1.06 counts per minute ($= c$)
Filtered volume	50 ml
Bottle volume	127 ml
Exposure time	5 hours

$k_1 = 126/50 = 2.52$
$k_2 = 1/5 \quad = 0.2$

$$\text{Rate of } ^{12}C \text{ assimilation} = \frac{500 \times 1.06}{100\ 000} \times 8320 \times 2.52 \times 0.2$$

$$= 22.2 \ \mu g \cdot l^{-1} \cdot h^{-1}, \text{ or } 22.2 \ mg \cdot m^{-3} \cdot h^{-1}.$$

5.4.4 *Analysis of chlorophyll content*

The determination of the chlorophyll content can be used as an indirect method for the estimation of the biomass and the photosynthesis rate of the primary producers. According to Sakamoto (70), as quoted by Vollenweider (152), certain chlorophyll *a* concentrations are associated with the trophic level of water:

Eutrophic lakes: 5–140 $mg \cdot m^{-3}$; 20–140 $mg \cdot m^{-2}$
Mesotrophic lakes: 1–15 $mg \cdot m^{-3}$; 10–90 $mg \cdot m^{-2}$
Oligotrophic lakes: 0.3–2.5 $mg \cdot m^{-3}$; 10–50 $mg \cdot m^{-2}$

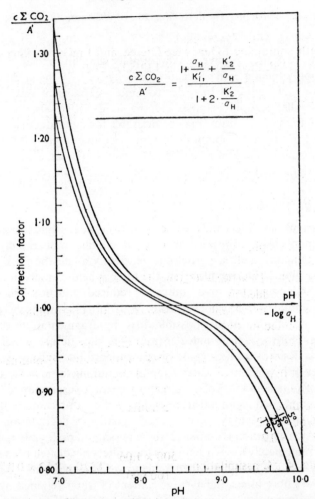

Fig. 28. Correction factors for deducing total CO_2 from titration alkalinity, pH and temperature, at ionic strength 0. Calculated according to formulae given by Buch (*155*). To be used in fresh waters of low salinity only.

According to Talling (*71*), the following values apply to marine water:

Unproductive areas: $<1 \text{ mg} \cdot \text{m}^{-3}$

Slightly productive areas: $1–30 \text{ mg} \cdot \text{m}^{-3}$

Highly productive areas: $>30 \text{ mg} \cdot \text{m}^{-3}$

Two methods suitable for chlorophyll analysis are described below: (*a*) spectrophotometric determination of chlorophyll *a*, *b*, and *c* (after Vollenweider, *45*); (*b*) determination with phaeophytin (after Golterman & Clymo, *72*).

5.4.4.1 *Spectrophotometric determination of chlorophyll* a,b,c

5.4.4.1.1 *Volume of water sample*

0.5–2 litres is often a convenient amount for sampling and appropriate for the commonly encountered concentration range of 1–20 mg of chlorophyll *a* per m^3 (= 1–20 µg·l^{-1}). In order to obtain extracts of suitable optical density, smaller sample volumes can be used with denser populations. Larger volumes (e.g., 5 litres) may be desirable for unproductive waters, but may be inconvenient to obtain or to filter. Consequently a more sensitive fluorimetric method has been developed for work on oceanic waters, in which concentrations are usually below 1 mg·m^{-3} (for details see *73, 74 & 75*).

5.4.4.1.2 *Filtration*

Both membrane filters and the finer porosity grades of glass fibre filters are now commonly used. The latter are cheaper and filter more rapidly, but they do not retain the smallest particles as efficiently as do the finer grades of membrane filters. During filtration, the filter is held clamped in a suitable support, and connected to a source of reduced pressure. The pressure reduction should probably not exceed 2–3 × 10^5 Pa (2–3 atmospheres) during filtration, to minimize the possible loss by fragmentation of delicate organisms. Filters of large diameter (e.g., 7-cm glass fibre) are useful if rapid filtration is desirable or if clogging by suspended solids is likely, as with silty river water or hypolimnion water samples containing ferric hydroxide. The addition of a small quantity of magnesium carbonate suspension to the filter is often recommended as an aid to retention and as a precaution against the development of acidity—and hence pigment degradation—in the extract. After filtration is complete, the filter should preferably not be dried but used immediately for extraction. Dried filters have often been stored for several days or weeks, but are then liable to yield less pigment. If necessary, as with glass fibre filters, the average content of water retained by the filter should be found by weighing and allowed for when calculating the composition of the solvent to be added.

5.4.4.1.3 *Extraction*

Either acetone (80% or 90% aqueous mixture) or methanol (90% or 100%) can be used as the solvent. The former is less efficient in extraction for some algae, but absorption characteristics of the principal photosynthetic pigments in it are better known (comparative tabulation in *76*). Originally, in most work with phytoplankton an extraction period of about 24 hours in cool dark conditions (refrigerator) was used. This may give good results, but because of possible changes in the extracted pigments a much shorter period is now often recommended, combined with some additional means for accelerating the extraction. Exposure to ultrasonic vibration ("sonification") is one such means, but is often inconvenient to apply and sometimes not very efficient. Grinding the filter and algae can be an effective method; practical details of one procedure are given in (72). With methanol, a brief (e.g., 30-seconds) exposure of the cells to the boiling solvent greatly accelerates the extraction, which can often be completed within 10 minutes.

After the extraction period, the extract is centrifuged and the clear supernatant solution used to fill a spectrophotometer cell (cuvette).

5.4.4.1.4 *Spectrophotometric estimation*

Used in the normal way, the spectrophotometer enables measurements of optical density ($\log_{10} I_0/I$) to be made at specified wavelengths for the pigment extract in a cell of known thickness (path length). A thickness of about 4 cm is generally most useful, as shorter cells (e.g., 1 cm) involve a loss of sensitivity, and longer cells (e.g., 10 cm) are less convenient, require more solvent, but can give increased sensitivity, which may be of value for unproductive waters.

The optical density measured at 750 nm can be taken as an approximate measure of non-selective " background " absorption by other materials (also scattering and cell-to-cell differences), and is subtracted from measurements of optical density in the red spectral region (600–700 nm) for which concentrations of chlorophyll *a* and its degradation products are calculated; it should normally be less than 0.005 unit per cm of cell thickness.

The procedure used to calculate the concentration of chlorophyll *a* from the values of optical density involves choosing between two pairs of alternatives:

Alternative 1a: one may disregard the possible contributions from degradation products, and express the result as the concentration of chlorophyll *a* equivalent to the optical density (-ies) measured. Alternative 1b: a differentiation may be attempted between the concentrations of chlorophyll *a* and its degradation product(s) (e.g., as phaeophytin). This differentiation can be based upon the relative changes of optical density (or of fluorescence) at the red absorption maximum induced by acidification, or upon a shift in the blue absorption maximum which accompanies the degradation of chlorophyll *a* (77, 78). It can be calculated either in terms of the proportions (%) of chlorophyll *a* and phaeophytin *a*, or by simple mathematical manipulation, in terms of concentrations of these pigments. (Examples are given in 73, 74, 78, 79 & 80).

Alternative 2a: the estimation of chlorophyll *a* concentration can be based upon the optical density measured at one wavelength near the red absorption maximum, or (alternative 2b) upon measurements at several wavelengths (e.g., 3-trichromatic methods). All such measurements are normally corrected by subtraction of the optical density at 750 mμ, as noted earlier. Examples of trichromatic methods include the much-used early procedure of Richards & Thompson (*81*) and later modifications—involving the same wavelengths of 630, 645, and 665 nm—outlined by Parsons & Strickland (*82*). Such methods were developed with the aim of distinguishing the contributions, in an extract mixture, of several pigments with overlapping absorption spectra.

In short, chlorophyll *a* is calculated from the following two equations of Parson & Strickland:

$$\text{Chlorophyll } a \ (\mu g \cdot l^{-1}) = C_a \cdot \left(\frac{v}{V \cdot l}\right)$$

where:

V = volume (in litres) of water filtered for extraction
v = volume (in ml) of acetone (90%) used
l = path length (in cm) of cuvette

and

$$C_a = 11.6 \ D_{665} - 1.31 \ D_{645} - 0.14 \ D_{630}$$

D_{665}, D_{645}, D_{630} being the optical densities in a 1-cm path length at the wavelengths 665, 645 and 630 nm, respectively.[a]

However, the dominance of absorption due to chlorophyll *a* in the region of its red absorption (663–665 nm) makes it doubtful whether the accuracy of estimation of chlorophyll *a* is improved by adopting a calculation based on three wavelengths rather than one. The latter (alternative 2a) is also more easily combined with the procedures intended to differentiate between chlorophyll *a* and its phaeophytin (alternative 1b). Judged on experience with the different alternatives, differentiation between chlorophyll *a* and phaeophytins appears to be more meaningful in primary production studies than the somewhat doubtful differentiation between chlorophyll *a*, *b* and *c*. For differentiation between chlorophyll *a* and phaeophytins, see section 5.4.4.2.

5.4.4.1.5 *Specific procedures*

Examples involving acetone as solvent are described in detail in (*72*) and need not be repeated here. Their relationship to the methods and alternatives generally available can be found by reference to the preceding section.

---

[a] Correspondingly, approximate values of chlorophyll *b* and *c* can be estimated by substituting the following values, respectively, in the second equation:

$$C_b = 20.7 \ D_{645} - 4.34 \ D_{665} - 4.42 \ D_{630},$$
$$C_c = 55.0 \ D_{630} - 16.3 \ D_{645} - 4.64 \ D_{645}.$$

Absorption characteristics of chlorophyll *a* in methanol are less well known, but relevant data are listed in (*76*), proposing the following simple approximate relationship for the concentration of chlorophyll *a* in 90% methanol which yields an optical density at 665 mμ of D_{665} measured with a path length of 1 cm:

$$\text{Chlorophyll } a \ (\text{mg} \cdot \text{l}^{-1}) = 13.9 \ D_{665}$$

5.4.4.2 *Determination with phaeophytin*

5.4.4.2.1 *Principle*

The absorption spectrum of chlorophyll has a maximum in acetone at 663 nm. Chlorophyll can be converted to phaeophytin by the addition of an acid, which removes Mg from the chlorophyll molecule. Both molecules occur under natural conditions. Phaeophytin also absorbs light at 663, but less strongly than the same concentration of chlorophyll. From the decrease in extinction when the sample is acidified, the amount of chlorophyll can be calculated.

An approximate correction for other coloured compounds and for turbidity can be made by subtracting the extinction at 750 nm (where chlorophyll and phaeophytin absorb an insignificant amount of light).

Accurate measurement of the concentration of chlorophylls is extremely difficult. The method described here is easy and rapid in use but the results should be interpreted with great care. For example the two most common chlorophylls, *a* and *b*, both absorb light at 663 nm and the extinction coefficients are not accurately known (see Table 6).

Table 6. Extinction coefficient (*K*) for chlorophyll *a* in aqueous acetone

Reference	Extinction coefficient (*K*)[a] for wavelength		Acetone concentration
	665 mμ	664–663 mμ	
Zscheile (*224, 225*)	65.0	68.5	90%
MacKinney (*226*)	84.0	—	100%
MacKinney (*227*)	76.0	82.0	80%
Zscheile et al. (*228*)	—	82.0	80%
Richards & Thompson (*81*)	66.7	71.0	90%
Vernon (*229*)	90.8	92.6	100%
		91.1	90%
Parsons & Strickland (*82*)	89.0	90.0	90%

[a] The extinction coefficient $K = \dfrac{\log_{10} I/I_o}{C \cdot l}$

where *l* is the light path in centimetres and C is the concentration in g · l⁻¹.

5.4.4.2.2   *Apparatus*

- Filter assembly for 47-mm diameter filters including filtering flask and device for producing a vacuum.
- Whatman GF/C or Gelman A filters.
- Grinding apparatus (Fig. 29). It is convenient to have this driven electrically at about $1000 \, r \cdot min^{-1}$, but a hand drill may also be used. Samples may even by ground by hand.
- 15–20 ml screwcap test tubes.

If no spectrophotometer is available a colorimeter and suitable optical filter may be employed. If possible the device should be standardized by comparing a range of extinction readings on a spectrophotometer with the colorimetric readings. The optical filter should have suitable cutoff properties so that it transmits only light within the principal chlorophyll absorption region centred about 663 nm. Suitable filters are Corning 2–58, Wratten no. 26 and Schott RG/2. The correction at 750 nm (described in section 5.4.4.2.4), cannot be made with this apparatus.

5.4.4.2.3   *Reagents*

- $MgCO_3$, reagent grade, powdered. Make a suspension in water in a plastic bottle.
- Acetone, 90% ($900 \, ml \cdot l^{-1}$), reagent grade.
- HCl, $4 \, mol \cdot l^{-1}$.

5.4.4.2.4   *Procedure*

Place a filter on the tower and apply vacuum. Deposit a film of $MgCO_3$ on the filter by filtering an aqueous suspension. (The $MgCO_3$ increases retention of particles on the filter). Pour a suitable measured volume of the fresh water sample through the filter and suck dry. Remove the filter, fold in half so that the side with the precipitate is not exposed, and drop it into the grinding tube. Add 2 ml of 90% acetone, insert the pestle and grind for 30 seconds at about $1000 \, r \cdot min^{-1}$ to release pigments from the cells. Remove the pestle and wash with 2 ml of 90% acetone, catching the washings in the grinding tube. Wash the contents of the grinding tube into the screwcap test tube and make up to a known volume, generally 10 ml. Centrifuge for 30 seconds. Measure the extinction of the supernatant in a suitable cell, with a ground stopper or lid (Fig. 30), at 663 nm and at 750 nm:

$$^{U}E_{663} \quad and \quad ^{U}E_{750}$$

Pour the contents of the cuvette back into the screwcap test tube, add 0.1 ml of

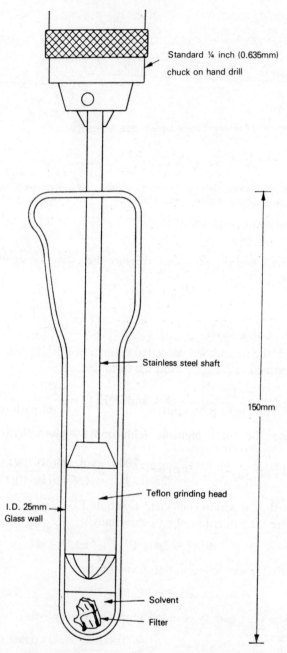

Fig. 29. Conventional tissue grinder as used for chlorophyll extraction

Reproduced from IBP Handbook (*50*)

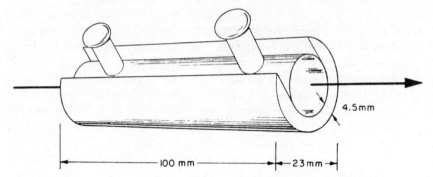

Fig. 30. Brass cuvette holder for small-volume, long light-path cuvettes. (Fits
Beckman DU type spectrophotometer). The arrow indicates the light-path.

Reproduced from IBP Handbook (*50*)

$4 \ mol \cdot l^{-1}$ HCl, and recentrifuge. Measure the extinction again at 663 nm
and 750 nm:

$$^{A}E_{663} \quad \text{and} \quad ^{A}E_{750}.$$

5.4.4.2.5 *Calculations*

Compute the unacidified corrected extinction ($^{U}E^{1 \ cm}_{663}$) and the acidified
corrected extinction ($^{A}E^{1 \ cm}_{663}$) from the formulae:

$$^{U}E^{1 \ cm}_{663} = \frac{^{U}E_{663} - ^{U}E_{750}}{\text{light path (cm)}} \quad \text{and} \quad ^{A}E^{1 \ cm}_{663} = \frac{^{A}E_{663} - ^{A}E_{750}}{\text{light path (cm)}}$$

Calculate the total pigment (chlorophyll + phaeophytin) from the
formula:

$$P_{t} \ (\mu g \cdot l^{-1}) = {}^{U}E^{1 \ cm}_{663} \times \frac{1000}{K} \times \frac{\text{vol. extract (ml)}}{\text{vol. filtrate (l)}}$$

where K is the extinction coefficient (see note E).
Calculate the extinction due to chlorophyll:

$$E^{1 \ cm}_{chl} = 2.43({}^{U}E^{1 \ cm}_{663} - {}^{A}E^{1 \ cm}_{663})$$

Compute the extinction due to phaeophytin:

$$E^{1 \ cm}_{phae} = {}^{U}E^{1 \ cm}_{663} - E^{1 \ cm}_{chl}$$

Calculate the quantity of chlorophyll (or phaeophytin):

$$P_{chl \ (or \ phae)} = E^{1 \ cm}_{chl \ (or \ phae)} \times \frac{1000}{K_{chl \ (or \ phae)}} \times \frac{\text{vol. extract (ml)}}{\text{vol. filtrate (l)}}$$

where K is the extinction coefficient (respectively 89 and 56, see note E).

5.4.4.2.6 *Notes*

A. If samples are to be stored for some reason, they should be stored in a darkened desiccator at around 0°C. It is, however, emphasized that best results are obtained when samples are analysed immediately. In no circumstances should extracts be stored for longer than 12 hours.

B. On the whole, methanol extracts better than 90% acetone. The specific absorption values are, however, not well known and changes in the pigment structure occur rapidly in methanol.

C. In the acidification step, 100% chlorophyll solution will yield a ratio $^UE/^AE$ of 1.7 or slightly higher. If the extract contains nothing but phaeophytin, the ratio will be 1.0 (Fig. 31).

D. From Fig. 31, the ratio $^UE/^AE$ can be converted directly to percentage as chlorophyll or phaeophytin.

E. There is about a 25% difference in the extinction coefficients given by different workers (Table 6). Because of the nature of the methods used for obtaining these values, one might recommend using the highest extinction coefficient for chlorophyll *a*. The recommended values for chlorophyll and phaeophytin are 89 and 56 respectively.

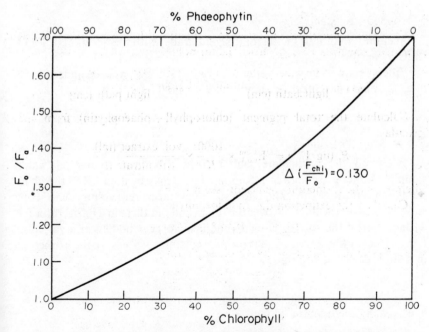

Fig. 31. Relationships between percentages of chlorophyll, phaeophytin and the acid ratio

Reproduced from IBP Handbook (*50*)

Many data, however, have been published using the value 65, which is close to the value given for phaeophytin.

F.   If very small algae are absent, then membrane filters and the method described in section 5.4.4.3 may be used.

5.4.4.3 *Approximate determination for samples containing little phaeophytin*

5.4.4.3.1 *Principle*

Where little phaeophytin is present, and most of the chlorophyll is chlorophyll *a*, an approximate determination may be made by measuring the extinction at 665 mμ of a methanol, ethanol or acetone extract.

5.4.4.3.2 *Apparatus*

Colorimeter and filter as described in section 5.4.4.2.2.

5.4.4.3.3 *Reagents*

Acetone, ethanol or methanol (reagent grade) with the addition of 1 g of $MgCO_3$ per litre.

Filters retain some water; after the organic solvent has been added to the filter, its final concentration should be 90% (900 ml·l^{-1}).

5.4.4.3.4 *Procedure*

Filter off the particulate matter from a known volume of water sample. Either glass fibre or membrane filters may be used. Roll the filter, put it in a centrifuge tube, and add a sufficient (measured) volume of ice-cold solvent to cover the filter. Cover the tubes, and put them in a refrigerator for 24 hours or, if the solvent is methanol, heat to near boiling in a very dim light. Decant the solvent, and if turbid, centrifuge. Measure the extinction in a suitable cell at 665 mμ.

5.4.4.3.5 *Calculation*

If $E^{1\,cm}$ is the extinction of the extract in a 1-cm cuvette;
chloroform *a* equivalent (mg·l^{-1}) $= 11.9 \times E^{1\,cm}$ (acetone); $13.9 \times E^{1\,cm}$ (ethanol and methanol) (76).

5.4.5 *ATP-technique*[a]

5.4.5.1 *Scope*

Determination of biomass by measurement of adenosine triphosphate (ATP) has been made by Holm-Hansen & Booth (*83*) in the ocean. Studies since that time in an aquatic environment have demonstrated that ATP is an excellent indicator of microbial biomass and that ATP determination is a practical and easy method. Adenosine triphosphate meets the following criteria:

(*a*) ATP is ubiquitous in all living organisms and the keystone of all cellular activity (*84*).

(*b*) The ratio of cellular organic carbon to ATP is fairly uniform if various unicellular and multicellular organisms (phytoplankton, bacteria, zooplankton) are compared. The ratio averages 286 for laboratory cultures; in the ocean a ratio of 265 in the epilimnion was found (determined separately for algae, bacteria, and zooplankton) (*85*, *86*).

(*c*) The steady state levels of ATP in algal cells are similar in light or dark; conditions; a sudden change in light conditions is followed by a change in the ATP level lasting only a few minutes, after which it returns to the steady state concentration (*86*). Studies with algae starved of nitrogen, phosphorus and silicon have shown some effect on the ATP level (*86–88*). Such laboratory data on nutrient-deficient algae would represent extreme conditions, but in the aquatic environment there is always a certain regeneration of nutrients.

(*d*) The adsorption of ATP by oceanic detrital material is insignificant; ATP adsorption occurred only in lake sediments (*89*).

ATP decreases sharply with the onset of autolysis of bacteria and in particulate algal material from the ocean that has been killed by repeated freezing or with cyanide (*83*). Activated sludge samples that had been dried at 103°C showed no residual ATP (*90*).

Sensitive methods for ATP analysis have been developed from McElroy's finding (*230*) that luminescence in fireflies has an absolute requirement for ATP. *In vitro* production by firefly lantern extract has been shown to depend upon the presence of luciferin, the enzyme luciferase, oxygen, magnesium ions and ATP. McElroy *et al.* (*91*) proposed the following firefly light reaction sequence:

$$\overset{\overset{\textstyle Mg^{2+}}{\longleftarrow}}{}$$

(1)   E   + LH_2 + ATP → E · LH_2 · AMP +   PP
   (luciferase)   (luciferin)   (luciferyl adenylate   (pyrophosphate)
                                          complex)

(2)   E · LH_2 · AMP + O_2 → E + Product + CO_2 + AMP + *Light*

---

[a] Based on Vollenweider (*45*).

The essential aspect of the reaction is that (*a*) for every molecule of ATP hydrolysed one photon of light is emitted (peak emission is about 560–580 nm); and (*b*) that if everything else is in excess, the light intensity will be directly proportional to the ATP concentration. When ATP is added to the enzyme preparation, there is a rapid emission of photons, the rate of which declines exponentially.

The light emission may be measured using:

- a photomultiplier tube which is housed adjacent to the reaction chamber in a black box and connected to a microphotometer (*92, 93*).

- a liquid scintillation counter (*94*).

- An ATP-photometer and a luminescence biometer.

It is possible to estimate the amount of ATP in a sample by measuring the peak height of light emission. However, this value is very dependent upon complete and rapid mixing of the sample with the enzyme preparation and is also influenced by the chemical composition of the enzyme preparation. Accuracy considerations indicate that the integral approach is better (*83, 95, 96*).

The size of the test sample depends on the fertility of the water. In oligotrophic lake water about one litre is advisable. The water samples are filtered through membrane filters (0.45 µm) or glass fibre filters (GF/C Whatman) as soon as possible to minimize any change in ATP levels caused by changing environmental conditions. The procedure outlined below is based on the work of Holm-Hansen & Booth (*83*).

5.4.5.2   *Procedure*

5.4.5.2.1   *Method of ATP extraction*

Place 5 ml of Tris-buffer (0.02 $mol \cdot l^{-1}$, pH 7.75) in each of several beakers, which are immersed in a boiling water bath and covered with watch glasses. Filter the samples through membrane filters or glass fibre filters (GF/C Whatman). As soon as no liquid remains above the filter, remove the filter and place it in a beaker. Extract the ATP for 5 minutes; then cool the beakers and transfer the extract to a centrifuge tube by means of a disposible syringe. Rinse the filter with 3 ml of Tris-buffer and heat for another 3 minutes. Bring up to volume (8 ml) with additional Tris-buffer and freeze the samples at $-20°C$ until ready for ATP analysis.

Studies have shown that ATP is not hydrolysed during the heating period and that it can be quantitatively determined after many months of storage.

5.4.5.2.2   *Luciferin-luciferase preparation*

Obtain extracts of firefly lanterns and freeze at $-20°C$ (until ready for use). Rehydrate 50 mg of the enzyme with 5.0 ml Tris-buffer and allow the suspension to stand at room temperature for 2–3 hours to reduce light emissions from endogenous ATP. Centrifuge at 1000 g and decant into a test tube. Dispense 0.2 ml (or less) of the enzyme reaction product into each vial and allow to stand for half an hour.

Shake the vial by hand and read the background light emission in the light measuring apparatus. Add to the vial 0.2 ml (or less) of the test solution or an ATP standard solution. Swirl gently for 3–4 seconds to effect complete mixing. After a 15-second period measure the amount of light emitted, and integrate the 1-minute period (if it is necessary to measure peak height, eliminate the 15-second mixing period).

5.4.5.2.3 *ATP-standard*

Weight 109 mg of crystalline adenosine—5-triphosphate disodium salt (mol. wt 551.2) into sterile Tris-buffer. Make a dilution (1 ml = 1 µg ATP) and pour 1 ml into individual test tubes, which are capped and stored at $-20°C$ until needed.

Some light meters achieve a detection of 10^{-13} g of ATP per ml injected with partially purified enzyme. At low concentrations, it is very important that the reagents and glassware are free of factors affecting the light reaction. Use the best sterile, distilled water. Suggested glass washing procedure: (1) soak in hot, soapy water, (2) boil for 1 hour in an acid bath and rinse several times with distilled water (*90*).

5.5 Methods for determining microbial decomposition of organic matter

5.5.1 *Scope*

Microorganisms such as bacteria, fungi, and yeasts are known to play a key role in the processes involved in the decomposition and mineralization of organic matter in the aquatic community. They attack any plants or animals that die, whether from natural causes, injury, or disease. Furthermore, a wide range of organic compounds continuously enter the environment in solution or suspension. This process also stimulates microbial activity. As a result, microorganisms are in a continuous state of flux as they adapt to changing sources of organic matter. Biodegradation of organic matter normally occurs under aerobic conditions with the production of carbon dioxide and water, the oxygen acting as the electron donor for energy transfer in the microbial cell.

The absence of dissolved oxygen does not inhibit biodegradation of organic matter. However, anaerobic decomposition is more or less incomplete, as it yields organic acids. Under natural conditions, anaerobic decomposition takes place in bottom sediments when aerobic metabolism in the upper layer of the sediment consumes too much oxygen.

The activity of microorganisms in water bodies and sediments can be assessed by means of oxygen consumption studies as well as by tracer techniques. The biochemical methods described below are suitable for the *in situ* estimation of microbial activity. They are based on the methods described in IBP Handbook No. 23, *Techniques for the assessment of microbial production and decomposition in fresh waters (50)*.

5.5.2   Decomposition of organic matter in bottom sediments

The method described below was developed by Romanenko & Romanenko (97) on the basis of the oxygen consumption methods reported by Hayes & Anthony (98) and Gambarjan (99).

5.5.2.1   Aerobic decomposition

The sample of sediment is removed with the aid of a sampler.[a] A column of sediment is taken from the sample with the aid of a glass tube 40 cm in length and 3.5 cm in diameter, using a weak vacuum in the upper part of the tube. This treatment does not disturb the vertical structure of the sediment. The bottom end of the tube is then closed with a rubber stopper. The tube with the sediment and the control tube are filled with water, which is taken from the bottom layer of water. It is important here to prevent the disturbance of the upper layer of the sediment. During the filling of both the experimental and control tubes the water is replaced several times. Then both tubes are stoppered with rubber stoppers so that no air bubbles escape.

The tubes are incubated in the dark *in situ* or at the simulated *in situ* temperature in the laboratory for 24 hours. At the end of the incubation period the tubes are held in the vertical position and are unstoppered. The water column over the sediment is mixed very carefully with a thin plastic rod having a loop at the end. This treatment eliminates errors connected with the uneven distribution of oxygen in the water column over the sediment surface. The mixing of water is made with both the experimental and control bottles. The water from the tubes is poured out with the aid of a tube into 60-ml bottles to determine the amount of oxygen in the water by the ordinary Winkler method. The volume of water in the tube is calculated geometrically.

The oxygen consumption by the sediment (D_1) is calculated using the formula:

$$D_1 \text{ (mg } O_2 \text{ per m}^2 \text{ per day)} = \frac{n \times H \times l \times 1600 \times 24}{y}$$

---

[a] For a survey of suitable types of samplers see (100).

where

n = difference between the oxygen titration value of water of the
   experimental tube and that of the control tube (50 ml of water)
H = concentration in $mol \cdot l^{-1}$ of the thiosulfate solution
t = the duration of exposure in hours
l = the length in cm of the water column in the tube.

When the respiratory coefficient is accepted equal to 0.85, 1 mg of O_2 consumed corresponds to 1.59 mg of CO_2 or to 0.44 mg of the organic carbon oxidized.

5.5.2.2 *Anaerobic decomposition*

As was pointed out above, the anerobic decomposition of organic matter in the bottom sediments can be assessed if the amount of evolved CO_2 is known. Where no oxygen is present in the bottom waters and the process proceeds only anaerobically, all the CO_2 formed has to be taken as a measure of anaerobic decomposition. The sampling and the arrangement of the experiments are identical to that described above. When incubation is complete, the water is poured off from the tubes and its content of free CO_2 is estimated by titration with $0.005 \; mol \cdot l^{-1} \; Na_2CO_3$ solution in the presence of phenolphthalein as indicator.

The calculation of the CO_2 formed (P) is made using the formula:

$$P \text{ (mg of C per m}^2) = \frac{n \times H \times l \times 2 \times 1200 \times 24}{t}$$

where

N = the difference between the titrations of 100-ml volumes of water from
   the experimental and the control tubes, in ml
H = concentration in $mol \cdot l^{-1}$ of the Na_2CO_3 solution
l = length of the water column in cm
t = time of the incubation in hours.

The rate of anaerobic decomposition in the sediment (D_2) can be expressed by the following equation:

$$D_2 \text{ (mg of C per cm}^2 \text{ per day}) = P - (D_1 \times 0.44)$$

5.5.2.3 *Measuring the dehydrogenase activity in bottom sediments by using triphenyltetrazolium chloride*

Close relationships are generally found between trophic conditions in lakes and the dehydrogenase activity (DHA) of their sediments. The DHA-values are especially valuable for comparison with oxygen consumption as well as formation of carbon dioxide, redox-potential, evolution of methane or nitrogen, and number of bacteria to be estimated separately in aliquot quantities of the same sediment.

Hydrogen from organic substances e.g., succinic acid is transferred by enzymes to triphenyltetrazolium chloride (TTC), which is thus converted to formazan. This red-coloured compound is nearly insoluble in water but soluble in some organic solvents.

5.5.2.3.1 *Reagents*

- TTC reagent: Dissolve 0.9 g of triphenyltetrazolium chloride and 1.5 g of cadmium nitrate in 300 ml of 0.1 mol·l^{-1} Tris-buffer (pH 7.5) containing 36.45 g of Tris-oximethylaminomethane dissolved in 300 ml of water and 60.9 ml of 0.1 mol·l^{-1} HCl. Finally, eliminate the dissolved oxygen by bubbling nitrogen through the reagent.

- Extraction mixture: 450 ml of acetone are added to 300 ml of tetrachloroethylene.

5.5.2.3.2 *Procedure*

The mud cores are conveniently taken from water bodies using a sampler of the corer type. Water covering the mud surface is sucked off and then the corer tube is opened along its length. The mud samples from different layers are taken by using a syringe (S in Fig. 32) the mouth of which fits into tube b of the incubation flask F. This flask is flushed with nitrogen to ensure that all the air is driven out. Just before the syringe is fixed to tube b, it must also be flushed with nitrogen. Instead of using the syringe, mud samples can be transferred to the flask by a spoon. However, in this case some oxidation of the mud occurs and produces inhibitory effects on anaerobic bacteria. After turning cock C_1 approximately 5 ml of the wet mud are expressed from the syringe into flask F. Then cock C_1 is turned again so that the nitrogen pressure expels the mud remaining in tube C. Weighing of the mud sampler in the flask is generally unnecessary because the syringe delivers quite accurate quantities of mud. Again nitrogen is used for flushing out O_2 from tube b. Immediately afterwards the burette B filled with TTC reagent is fixed to tube b. Allow 10 ml of the solution to run into flask F and empty tube c by nitrogen flushing again. The cocks C_1 and C_2 are closed and the flask is incubated for 24 hours on a shaking apparatus in the dark at 30°C. Open flask F and pour in approximately 40 ml of the extraction mixture, close again and shake for 1 hour on the shaking apparatus in the dark. Filter the mixture through paper (e.g., No. 589, 3 Schleicher and Schüll) into a measuring flask, wash the filter, fill up with extraction mixture under shaded light conditions

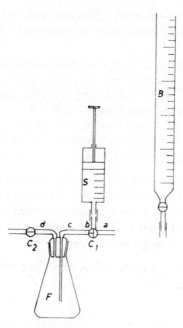

Fig. 32.   Incubation flask and filling apparatus used for measuring the dehydrogenase activity of mud samples

Reproduced from IBP Handbook (50)

and put in the dark immediately afterwards. A blank sample is run, i.e., by using the same procedure without TTC in the Tris-reagent. The extinction of the formazan solution is measured immediately at 540 nm in a spectrophotometer. The resulting values can be used for comparison by referring to the quantities of applied wet mud, the dry substance of which has to be determined separately. It is more advantageous to calibrate the extinction values in terms of H^+ by using 0.01 mol $\cdot$ l^{-1} ascorbic acid, which delivers 0.01 equivalents H^+/L. The factor for computation may be, for example, 4.66 µg H^+ per extinction value 0.001 and has to be related to unit weight of wet or dry substance.

5.5.2.4   *Measuring the evolution rate of gases from bottom sediments*

The process of microbial fermentation in bottom sediments results in the production of methane and other gases. Their quantity depends on the concentration of organic substances and nutrients in the sediment. Remarkable differences are found in gas-producing activity between muds from lakes of low and high productivity. The largest values, up to 1000 times those obtained with uncontaminated water bodies, occur in lakes receiving sewage waters.

5.5.2.4.1   *Measurements by direct use of mud cores*

Using a core sampler, take mud cores 20–50 cm in length and 10 cm in width, together with the contact water layer 40–70 cm in height. The most convenient sampler for this purpose is the Iris-Mud-Sampler, the bottom of which is closed in the sediment by an iris-shutter (Fig. 33). Insert the

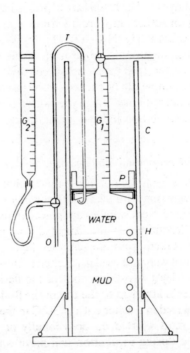

Fig. 33. Experimental set-up with a core tube for measuring evolution rates of fermentation gases

Reproduced from IBP Handbook (*50*)

special piston P which is combined with the gas burette G_1 and tube T as well. By this means a part of the lake water will be forced out at the top of burette G_1 and a part through tube T into the levelling burette G_2, in which the surface of the water is covered by liquid paraffin. This surface has to be adjusted to the level of burette G_1 by opening the outflow O of tube T. Thus the piston P separates water and compresses the sample of mud and water firmly. The height of the water column should be a few cm only. The core is incubated in the dark at 30°C or at such a temperature as might be more representative of natural conditions. Then adjust the liquid level to point " zero " in burette G_2 after the temperature of the whole apparatus has been allowed to reach equilibrium. Read the volume of gas evolved in burette G_1 at short time intervals, depending on the intensity of bacterial de-composition. Measure the total quantity of gas formed by reading the pressure in burette G_2 after having levelled it against the water surface in burette G_1. Compute the volume according to normal gas conditions (0°C, 1.01×10^5 Pa). The gas volume collected in burette G_1 is used for chromatographic analysis. The results are expressed as cm^3 of gas per m^2 per day or per month or other appropriate time interval. The volumetric composition of the gases (CH_4, N_2, CO_2, H_2, O_2) is also described.

Additionally, the content and composition of the gases dissolved in the contact layer of water can be measured by gas-chromatographic methods. The water sample can be sucked out by inserting a syringe through one of the rubber stoppered holes (H) in the wall of tube C. The same holes are useful for injecting solution in experimental series.

5.5.2.4.2 *Measurements using homogenized mud samples* in vitro[a]

This method differs from the preceding one in that the mud samples are first homogenized by mixing with near-bottom water during the incubation.

The homogenized sediment samples are placed in flasks of 250, 500, 1000 or 2000 ml volume depending on the expected volume of the gas evolved (Fig. 34), and water taken from the contact layer of the same lake is added. The quantity of wet mud used is weighed in the flask. The volume of the mud should be at least two-thirds that of the flask. A 100-ml burette acting as a manometer is attached to the top of the flask. For incubation of the mud the flask is placed in a water bath at 30°C in the dark. The contents are shaken and the mud whirled up occasionally or stirred constantly if possible. Gas evolved during incubation will drive water into the burette. The water level gives the quantity of gas at normal conditions after reduction to 0°C and 1.01×10^5 Pa according to barometric pressure, temperature, and hydrostatic pressure of the water column in the burette. Results are expressed as cm^3 of gas per g of wet sediment, or dry substance, per time interval, e.g., month or 100 days. The standard deviation of the values is 10% approximately.

The quantity of gases dissolved in the water cannot be determined precisely because the initial gas content of the water is unknown. However, for comparative work these errors can be neglected in the case of observation

---

[a] This procedure was developed by A. Hamm, Munich (see *101*).

Fig. 34.   Apparatus for determining activities of gas evolution of homogenized mud samples

Reproduced from IBP Handbook (*50*)

periods of a month or longer.   According to the absorption coefficients of the participating gases at 30°C and 1.01×10^5 Pa, for equal volumes of gas and solution the volumetric errors would be 2.3% CH_4, 0.1% N_2 and 4.7% CO_2, assuming an average volumetric composition of 85.2% CH_4, 7.5% N_2 and 7.1% CO_2.

5.6   Methods for estimating self-purification processes

5.6.1   *Principles*

The principal mechanisms responsible for reducing the concentration of organic matter are:

- permanent loss due to microbial decomposition
- biomass production at the established trophic levels
- permanent loss of energy due to the respiration rate at each trophic level (community respiration).

The mechanisms responsible for the elimination of organic matter other than by biochemical processes, are:

- storage of detritus or particulate organic matter at the bottom, or export into the downstream reach
- loss of volatile matter to the atmosphere
- chemical reactions, oxidation-reduction processes, adsorption, flocculation.

Lakes usually have little outflow in comparison with the volume of the water masses. Therefore the export of detritus is too small, in most cases, to compensate for the input of polluting matter. Of much more importance is the fact that detritus and even living cells are allowed to settle on the bottom. Here the stored matter becomes subject to anaerobic decomposition.

Running waters have other properties. Owing to the fact that the flow is only in one direction, the export of detritus, biomass, and dissolved organic compounds to the downstream reaches plays an important role in self-purification processes.

It is assumed that the river represents a continuous fermentation system. The input of large quantities of organic matter forces the community in the direction of heterotrophy and microbial decomposition of the organic matter is highly stimulated. Under these conditions the ratio P/R between primary productivity (P) and heterotrophic activity, e.g., respiration (R), is often < 1, or in cases of severe pollution $\ll 1$. As a result of the self-purification processes in the flowing water, photoautotrophic organisms become progressively more abundant downstream. The quotient $P/R = 1$ represents this situation on the trophic scale.

5.6.2 Definition

Self-purification may be defined as the ability of the community involved to cause a decrease in the concentration of pollutants (organic matter) per unit time, or to reduce the mass flow of these substances within a certain flow distance. A more general approach is given in (*102*).

5.6.3 Field of application

Self-purification processes can be estimated either in terms of quantitative units or in terms of secondary effects, such as changes in the oxygen balance of the receiving water body, the heterotrophic activity (oxygen consumption) of microorganisms, the abundance and distribution of organisms (species diversity), the ratio of photoautotrophic and heterotrophic reactions, and, last but not least, the presence of indicator organisms due to the various saprobic systems.

According to Wuhrmann (*102*), the following quantities are useful for estimating self-purification (the explanation of the symbols is given at the bottom of this page).

(a) Amount of self-purification (decrease of mass transport within a river reach), S_m, assuming no additional load between points of observation (in $mol \cdot s^{-1}$):

$$S_m = Q(c_o - c_u) \tag{1}$$

(b) Rate of self-purification (decrease in concentration of pollution per unit time at constant flow), S_r (in $mol \cdot m^{-3} \cdot s^{-1}$):

$$S_r = \frac{dc}{dt} = \frac{c_o - c_u}{t} \tag{2}$$

S_r may also be expressed in units of travel distance. The precision of its determination depends largely on the definition and the measurement of flow time between the points of observation.

These quantities acquire much greater significance when related to ecological parameters. For instance, the amount of self-purification may be expressed as a function (S_e) of the biomass in the river (in $mol \cdot g^{-1} \cdot s^{-1}$):

$$S_e = \frac{S_m}{G} = \frac{Q(c_o - c_u)}{t(g'Pv + g''Q)} \tag{3}$$

Similarly, the rate of self-purification may be expressed as a function of the biomass and the settled wetted surface (in $mol \cdot m^{-3} \cdot s^{-1}$):

$$S_r = S_e\left(\frac{g'}{R} + g''\right) \tag{4}$$

S_e is equivalent to the specific elimination rate exerted by the total biomass in direct contact with the flowing water (i.e., the suspended organisms plus the sessile epibenthic flora and fauna). The introduction into Equation 2 of S_e and the hydraulic radius (R) as a geometrical parameter gives in Equation 4 a value for S_r that emphasizes the space distribution of the biomass within a cross section.

Q: flow $(m^3 \cdot s^{-1})$
c_o, c_u: concentration of compounds at the upstream (c_o) and the downstream (c_u) end of the self-purification reach $(mol \cdot m^{-3})$
t: flow time within the self-purification reach (s)
G: total biomass (g)
g':   attached biomass $(g \cdot m^{-2})$
g'':   suspended biomass $(g \cdot m^{-3})$
P: length of wetted cross profile (m)
R: hydraulic radius (m)
v: flow velocity $(m \cdot s^{-1})$

5.6.4 *Determination of the biochemical oxygen demand (BOD)*

This method was originally developed for wastewater analysis and the control of the degradation efficiency of sewage treatment plants. BOD has been used as a parameter for a variety of purposes, in particular in connexion with surface water quality assessment. As a measure of the intensity of the degradation of organic substances in water, however, the BOD method can be used only with reservations, because the values thus measured are influenced by a variety of factors. The details of the laboratory procedure are given in volume 2, chapter 4, section 2.

5.6.5 *Assimilation and depletion test*

The assimilation and depletion test (A–D test) is used for the toxicological and biochemical examination of wastewater and wastewater constituents, and serves primarily for the determination of the biochemical effect of such constituents as a function of their concentration, thus providing information on the influence of a specific wastewater on the oxygen balance of the receiving stream.

5.6.5.1 *Theory*

The two basic reactions of biochemical self-purification serve as a measure of the effects, in particular the toxic effect, of a wastewater. They are:

(*a*) the bacterial degradation of organic substances; this is assessed by determining the resultant oxygen consumption as a function of wastewater concentration (depletion test);

(*b*) the assimilation by green plants (phytoplankton); this is assessed by determining the oxygen production as a function of wastewater concentration (assimilation test).

As these processes correspond to the main reactions involved in self-purification, the results of the tests enable direct qualitative conclusions to be drawn about the effect of a wastewater on the oxygen balance of a stream, provided the dilution conditions in the receiving stream are known. Quantitative conclusions are possible if the extent of the so-called biochemical processes in the receiving stream, as observed in the absence of wastewater influences, is also known.

5.6.5.2 *Interferences*

In principle, A–D tests can be interfered with by all substances that affect the determination of oxygen, in particular by those with heavily oxidizing or reducing effects. Where such disturbances are to be expected, the iodine difference method of Ohle, or electrometric measurement with the aid of membrane-covered electrodes, should be applied; alternatively, the examinations should be carried out with pretreated wastewater (e.g., following aeration to satisfy the chemical oxygen demand). Where the original pollution load of the receiving stream is to be taken into account, the dilution water should be taken from a point upstream of the wastewater inflow.

5.6.5.3   *Apparatus and reagents*

All the apparatus and reagents listed in the method for the determination of dissolved oxygen (volume 2, chapter 3, section 16), are required and, in addition, the following:

(a) *For the determination of oxygen consumption:*

- Graduated pipettes, 10 ml capacity, graduated in increments of 0.1 ml
- Volumetric pipettes, 20 ml and 50 ml capacity
- Non-toxic BOD dilution water (see volume 2, chapter 3 section 2.2.5.1)
- Peptone solution: 1 g of peptone, from meat, dried, is dissolved in 100 ml of distilled water; the solution should always be prepared shortly before use.

(b) *For the assimilation test:*

- Light box or light cabinet in which a constant illumination intensity of about 4000 lux can be produced at a constant temperature of 20–22°C.
- Erlenmeyer flask for use as culture tube, 100 ml capacity
- Non-toxic BOD dilution water, as above, with the addition of 700 mg of sodium bicarbonate ($NaHCO_3$) and 5 mg of ethylene diaminetetracetic acid, disodium salt, per litre
- Filtering device for membrane filter
- Membrane filter, pore size 5 μm
- Tragacanth solution: about 0.1 g of tragacanth, finely powdered, is left to swell in several ml of distilled water; a fresh solution should be prepared daily.
- Non-sterile mixed culture of algae of the order Protococcales. This culture is produced as follows: Culture flask with inorganic nutrient solutions are left open and exposed to light until green turbidity occurs

following infection from natural sources in the air.[a] The nutrient solutions best suited for the purpose are those produced by dissolving in distilled water commercially available nutrient salt tablets for hydroponic cultures; as a substitute, one of the following nutrient solutions may be used:

(i) Nutrient solution I: 1 g of potassium nitrate, KNO_3, analytical reagent grade (AR), 0.1 g of calcium nitrate, $Ca(NO_3)_2 \cdot 4H_2O$, AR, 0.2 g of dipotassium hydrogen phosphate, K_2HPO_4, purest grade, 0.1 g of magnesium sulfate, $MgSO_4 \cdot 7H_2O$, AR, and 0.01 g of ferric chloride, $FeCl_3$, AR are dissolved in 1 litre of distilled water.

(ii) Nutrient solution II: 0.08 g of diammonium hydrogen phosphate, $(NH_4)_2HPO_4$, AR, 0.04 g of dipotassium hydrogen phosphate, K_2HPO_4, purest grade, 0.04 g of magnesium sulfate, $MgSO_4 \cdot 7H_2O$, AR, and 0.4 g of calcium sulfate, $CaSO_4 \cdot 2H_2O$, AR are dissolved in 1 litre of distilled water. Ten drops of a 10 $g \cdot l^{-1}$ aqueous solution of ferrous sulfate $FeSO_4 \cdot 7H_2O$ are added.

Depending on the light conditions, the original growth of the cultures requires about 8–14 days. For continued growth, 2 ml of a parent culture aged about 10 days are transferred into approximately 100 ml of one of the above nutrient solutions.

5.6.5.4 Depletion test (plotting the oxygen consumption curve)

5.6.5.4.1 Procedure

Seven or eight oxygen bottles are filled with non-toxic, oxygen-saturated BOD dilution water. In one sample (reference sample), the oxygen is at once chemically fixed. The other samples are adjusted to BOD of about 5 $mg \cdot l^{-1}$ by adding 2–3 ml of a peptone solution for each litre of dilution water; the exact volume must be determined by preliminary tests.

---

[a] In order to shorten the time needed for the growth of a sufficient quantity of algae, the culture may be seeded with protococcal algae using the following new algal assay medium as nutrient solution:

	$mg \cdot l^{-1}$		$\mu g \cdot l^{-1}$
$NaNO_3$	25.5	H_3BO_3	185.64
K_2HPO_4	1.044	$MnCl_2$	265.27
$MgCl_2 \cdot 6H_2O$	12.39	$ZnCl_2$	32.7
$MgSO_4 \cdot 7H_2O$	14.7	$CoCl_2$	0.78
$CaCl_2 \cdot 2H_2O$	4.41	$CuCl_2$	0.009
$NaHCO_3$	15.0	$Na_2MoO_4 \cdot 2H_2O$	7.26
$Na_2SiO_3 \cdot 5H_2O$	92.7	$FeCl_3 \cdot 6H_2O$	160.0
		$Na_2EDTA \cdot 2H_2O$	300.0

One of these samples remains unaltered to serve as a blank test sample. To the other samples, different quantities of the wastewater to be examined are added, e.g., 1, 2, 5, 10, 20, and 50 ml per litre of sample. The wastewater must be added at the bottom of the bottle, using suitable pipettes, so that when the stopper is replaced, dilution water only (and under no circumstances wastewater) will be displaced and spill over.

All bottles are then closed, taking care that no gas bubbles remain, and shaken vigorously. After 24 hours of incubation in the dark at a temperature of 20–22°C, the residual oxygen content of all samples is determined.

5.6.5.4.2 *Calculation*

The residual oxygen content of each sample is computed according to the formula:

$$G = \frac{a \times 80}{b - c}$$

where

G = the oxygen content of the sample in $mg \cdot l^{-1}$

a = the volume (ml) of $0.01\ mol \cdot l^{-1}$ sodium thiosulfate solution required

b = the volume (ml) of the oxygen bottle

c = the sum of the volumes (ml) of the added peptone solution and the wastewater.

The change in the oxygen consumption of each sample containing wastewater, as compared with the "reference sample", is computed according to the following formula:

$$\Delta Z = \frac{G_B - G_X}{G_K - G_B} \times 100$$

where

ΔZ = change (%) in the oxygen consumption of the sample to which wastewater has been added, as compared with the reference sample not containing wastewater

G_B = oxygen content $(mg \cdot l^{-1})$ of the blank test sample after incubation

G_X = oxygen content $(mg \cdot l^{-1})$ of the sample, which in 1000 ml contains X ml of wastewater

G_K = original oxygen content $(mg \cdot l^{-1})$ of the reference sample.

Negative ΔZ values are a measure of the toxic effect of the wastewater. Positive ΔZ values result from nontoxic but oxygen-depleting wastewaters in which the biological and chemical oxygen demand prevails over any toxic effect that may be present.

Further data can be obtained as follows:

$G_K - G_B = Z_B = BOD_1$ of the blank test sample

$G_K - G_X = Z_X = BOD_2$ of the sample containing wastewater and peptone

$G_B - G_X = Z_Z = BOD_1$ of a sample containing X ml of wastewater and $(1000 - X)$ ml of dilution water. Negative values indicate toxic effects.

5.6.5.5 *Assimilation test (plotting the "assimilation curve")*

5.6.5.5.1 *Procedure*

Thirteen to fifteen oxygen bottles (the actual number depends on the number of the wastewater dilutions to be examined) are filled with BOD dilution water. In one sample ("reference sample"), the oxygen is at once chemically fixed; this sample is stored in the dark at 20°C for later titration. The other samples are used to prepare two series of duplicate samples. First, a quantity of non-sterile algal culture is filtered through a membrane filter until the membrane has an intense green colour. Care should be taken to prevent the filtration residue from becoming dry. Before filtration, several ml of tragacanth solution should be added to the culture to prevent the algae from floating off during the subsequent procedure. The filter membrane is carefully subdivided into eight equal parts. One-eighth of the algal filter is placed in one of the two bottles of each duplicate sample. Thus, each pair of samples in the series consists of one bottle containing algae and one bottle with no algae.

One pair of samples remains without further additives (pair of blank test samples). The other sample pairs are mixed with different quantities of the wastewater to be examined, e.g., with 1, 2, 5, 10, 20 and 50 ml·l⁻¹ in such a way that the quantity of wastewater added is the same for the two samples of each pair.

The wastewater should always be added at the bottom of the bottle, using suitable pipettes so that, when the stopper is replaced, dilution water only (under no circumstances wastewater) will be displaced and spill over. All bottles are then closed, taking care that no gas bubbles remain, and shaken vigorously to ensure even distribution of the added wastewater; they are then incubated in the light cabinet for 24 hours at a light intensity of about 4000 lux and a temperature of 20–22°C. Care should be taken to make sure that in all samples containing algae the filter membrane comes to rest with the filtration residue on the top side. On expiration of the test period, the oxygen content in all samples is determined. The assimilation rate of each pair of samples is defined as the difference in oxygen content between the sample with and the one without algae. In the blank test sample, this rate should be about 5–8 mg of oxygen per litre.

5.6.5.5.2 *Calculation*

Variations in the assimilation rate are computed for each wastewater concentration according to the following formula:

$$\Delta A = \frac{(S_{Xm} - S_{Xo}) - (S_{Bm} - S_{Bo})}{S_{Bm} - S_{Bo}} \times 100$$

where

ΔA = change % in the assimilation rate of a sample contaminated with X ml of wastewater per litre compared to a non-contaminated blank test sample

S_{Bm} = oxygen content (mg·l^{-1}) of blank test sample containing algae, after incubation

S_{Bo} = oxygen content (mg·l^{-1}) of blank test sample without algae, after incubation

S_{Xm} = oxygen content (mg·l^{-1}) of sample containing X ml of wastewater per litre plus algae, after incubation

S_{Xo} = oxygen content (mg·l^{-1}) of sample containing X ml of wastewater per litre but no algae, after incubation

Negative ΔA values are a measure of the toxic effect of the wastewater. Positive ΔA values result from nontoxic, eutrophic wastewaters and from wastewaters in which any toxic effect that may be present is exceeded by the enrichment effect of the wastewater (e.g., wastewater containing phosphate or nitrate).

5.6.5.6 *Presentation of the results*

Values of ΔZ and ΔA are rounded up or down to the nearest 1%. All values should be tabulated. The ΔZ and ΔA values should be represented graphically as functions of the wastewater concentration plotted on the x-axis, and the ΔZ and ΔA values on the y-axis. Where only one wastewater concentration was examined in the A–D test, or where the result obtained with a specific concentration (e.g., the dilution ratio of the examined wastewater in the receiving stream) is to be discussed separately, the corresponding values should be given.

Example:
  In the A-test, ΔA (20 ml·l^{-1}) = -35%
  In the D-test, ΔZ (20 ml·l^{-1}) = -28%
The value in parentheses indicates the concentration used in the test.

5.6.5.7 *Modifications in the procedure*

Where the comparative toxicological examination of different wastewaters is less of interest than the experimental determination of the effect of a certain wastewater on the oxygen balance of the receiving stream, it may be advisable to calibrate the inoculation material used in the A–D test (e.g., dilution water, algal cultures) by comparative tests with water from the receiving stream upstream of the point of wastewater inflow and using the micro-organisms it contains. Experience shows that the critical limiting values (i.e., the lowest concentrations still having a measurable toxic effect) thus obtained are similar but that the toxic effect of the wastewaters is slightly less than with culture material (probably as a result of adaptation of the organisms in the receiving stream). This is especially true for the A-test.

When using electrometric methods for measuring oxygen, chemical fixation is not possible; oxygen consumption may be stopped by adding, in the form of a concentrated solution, 20 mg of mercuric chloride ($HgCl_2$), analytical grade, for each litre of sample. The sample bottles are then closed again, taking care that no gas bubbles are present, and kept this way until measurement commences.

5.6.6 *Oxygen balance measurements*

Oxygen is released by primary production and consumed by heterotrophic organisms and by the chemical oxidation of reduced substances; it is also supplied from the atmosphere. Depending on the water temperature, organic pollution and light conditions, a dynamic equilibrium results, which manifests itself in a day and night variation in the dissolved oxygen content of the surface water. By simple measurement of the oxygen content of the water during a day and night period, an oxygen curve is obtained, which can be evaluated by means of the Brujewitsch formula (*103*):

$$P_{O_2} = O_{2_{max}} + K \times O_{2_{night}} \times \frac{N}{24 - n}$$

where P_{O_2} = oxygen production, $O_{2_{max}}$ = the difference between the maximum and minimum oxygen content during a 24-hour period, $O_{2_{night}}$ = the decrease in oxygen content during the night, n = the length of the day in hours, and K is a coefficient, which is equal to the ratio of the time between sunrise and afternoon maximum to the length of the day in hours. Generally, the value of the coefficient is 0.85. It is assumed that the respiration measured at night is the same as in daytime.

According to McConnell (*104*), a three-point evaluation can be made to determine the 24-hour oxygen production:

$$P_{O_2} = O_{2su2} - O_{2su1} + \frac{(O_{2su1} - O_{2sa}) \times 24}{\text{night hours}}$$

where P_{O_2} = oxygen production, O_{2su1} = oxygen content at sunset,

O_{2su2} = oxygen content at the expiration of a 24-hour period, and O_{2sa} = oxygen content at sunrise (see also *105*).

The biogenous oxygen supply is of special importance when, owing to heavy oxygen consumption in consequence of anthropogenic pollution, oxygen diffusion from the atmosphere is no longer sufficient to ensure saturation values in the water. The determination of the biogenous aeration rate offers the possibility of quantifying this interesting metabolic state of the water.

The biogenous aeration rate can be measured directly *in situ*, i.e., in the surface water, by determining the oxygen balance of water samples confined in gas-tight containers. By converting the measured values according to the assimilation formula, it is also possible to calculate the primary production (see section 5.4.2.5).

On the other hand, under the dark conditions of the BOD test, phytoplankton only consume oxygen as a result of respiration. Thus, the measurement of BOD for waters containing phytoplankton may show a considerable oxygen consumption that is not the result of degradation processes by bacteria. Under uniform laboratory conditions, the determination of the oxygen production potential provides characteristic values for oxygen production by the phytoplankton contained in a sample of river water. These characteristic values are therefore used as a measure of the development of algal blooms; they aid the physiological detection of active phytoplankton and of the aeration of the water, and allow a correct interpretation to be made of BOD measurements in surface waters.

5.6.6.1   *Determination of the oxygen production potential*

5.6.6.1.1   *Theory*

The oxygen production potential (OPP) is the quantity of oxygen produced by the naturally present phytoplankton in a water sample within a period of 24 hours under constant laboratory conditions (*106, 107*).

5.6.6.1.2   *Interferences*

Interferences by oxidizable substances are possible if the BOD_1 of the sample to be examined exceeds its oxygen content; substances that influence the oxygen determination may also disturb the determination of the OPP. The presence of pollutants such as industrial wastewater should not be considered as an interference factor, as a similar effect will also take place in the surface water concerned.

5.6.6.1.3 *Apparatus and reagents*

All the apparatus and reagents required for oxygen determination are needed and, in addition:

- Light box or light cabinet in which a constant light intensity of approximately 4000 lux can be produced at a constant temperature of 20–22°C

- Opaque plastic foil covers, shaped to fit the oxygen bottles used.

5.6.6.1.4 *Procedure*

Fill three oxygen bottles with the water to be examined and close them, making sure that all gas bubbles are excluded. In one sample, the oxygen should be fixed at once; this sample is stored in the dark at a temperature of 20–22°C for later oxygen determination. Sample No. 2 is enclosed in a light-tight cover (darkened sample); sample No. 3 remains unaltered (illuminated sample). Sample No. 2 and Sample No. 3 are then incubated in the light box or cabinet for 24 hours at 20–22°C and under a continuous light intensity of approximately 4000 lux. At the end of the incubation period, the oxygen is also fixed in these two samples, and the oxygen content in all three samples is determined.

The darkened samples must always be kept in the same incubator as the exposed samples, since even the slightest difference in temperature between the exposed and darkened samples may lead to faulty results.

5.6.6.1.5 *Calculation*

The oxygen production potential is calculated according to the following formula:

$$OPP = S_h - S_d$$

The biochemical oxygen demand is determined from:

$$BOD_1 = S_e - S_d$$

where

OPP = oxygen production potential, in $mg \cdot l^{-1}$
BOD_1 = one-day biochemical oxygen demand, in $mg \cdot l^{-1}$
S_e = oxygen content ($mg \cdot l^{-1}$) of the water sample at the time of sampling
S_h = oxygen content ($mg \cdot l^{-1}$) of the illuminated sample
S_d = oxygen content ($mg \cdot l^{-1}$) of the darkened sample.

5.6.6.1.6   *Presentation of the results*

Values should be rounded up or down to the nearest 0.1 mg·l^{-1}. Light intensity, temperature, and incubation time should be given together with the results.

Example:
OPP (22°C, 4000 lux, 24 h) = 12 mg oxygen per litre.

6. TROPHIC AND SAPROBIC LEVELS

Organisms have been used as indicators of certain properties of the aquatic environment since the middle of the 19th century but the first indicator system was not established until the beginning of the 20th century.

There are now 3 main approaches:

(1) determining the state of the communities and detecting changes in their structure;

(2) using organisms as indicators of water quality, especially with respect to the content of putrescible organic matter; and

(3) measuring the quantity of organisms that are in excess of their natural level, thus causing nuisances and deterioration in water quality.

6.1   Numerical values as expressions of community structure

6.1.1   *Similarity quotient*

The simplest approach to biological monitoring or river water quality is by means of an ecological survey of the river carried out by an experienced team of river biologists. The results are then interpreted, comparisons being made between the community structure at successive stations downstream. For this purpose similarity coefficients may be calculated such as Sørensen's Quotient of Similarity, Q_s, given by the following formula:

$$Q_s = \frac{2c}{a+b}$$

where

   a = number of species in one sample
   b = number of species in a second sample
   c = number of species common to both.

Because of the longitudinal distribution of species along the river, there is a natural change in community structure between successive stations. Where, however, a marked discontinuity in this transition occurs, which cannot be explained by natural ecological changes in the river, pollution is indicated. A more intensive study, backed up by physicochemical analysis, is then needed in that section of the river to identify the cause and source of pollution. The effectiveness of any remedial action can be assessed by subsequent examination of the affected stations.

For administrative and recording purposes, however, it is often necessary to report the results of such biological surveys in the form of a descriptive grading or numerical score. Where this is required, one of the following diversity indices may be used.

6.1.2 *Diversity indices*

Diversity is a characteristic of community structure expressing the richness or the variety of the component species. It is generally considered that communities subject to environmental stress undergo reduction in community diversity. A diversity index is a numerical value expressing the numbers of different species present in a community in relation to the total population. Pollution, by subjecting the community to environmental stress, results in a reduction in the diversity index. It is assumed that the degree of change in the diversity index is proportional to the intensity of pollution. Different formulae have been suggested for computing the diversity index (*d*).

(*a*) *Menhinick's Index (108)*

$$d = \frac{s}{\sqrt{n}}.$$

where

s = number of species in sample
n = total number of individuals in sample.

(*b*) *Margalef's Index (109)*

$$d = \frac{s-1}{\log_e n}.$$

Both Menhinick's and Margalef's indices, although readily computed, are dependent on sample size. Furthermore, they do not reflect significant changes in community structure; they do not take into account the relative number of individuals nor the different species, so that communities with markedly different percentage species composition could have the same diversity index.

(*c*) *Shannon and Weaver Index (110)*

$$d = -\Sigma \left(\frac{n_i}{n}\right) C \log\left(\frac{n_i}{n}\right)$$

where

n_i = number of individuals in each individual species in sample
n = total number of individuals in all species in sample
$C = 1$ for $\log_{10}$
$C = 3.3219$ for $\log_2$ (binary digits, most often used)
$C = 2.3026$ for $\log_e$

Although this index is more difficult to compute than Menhinick's and Margalef's indices, it does take into account the relative abundance of different species in the community. It is therefore more sensitive in detecting changes in community structure.

6.1.3   *Application*

Diversity indices can be applied to any community—benthos, periphyton, or plankton. They have the advantage of providing an objective assessment. They respond to all types of environmental stress and therefore indicate different types of pollution—organic, physical, and toxic. However, they also respond to environmental stresses other than those due to pollution; for example, the diversity index is often low in head stream where physical conditions are severe but the water quality usually very good. Diversity indices, although reflecting an important feature of community structure, do not describe all their characteristics. The presence or absence of species of known tolerance to pollution is not made use of. The ecological significance of diversity, although often claimed in theory, has not been widely established in practice. Consequently, one should not rely solely on diversity indices but they can be used to advantage to supplement other methods. A change in the diversity index reflects a change in the ecological conditions; the cause of this change must, however, be ascertained by other means.

6.2   Extended saprobic index

Saprobity is one of the main determinants of water quality. The others are toxicity, physical factors (e.g., suspended solids, oil, heat), radioactivity, and in some circumstances, also trophism and salinity. Although these properties vary independently, they also interact.

Saprobity is an expression of the complex of properties of the aquatic environment that result from the presence of organic matter accessible to microbial exoenzymatic decomposition. It affects the oxygen regime and the species composition, as well as the development of communities of aquatic organisms. The structure of these communities reacts in dynamic equilibrium with the changes in environmental conditions. Changing communities show two distinct saprobic successions, which can be marked on a conventional scale of saprobity. Saprobity itself is dimensionless, but it is directly dependent on the mean BOD value, so that it can be stated that the saprobic degrees (or levels) are an ecological expression of BOD reflected in the species composition of the communities. Saprobic degrees can be determined by qualitative biological analysis.

The structure of saprobic communities is shown in Fig. 35, which also indicates the saprobic successions.

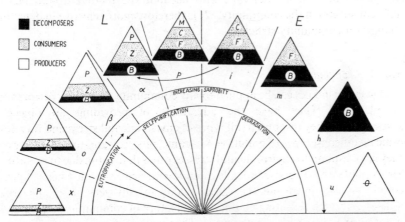

Fig. 35. Structures of communities at individual saprobic levels: x—xenosaprobity; o—oligosaprobity; β—β-mesosaprobity; α—α-mesosaprobity; p—polysaprobity; i—isosaprobity; m—metasaprobity; h—hypersaprobity; u—ultrasaprobity; L—limnosaprobity; E—eusaprobity; B—bacteria; F—colourless flagellates; C—ciliates; M—mixotrophic phytoflagellates; Z—zooplankton and other animals; P—phytoplankton and other producers.

Reproduced from Sládeček (*111*)

The two saprobic successions are as follows:

1. The primary (progressive, ascending) series, in which the initial stage of katharobity is gradually changed by the addition of mineral salts and organic matter into higher levels of saprobity, culminating in hypersaprobity or even abiotic ultrasaprobity. Eutrophication is a particular type of initial process that culminates in beta-mesosaprobity. There are two trends within this series: eutrophication, both natural and induced, and saprobization, which can also be both natural and induced.

2. The secondary (regressive, descending) series begins at the stage of hypersaprobity and gradually descends through all the stages of saprobity, ending with β-mesosaprobity in temperate climates or with oligosaprobity in cold climates and in the sea. This series can be artificially shortened in

sewage and industrial waste plants. The general trend is decomposition or self-purification.

Both successions are objective realities, but they may be described and interpreted in various ways. Both are very old and can be dated back to the Precambrian period.

In the circular scheme of water quality shown in Fig. 36, the quadrants represent katharobity (K), corresponding to drinking water, limnosaprobity

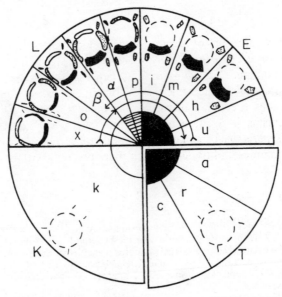

Fig. 36.   Circular scheme of water quality, representing a synthesis of the ecological and physiological points of view: K—katharobity; T—transsaprobity; a—antisaprobity; r—radioactivity; c—physical factors.   The other letters indicate the saprobic degrees as listed in Fig. 35.   The interior arrow shows the direction of eutrophication and increase of organic pollution, while the exterior one shows the direction of decomposition and selfpurification.

(L), i.e., clean and polluted underground and surface water, eusaprobity (E), i.e., sewage and organic industrial waste, and transsaprobity (T), comprising the following interfering factors: antisaprobity (a), which may be equated with toxicity, radioactivity (r), and physical factors (c). The diagram also illustrates the inner metabolism of each saprobic degree according to the 6 schemes of Caspers & Karbe (*112*). These schemes are included at x, o, β, α, p, h; two analogous schemes were added at i and m; the possibility of such schemes was marked at k and r. The degrees u, a, c are abiotic and the same is often true at k. This is in accordance with the Prague convention defining saprobity, within the bioactivity of a body of water, as the sum of all those metabolic processes that are the antithesis of primary production and therefore the expression of all processes leading to the loss of potential energy. In combination with the biogenic as well as the physical oxygen supply, the degree of saprobity can be estimated either by measuring the dynamics of metabolism or by analysing the communities of aquatic organisms present.

6.2.1 *Scope*

The level of saprobity of a water body provides an estimate of organic pollution. Several degrees of saprobity can be recognized by noting the presence of different communities of aquatic organisms. Both the communities themselves and some of their constituents can serve as indicators of the conditions prevailing in the environment. A broad knowledge of aquatic organisms is a prerequisite for the biological analysis. Skilled hydrobiologists are able to make a rough estimate of the degree of saprobity within a few minutes and to determine it more precisely within a few hours.

6.2.2 *Field of application*

Water inhabited by aquatic organisms can be evaluated for saprobity if the species composition and at least the abundance of the organisms is known. Underground water, running waters, standing water bodies, sewage and industrial waste are all susceptible to saprobiological examination and classification.

6.2.3 *Definitions*

Saprobic degrees and their abbreviation are listed in Table 6a. Also given are the ranges and mean values of the saprobic index S, introduced by Pantle & Buck (*114*) and extended by Sládeček (*115*).

The relationship of individual saprobic degrees to some quantitative chemical and bacteriological data is shown in Table 7.

The relationship between saprobic degrees and dissolved oxygen content at various water temperatures is illustrated diagrammatically in Fig. 37. Class I represents xenosaprobity plus oligosaprobity, class II—β-meta-saprobity, class III—α-mesosaprobity, and class IV—polysaprobity.

The original equation for the saprobic index, S, given by Pantle & Buck (*114*) is:

$$S = \frac{\Sigma(h \cdot s)}{\Sigma h}$$

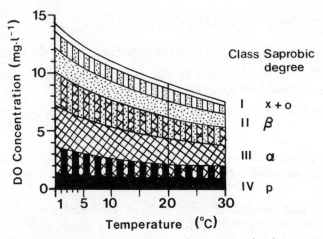

Fig. 37. Dissolved oxygen content of running waters related to water quality or saprobic degrees and water temperature

After Hamm et al. (*116*)

Table 6a. Ranges and mean values of the extended saprobic index, S

Degree	Abbreviation	Range	Mean
Xenosaprobity	x	−0.5–0.5	0
Oligosaprobity	o	0.51–1.5	1.0
β-mesosaprobity	β	1.51–2.5	2.0
a-mesosaprobity	a	2.51–3.5	3.0
Polysaprobity	p	3.51–4.5	4.0
Isosaprobity	i	4.51–5.5	5.0
Metasaprobity	m	5.51–6.5	6.0
Hypersaprobity	h	6.51–7.5	7.0
Ultrasaprobity	u	7.51–8.5	8.0

Table 7. Comparative values limiting the individual saprobic degrees (upper limits)

Degree	Saprobic index (S)	BOD_5[a] $(mg \cdot l^{-1})$	Coliforms per litre	Psychrophilic organisms per ml (agar plate)
x	0.5	1	10^4	10^3
o	1.5	2.5	5×10^4	10^4
β	2.5	5	10^5	5×10^4
a	3.5	10	10^6	25×10^4
p	4.5	50	3×10^7	2×10^6
i	5.5	400	3×10^9	10^7
m	6.5	700	10^{10}	10^8
h	7.5	2×10^3	10^6	10^9
u	8.5	12×10^4	0	10

[a] BOD_5 values in limnosaprobic standing water bodies (x–p) may be as much as twice those indicated in this table.

where

h = abundance according to a scale of estimation (e.g., 1, 3, 5 or 1, 2, 3, 5, 7, 9),

s = the saprobity value of individual species found in the sample under examination.

In its extended form (*115*), the equation becomes:

$$S = \frac{0\Sigma h_x + 1\Sigma h_o + 2\Sigma h_\beta + 3\Sigma h_\alpha + 4\Sigma h_p + 5\Sigma h_i + 6\Sigma h_m + 7\Sigma h_h + 8\Sigma h_u}{\Sigma h}$$

where

h_x = the sum of all values for abundance of xenosaprobic species,

h_o = the sum of all values for abundance of oligosaprobic species and so on.

In this case, instead of using only an estimated value for h, it is advantageous to use either a percentage value or actual quantitative data. The calculation is, however, a little more difficult.

When making the calculation, the mean values for the species, as listed in Table 6a, are used, i.e., 0 for xenosaprobic species, 1 for an oligosaprobic species, etc.

The concept of saprobic valency was proposed independently by Zelinka (*117*) and by Dittmar (*118*). These authors found that a species is rarely confined to only one saprobic degree. For every aquatic organism, the abundance follows a characteristic curve of Gaussian (or other) distribution in relation to the content of organic matter. Some typical examples are presented in Fig. 38.

To obtain such a graphic representation of the Gaussian distribution of a species, saprobic valencies are plotted on an arbitrary scale of 10 units for each of the saprobic degrees. This allocation is preferably based on a statistical analysis, but where such a procedure is not possible the personal experience of the investigator can be taken as an approximate guide. Examples of saprobic valencies are given in Table 8, which also shows the individual saprobic indices, S, and the indicative weights of the species, I (see below).

The indicative weights of the species range from 1 to 5, the best indicators having the highest indicative weights. The value of I is determined from the saprobic valency in the following manner:

$I = 5$ (best indicators) where all 10 units of saprobic valency belong to one saprobic degree or where the units show a ratio of 9:1 in 2 successive degrees.

$I = 4$ (very good indicators) where the ratio of the saprobic valency units is 8:2 or 7:3 in two successive degrees or 1:8:1 in 3 successive degrees.

$I = 3$ (moderately good indicators) where the ratio is 6:4 or 5:5 in 2 successive degrees or where the highest number of units equals 7 or 8 in 3 successive degrees.

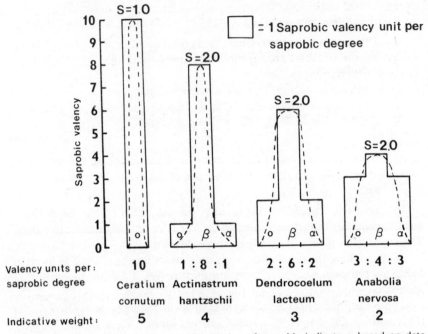

Fig. 38. Four cases of Gaussian distribution of saprobic indicators, based on data shown in Table 8

Table 8. Some examples of saprobic valencies, with indicative weights and saprobic indices

Taxon	x	o	β	α	p	I	S
Sphaerotilus natans Kützing)	—	—	+	4	6	3	3.6
Apodya lactea (Ac.)	—	—	—	9	1	5	3.1
Hydrurus foetidus ((Vill.) Trev.)	5	4	1	—	—	2	0.55
Cymbella cesatii (Grunow)	9	1	—	—	—	5	0.1
Melosira varians (Ag.)	+	3	5	2	—	2	1.85
Ceratium cornutum ((Ehr.) Clap.)	—	10	—	—	—	5	1.0
Actinastrum hantzschii (Lagerh.)	—	1	8	1	—	4	2.0
Closterium acerosum (Ehr.)	—	—	2	8	—	4	2.8
Stigeoclonium tenue (Kützing)	—	—	3	7	—	4	2.7
Lemanea fluviatilis ((L.) Ag.)	1	7	2	—	—	3	1.15
Desmarella moniliformis (Kent)	—	—	4	6	—	3	2.6
Vorticella alba (Fromentel)	—	—	—	5	5	3	3.5
Vorticella microstoma (Ehr.)	—	—	—	—	10	5	4.2 E[a]
Dendrocoelum lacteum (O.F.M.)	—	2	6	2	—	3	2.0
Rotaria rotatoria (Pallas)	—	+	1	6	3	3	3.25
Bosmina longirostris (O.F.M.)	1	4	4	1	—	1	1.55
Baetis rhodani (Pictet)	3	3	3	1	—	1	1.05
Anabolia nervosa (Leach)	—	3	4	3	—	2	2.0

[a] E indicates an extension into eusaprobity.

$I = 2$ (bad indicators) where the highest number of units is 5 or 4 in 3 degrees, or 7 or 6 in 4 degrees.

$I = 1$ (no use as indicators) where the highest number of units is 5, 4 or 3 in 4 degrees, or where there are any number of units in 5 degrees. This method of rating is summarized in Table 9.

Table 9. Allocation of the indicative weight I, to species according to the number of saprobic degrees and the highest unit of the saprobic valency (*119*)

I	Ratio of saprobic valency units in successive saprobic degrees							
5	10	9:1						
4	8:2	7:3	1:8:1					
3	6:4	5:5	1:7:2	1:6:3	2:6:2			
2	1:5:4	2:5:3	2:4:4	3:4:3	1:7:1:1	1:6:2:1		
1	1:2:5:2	1:1:5:3	1:2:4:3	1:4:4:1	1:3:3:3	1:2:3:2:2 etc.		

6.2.4 Principles

The saprobic valencies and the individual saprobic indices of several thousands of aquatic organisms have now been determined. Many lists of indicator organisms have been published, the most detailed one by Sládeček (*120*).

According to the organisms found, it has been possible to estimate the saprobic degrees of the environment and related factors, as listed in Table 7. There can be differences in regard to conditions between plankton and benthos, the presence of the latter usually indicating inferior conditions. The most important relationship is that between saprobity and BOD_5. Fig. 39 presents an approximate correlation between saprobity, expressed by the extended saprobic index S, and the arithmetic mean values of BOD_5 (*121*). In the absence of such a correlation, the saprobic index should be preferred.

6.2.5 Sampling

Sampling is carried out in the same manner as described for individual communities, i.e. plankton, periphyton, microbenthos, and macrobenthos. The main concern is the qualitative composition of the communities (species composition). Exact quantitative sampling and subsequent procedures can be replaced by simple estimation of abundance.

For comparison, exactly the same communities must be sampled along a river or in a number of lakes or other standing water bodies. It is not fair to compare, for example, plankton in one locality with periphyton in a second and with macrobenthos in a third.

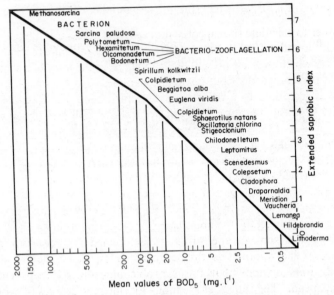

Fig. 39.   Relation of arithmetic mean values of BOD_5 to the extended saprobic index, S.   The given BOD_5 values are arithmetic means for the period necessary for development of the community studied.

Because a biological analysis can be made very quickly in the field, a portable microscope is highly recommended for field studies.

If possible, a preserved sample should always be kept for future reference, comparison, and re-examination.

6.2.6   *Procedure*

Saprobity can be either estimated or calculated.

6.2.6.1   *Estimation*

The original procedure of Kolkwitz & Marsson (*122–124*) used only a simple estimation of the saprobic degree according to the experience and subjective feeling of the investigator. This can still be done today if the investigator has enough knowledge and experience. However, a more objective approach is preferred. Two methods are in use in Central Europe.

6.2.6.2   *Calculation of the saprobic index, S*

In order to calculate the saprobic index, S, it is necessary to have a list of the species found within the community examined and information on the amounts in which they are present, which may be in the form of quantitative data, the percentage distribution in the sample, or an estimation of the abundance according to a more or less simple scale. The next step is to determine from the literature the indicator values according to the various species (*120, 126–132*). In some cases, it may be possible to find directly the desired individual S values, in others only the names of the saprobic degrees for which the species are indicators. In the latter case, the names of the Latin taxons are replaced by the mean values for the species (see Table 6a), i.e., an oligosaprobic species is replaced by " 1 ", a β-mesosaprobic species by " 2 ", an α-mesosaprobic species by " 3 ", etc. Each of these approximate saprobic indices, S_i, is multiplied by the abundance, or other quantitative data, for the species and the sum of the products is divided by the sum of the abundances. The quotient is the saprobic index, S, of the community examined. It is obvious that this saprobic index merely represents an arithmetic mean. The ranges of the index for different degrees of saprobity are listed in Table 6a and a corresponding scale of saprobity is depicted in Fig. 40.

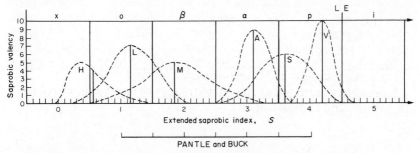

Fig. 40.   Part of the scale of saprobity showing the position of 6 benthic species: *Hydrurus foetidus, Lemanea fluviatilis, Melosira varians, Apodya lactea, Sphaerotilus natans* and *Vorticella microstoma.* 1–4 represents the original scale of Pantle & Buck (*114*).

By way of an example, Table 10 summarizes the relevant data for a sample of plankton taken from a gravel pit in Kvasice, Czechoslovakia, on 22 August 1973.

In this example,

$$S = \frac{(h \times S_i)}{h} = \frac{41.2}{28} = 1.5$$

This saprobic index corresponds to an intermediate degree between oligosaprobity (1) and β-metasaprobity (2).

Table 10. Abundance of plankton species found in a Czech gravel pit, with corresponding S_i values

Taxon	Abundance (h)	$S_i{}^a$	$h \times S_i$
Aphanizomenon flos-aquae	3	1.7	5.1
Anabaena macrospora	2	1.5	3.0
Ceratium hirundinella	5	1.15	5.7
Asplanchna priodonta	2	1.55	3.1
Brachionus calyciflorus	1	2.5	2.5
Keratella quadrata	2	1.55	3.1
Polyarthra vulgaris	1	1.85	1.8
Bosmina longirostris	2	1.55	3.1
Daphnia cucullata	1	1.75	1.7
Diaphonosoma brachyurum	1	1.4	1.4
Nauplius *Cyclops* (species not determined)	2	1.5	3.0
Cyclopids (species not determined)	3	1.5	4.5
Thermocyclops hyalinum	2	1.85	3.7
	28		41.2

[a] The S_i values for naupli and cyclopids were only estimates because no exact determination was made at this locality and at least 5 different species of *Cyclops* had been found earlier.

6.2.6.3   Calculation of saprobic valency

For the calculation of saprobic valency, it is necessary to have a list of the species found within the community examined and information on abundance, percentage distribution, or other quantitative data (see Example Table A). The saprobic valencies of the different species are determined from the literature (*120, 130*) and a second table is then constructed in which the taxons are listed together with the corresponding saprobic valencies and the indicative weights, as shown in the Example Table B. The calculation is based on the following formula:

$$X = \frac{\sum\limits_{i=l}^{h} (h \cdot g \cdot x)}{\sum\limits_{i=l}^{h} (h \cdot g)}$$

where

X = degree of saprobity of the area of limnosaprobity,
h = abundance, percentage distribution, or other quantitative value,
g = indicative weight of species, I, on a scale of 1–5,
x = the number of units of saprobic valency allocated to the particular species.

In order to perform this calculation, a third table is prepared in which the taxons are again listed but the columns representing the various saprobic degrees show, for each taxon, the product obtained by multiplying together

Table A.   The rotifer fauna of a stabilization pond at
Podolánka, Czechoslovakia, 10 July 1950

Taxon	Number of individuals per 10 ml (h)
Brachionus angularis bidens (Plate)	5
Brachionus rubens (Ehrenberg)	4
Filinia longiseta longiseta (Ehr.)	5
Keratella quadrata (O. F. Müller)	41
Keratella cochlearis cochlearis (Gosse)	66
Polyarthra vulgaris (Cardin)	1
Pompholyx sulcata (Hudson)	112
Synchaeta pectinata (Ehrenberg)	3
Synchaeta oblonga (Ehrenberg)	2
Total number of rotifers in 10 ml	239

Table B.   Saprobic valencies and indicative weights, I, of the various
species, based on various literature sources

Taxon	x	o	β	a	p	I
Brachionus angularis bidens	—	1	9	—	—	5
Brachionus rubens	—	—	1	6	3	3
Filinia longiseta longiseta	—	1	5	4	—	2
Keratella quadrata	2	3	5	—	—	2
Keratella cochlearis cochlearis	2	3	5	—	—	2
Polyarthra vulgaris	+	3	5	2	—	2
Pompholyx sulcata	—	2	8	—	—	4
Synchaeta pectinata	—	5	4	1	—	2
Synchaeta oblonga	—	3	6	1	—	3

the saprobic valency, the abundance, and the indicative weight (see Example Table C).   For each saprobic degree, the total of these products is shown at the bottom of the table and the sum of all these totals is shown on the extreme right of the table.   By dividing the individual totals by their sum, the weighted arithmetic means are calculated (the sum of all the means = 10) and, if necessary, the results are converted to percentages by multiplying by 10.   By rounding off the weighted means, a saprobic valency profile for the whole community is obtained and it is also possible to determine the saprobic index, S.

From the results, it is possible to construct a distribution curve of saprobic valency for the whole community, the peak of the curve corresponding to the degree of saprobity of the community.   Because the sum of the units of saprobic valency is always 10, it is possible to make comparisons between different localities and different water basins, provided that the same communities are always compared.

Table C. Products of saprobic valency, abundance and indicative weight of
each species for each saprobic degree

Taxon	x	o	β	α	p
Brachionus angularis bidens	—	25	225	—	—
Brachionus rubens	—	—	12	72	36
Filinia longiseta longiseta	—	10	50	40	—
Keratella quadrata	164	246	410	—	—
Keratella cochlearis cochlearis	264	396	660	—	—
Polyarthra vulgaris	—	6	10	4	—
Pompholyx sulcata	—	896	3584	—	—
Synchaeta pectinata	—	24	30	6	—
Synchaeta oblonga	—	18	36	6	—
Total	428 +	1621 +	5017 +	128 +	36 = 7230
Weighted arithmetic means:	0.59 +	2.24 +	6.95 +	0.17 +	0.5 = 10.00
Percentage values:	5.9 +	22.4 +	69.5 +	1.7 +	0.5 = 100

As can be seen, the highest value for the weighted arithmetic mean corresponds to β-mesosaprobity, but the peak of the distribution curve is shifted a little towards oligosaprobity. If the figures are rounded off, the saprobic valency profile for this rotifer plankton becomes:

$$x = 0, \text{ o} = 3, \beta = 7, \alpha = 0, \text{p} = 0, I = 4.$$

The saprobic index, S, works out at 1.7.

Conclusion: The stabilization pond has a saprobity rather better than β-mesosaprobity, with a saprobic index of 1.7 and a tendency to self-purification (as judged from previous analyses).

6.2.7 *Expression of results*

Saprobity can be indicated in the following ways:

(a) by a simple expression of the saprobic degree, in words (not in numbers), e.g., α-mesosaprobity;

(b) by the extended saprobic index, S, indicating the position on the scale of saprobity as shown in Fig. 39, e.g., $S = 3.1$;

(c) by the 10 units of saprobic valency expressed for the whole community, e.g., $\beta = 2, \alpha = 7, \text{p} = 1, I = 3$;

(d) by representing the saprobic valencies graphically as histograms (Fig. 37) or as curves of Gaussian distribution (Fig. 39).

Of the above alternatives, (b) is to be preferred as it shows the position of the community on a universal scale of saprobity.

It is recommended that the results be summarized as maps of water quality. Such maps may either present all the criteria, i.e., chemical, bacteriological, saprobiological, toxicological, etc., or only one factor (*126, 133 & 134*).

6.2.8 *Interference*

As far as is known, the following factors interfere with saprobity and may affect the results:

1. Toxicity. This is determined by bioassays as described in section B.

2. Radioactivity must be determined by radiological analysis (see volume 2, chapter 5).

3. Physical factors, e.g., fine mineral suspensions, coal powder, mineral oils, elevated temperature, freezing. In some cases toxicity tests can be applied, although the majority of cases must be designated as "inert" pollution.

4. Trophism. In some cases this cannot be distinguished from saprobity, but its importance increases with eutrophication.

5. Salinity, which may be considered a special subfactor of toxicity.

6. Velocity of the current. According to Zimmermann (*135*) at a rate of flow of about 80 cm·s^{-1} the species composition of the benthic communities is changed so that it indicates exactly the next higher degree of saprobity than at 5 cm·s^{-1}.

7. Climatic, regional and edaphic factors. These have only a small influence.

6.2.9 *Validity*

The prime objective of the saprobiological analysis is the rapid classification of the community under examination. For this purpose, the extended saprobic index, S, is of unique value in providing a universal scale, from the purest underground water to highly loaded wastewater. However, for the proper application of this method detailed taxonomic knowledge is a prerequisite. If communities are poor in species and/or biomass, possible interactions of saprobity with toxic, radioactive and physical effects must be considered.

6.3 Biotic indices based on macrofauna

The saprobic systems make use of a whole range of taxa. Other indices have been developed that make use of macro-invertebrates only. To present the results of invertebrate surveys in a form acceptable to the non-biologist, especially when carried out over an extended period, different biotic indices have been developed. Such indices, however, are descriptive gradings and although expressed numerically they are not in any way quantitative and should not be subjected to parametric statistical processing. Details of such methods are given below.

6.3.1   Trent biotic index

This index was developed by Woodiwiss (*136*) for use in the former Trent River Authority area in England and has since formed the basis of systems that are in use in various parts of the world. It takes account of two basic principles:

1.   Pollution tends to restrict the variety of organisms.

2.   In streams, Plecoptera, Ephemeroptera, Trichoptera, *Gammarus*, *Asellus*, *Chironomus riparius* and tubificid worms may be regarded as key organisms that tend to disappear in the order listed as the degree of pollution increases. (This is in accord with their saprobic classification). Accordingly a number of readily identifiable groups are recognized; some of these are species, others are families (Table 10a).

From the specific groups and the total number of groups present the Trent Biotic Index (0–X) can be derived according to the system shown in Table 11.

The Trent Biotic Index has proved most successful when eroding substratum (riffle) communities have been sampled. Although these are

Table 10a. Taxonomic "Groups" used in the determination of the Trent Biotic Index
(*136*)

The term " Group " used for the purpose of the Trent Biotic Index means any one of the species included in the following list of organisms or sets of organisms:

Each known species of Plathyhelminthes (flatworms)
Annelida (worms) excluding the genus *Nais*
Genus *Nais* (worms)
Each known species of Hirudinae (leeches)
Each known species of Mollusca (snails)
Each known species of Crustacea (hog-louse, shrimps)
Each known species of Plecoptera (stone-fly)
Each known genus of Ephemeroptera (mayfly, excluding *Baetis rhodani*)
Baetis rhodani (mayfly)
Each family of Trichoptera (caddis-fly)
Each species of neuroptera larvae (alder-fly)
Family Chironomidae (midge larvae) except *Chironomus Ch. thummi*
Chironomus Ch. thummi (blood worms)
Family Simuliidae (blackfly larvae)
Each known species of other fly larvae
Each known species of Coleoptera (beetles and beetle larvae)
Each known species of Hydracarina (water-mites)

Table 11. The assessment of the Trent Biotic Index (*136*)

Clean				No. of groups present			
			0–1	2–5	6–10	11–15	16+
					Biotic Index		
Plecoptera	More than one species		—	VII	VIII	IX	X
nymph present	One species only		—	VI	VII	VIII	IX
Ephemeroptera	More than one species[a]		—	VI	VII	VIII	IX
nymph present	One species only[a]		—	V	VI	VII	VIII
Trichoptera	More than one species[b]		—	V	VI	VII	VIII
larvae present	One species only[b]		IV	IV	V	VI	VII
Gammarus present	All above species absent		III	IV	V	VI	VII
Asellus present	All above species absent		II	III	IV	V	VI
Tubificid worm and/or Red Chironomid larvae present	All above species absent		I	II	III	IV	—
All above types	Some organisms such as *Eristalis tenax* not requiring dissolved oxygen		0	I	II	—	—
Polluted							

[a] *Baetis rhodani* excluded.
[b] *Baetis rhodani* (Ephem.) is counted in this section for the purpose of classification.

available in the upper zones of rivers (rhithron) they may not be available in the lower reaches (potamon). For the same water quality, the eroding substratum biotope would give a higher biotic index than the depositing substratum biotope. In comparing different stations along a river, therefore, the type of biotope should be taken into account. This Biotic Index has shown that it may be adjusted by relating it to its maximum possible value for the type of river zone being sampled.

6.3.2 French Biotic Index

This index, proposed by Tuffery & Verneaux (*137*), was derived from the Trent Biotic Index but is more refined in that it takes into account both lentic and lotic zones in the river and the type of river zone. Using Tables 12 and 13, indices are derived for three pooled lentic samples, I_e, and for three pooled lotic samples, I_c, taken from the same station. Groups of less than three individuals of any species are discarded as being accidental (e.g., drift).

The Biotic Index, I_m, is also determined for an unpolluted station as the highest index for the type of river being surveyed, this being considered as the reference station. Using these values, a river is considered polluted when

$I_m - \dfrac{I_e + I_c}{2} > 1$ and no other natural ecological factor, e.g., slope, entry of tributary, shading, could be responsible.

Self-purification is considered complete when $\dfrac{I_e + I_c}{2} = I_m - 1$.

Table 12. Taxonomic groups used for the French Biotic Index (*137*)

	Level of identification
Plecoptera	Genus
Trichoptera	Subfamily
Ephemeroptera	Genus
Odonata	Genus
Coleoptera	Family
Mollusca	Genus
Crustacea	Family
Megaloptera	Genus
Hemiptera	Genus
Diptera	Family
Planarians	Genus
Leeches	Genus
Oligochaeta	Family
Nematoda	Order
Hydracarina	Order

Table 13. Assessment of the French Biotic Index (*137*)

		No. of groups present:				
		0–1	2–5	6–10	11–15	≥16
				Biotic Index		
1. Plecoptera or Ecdyonuridae (Heptageniidae)	>1 group 1 group	— V	VII VI	VIII VII	IX VIII	X IX
2. Case-bearing Trichoptera	>1 group 1 group	— V	VI V	VII VI	VIII VII	IX VIII
3. Ancylidae Ephemeroptera except Ecdyonuridae	>2 groups ≤2 groups	— III	V IV	VI V	VII VI	VIII VII
4. *Aphelocheirus* (Hemiptera) Odonata, Gammaridae, or Mollusca (except Sphaeridae)	All above groups absent	III	IV	V	VI	VII
5. *Asellus* or Hirudinae or Sphaeridae or Hemiptera (except *Aphelocheirus*)	All above groups absent	II	III	IV	V	—
6. Tubificidae or Chironomidae of the *thummi-plumosus* group	All above groups absent	I	II	III	—	—
7. Eristalinae	All above groups absent	0	I	I	—	—

6.3.3   *Assessment of the biotic index by the " Score " System*

The Trent Biotic Index, like the original Saprobic System does not take into account the relative abundance of the organisms present. The " Score " System proposed by Chandler (*138*) is a modification of the Trent Biotic Index system in which account is taken of the relative abundance of the groups identified. Five levels of abundance are recognized, based on the numbers taken during a 5-minute sampling period using a hand-net (Table 14).

Table 14. Level of abundance used
in the " Score " system

Level of abundance	No. per 5 minutes of sampling
P—present[a]	1–2
F—few	3–10
C—common	11–50
A—abundant	51–100
V—very abundant	>100

[a] May be drift from upstream, probably indigenous, but rare.

Using Table 15, in which the groups are arranged in order of their tolerance to organic pollution, a score is given for each group according to its level of abundance. For species characteristic of clear water, the score increases with increasing abundance, whereas for species tolerant of pollution the score decreases with increasing abundance. The individual scores for the different groups present are added to give the Biotic Index for that station. There is a continuous graduation from polluted to clean water conditions and no theoretical upper limit.

6.4   Applicability of methods

If practicable, preliminary surveys should be carried out on river systems where the sources of pollution are known. The results should be processed testing the different methods available to determine the ones most suitable for the region.

The selection of the method to be used will depend on the objectives of the survey (see section 6.4.2) and the available resources.

6.4.1   *Resources*

Relative assessments of the effort needed for sampling and processing using the different methods are presented in Table 16.

Table 15. Biotic Index by the " Score " system (*138*)

Groups present in sample	Increasing abundance				
	P	F	C	A	V
	Units scored				
Each species of *Planaria alpina*, Taenoptergidae, Perlidae, Perlodidae, Isoperlidae, Chloroperlidae	90	94	98	99	100
Each species of Leuctridae, Capniidae, Nemouridae (excl. *Amphinemura*)	84	89	94	97	98
Each species of Ephemeroptera (excl. *Baetis*)	79	84	90	94	97
Each species of Cased caddis, Megaloptera	75	80	86	91	94
Each species of *Ancylus*	70	75	82	87	91
Each species of *Rhyacophila* (Trichoptera)	65	70	77	83	88
Genera of *Dicranota, Limnophora*	60	65	72	78	84
Genera of *Simulium*	56	61	67	73	75
Genera of Coleoptera, Nematoda	51	55	61	66	72
Genera of *Amphinemura* (Plecoptera)	47	50	54	58	63
Genera of *Baetis* (Ephemeroptera)	44	46	48	50	52
Genera of *Gammarus*	40	40	40	40	40
Each species of Uncased caddis (excl. *Rhyacophila*)	38	36	35	33	31
Each species of Tricladida (excl. *P. alpina*)	35	33	31	29	25
Genera of Hydracarina	32	30	28	25	21
Each species of Mollusca (excl. *Ancylus*)	30	28	25	22	18
Each species of Chironomids (excl. *C. riparius*)	28	25	21	18	15
Each species of *Glossiphonia*	26	23	20	16	13
Each species of *Asellus*	25	22	18	14	10
Each species of Leech excl. *Glossiphonia, Haemopis* (*1*)	24	20	16	12	8
Each species of *Haemopis*	23	19	15	10	7
Each species of *Tubifex sp.*	22	18	13	12	9
Each species of *Chironomus riparius*	21	17	12	7	4
Each species of *Nais*	20	16	10	6	2
Each species of Air-breathing organism	19	15	9	5	1
No animal life	0	0	0	0	0

Table 16. Relative assessments of the effort involved in different biological monitoring methods, arranged in decreasing order

Sampling	Taxonomy	Data processing
● Diversity Index	● Saprobic System	● Shannon-Weaver Diversity Index[a]
● Pantle & Buck Saprobic Index	● Pantle & Buck Saprobic Index	● Margalef Diversity Index
● Chandler Score		
		● Pantle & Buck Saprobic Index[a]
● Trent Biotic Index	● Biotic indices	● Chandler " Score "
● Saprobic System	● Diversity indices	● Trent Biotic Index
		● Saprobic System

[a] Effort appreciably reduced by use of computer.

Apart from effort a degree of expertise is required; generally best results will be obtained by trained hydrobiologists who are capable of interpreting the results in relation to other environmental and seasonal conditions.

6.4.2 *Selection of method*

The choice of method will be influenced by the objectives of the survey and the nature of the water pollution. Most systems have been developed to monitor the most common form of pollution, namely, organic.

Where the pollution load is known to be organic or eutrophic, gross pollution can be monitored by either the Saprobic System or the Biotic Index. Where the environmental changes are slight, however, the " Score " System is probably the most sensitive method.

In cases of toxic and physical pollution, although these may be indicated by the Saprobic System and Biotic Index, the results are sometimes difficult to interpret. In such cases, the Shannon-Weaver, Diversity Index is probably the most sensitive indicator system. Where the source of pollution is not known, or where different types of pollution occur, then the Saprobic System or the Biotic Index and the Diversity Index should be used.

The procedures to be adopted for the different methods are indicated schematically in Fig. 41.

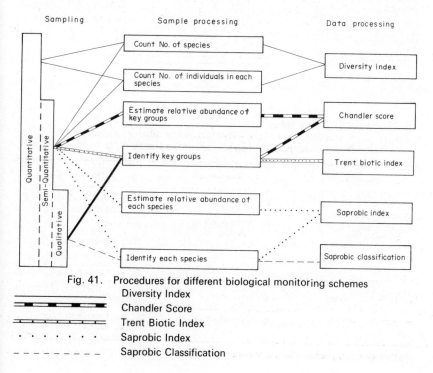

Fig. 41. Procedures for different biological monitoring schemes
Diversity Index
Chandler Score
Trent Biotic Index
Saprobic Index
Saprobic Classification

6.5 Conversions

Table 17 shows the conversion of the values of the Extended Saprobic Index S into the Trent and Score biotic indexes.

Figure 41 compares the Extended Saprobic Index, S (for aerobic conditions only) with that of Pantle & Buck (*114*) and with the modification of Dresscher & van der Mark (*125*).

Tables 18 and 19 show how the most important communities of phytobenthos, zoobenthos and the biocenotic classification are related to saprobic degrees within the limnosaprobity and to some quantitative values for eusaprobity.

Table 17. Approximate comparisons between the extended saprobic index, S, the Trent Biotic Index and the " Score " system (*120*)

Saprobity name	Abbreviation	Saprobic index (S) Range	Mean	Trent Biotic Index	" Score " system
Katharobity	k	negative	−1	0	0
Xenosaprobity	x	−0.5–+0.5	0	VI–X	90–100
Oligosaprobity	o	0.5–1.5	1	IV–IX	56–81–98
β-Mesosaprobity	β	1.51–2.5	2	III–VII	15–51–72
α-Mesosaprobity	α	2.51–3.5	3	III–VII	7–13–26
Polysaprobity	p	3.51–4.5	4	I–IV	1–9–22
Isosaprobity	i	4.51–5.5	5	I–II	0
Metasaprobity	m	5.51–6.5	6	0	0
Hypersaprobity	h	6.51–7.5	7	0	0
Ultrasaprobity	u	(7.51–8.5)	(8)	0	0

Note: Toxicity (= antisaprobity), radioactivity and extreme physical factors (= cryptosaprobity) are excluded and must be evaluated separately. They can interfere with any one saprobic degree.

6.6 Indices of traphic levels

A skilled hydrobiologist is able to recognize the two basic trophic levels according to a biological analysis: oligotrophic water bodies are poor in nutrients and biomass, but excellent for water supply; eutrophic ones are rich in nutrients and biomass, forming water-blooms, vegetative colourings, excessive growth of filamentous algae, and aquatic macrophytes, and are therefore less useful or unacceptable for water supply.

The terms apply to lakes where the conditions in the hypolimnion during the summer stratification period determine the fundamental limnological classification. Oligotrophic lakes are aerobic in the whole water column throughout the year; in eutrophic ones, the oxygen is completely exhausted once or twice a year in the near-bottom zones.

Oligotrophy is a natural phenomenon in mountain and sub-mountain lakes and eutrophy in lowland ones. In the course of time, the oligotrophic lakes change into eutrophic ones. This process is, under natural conditions,

Table 18. Comparison of saprobity degrees and biological zones within limnosaprobity (139)

Degree of saprobity	Classes of water quality (126) (140) (141)	Communities of phytobenthos (131)	Communities of ciliates (142)	Zones of zoobenthos (143, 144)	Fish zones, (145, 146)	Biocenotical classification (147)
Xeno-saprobity	I / I / Ia — (1)	Hildebrandia rivularis, Draparnaldia plumosa and Chlorotylium cataractarum	Very rare	Ameletus	0, Spring rillet	Krenon
Oligo-saprobity	II — 2.5	Phormidium inundatum, Vaucheria sessilis, Lemanea annulata, Batrachospermum vagum or Hildebrandia rivularis, Meridion circulare, Draparnaldia glomerata	Oligosaprobic ciliat. (Spathididae)	Rhitrogena	(Upper) Trout / (Lower)	Epirhitron / Metarhitron
β-mesosaprobity (better) (γ-meso-saprobity Fjerd.)	I, II	Batrachospermum moniliforme or Lemanea fluviatilis, Cladophora glomerata or Ulothrix zonata (clean water type)	β-mesosaprobic community: Coleps hirtus, Dileptus anser, Euplotes patella, Hemiophrys procera, Frontonia leucas, Lacrymaria olor, Lembadion lucens etc.	Edyonurus	Grayling	Hyporhitron
β-mesosaprobity (typical)	III — 5	Phormidium div. sp. (P. subfuscum, favosum, retzii)		Oligoneu-riella	Barbel	Epipotamon
β-mesosaprobity (inferior)	II	Cladophora fracta		Ephemera		Metapotamon / Hypopotamon
α-Meso-saprobity	III, IV — 10	Stigeoclonium tenue; benthic Oscillatoriae (O. brevis, limosa, splendida) Ulothrix zonata (polluted water type)	Chilodonelletum cucullulae	Herpobdella	Bream	0
Poly-saprobity	IV, V, N — 15 / 50	Sphaerotilus natans (Mucor, Fusarium, Oscillatoria chlorina), Euglena viridis (and E. deses)	Colpidietum colpodae	Tubificidae	(Carp, crucian carp, tench)	0

Table 19. Comparison of saprobity degrees within eusaprobity (139)

Degree of saprobity	Abbrev.	Characteristic according to Sládeček (148)	Characteristic according to Fjerdingstad (131)		H_2S (mg·l⁻¹)	Psychrophilic per ml	Coliforms per litre	BOD_5 (mg·l⁻¹)
Isosaprobity	i	Degree of ciliates Ciliata: 10–50.000 per 1 ml Flagellata: 1.000–20.000 (Amoebina: 0–1.000) Bacteria: in mass (Mycophyta: in mass)	*Euglena* community	II. 1.	<1	<10^7	<3×10^9	<50–400 (600)
Metasaprobity	m	Degree of colourless flagellates Flagellata: 5.000–300.000 Ciliata: 0–5 Bacteria: in mass	*Thiothrix nivea* community *Beggiatoa* community Chlorobacterium community Rhodobacterium community *Bodo* community Bacterium and *Bodo* community	III. 1. III. 1. II. 3. II. 2. I. b. I. c.	<100 (1.000)	<2×10^7	<10^{10}	<200–700
Hypersaprobity	h	Degree of bacteria and Mycophyta Bacteria: in mass Mycophyta: in mass Flagellata: 0–5	Bacterium community (= coprozoic zone)	I. a.	<10	<5×10^7	<10^6	<500–1500 (2000)
Ultrasaprobity	u	Abiotic (but not toxic) degree Bacteria:0–10 (Mycophyta: 0–10)	0		0	<10	0	<1–120 × 10^3

slow and requires thousands of years. The activities of man (e.g., deforestation and cultivation of land) accelerate this process and cultural or induced eutrophication occurs within a few decades (*149*).

Natural eutrophication can be reversed only with difficulty. However man-induced eutrophication can be reversed by nutrient-stripping or by diverting nutrient-rich effluents or other appropriate means.

Eutrophication means the increase of growth of algae and other aquatic plants as a consequence of increased nutrient supply. The growth can reach such an extent that the use of the water for water supply, recreation, etc., is limited or even prevented. Eutrophication is connected with organic pollution, as mineral nutrients are evolved from organic waste matter by microbial decomposition and self-purification.

6.6.1 Analysis

Any biological method able to determine quantitatively the organisms present, their biomass and their rate of production is convenient for analysis of the trophic level. The temporary changes indicate the progress of eutrophication or the stability of the trophic state of the water body under examination. The same community must be compared in every case: plankton with plankton, fish with fish, benthos with benthos.

Another way is to determine the species composition using organisms as indicators of the trophic state. There is a distinct connexion with the saprobic degree: xenosaprobic and oligosaprobic organisms are associated with the oligotrophic level, β-mesosaprobic and α-mesosaprobic organisms with the eutrophic level.

6.6.2 Evaluation

There is not yet a final classification of individual trophic levels. However, a tentative comparison is given in Table 20.

6.6.3 Comparison of saprobic and trophic levels.

Figure 42 provides a scheme of longitudinal successions in flowing water showing the two saprobic successions and their relationship to the values of BOD_5, production/respiration ratio, and saprobic levels (*151*). A precise correlation between saprobic and trophic levels has not yet been established. On the other hand, for lakes some good correlations have been demonstrated with respect to biomass and nutrients (*152, 153*).

6.6.4 Trophic potential

A number of laboratory methods, analogous to the BOD_5 test, have been developed to demonstrate quantitatively the ability of a water sample to

Table 20. Tentative comparison of saprobic and trophic levels showing the upper limits of various determinands for each level [a] (150)

Extended saprobic index (S)	Degree of saprobity	Trophic level	Plankton algae (individuals per ml)	Chlorophyll (mg·m⁻³)	Primary production expressed as C mg·m⁻²·d⁻¹	g·m⁻²·y⁻¹
−0.5	k	Katharobic = atrophic	1	0	0	0
0.5	x	Ultra-oligotrophic	10^2	1	50	10
1.5	o	Oligotrophic	10^3 (10^4)	5 (20)	10^2 (15×10^2)	30 (5×10^2)
Intermediate level [b]						
2.0	y	Mesotrophic = γ-eutrophic	10^4 (10^5)	20 (10^2)	250 (4×10^3)	10^2 2×10^3)
2.5	β	β-eutrophic = eutrophic	10^5 (10^7)	3×10^2 (15×10^3)	5×10^2 (12×10^3)	150 (4×10^3)
3.5	a	α-eutrophic	10^6	10^3	(15×10^2)	3×10^2
4.5	p	Polytrophic	10^7	15×10^3	12×10^3	4×10^3
Sewage and industrial water—predominantly heterotrophic production:						
5.5	i	Isotrophic	10^3	3	10^2	30
6.5	m	Metatrophic = thiotrophic	0	+	+	+
7.5	h	Hypertrophic	0	0	0	0
8.5	u	Ultratrophic = atrophic	0	0	0	0

[a] The values in parentheses correspond to induced eutrophic conditions.
[b] The intermediate (mesotrophic) level is equivalent to γ-mesosaprobity (131).

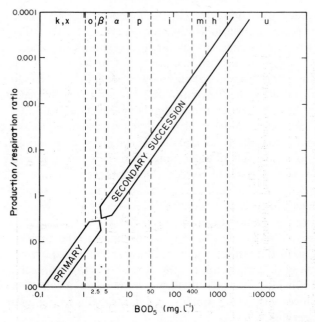

BOD$_5$ (mg. l^{-1})

Fig. 42. Relationship between BOD$_5$, production/respiration ratio, saprobic levels, and saprobic successions

Reproduced from Sládeček (*151*).

supply nutrients for algal growth. However, none has yet proved completely satisfactory. The maximum value of algal biomass reached in the steady state of the growth curve is a quantitative measure, which is useful for comparative purposes.

As test algae, *Selenastrum capricornutum* or *Scenedesmus quadricauda* are often used (*154*). Algal dry weight of up to 50 mg · l^{-1} indicates oligotrophic conditions, 50–100 mg · l^{-1} indicates mesotrophic conditions and above 100 mg · l^{-1} eutrophic conditions, but other values are also given in the literature.

B. BIOLOGICAL TESTS

1. PRELIMINARY CONSIDERATIONS

The term " Biological tests " includes any procedure in which living material is used in the detection or measurement of the presence or effect of one or more substances or conditions. The Whole-Organism Tests described in this Manual are of the type known as Toxicity Tests in the European Inland

Fisheries Advisory Committee (EIFAC) Report of Fish Toxicity Testing Procedures (*156*), i.e., tests in which living material is used to define the nature and degree of harmful effects produced by single or mixed poisons. The term " Bioassay ", often erroneously equated with " toxicity test ", is restricted in this section of the Manual to the following definition: " The use of living material to measure the concentration of a substance by determining the potency of the substance in producing some specific effect. "

Biological tests may be used in helping to assess (*a*) the suitability of environmental conditions for aquatic life, (*b*) favourable and unfavourable concentrations or levels of environmental factors for aquatic life, such as concentrations of dissolved oxygen (DO), pH, temperature, salinity, and turbidity, (*c*) the effect of various combinations of these environmental factors on the toxicity of wastes, (*d*) the relative toxicity of different wastes to a selected species or a number of species, (*e*) the relative sensitivity of different aquatic organisms to an effluent or toxicant, (*f*) the amount of waste treatment needed to meet water pollution control requirements, (*g*) the effectiveness of different waste treatment methods, (*h*) permissible discharge rates for effluents, (*i*) water quality requirements for aquatic life, and (*j*) compliance with water quality standards, effluent requirements and discharge permits.

No single biological test can supply all the information required for environmental protection as set out in the Introduction to this chapter (see above), but 5 principal types have been distinguished by EIFAC (*156*). These are: (*a*) preliminary screening tests; (*b*) tests providing information for water quality criteria; (*c*) effluent monitoring tests; (*d*) legal tests; (*e*) river/lake monitoring tests. The general aspects of the methods are considered in section 2 and the individual methods are described in detail in sections 3 to 8.

An important concept recently identified by a number of authors (for example, in *157*) is that of *sequential assessment*. This concept recognizes the need to focus effort on the most appropriate types of test when assessing the degree of risk attached to the release of any chemical in the environment. The temptation to apply a rigid standardized testing programme should be resisted and preference given to a sequential review and assessment of experimental and other data. As a preliminary to any decision on the need for a toxicity testing programme the following information should be examined.

(1) The proposed or existing rate of production of the material and its patterns of usage and disposal (e.g., whether the material is likely to become widely distributed at low concentrations from diffuse sources, or discharged at high concentrations to a restricted area from point sources, such as sewage disposal works).

(2) The chemical and physical nature of the material (or closely related

substances) and its potential for biodegradation or bioaccumulation in the environment.

(3) Existing toxicity data on the material or on closely related substances.

From repeated assessments of such data decisions can be made: whether, for instance, to continue toxicity testing, abandon the proposed production of the material, call for further data, or permit certain patterns of usage. This approach can provide a sound basis for using limited scientific resources in an economic manner to assess environmental hazard.

Obviously the sequences of acquisition and review of data are carrried out not merely by means of one of the classes of test outlined by EIFAC (above), in conjunction with the information referred to in paragraphs (1)–(3) above, but require the versatile use of many types of test not listed here, including those concerned primarily with bioaccumulation, biodegradation, and hazard to man.

In any of these tests the measured response of the organisms may be a stimulatory or an inhibitory one and may include differences (compared with control organisms) in growth, survival, fecundity, morphology, metabolism, behaviour and chemical composition. Observations in routine tests have often been limited to gross effects of a substance on an organism, such as acute lethal toxicity, but possible alternatives to this approach are included throughout the subsequent sections.

It is evident from the previous paragraphs that in order to make a useful statement about the possible effects of a substance on the environment a " package " of tests may be required, perhaps consisting of, for example, tests with an alga, an invertebrate, and a fish, rather than confining tests to a single taxonomic group. The sections that follow should help to make those concerned with the protection of the environment more familiar with the diversity of relevant whole-organism biological tests.

In order to compare results of biological tests, a number of standardized procedures have been adopted. Standardization allows comparisons to be made between the toxicities of two substances or mixtures; it may also facilitate basic toxicological research into the metabolism and detoxification of substances by organisms and play a valuable role in the control of production or waste purification processes. On the other hand, it has considerable disadvantages. Strictly, the results can refer only to the single test species and to the single set of environmental conditions and the measured response adopted in the standard procedure. It cannot be emphasized too strongly that any extrapolation to other species, conditions or responses, with the object of establishing a maximum safe concentration of the test material in the environment, should be avoided. Nevertheless, the value of standardized procedures in initial screening tests, particularly with whole organisms, has been recognized, e.g., in the US Standards Methods (*158*):

" Reasonable uniformity of bioassay [in the sense of toxicity testing procedures] procedures and of the manner of presenting the results are essential for effective use of acquired data. Widespread adoption of uniform methods will promote the accumulation of comparable data and increase their effective use. The standardization of bioassay methods and experimental procedures will ensure adequate uniformity, reproducibility and general usefulness of bioassay results without interfering unduly with the adaptability of the tests to local circumstances and problems. " For these reasons standard test procedures are included.

The "average" biological laboratory should be capable of handling most of the methods presented, although in some a knowledge of other skills, such as basic electronics, would be required. Complexity of apparatus is not necessarily equivalent to reliability; in fact the opposite may obtain at times. The guiding principles in the design of apparatus in which living organisms are to be kept should be reliability, fail-safety, and simplicity, so that faults, when they occur, do not jeopardize the results or further endanger the test organisms and can be easily and quickly remedied by staff after minimal training.

The average laboratory (see vol. 1, chapter 7) should be equipped to maintain adequate stocks of the chosen test organisms in such a manner that their health is maintained at a high level. This can limit the choice of test organisms. National or international standards or legislation governing experimentation on living organisms must, of course, be complied with. Facilities for chemical analysis and data handling at the " desk top calculator " level should be available. Staff should possess the necessary skills for maintaining the test organisms, preparing and executing the tests, handling the data, and drawing relevant conclusions.

The detailed purposes, procedures, and methods of interpretation for the whole-organism tests may be found in subsequent sections.

2. GENERAL ASPECTS

2.1 Objective

The initial objective in a whole-organism toxicity test is to define the concentrations (and their confidence limits) at which a poison is capable of producing some selected harmful response in a sample of organisms under controlled conditions of exposure. The appropriate way to do this is by use of the quantal response, from which the relation between concentration and percentage effect can be defined (Fig. 43).

The combination of data from a number of such observations is the basis of a toxicity curve (Fig. 44); in effect the concentration of a substance above

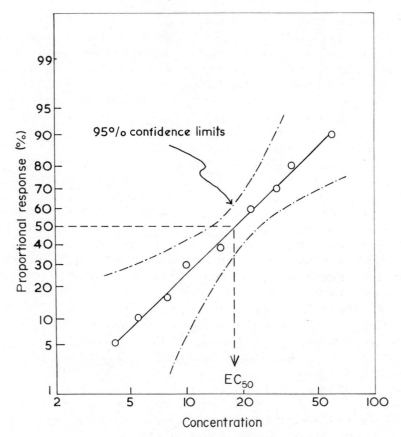

Fig. 43. Quantal response of 9 test populations after time t_1

After Brown (*159*).

which a percentage of the test organisms cannot achieve homeostasis in a given period is established. The descriptive value thus identified is then used to infer how the rest of the population from which the sample was drawn might respond.

2.2 Types of test

To indicate the types of testing procedure that would provide appropriate data for the control of pollution, EIFAC (*156*), categorized the following 5 types of toxicity test, which, although originally considered for use with fish, are equally appropriate to other whole-organism tests.

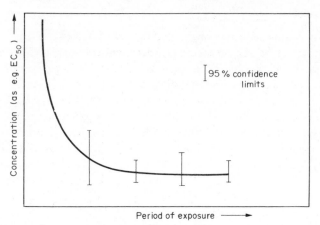

Fig. 44.   Toxicity curves using quantal data

After Brown (*159*)

(1) Screening tests to determine the acute toxicity of chemicals or products under standard conditions.

(2) Tests to establish water quality criteria.   These tests are designed not only to assess hazard, but to enable water quality objectives to be prepared.   Since hazardous effects may only become apparent in the long term, a variety of specially designed tests in addition to short-term acute toxicity tests, is necessary.

(3) Effluent monitoring tests.   Effluents are frequently complex mixtures of substances that are difficult to analyse and in such circumstances the imposition of normal chemical standards for assessing quality may be impossible.   Simple toxicity tests may therefore be used for monitoring these discharges to assess effluent quality and may be utilized in preliminary surveys of polluted catchments.

(4) Legal tests.   Where quality standards set for those effluents described above need to be legally binding, closely defined reproducible test procedures are necessary to establish acceptable evidence in a court of law of failure to comply with a toxicity standard.

(5) River monitoring tests.   Rivers and lakes can be suddenly polluted by a variety of causes, giving rise to hazards for water users downstream.   In such cases a monitoring system using whole organisms can provide an early warning of unfavourable conditions.

These tests should not necessarily be confined to the laboratory; field tests may prove particularly valuable for establishing water quality criteria and for monitoring purposes.

2.3 Selection of test organisms

The prime considerations in the selection of organisms for toxicity tests are (not in order of importance): (1) their sensitivity to the material or environmental factors under consideration, (2) their geographical distribution, abundance, and availability throughout the year, (3) their recreational, economic, and ecological importance locally and nationally, (4) the availability of culture methods for their rearing or maintenance in the laboratory and knowledge of their environmental requirements, (5) their general physical condition and freedom from parasites and diseases.

Very few studies have been made to determine the species most sensitive to a potential toxicant or waste. When selecting a test species for investigating a particular material, environmental factor, or effluent, consideration is given to available information on sensitivity, or sensitivity is determined by short-term toxicity tests and the selection is then made on the basis of the other considerations listed above. Since space is usually limited, attention must be given to the size of the organisms and the length of the life cycle. Small organisms less than 50–80 mm in length and having a short life cycle are the most useful for general toxicity studies. Some specific studies, however, will require larger organisms with long life cycles.

2.3.1 *Condition and health of selected organisms*

When conducting studies to determine maximum safe concentrations of an effluent, the most sensitive locally important species and the most sensitive life stage should ideally be used. When circumstances necessitate the regular use of some other test species, comparative tests using the effluent of concern should be performed to relate the sensitivity of this species to that of the most sensitive of the locally important species. For any one series of toxicity tests, the species should be obtained from a common source and collected at one time. The organisms used must be within a narrow size range; in general, the largest individual should not be more than 50% longer than the shortest one in the group. They should also be of the same age-group or life stage.

Information on the conditions required for holding and culturing organisms in the laboratory throughout the life cycle is available for only a few species. In many instances, therefore, it will be necessary to collect from the field certain life stages of selected organisms for toxicity tests. In these cases, the availability of knowledge of the environmental requirements and of the food habits is particularly important in the selection of test organisms.

The past history of test organisms should be determined, including when and where they were collected, the method of collection and how they were subsequently transported and handled. Test organisms should not be taken from polluted areas where the organisms are in poor condition or where they have unusually high body burdens of potential toxicants, especially those under test. They should not be taken from areas where disease and parasites are prevalent or where deformed individuals are commonly found.

2.4 Test endpoints

The choice of response will obviously depend on the type of test. Mortality, for example, may be a suitable response for initial screening but would be quite inappropriate on its own in tests designed to provide information on maximum safe concentrations in the environment. For the latter, a decrease in fecundity or growth rate or a change in behaviour might be more pertinent than individual survival in assessing the long-term potential of a population for success.

2.5 Apparatus

All components of a testing system, including culturing, acclimation and exposure chambers, water heating and cooling units, piping, constant head tanks, valves, fittings, and pumping and mixing equipment must be constructed with nontoxic and nonabsorptive materials. Details of the composition and preparation of acclimation and dilution waters are presented separately for each type of test.

Despite the relative complexity of the apparatus required, flow-through tests are regarded as essential in all but a few procedures, and the basic components of a flow-through test system are shown in Fig. 45. Static tests,

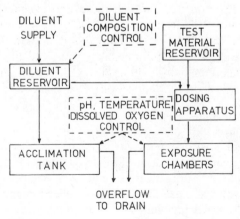

Fig. 45. Basic components of a flow-through test system

that is tests in which the test solutions are not frequently replaced, have a number of disadvantages that cannot be reconciled with good experimental practice. Without renewal, the concentration of the test substance may be reduced by biodegradation, volatilization, adsorption on the surface of the apparatus, uptake by test organisms, or complexation with materials excreted or secreted by the organisms or contained in the dilution water itself. At the same time, secretions and excretions of the test organisms may build up within the test chamber, modifying the original composition of the test solution (for example, in the case of ammonia excreted by ammonotelic organisms) and contribute to the total toxicity. Exceptionally, static tests may be superior where the test substance is an insoluble material or where a known conservative substance is presented in a large volume of dilution water to a small or physiologically relatively inactive biomass.

Dilution water and stock solutions of test materials can be measured, mixed, and delivered to the exposure chambers by a variety of methods, most of which have been described or listed (*158, 160 & 161*).

The requirements of simplicity, fail-safety, and reliability have been fulfilled most closely by Stark (*162*) whose " siphon-doser ", a modified form of which is shown in Fig. 46, was based on earlier designs by Abram (*163*) and Grenier (*164*). Simple laboratory glassware is required in assembling a siphon-doser; flows of stock solutions, dilution water, and mixed water to the exposure chamber are all achieved by gravity and if the diluent flow is interrupted the poison flow is also stopped.

Flow rates through the test containers must be at least 4 exposure-chamber volumes per 24 hours and in many cases it is desirable to construct the toxicant delivery system so that it can provide 10 or more exposure-chamber volumes per 24 hours, thus ensuring an adequate supply of dissolved oxygen in the chamber when direct aeration of the test solution is impracticable. The flow-rate through the exposure-chambers should not vary by more than $\pm 10\%$ from any one chamber to any other, or from one time to another within a given test. The calibration of the toxicant delivery system should be checked carefully, before, during, and after each test. This should include determining the volume of stock solutions and dilution water used in each portion of the toxicant delivery system and the flow-rate through each test container. The general operation of the toxicant delivery system should be checked daily during the test.

There is a wide choice of types of dosing apparatus now available, the apparatus of choice will depend on the availability of the components and the requirements simplicity, fail-safety, and reliability.

2.6 Procedures

Procedures specific to each type of test will be given in sections 3–7 and 9.

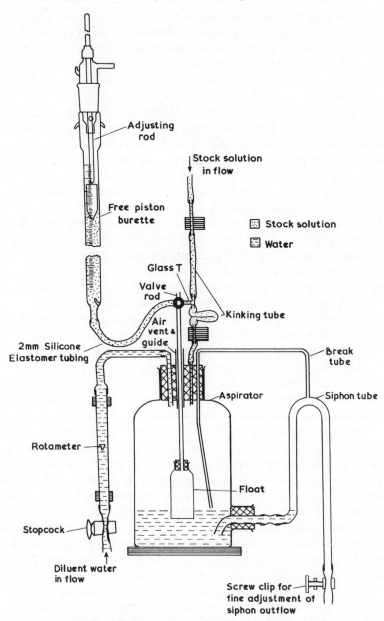

Fig. 46. Siphon-operated dosage apparatus. The rise and fall of the float, as the aspirator continually fills and empties, kinks and straightens the T-valves. On the fall, poison passes from the reservoir into the metering burette (or syringe); on the rise, the metering device empties into the aspirator.

After Stark (*162*)

2.6.1 *Pretest procedures*

Having chosen the test species by the criteria set out in sections 2.1–2.4, or as dictated by the individual methods, the organisms should be collected, for example, from their natural habitats, or fish farms, ensuring that they are not harmed, either physically or physiologically, during collection and transportation.

Water temperature, total hardness, dissolved oxygen concentration, and pH value should be determined at the collecting site to indicate the water quality into which the organisms should be transferred on arrival at the laboratory. Organisms should not be handled any more than necessary and transfer should be made with suitable containers or hand nets or, if they are small, by large-bore pipettes into which they can be drawn without damage and then transferred to holding containers. Hand-nets should be made of soft material with several layers around the rim of the net and there should be no sharp points or projections. All equipment must be kept clean and sterilized before use. The organisms should not be crowded during transportation, should be kept at a suitable temperature, provided with sufficient dissolved oxygen, and watched carefully for signs of distress. They should be protected from strong light and provided with shelter.

Collected animals must be observed for possible injury as a result of the procedures in transport to the laboratory. Fish injured during seine-netting, for example, should be kept in isotonic saline solution for a few days. Smaller forms can be examined under the dissecting microscope. Criteria for assessing if an animal is injured depend on the species and such assessment is more difficult for sluggish species. Useful criteria for denoting injury include loss of appendages, inability to maintain a normal body posture (e.g., with dorsal side uppermost), abnormal locomotion and uncoordinated movements of the mouth parts or other parts of the body, and colour change.

Newly collected organisms should be quarantined for at least 7 days after arrival before being added to the test station stocks. Any excessive mortality (say 10% after any post-transportation mortality) among quarantined organisms should cause the whole batch to be rejected.

After quarantine the organisms should be acclimated to the dilution water and the environmental factors (temperature, pH, DO) chosen for the test. The acclimation period depends on the difference between conditions at the collecting site and the test conditions. The period must be sufficiently long for the subsequent responses of the newly collected organisms to resemble those of organisms held under acclimation conditions for an extended period. If there are differences only in temperature, dissolved oxygen, or pH, it may be that acclimation periods of less than one week will be sufficient. If the total hardness value of the test differs markedly from that of the collection site, as much as 28 days acclimation may be required. If a long-term test is proposed and the test organisms have therefore to be fed on novel food it must be established that their new diet is acceptable and sufficient before the test can be started.

The selection and number of test concentrations depend on the nature of the test and the results of the preliminary " sighting test " (see section 2.6.2). Generally, the chosen concentrations form a geometric progression because a logarithmic increase in stimulus is usually required to elicit an arithmetic increase in response from a sample of organisms. A convenient method of finding a given number of concentrations that are logarithmically equally spaced between the maximum and minimum dictated by the sighting test is shown in Fig. 47. A ruler is placed on a suitable sheet of logarithmic

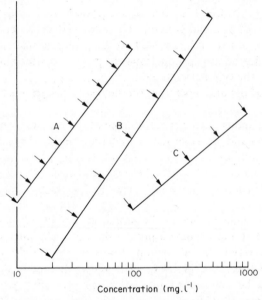

Concentration (mg.l⁻¹)

Fig. 47. A graphical method for determining a series of test concentration levels. Examples: A—9 tanks from 10–100 mg · l⁻¹; B—7 tanks from 20–500 mg · l⁻¹; C—5 tanks from 100–1000 mg · l⁻¹.

graph paper so that simple measurements, e.g., 0, 20, 40, 60 mm, refer to each test tank with 0 adjacent to the minimum concentration and 60 to the maximum; the concentrations adjacent to 20 and 40 mm are those of the intermediate solutions in a test with 4 concentrations.

Solutions of toxicants should be prepared in advance so that they may be added immediately to the dilution water in the required amount at the beginning of the test to obtain the different test concentrations of material under study. If a toxicant is unstable in solution, its half-life should be determined if appropriate so that it may be replaced as necessary. All solutions required for each series of toxicity tests must be prepared from the same sample of material. Any undissolved material present in the stock solution must be uniformly dispersed by agitation before being withdrawn and added to the dilution water in the test containers.

Some materials present serious problems if there is difficulty in distributing them evenly throughout the test solutions. This is especially true for oil. Agitation may be necessary in the stock solution as well as in the test containers to maintain solids or immiscible liquids in suspension.

The nature of the material being tested governs the selection of test containers (size and shape), preparation of the test solutions, and the frequency of test solution replacement. Problems associated with various substances include insolubility, adsorption on to exposed surfaces, decomposition, hydrolysis, photolysis, volatility, oxidizability, and encouragement of bacterial growth. These can reduce the concentration of material being tested and can lead to an underestimate of its harmful effects. Also, degradation products may be produced, which may be more or less toxic than the original material.

The effect of pH and teperature on the test solutions must be taken into consideration.

Samples of industrial or other effluents that are not constant in their composition should be collected at different times; they should not be unnecessarily combined to make composite samples because knowledge of the maximum toxicity, rather than the average toxicity, of a variable effluent is often required in connexion with the control of waste disposal to the aquatic environment.

Samples of effluents should be stored in completely filled stoppered containers and at a low temperature. If the waste contains organic matter subject to bacterial decomposition, the samples should be held at a temperature between 0°C and 4°C. The allowable time of storage prior to testing should be determined by testing samples after given periods of storage. Samples should not be stored longer than absolutely necessary.

2.6.1.1 *Preparation of dilutions*

Many effluents to be tested are complex mixtures, having solid, liquid, and gaseous components. When test media are being prepared, the waste toxicant should be shaken thoroughly before use. Waste may be used directly as a stock solution or a stock solution of the toxicant may be prepared by diluting with fresh water to the desired concentration and volume for mixing with the dilution water.

(*a*) *Soluble substances*

Stock solutions should be prepared on a volume-to-volume ratio of the dilution water and the waste effluent so that the percentage of waste in each of the test concentrations can be easily designated. If it is a soluble solid, it should be prepared on a weight-to-volume basis (e.g., $g \cdot l^{-1}$, $mg \cdot l^{-1}$, $\mu g \cdot l^{-1}$). If a volume-to-volume basis is used and it is desired to convert it to weight-to-volume, a correction must be made for the specific gravity of the material being tested.

Problems of extent and rate of solubility should be solved by mechanical means if possible, but if necessary solvents and/or emulsifying agents or water-miscible solvents may be used.

Acetone, dimethylformamide (DMF), ethanol, methanol, and triethylene gylcol may be used as solvents for the preparation of stock solutions. If these are not satisfactory the following may be considered: isopropanol, acetonitrile, dimethylacetamide, and ethylene glycol. A suggested surfactant is Triton X-100 or an equivalent material. Only the minimum amount of solvent necessary to disperse the toxicant should be used.

When an additive is used, two sets of controls must be employed, one containing no additives and one containing the highest concentration of additives to which any organisms in the test are exposed.

(b) Insoluble substances

If a substance is part settleable solid and part liquid, it should be shaken up thoroughly to ensure even dispersion; the desired volume should then be removed before the two phases can separate and either used as a stock toxicant or diluted with water to the desired concentration or percentage of waste for addition to the dilution water in the test solutions. It is necessary to provide agitation in the stock reservoir and in the test concentrations to keep the material in suspension. If small organisms are being used for the test, a magnetic stirrer may be used in the test chamber. If larger organisms are being tested in tanks, a screen or perforated false bottom may be placed in the tank over a revolving propellor. However, if the solids settle out quickly in nature and are not contacted by pelagic organisms, only tests in the supernatant liquid portion may be relevant. If the solid portion of the waste is thought to be toxic, test chambers should be set up in which benthic and burrowing organisms can be exposed to the settled material. Wastes should be mixed and allowed to settle before organisms are added. Test organisms might include tubificid worms and other silt-inhabiting annelids, burrowing mayflies, chironomids and other Diptera living in or on bottom materials, and freshwater snails, as well as bottom-living or bottom-feeding fish.

2.6.2   Test procedures

The number of organisms to be exposed in each test concentration is governed by several considerations: (a) the size of the organism in relation to that of the exposure chamber; (*b*) the expected normal mortality; (*c*) the extent of cannibalism; (*d*) the availability of dilution water, toxicant, and test organism, and (*e*) the desired precision of the estimate of the toxicity of the test material. In turn the precision obtained also depends on a number of factors: (*a*) the variability in response of the organism; (*b*) the number of individuals exposed to each test concentration; (*c*) the number of replications; (*d*) the toxicant being tested; (*e*) how close the mid-concentrations tested happen to be to the median lethal concentration (LC_{50}); (*f*) how closely the concentrations of the toxicant solutions being tested cluster around the LC_{50}; and (*g*) the variability in concentration of the toxicant being tested.

In a sighting test, a small number of organisms may be exposed to a wide range of concentrations, whereas, in the " definitive test " the range is reduced and a greater number of organisms exposed to each concentration, as detailed later for each type of test. Suitable controls are used in the main test, including those receiving solvents, as outlined in section 2.6.1.

Sufficient acclimated test organisms are randomly distributed among the exposure-chambers, the location of each organism being dictated by use of a table of random numbers in such a manner that some may be returned to the acclimation system.

It is usual to allow organisms at least 24 hours in which to recover from any handling stress incurred in the transfer from acclimation to exposure chamber, before the test materials are added to the tank. Where continuous-flow tests are used, an initial dose of material may be added so that the test concentration is immediately achieved, after which the concentration is maintained by the dosing apparatus. The initial dose may be " matured ", either in the dilution water in a separate container for a period equal to the median (or some other given percentile) retention period of the exposure chamber, or in dilution water in which the test organisms have previously lived for some hours so that any materials derived from the organisms have had a period of contact with the test substance, simulating as closely as possible subsequent events in the test chamber.

During the test, sufficient observations of physicochemical variables in the test chamber should be made to enable suitably detailed descriptions of exposure conditions to be made, particular attention being paid to the material under test and to those variables thought to affect its toxicity to the chosen organism. Where analysis of the waste material is impracticable, the accuracy of the dosing apparatus should be checked, as indicated in section 2.5; inert dyes or other conveniently analysed conservative substances should be used, preferably at least before and after each test.

Observations of the organism should be made at intervals and any unusual change in behaviour or appearance should be recorded. Some tests may require only infrequent observation, as detailed later. Dietary requirements of test animals are also dealt with later.

At the end of a test, surviving individuals that are obviously severely affected and those required for tissue analysis (e.g., for analysis of accumulated materials, enzyme studies, and histology) should be killed. Other surviving test individuals, including controls, should be placed in uncontaminated water, since further observations on them during this post-test period can be valuable where poisoning effects are delayed. If no delayed effects become apparent within an adequate period, organisms may eventually be released to suitable natural waters if their release is considered safe on medical, legal, and scientific grounds.

2.7 Expression of results

Whether the response of the test organisms is quantal ("reacted" or "did not react") or quantitative (degree of reaction) the results of toxicity tests should include a measure of the location of an effective concentration (EC), a definition of the percentage of the sample of organisms to which this figure refers (e.g., EC_{50} = median effective concentration), a measure of dispersion (often, but not necessarily, an estimate of 95% confidence limits—see Fig. 43 and 44) and the duration of the exposure period. When the response is death, the EC is known as lethal concentration (LC). Percentages other than the median may be reported, but their definition to the same confidence limits as those of the median requires larger numbers of organisms to be tested and the experimenter must reconcile the increased value of data referring to a response by smaller percentages of the population with the extra resources required. The measure of dispersion (an expression of the inherent variability of response of the sample) may be defined by the slope of the regression line relating response and concentration of test material (see below).

The different types of test require data analysis of various degrees of complexity, the simplest being perhaps to calculate the concentration of a substance to which 5 out of 10 organisms would respond (see, for example, section 8.1.4). The most complex method commonly used is probit analysis (165) for which computer programs are now available. Useful graphical methods also exist for the solution of time-percent of population responding curves (166) and for evaluating dose-effect experiments (167). Sprague (161) has reviewed most of the methods currently available.

The new "trimmed Spearman-Karber method" has been described (168). Comparison with probit and logit methods indicates that the new method is not subject to the problems of the two older methods, has good statistical properties, and is easy to use.

Where the concentrations of test material in the test solutions have not been measured directly but are nominal, through having been estimated from the "known" dilution of a made-up stock solution, this should be indicated when expressing the results, e.g., by adding in parenthesis the letter " I " (Initial nominal concentration) (*169*). Thus a nominal 24h LC_{50} would be expressed 24h $LC(I)_{50}$.

2.7.1 *Calculating, analysing and reporting results of toxicity tests*

In the past, simplified methods have been used for determining LC_{50} and EC_{50} values. Such methods of interpolation have given values that were generally accurate within the precision of the test (see, for example *170*). Since many will wish to handle their data by the simpler methods, it is recommended that the following procedures may be used in these situations and the more sophisticated approaches described in section 2.7.1.2 can be used where greater precision is required.

2.7.1.1 *Estimation of results by interpolation*

An LC_{50} is an interpolated value, based on the percentages of test organisms dying in one or more concentrations in which less than half died and one or more concentrations in which more than half died. Estimation of the LC_{50} by interpolation involves plotting the data on semilogarithmic coordinate paper with concentrations on the logarithmic scale and percentage of dead organisms on the arithmetic scale. A straight line is drawn between the two points representing the percentage dead at the two successive concentrations that were lethal to more than half and to less than half the test organisms. The concentration at which this line crosses the 50% mortality line is the estimated LC_{50} value. Figure 48 illustrates this procedure, which is

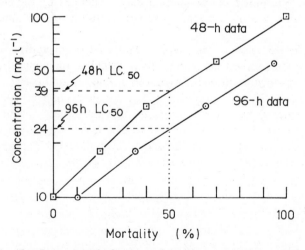

Fig. 48. Estimation of LC_{50} by straight-line graphical interpolation

referred to as straight-line graphical interpolation. Hypothetical results used in developing the graph are in Table 21. The LC_{50} values for 48-h and 96-h exposures are 39 and 24 mg·l^{-1}, respectively. Another approach is to plot the data on logarithmic-probability paper with concentration on the logarithmic and percentage dead on the probability scale, in which case a 10% mortality is plotted as 5%, a 20% mortality as 15%, etc., where 10 organisms are exposed in each chamber.

Table 21. Experimental data (hypothetical) plotted in Fig. 48

No. of test organisms	Concentration of material (mg·l^{-1})	No. and % of test organisms dying 48-h		96-h	
		No.	%	No.	%
20	10	0	0	2	10
20	18	4	20	7	35
20	32	7	35	13	65
20	56	14	70	19	95
20	100	20	100	20	100

2.7.1.2   *Analysing results of quantal toxicity tests*

Responses arising from toxicity tests are of two kinds, and methods of analysis are described for each. The first kind is the *quantal* test, in which a given organism either shows the response that is under study or does not show it—for example, it dies or it does not die. Thus, at any concentration greater than that tolerated in the environment without effect, a certain percentage of test organisms will show the response within some stated time period. The second kind is the *quantitative* or graded test, in which each organism yields a response that is variable in degree, such as amount of growth.

2.7.1.2.1   *Calculating LC_{50} and EC_{50}*

Methods for quantal tests are designed to estimate the concentration of a test material that just causes a response by the median or " typical " test organism.

The same procedure is used for estimating the median lethal concentration or the median effective concentration for any sublethal response. The latter might be immobilization, turnover, fatigue in a swimming test (*171*), avoidance reaction (*172*), or a significant effect on, for example growth, fertility or tissue structure. For sublethal responses or effects, the term EC_{50} should be read instead of LC_{50} in the text below and an appropriate word or phrase that describes the sublethal response should be inserted.

The lethal concentration for 50% of the individuals should be used to report results of toxicity tests in which death is the criterion of effect. The quantal test is used for acute mortality, which is usually considered to occur within 4–7 days, depending on the test organism, but may also be used for any longer period, such as 30 days or 3 months.

The LC_{50} may be estimated by probit analysis. In routine tests, this requires as a minimum that a line be drawn by eye to fit the results plotted on logarithmic-probability paper (Fig. 49). Such plotting is always the first stage of analysis, even in the more complex methods that are described below.

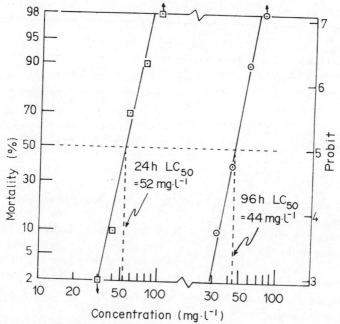

Fig. 49. Examples of determining median lethal concentrations at two representative times using probit analysis and the line of best fit

From US Standard Methods (*158*)

Observations of mortality are tabulated as in Table 22 for at least 1 and preferably 4 selected exposure times for the subsequent construction of a concentration-response curve (see section 2.7.1.2.2). The selected times should include the longest one used in the test. Only one successive 0% and one successive 100% mortality value should be used, the values selected being the ones nearest the centre of the range of concentrations. To construct the graph, percentage mortality should be plotted on the vertical axis (*probit* or probability scale) against the concentration on the horizontal axis (logarithmic scale) (Fig. 49). Since the probit scale never reaches zero or

Table 22. Hypothetical data from a toxicity test subjected to probit analysis (*158*)

Concentration of material ($mg \cdot l^{-1}$)	No. of test organisms	Number of test organisms dead at							
		2 h	4 h	6 h	8 h	24 h	48 h	72 h	96 h
100	10	1	4	7	9	10	10	10	10
75	10	0	1	2	6	9	9	10	10
56	10	0	0	0	2	7	7	8	9
42	10	0	0	0	0	1	4	4	4
32	10	0	0	0	0	0	1	1	1
0	10	0	0	0	0	0	0	0	0
LC_{50}, estimated from graph ($mg \cdot l^{-1}$)		100	100	90	71	52	47	45	44
LC_{50}, calculated by probit analysis		—	—	89.6	70.2	52.7	47.0	44.6	43.4
95% confidence limits		—	—	76 105	58.2 84.2	45.3 61.2	39.5 55.9	38.7 51.4	34.9 54
Slope of probit line		—	—	10.9	8.42	10.1	7.03	9.54	11.3

100%, any such points must be plotted with an arrow indicating their true position.

A line is next fitted to the points by eye. Most consideration should be given to points between 16 and 84% mortality (i.e. between 4 and 6 probit units or standard deviations) and an attempt should be made to minimize total vertical deviations of the line from the points. If there is doubt about placing the line, it should be drawn as horizontally as possible (Fig. 49) since this acknowledges more variability in the data.

The concentration causing 50% mortality is read from the fitted line and this is the estimated LC_{50} for the selected exposure time. This is one result of the toxicity test and should be reported. In the example, the estimated 96-h LC_{50} is approximately 44 $mg \cdot l^{-1}$. This is the estimated concentration that would be expected to kill the average or typical test organism in 96 hours. The LC_{50} estimated by graphical procedures is almost always sufficiently accurate for the purposes of the test. For example, the first graphical estimates shown in Table 22 are very close to those calculated by formal probit analysis using a computer.

In order to estimate an LC_{50} with reasonable accuracy, the data used to obtain it should satisfy certain guidelines. Each concentration of the toxic material being tested should be about 60% of the next higher one, estimates of the LC_{50} thus obtained being usually satisfactory for routine toxicity tests of waste effluents and screening tests of chemicals. In addition, it would usually be sufficient if one concentration produced a lethality between 10% and 50%

and a higher concentration produced a lethality between 50% and 90%. Alternatively, one of these values could be exactly 50%.

In more exacting tests and for research purposes, it is desirable to have several partial mortalities at different concentrations. To secure these, it is necessary to test a larger number of concentrations. In research studies, preferably at least one of the responses should be in the range 16–84% mortality because these represent ± 1.0 probit about the median response. At least two partial mortalities are required in order to estimate the LC_{50} and its confidence limits by Finney's method of formal probit analysis.

2.7.1.2.2 *Plotting toxicity curves*

Most toxicity tests will provide information on mortality at times before the final selected time. It will usually be beneficial to the investigator to use such information, as soon as it becomes available, to plot a toxicity curve. The procedure is to estimate the LC_{50} from a graph plotted in the same way as Fig. 49 for each of the observation times. The series of LC_{50} values should be used to construct a toxicity curve on log-log graph paper as the experiment proceeds, ending with something similar to Fig. 50.[a]

The purpose of a toxicity curve is to give the investigator an overall picture of the progress of the test and to indicate when acute mortality has stopped. This will be indicated by the curve becoming asymptotic to the time axis (*161*). In Fig. 50 the toxicity curve is closely approaching an asymptote of time but may not have quite reached it.

The LC_{50} for an exposure time that is in the asymptotic part of the curve could be termed the *asymptotic*, *threshold*, or *incipient* LC_{50}. Such a threshold of acute lethality for the median organism has greater theoretical and practical significance than an LC_{50} for some arbitrary time, such as 96 hours.

Asymptotic LC_{50} values may usually be determined for most macro-invertebrates and fish within a 96-h to 168-h exposure (*161*). However, sometimes a threshold is not apparent at that time. In such a case, the absence of a threshold for acute mortality is obviously of great practical importance, since lower concentrations than those producing mortality within the test period may be harmful with longer exposure times. In

---

[a] Although the dependent variable is plotted on the horizontal axis, it is customary and probably best to maintain this format. If such a graph were derived from estimates of median lethal times at various concentrations, the graph would be correct, inasmuch as time would be the dependent variable axis. Since the same set of observations could be used to produce either a series of LC_{50} values or a series of median lethal times, there would seem to be little reason to have two different formats for toxicity curves and the form shown in Fig. 49 is historically conventional.

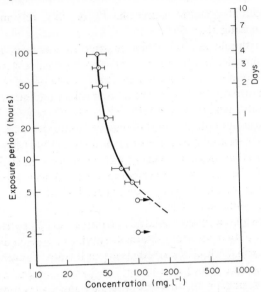

Fig. 50.   Toxicity curve using data from Fig. 49.   Bars indicate 95% confidence limits

From US Standard Methods (*158*)

research tests, it is advantageous to continue beyond 96–168 hours to determine if a threshold exists. If no threshold is found, that should be reported.

2.7.1.2.3   *Confidence limits of the* LC_{50}

Confidence limits of the LC_{50} are essential in research and also helpful in routine testing.   They may be calculated by probit analysis (*165*). Confidence limits should be included for the LC_{50} of the longest exposure time.   It is not necessary to estimate confidence limits at every exposure time, although this has been done in Table 22 for illustrative purposes.

The simplified nomographic methods of Litchfield & Wilcoxon (*167*) are acceptable for field work or when it is impossible or inconvenient to use a computer.   Results should be plotted for the selected time interval as in Fig. 49.   These graphic procedures are then used to estimate the goodness of fit of the eye-fitted line, its slope function, and the 95% confidence limits of the LC_{50}.   In doubtful cases, a number of different lines may be placed and the best-fitting one chosen.   The LC_{50}, its limits, and the *slope function* should be reported.   An approximate probit line may be constructed by this method, and confidence limits can be estimated even if there is only one partial mortality between 16% and 84% and one 0% or 100% response, as long as one of these is greater than 50%.

A computer should be used when possible to carry out the otherwise tedious iterative calculations of Finney's probit analysis, which give a maximum likelihood solution of the LC_{50}, its confidence limits, slope of the probit line, and other data. There are many packaged computer programs; one that is easily available is BMD 035 (*173*) using FORTRAN. Unfortunately, the output of that program requires some modification to enable statements of such desired parameters as confidence limits to be expressed in common terms so that they can be easily utilized by non-statisticians. Probit analysis may also be used with other computer languages, such as APL, in which the investigator can type in the data directly, without the intermediate step of preparing punched cards.[a]

A formal arithmetic probit analysis requires partial mortality at two concentrations. If two are not obtained, results can be analysed by the Litchfield-Wilcoxon method described above, or by moving average methods mentioned in the next section.

Even when a formal probit analysis is carried out with a computer, a graph such as Fig. 49 should always be made to check that the computed LC_{50} is reasonable. In some cases, a variable response can lead to truncated and split results; such information is useful to the investigator and would be missed or distorted if the data were processed only by a computer.

The significance of the difference between two LC_{50} values may be tested once confidence limits have been estimated, the simplest way being to look at the confidence limits of the two values. If the limits do not overlap, then the two LC_{50} values are significantly different. However, even if the confidence limits overlap, the LC_{50} values may still differ significantly, as can easily be established graphically (*167*).

The confidence limits about the LC_{50} do not describe variability of the LC_{50} when it has been estimated with another stock of organisms at another time of year. The limits merely indicate the accuracy of the estimate that would be expected from replicate tests carried out at the same time with exactly the same conditions and components. A precision within about 10% is sometimes attainable but better than that is not to be expected, even under favourable circumstances, unless more than 10 organisms are exposed at each concentration.

2.7.1.2.4 *Other methods of analysing results*

The graph for estimating the LC_{50} (Fig. 49) is sometimes constructed using an arithmetic scale for percentage mortality instead of a probability

---

[a] Such a program, APL Plus, may be obtained from the Institute of Computer Science, University of Guelph, Guelph, Ontario, Canada.

scale. However, the probit scale is generally better since the experimental points are then usually fitted by a straighter line.

Logits have been used instead of probits with equivalent results (*174*). Reciprocal transformations have also been used as well as arcsine transformations with estimation of the LC_{50} by a moving average (*175*). All these methods have some limitations but the last one is recommended for estimating LC_{50} and confidence limits when fewer than two partial percentage kills have been obtained.

Highly sophisticated computerized approaches describing multivariate response surfaces are available and can be advantageous for advanced research (*176*). However, for most work, the basic method given above has advantages of speed and simplicity.

For some purposes, it may be more informative to estimate the median effective time (ET_{50}) for mortality at each concentration. This may be done by plotting percentage mortality on a probit scale against time on a logarithmic scale. The ET_{50} values may then be estimated by techniques of probit analysis similar to those given above. Toxicity testing procedures are the same, although somewhat more frequent observations of mortality may be required, especially in the early stages of the test, and construction of the concentration-response curve as in section 2.7.1.2.2. For research purposes, this method sometimes allows easier interpretation of irregular results. It may also be useful in assessing the effects of mixing zones or other situations in which high concentrations prevail and where it would be desirable to estimate a time for passage of fish that would cause only a small percentage mortality.

2.7.1.2.5 *Mortality in controls*

Control mortality should be not greater than 10% and preferably not more than 5%, a figure that would correspond to the presence in a group of an occasional weak organism. Anything more than this should be regarded as unsatisfactory and the test should be repeated under more suitable conditions. If this is impossible, corrections for higher mortality in controls may be made using Abbott's formula (*177*):

$$P = \frac{P^* - C}{1 - C}$$

Where P and P^* are the corrected and observed proportions responding to the experimental stimulus and C is the proportion responding in the control test. Use of this formula does not solve the problems of probable interaction of stress from the toxicant with whatever stress is causing mortality in the control. However, with some long-term tests and with some invertebrates where mortality occurs even under the best possible conditions, it is necessary to use Abbott's formula or to consider the threshold lethal concentration as that in which the mortality equals the mortality in controls.

2.7.1.2.6 *Reporting of results*

The LC_{50} must always be given with specified exposure time. Also to be reported, if they have been calculated, are the confidence limits of the LC_{50} and the slope of probit line (or the slope function, *167*). These are the key data, from which other investigators can reconstruct the probit line if desired. Also highly useful is a figure showing the toxicity curve, or else a list of the LC_{50} values for different exposure times. If neither of these is given, the mortality in each concentration at the end of each 24-hour period must be reported. Mortality in controls must always be stated.

These experimental results must be accompanied by the following information: (*a*) the species of test organism, their source, weight and condition, acclimation to test conditions, treatment for disease and parasites prior to use, and observations on behaviour during the test; (*b*) the tested material, its source, storage and known physical and chemical properties; (*c*) the source of the experimental water or diluent, its physical and chemical properties, and variations in these properties during the test, as well as any pretreatment, additives, unusual constituents or known contaminants; (*d*) the physical and chemical properties of the test solution, especially a complete description of the concentration of the toxic component, if measurable, and the temperature, pH, and hardness at which the tests were made; (*e*) brief mention of the method, if standard, or its description, if different from a standard procedure, plus the specific experimental design; (*f*) the type of test container with volume and depth of solution, number of organisms and loading rate, toxicant delivery system, flow rate or frequency of renewal, and (*g*) the criterion of response and any observations on reaction or behaviour of the organisms during tests.

2.7.1.3 *Analysing results of graded or quantitative toxicity tests*

In quantitative or graded toxicity tests, each organism gives a response that is measurable on a continuous graded scale. For example, each organism in a test might show a measurable percentage increase in body weight.

Since there are usually many test organisms, a series of several graded measurements is generated for each test concentration; such data are easily analysed by standard techniques. A simple one-way analysis of variance may be used initially to assess whether significant differences have been found.

If differences exist, the investigator may proceed to determine whether responses for a given concentration are significantly different from responses for the controls. Several good techniques are available and are described in most standard statistical text books. One sound test is the Student-Newman-Keuls test (*178*) and a similar one is Duncan's multiple-range test (*179*). A particularly appropriate method is Dunnett's test (*180*), in which the responses at each concentration are compared with the responses of the control.

These techniques are applicable to most of the graded responses described for specific test organisms in the sections that follow.

2.8 Interpretation and application of results

Interpretation and application of results are specific to each type of test and cannot be used for other purposes. For example, data from short-term tests should not be used in establishing standards for long-term safeguarding of a population or community. The laboratory test has a limited application because it cannot reflect the intricacies of a natural habitat. The artificial ecosystem test (see section 4.6) overcomes some of these difficulties, but extreme caution should be taken in any extrapolation within and between laboratory and natural systems. Although relationships between the success of a community and water quality (as defined from short-term toxicity data) have been established for fish, the hazards inherent in extending this approach have been recognized (*181*). Application factors relating maximum acceptable toxicant concentration (MATC) to lethal concentrations have also been determined, and it has been demonstrated that these factors vary, with the toxicant (*182–184*). Where mixtures of toxicants occur their combined effects—additive, antagonistic or synergistic—should be measured.

The fundamental tenet must be that where the presence of a polluting substance is likely to cause harm to an aquatic community, tests must be made with the species at risk under the environmental conditions in which the stress is to be applied, in order to assess with reasonable accuracy the maximum safe exposure (time and concentration of the pollutant).

3. SCREENING TESTS

Theoretically, most chemicals could find their way into the aquatic environment as a result of accidental discharges, either from storage depots or while being transported by air, land, or water; they might also result from irresponsible or ill-informed disposal of unwanted surplus material. Many such discharges are likely to be isolated, single occurrences, causing an initial concentration of chemicals that will gradually decrease owing to their subsequent dispersal, dilution, and degradation. Information is required on the degree of risk attending such accidents so that the necessary steps can be taken to minimize their possible effects.

Some chemicals may find their way into lakes or rivers as a result of normal use or misuse, and again it is necessary to assess the degree of risk involved for aquatic life. To take the protection of fish population as an example, if the likely maximum concentration of a particular chemical in the environment is very much smaller than the acute lethal level for a particular species of fish,[a] then it might be safe to assume that such a chemical poses no pollutional problems for fisheries. The type of test procedure required to give a measure of the acute lethal concentration for fish can be termed a preliminary *screening test*. Such a screening test can also be used to determine the potentially least toxic of a group of chemicals or products that might find their way into rivers and lakes from normal usage, so that the use of the least hazardous substance can be investigated further.

The above definition of a screening test for fish (*156*) was examined in 1976 by the International Organization for Standardization (ISO) (*185*), which stated:

(1) The formulation of a single standard fish toxicity test to cover all categories of risk assessment was unrealistic and an impossible task.

(2) A standard acute toxicity test to be used solely for screening purposes was feasible and might prove to be internationally acceptable; this would enable a wide range of chemical substances and products to be placed in broad categories of toxicity and give some indication of the degree of risk involved in their appearance in the aquatic environment.

(3) There was a real danger that the results of the screening test could be misused, particularly when used alone, for setting water quality standards.

(4) Because of the need for reproducible results, fish toxicity tests should be carried out in properly equipped laboratories where competent technical staff were available, not only to carry out the tests but to interpret the results. Collaborative studies between laboratories with reference substances were highly desirable in order to assess the comparability of results.

(5) Because the problems associated with the marine environment were vastly different from those of freshwater, separate screening tests had to be developed for measurement of acute toxicity to marine and freshwater fish. It could not be assumed that the results of toxicity tests using freshwater fish gave a true indication of the level of toxicity of a substance to marine fish and therefore any such extrapolations should generally be avoided.

---

[a] A value of 10^{-4} times the acute lethal concentration can be taken as an approximate guide. The safety factor for persistent or accumulating toxic substances may be less than this value.

(6) It had so far been possible to propose a standard acute toxicity test for freshwater fish only. However, consideration should be given to the same general principles when designing a test for marine fish and until a standard procedure could be defined, details of salinity, pH, temperature, suspended solids, and other aspects of the procedure should be reported, together with precise details of the test species used, and its method of collection and maintenance.

A number of screening tests using fish and other organisms are described briefly in sections 3.1–3.6 and set out in detail in section 8.

3.1   Screening tests using fish

3.1.1   *Test based on a procedure proposed by ISO*

The object of this test (*185*) is to obtain an indication (within an order of magnitude) of the acute lethal concentration of a substance to fish. The species adopted is the zebra fish (*Brachydanio rerio*, Hamilton & Buchanan) and the principal result of the test is the LC_{50} value after 24 h, 48 h, and 96 h of exposure.

The test will allow the acute toxicities of different substances to be compared under standardized conditions of testing and therefore the substances may be placed in an order of toxicity. Such results are only a guide to the implications of the presence of these substances in the environment and should not be used for an accurate prediction of the ecological risk involved.

Details of the test are given in section 8.1. In addition, a static test using zebra fish is described in section 8.2, in which the 96-h LC_{50} is determined under defined conditions.

3.1.2   *The Carter bottle test*

The test was originally developed as a simple means of testing the toxicity of industrial effluents (*186*). It will become apparent that the test could have been included as an effluent monitoring test or (because of its use in synoptic surveys of rivers receiving pollutants from many sources) as a river monitoring test, as well as a screening test.

In the test, small fish of a given size are sealed in containers filled with air-saturated waters of different qualities (e.g., a clean "control" water and effluent or diluted effluent). A third set of containers, without fish, is also often used to assess the microbial oxygen demand of the test water. The fish consume oxygen from the water and become asphyxiated. The residual dissolved oxygen (DO) concentrations are then measured. In clean water, the residual DO will normally be lower than when poisons are present, suggesting that the lethal threshold DO is increased in the presence of other stresses to the fish. The residual DO is therefore used to compare the degree of contamination of the water.

Details are given in section 8.3.

3.2 Screening tests using macroinvertebrates

Within the limitations of screening tests set out in section 3 above, macroinvertebrates can be effective test organisms. They have advantages over fish in this respect, owing to their smaller size, relative ease of culture, short life cycles, and availability.

Brief descriptions are given below of tests using the crustacean *Daphnia magna* (section 3.2.1) and the mollusc *Biomphalaria glabrata* (section 3.2.2). The use of other species is briefly mentioned in section 3.2.3.

3.2.1 *Determination of the inhibition of the motility of* Daphnia magna Straus *(Crustacea, Cladocera)*[a]

The concentration of the test material that immobilizes 50% of a sample of *Daphnia* exposed for 24 h under the conditions described in section 8.4 is determined. The test has been proposed as suitable for determining the acute toxicity of chemical substances, industrial effluents (treated or untreated), and raw and treated sewage, as well as any fresh surface or ground water.

A similar 96-h test using *Daphnia pulex*, which can be used for evaluating the quality of oil refinery waste has been described (*187*).

3.2.2 *Toxicity tests using* Biomphalaria glabrata

Snails are suitable indicators of the chemical characteristics of littoral waters; they are sensitive to several pollutants and particularly to heavy metals. They are available in any season and large numbers can be easily reared in a small volume of water. Reproduction is continuous, fecundity high (4–5 embryos per adult per day), and viability about 90%. The duration of embryonic development is about 8–10 days at 20°C and snails become mature in about 3 months; the mean life of the adult varies from 1 to 2 years.

The tests described in section 8.5 (O. Ravera, personal communication) cover several aspects:

(*a*) a 24-h test of the rate of heart-beat in 3-month old snails,
(*b*) a 72-h lethal toxicity test using adult snails,
(*c*) a 10-d lethal toxicity test using snail embryos.

In the last test, a note is also made of the occurrence of morphologically anomalous individuals.

---

[a] This method is based on draft proposals by ISO.

3.2.3   *The use of other macroinvertebrates in screening tests*

Methods of observation and interpretation of data similar to those described in sections 8.4 and 8.5 may be applied to other species of invertebrate, such as tubificid worms and the larger freshwater crustaceans (e.g., *Asellus* and *Gammarus*), although the taxonomic skill required to identify the Tubificidae (of importance since members of this family have widely differing tolerances to pollutants) may not favour the use of the latter in routine screening tests. Alabaster (*188*) described a system in which these 3 groups, and *Daphnia*, are exposed in 96-h screening tests using flow-through apparatus. Maki (*189*), described a system for continuous-flow testing of small aquatic organisms.

One species that has recently received detailed attention as a test organism is *Hydra littoralis*, the methodology being adapted from, and thus being similar to, that for a marine colonial hydroid (*190*). This species appears to be easily reared in the laboratory and is very sensitive to certain poisons, responses including changes in rate of growth and in morphology at sublethal concentrations (A. R. D. Stebbing and V. A. Cooper, personal communications).

3.3   Screening tests using macrophytes

The use of plants in screening tests may have direct relevance where there is a possibility that a contaminated water may be used for crop irrigation, but such tests may also be of value in detecting changes in water quality *per se*. It must be recognized that the effects of a test substance on a submerged aquatic plant (for example, Canadian pondweed, *Elodea canadensis*) may differ from the effects on a terrestial species, and that effects on a germinating seed such as white mustard (*Sinapis alba*) may be different from those on a seedling or a more fully developed crop.

3.3.1   *Test using Canadian pondweed* (Elodea canadensis *Michaux* (Hydrocharitaceae))

The following responses have been used in screening tests: loss of green colour, cessation of photosynthesis, degradation of leaves, cessation of rotation of plastids within the cells, and sinking of the stem. The last response is due to inhibition of the photosynthetic production of oxygen, bubbles of which would otherwise increase the buoyancy of the plant when exposed to light for a period. (This reaction has also been applied in tests using the alga *Rhizoclonium hieroglyphicum* Kützing, which are not further described.)

Details of culture and test methods using *Elodea* are given in section 8.6.

3.3.2 *Test using white mustard* (Sinapis alba L. (*Cruciferae*))

The seed of white mustard, *Sinapis alba*, can be obtained throughout the year. The germination of the seed and the early development of the seedling may be used in a number of ways to determine the toxicity of the water. These include effects on the efficiency of germination, the speed of growth of the rootlets, and the relative rates of growth of the rootlet and hypocotyl. The methods are described in section 8.7.

3.3.3 *Tests using lesser duckweed* (Lemna minor L.)

Parker (*191*) has published a method for the rapid detection of herbicides that inhibit photosynthesis, using *Lemna minor*. The paper provides a description of the principle, methods, and examples of the test.

3.4 Screening tests using algae

The tests outlined below and detailed in section 8.8 are largely based on the US Environmental Protection Agency (EPA) algal assay procedure: bottle test (*192*), to which reference should be made for general guidance. In its original form the EPA procedure was intended primarily for use in a variety of general situations but its inclusion (in edited form) in this chapter is intended to enable assessment of whether or not various compounds or water samples are toxic or inhibitory to algae.

The maximum specific algal growth rate in unpolluted water is related to the concentration of the rate-limiting nutrient present, and the presence of toxicants can prevent or inhibit this growth rate.

All comparative growth responses should be analysed statistically and significant levels of the differences reported. For most purposes, a 95% significance level can be considered statistically significant.

3.4.1 *Screening tests using* Selenastrum capricornutum, Microcystis aeruginosa *and* Anacystis cyanea

The tests utilize biomass determinations and two parameters of growth: maximum specific growth rate and maximum standing crop.

Details are given in section 8.8. In addition, reference should be made to other work on using algae in water pollution research, (*193 & 194*).

3.5 Screening tests using protozoa

Protozoa, with algae and bacteria, form the broad base of aquatic food chains. US Standard Methods (*158*) gives procedures for toxicity testing using ciliated protozoa, *Tetrahymena pyriformis* being the recommended organism.   Responses include changes in population growth rate and effects on maximum population density.

Two European methods based on studies by Bringmann & Meinck (*195*) are detailed in sections 8.9 and 8.10. They utilize (*a*) the ability of uninhibited cultures of *Colpoda maupasi* to decrease the numbers of bacteria (measured as turbidity) from a standard suspension (section 8.9) and (*b*) the morphological and physiological responses of *Paramecium caudatum* Ehrenberg to dilutions of test materials (section 8.10). The protozoa can be obtained through the Culture Centre of Algae and Protozoa (see section 8.8.2.1).

3.6   Screening tests using bacteria

The ability of *Pseudomonas fluorescens* to convert glucose into organic acids and thus lower the pH of a sample is used to screen test materials that may inhibit the conversion.   The test is described in detail in section 8.11, and is based on the method of Bringmann & Meinck (*195*).

Pseudomonas fluorescens (NCIB 9046) may be obtained from the National Collection of Industrial Bacteria, Torry Research Station, 135 Abbey Road, Aberdeen AB9 8DG, Scotland.

Other tests measure the saprobic level of a given water, but these are not considered to be screening tests.

4. TESTS FOR ESTABLISHING WATER QUALITY CRITERIA

4.1   Introduction

The need for tests other than screening tests to provide information for the formulation of water quality criteria was expressed by EIFAC (*156*) as follows:

There are many poisons that appear in the environment at levels greater than 10^{-4} times the acute lethal level, as a result of industrial, agricultural, and domestic effluent discharges, or from direct application to water (as with aquatic herbicides).   Such chemicals may remain in the aquatic ecosystem for long periods of time, perhaps permanently, and for these substances much more information is required to assess the hazard, formulate water quality criteria, and impose water quality standards.   The nature and extent of the additional tests depend upon the nature of the substance and the degree of risk that its use entails.   The test procedures necessary to provide such information can be described as tests to establish water quality criteria.

The Commission's conclusions in relation to fish can equally be applied to the other members of the freshwater biota:

Where the predicted or measured concentration of a potential pollutant in the aquatic environment is greater than 10^{-4} times the 48-h or 96-h LC_{50}, as determined by a screening test, it is clear that further tests may have to be made to determine more accurately the degree of risk entailed so that suitable control measures can, if necessary, be applied to the use and disposal of the substance. The extent to which other tests have to be used, and their type, is a function of the degree of risk subsequently found and the nature of the pollutant. The experience of the Working Party on Water Quality Criteria, Sub-Commission III, EIFAC, is that, for common pollutants, an extensive knowledge is required of their chemistry and toxicity to fish under a wide range of conditions, both lethal and sublethal, before even tentative quality criteria can be established. On the other hand, a less comprehensive programme of testing would be required to assess the hazard arising from the discharge of a specific effluent at a single location. Tests to provide such information cannot be standardized since much depends on the nature of the substance and its harmful effect. For example, a constant-flow type of apparatus is unnecessary if the required concentration of poison can be maintained in fixed-volume test vessels with infrequent replacement of solutions. However, certain basic guidelines can be laid down that will enable the test results to be fully used in the preparation of water quality criteria.

In all tests, the guidelines set out in section 2 should be followed. The following sections (4.2–4.4 and 5–7) are based largely on the EIFAC report on fish toxicity testing procedures (*156*).

4.2 Lethal toxicity tests using fish

4.2.1 *Scope*

The role of lethal toxicity tests in establishing water quality criteria is extremely limited, since under natural conditions subtle effects of poisons at sublethal concentrations could severely affect a fish population by, for example, preventing breeding or the efficient utilization of food. However, the tests described below are included in this section because they can indicate relevant concentrations that should be used for sublethal toxicity studies, as well as providing information on gross responses and perhaps suggesting which aspects and possible target systems might be examined at more relevant concentrations.

4.2.2 *Effect of chemical and physical variables*

For most poisons, the relation between the logarithm of concentration and the logarithm of median period of survival of the test fish is curvilinear and a concentration exists where the curve becomes asymptotic to the time axis. This is known as the threshold or asymptotic LC_{50} value (see section

2.7). The effect of water hardness, pH value, temperature, salinity, and dissolved oxygen concentration on the LC_{50} value and the shape and position of the concentration response curve should be measured over the whole range likely to be encountered by the fish and these factors controlled to within close limits during the experiments (for example, pH value $\pm$ 0.1 unit, temperature $\pm$ 1°C). It should be remembered that variables such as pH value and temperature are important for those poisons that dissociate in solution to form ionized and un-ionized molecules, such as ammonia, of which only one type may be predominantly toxic; bicarbonate and free carbon dioxide concentrations can also affect the toxicity of such poisons. A review of the factors that can affect the chemical nature of pollutants and their subsequent harmful effects has been published (*196*). Other factors, including temperature and dissolved oxygen concentrations, can affect the susceptibility of fish to poisons.

4.2.3 *Species used and their pre-test maintenance*

Tests should be made to compare the sensitivity of the major fish species of commercial or sport value at different stages in their life cycle, from egg to adult. The care of the fish should be similar to that outlined in section 2 and, as wild fish may have to be used, great care has to be taken to avoid injury by the method of capture. Precautions against disease in the laboratory stock are even more important and the degree of parasitism should be investigated and recorded in the published results, as also should be the size, weight and (where possible) age of the fish used. During lengthy tests the fish should be fed (although this may not be necessary for short periods at very low temperatures) and the test vessels should be designed in such a manner that they can be kept as free as possible from unconsumed food and faeces.

4.2.4 *Analysis of results*

The tests should be continued until a definite threshold LC_{50} is obtained; construction of log concentration/log survival time curves can be obtained in two ways. If individual survival times of fish are recorded, the median survival time at each concentration can be derived graphically using log-probit paper and a line drawn through the resultant values (see section 2.7.1). This method is capable of providing more information than the fixed-time inspection procedure recommended in many of the screening tests (e.g., sections 8.1.4 and 8.4.3) for reasons given by Sprague (*197*), although it is also somewhat time-consuming since the fish may have to be inspected at more frequent intervals. The effect of different environmental variables on the toxicity of a poison to fish can be more readily perceived if the data are expressed graphically than if they are presented in tabular form only; published results should include both forms of data presentation.

4.2.5 *Special case of accumulative poisons*

For those poisons that are persistent in the environment and that accumulate in the fish, it is necessary to know the rate of uptake, the levels in the tissues that are associated with mortality, and the rate of loss when fish given a non-lethal exposure to the poison are returned to clean water. Such data on the level of residues at death are much more relevant to environmental monitoring programmes than are LC_{50} values of aqueous solutions.

4.2.6 *Other uses of fish tissues derived from lethal toxicity tests*

As indicated in section 4.2.1, the tissues of dead, or severely affected, fish can provide valuable material, for example for the biochemist. Apparatus for preparation of tissues in a suitable form to permit later analysis should be assembled in good time, and optimum storage techniques (e.g., deep-freezing, freeze-drying, fluid fixatives) should be established.

4.3 Sublethal toxicity tests using fish

In the preceding sections, the measured response to a pollutant has generally been death, whereas in setting a standard for a pollutant it is necessary to know the concentration that will not adversely affect fish. Considerable attention has been given in recent years to nonlethal responses of fish to low levels of pollutants. Such tests have measured changes at the cellular, tissue and organ level, and in the whole animal, involving a wide range of experimental technique and apparatus. No one test published so far has been shown to be capable alone of providing data on which criteria or standards can be set; information has to be gathered from experiments covering a wide range of responses by fish to the pollutant under review. It is not the intention here to describe the tests used in detail, but only to give a brief indication of the general principles to be followed when such tests are designed. The following examples have been selected to provide illustrations rather than a comprehensive review; the general rules laid down in section 2 for the care of fish and for the preparation of dilutions of pollutant apply also to all these tests (see e.g. *198*).

The chemical and physical factors known to affect the toxicity of the pollutant should be closely controlled and the values for the mean, standard deviation and range should be reported.

4.3.1 *Biochemical studies*

The biochemical studies most often undertaken are those on enzyme induction and inhibition; such experiments are useful if they shed light on the nature of the toxic action, which may then provide a wider understanding of the effect of the poison on the animal and lead to the prediction of important side-effects. But too often the significance of the results in terms of the effect on the viability of the species is not given, nor can it be readily obtained.

4.3.2 *Histological studies*

Prepared sections of tissues and organs from animals exposed to lethal and sublethal levels of toxic substances can give an indication of the site of toxic action, particularly where the tissue damage is severe, for example, the destruction of the gill epithelial tissue of fish exposed to acutely lethal levels of heavy metal salts. It is more difficult to assess the significance of slight tissue aberrations because these may be the result of adaptation by the fish to the stress imposed by the pollutant. Any such tests should show both the existence of a graded response and the concentration of poison that represents a no-effect level. Techniques are now available for measuring such histological effects and these should become more widely used.

Histochemical studies as used, for example, for heavy metals, can be of value if the target organ for the poison is either small or cannot readily be excised for chemical analysis, since in those cases, if coupled with other sublethal tests, they could be used in monitoring programmes. Haematological parameters have been measured to assess a sublethal response and such studies may increase in value with more experience in the interpretation of the results; at present, the range of normal variations is not fully understood.

4.3.3 *Physiological effects*

These include tests on the effect of poisons on the ability of fish to osmoregulate, to adapt to temperature changes, and on changes in heart and respiration rates. Again, it is important to demonstrate that the reaction being studied is of vital importance, that a graded response exists, and that a no-effect level is obtained. However, such tests are normally of short duration and the possibility remains that a longer exposure to sublethal levels may adversely affect a system not studied.

4.3.4 *Growth rate*

Measurements of changes in growth rate have much to commend them, since an organism growing at a normal rate can be presumed to be healthy (although it may at the same time have become sterile) and the growth rate is an important factor for species of commercial importance.

When persistent poisons are being tested, the fish should first be allowed to accumulate them to a predetermined level, otherwise the growth rate will be measured during a period when the toxic substance rises from zero to a low level in the tissues and the toxic effect may not be immediately apparent. Both the food supply and its presentation should be as natural as possible.

Growth rate is normally measured by making repeated measurements of length and weight over a period of several weeks or more. However, a recent method of estimating instantaneous growth rates from the uptake a ^{14}C-glycine by removed fish scales has been reported (*199*).

4.3.5 *Life cycle tests*

Tests in which fish are exposed to a pollutant for a year or longer are probably more illuminating than any other type, and quite unsuspected effects of poisons can be discovered. Not only can fecundity and viability of progeny be measured but also growth rate and resistance to disease. Their drawback is that the number of species that can be investigated in this way is limited and, because of the length of time taken, only a few poisons under a limited range of environmental conditions can be investigated unless considerable experimental facilities are available. Also, as in most other tests, the test species are normally exposed to a constant level of poison, a situation that is unlikely to be approached in the natural ecosystem except, perhaps, in lakes. Too little is known at present about the effect of fluctuating levels of poison around the no-effect concentration. Standard procedures for chronic " bioassays " have been published (*200*).

4.3.6 *Behaviour*

Because fish may actively avoid polluted areas, laboratory tests have been made to measure their reaction to a choice of clean or contaminated water. Such tests are normally made in a small apparatus with a clear interface between the two conditions; the results indicate the ability of fish to discriminate between the two by its reaction toward them in the absence of other environmental stimuli. It is often difficult to extrapolate from such data to field conditions where a sharp interface between clean and polluted water is lacking, and where other stimuli, such as territorial, migratory, or feeding behaviour patterns may have an overriding effect. Other aspects of behaviour, such as learning or physical reaction to stimuli, have also been tested in the presence of poisons. Those in which the species are exposed to a poison for a short period of time and their behaviour pattern then tested, may be of doubtful value if the ecological significance of the altered behaviour pattern is difficult to ascertain. However, poisons that act on the sensory mechanisms may affect fish-feeding behaviour or migration and may also influence their response to other poisons.

4.3.7   *Activity*

It has been shown that an increase in activity in freshwater fish makes them more susceptible to poisons, but the increase in sensitivity in terms of threshold LC_{50} values is small. Also, swimming speeds are affected by concentrations lower than the lethal levels.

It should be noted that both the activity and behaviour of fish are being used in monitoring systems to detect deleterious changes in water quality at effluent outfalls (section 5.2) and potable water intakes (section 7.2).

4.3.8   *Hazard to fish predators, including man*

Some toxic substances can exist in fish at low, nonlethal concentrations that may affect their quality or wholesomeness. For example, phenolic substances produce undesirable tainting in fish flesh at concentrations well below the lethal level and this aspect of pollution should be investigated where commercially important species are at risk (*201*). The problems associated with organochlorine and mercury compounds are well documented.

4.3.9   *Summary*

Of the tests described above, it is clear that none can be used on its own for the formulation of reliable, safe concentration criteria; the life cycle test is basically superior, but is limited by the species that can be used, and the time and space requirements. The remaining tests, and others not described here, contribute only partially to the knowledge required on the effects of pollution on the ability of fish and fisheries to survive. It cannot be stressed too strongly that the results of the experiments should be obtained in such a way that they should be capable of interpretation in terms of the survival of the species in the ecosystem and, especially where persistent poisons are used, the observed effect related to the concentration of toxic substance in the tissues. Furthermore, data obtained in the laboratory may not be relevant to the field situation and should be supplemented wherever possible by carefully conducted studies in the field (see section 4.4).

4.4   Field observations on fish

In sections 4.2 and 4.3 only the interaction between a fish and a pollutant under laboratory conditions has been considered; it is necessary, however, to relate such findings to the effect of pollutants on fish and fisheries in natural ecosystems.

Generally, a laboratory experiment is designed to run under constant conditions, although in some (e.g., life cycle studies) certain factors, such as light and temperature, are left uncontrolled so that the development of gonads can be suitably " triggered " at the correct time of year. Also, pollutants in laboratory experiments, even though they may be added intermittently and in mixtures with a few other pollutants, are added to a dilution water generally having a very low level of heavy metals and of organic and suspended matter. Food, although it may occasionally be " natural ", is presented to the test animals at regular intervals. The animals generally occupy a volume of water many times lower than their natural requirement and may be subject to overcrowding stresses, as well as extraneous noise, artificial light, and the close proximity of testing personnel.

The lack of space, diversity and change in their environment, the " purity " of the dilution water, and the occurrence of novel stresses in laboratory animals lead to the possibility that their responses may be quite different from those of animals in more natural environments. Field observations must therefore be used to help assess the relevance of laboratory-based data.

For a pollutant already present in significant amounts in the aquatic environment, surveys can be made of the status of fisheries at various pollution levels and the results compared with data obtained from laboratory tests. However, difficulties may occur if the fish are exposed to more than one pollutant; also, an extensive chemical sampling programme is required.

Useful data can be obtained from experiments with caged fish in rivers and lakes, in which observed mortalities are correlated with predictions based on the concentration of the pollutants as determined by chemical analysis and their known lethal effects from laboratory experiments. Again, it is important for such experiments to be accompanied by an extensive monitoring programme for the pollutant, since the concentrations in the water can fluctuate widely over short periods of time. However, it may be much more convenient (and essential for those substances that are present in the environment at levels too low to cause mortality or for those whose use is under consideration) to obtain pertinent data from artificial ecosystems (section 4.6), such as small streams supplied with controlled dilutions of effluents, or ponds to which the pollutant has been added. Such tests can provide useful information on the effect of a pollutant on fisheries within the natural ecosystem. Again, it is of the greatest importance that those chemical and physical variables that have been shown to affect the toxicity of the pollutant in laboratory tests should also be monitored in field surveys and experiments.

4.5 Tests using other organisms

Water quality criteria cannot be based on studies of one class of aquatic organism alone. Other aquatic organisms should receive attention and indeed the relatively short life cycles and high fecundity of invertebrates such as *Daphnia* and freshwater snails makes them very suitable for life cycle studies. Justification for the preponderance of studies on fish is based on their commercial and recreational importance, on their position towards the end of many energy chains, and, according to the limited information so far available, on their greater sensitivity to many substances compared with invertebrates. However, since most fish readily change their feeding habits when forced to do so, the existence of a thriving fish community is no guarantee that their original food organisms, or the rest of the biota, are all still in a healthy condition.

4.6   Artificial ecosystems

4.6.1   *Types of ecosystem*

The use of artificial ecosystems in screening the effects of pollutants is not yet amenable to standardization but can provide a valuable input of data in the establishment of water quality criteria. Two types of artificial ecosystem may be distinguished: (*a*) the small-scale, laboratory ecosystem differing from the laboratory-based toxicity tests described above chiefly in the use of several, often interdependent, species in the same chamber (e.g., an autotroph, a herbivore, and a carnivore); (*b*) the large-scale, outdoor, ecosystem colonized by a wide variety of producing and consuming organisms, whose interdependence is neither necessarily so complete nor so simple as in (*a*).

4.6.2   *Laboratory-scale ecosystems*

An example of a laboratory ecosystem is given in section 8.12. Observations are made on plant growth, the persistence of the herbicide in the water and in fish tissue, the survival and growth of fish, and the abundance of phytoplankton and zooplankton. Similar approaches could be adopted for the testing of other materials.

4.6.3   *Other examples of laboratory-scale ecosystems*

Descriptions of other model ecosystems may be found in (*203*) and, for flow-through systems, in (*204*).

4.6.4   *Conclusions*

It is obvious that model ecosystem studies are not yet at a stage where standardization can be applied. Quite possibly, by their very nature, they will never be subject to standardization because their efficiency in indicating possible hazards to the environment is based on the complexity of interspecific reactions of the test material. The ultimate extension of work on laboratory ecosystems is to study the natural environment itself, as indicated for fish in section 4.4 above. The intermediate step, however, is to work on artificial but large-scale extralaboratory systems.

5. EFFLUENT MONITORING TESTS

Normally, the quality standards set for an effluent are described in chemical terms and the subsequent monitoring of the effluent is carried out by chemical analysis. However, where effluents contain substances or complex mixtures that may prove hazardous to freshwater organisms and that are difficult to analyse, toxicity tests have to be carried out to estimate the extent of the risk and a simple test used for subsequent monitoring of the effluent. Such a test can be called an *effluent monitoring test*.

5.1 Effluent monitoring tests using fish

5.2.1 *Introduction*

The practice of keeping fish in aquaria or ponds supplied with effluent from industries or sewage disposal works to demonstrate that the effluent is not harmful to fish is increasing and should be encouraged. However, there are many situations where effluents, mainly from industries, are lethal to fish and where this practice cannot be used. In such cases, the effluent can often be monitored for its toxic constituents by chemical analysis, but there are other instances where the toxic substance or substances are difficult to detect or measure by such means, and only a fish toxicity test can provide a quantitative measure of the harmfulness of the effluent. Each such pollutional situation is usually unique in that the individual characteristics of both the effluent and the water in the receiving river or lake are unlikely to be found elsewhere. What is required, therefore, is a simple toxicity test to enable the harmfulness of the effluent to be monitored by unskilled personnel.

5.1.2 *Test procedure*

There are two ways in which this can be done:

(1) The effluent can be passed to an aquarium containing fish, after dilution with the receiving water, to give final concentrations equal to or greater than the concentration obtained in the river or lake. Alternatively, a series of dilutions can be prepared to give a range of concentrations to which fish are exposed. Such a test will show whether the effluent is causing harm and is useful if the discharge varies considerably in quality over a period of

time, or contains volatile or degradable pollutants, and when a single sample would not be representative of the daily or weekly discharge. More detailed information on this type of test will be found in section 7.

(2) Samples of effluent can be taken at regular intervals, serial dilutions with receiving water prepared in simple aquaria, and fish exposed to them without replacement of the test solutions. Such a test has value if the effluent quality is fairly constant and the pollutants are stable, and it has the advantage of providing a quantitative measure of the toxicity of the discharge. This, together with information on the dilution of the effluent after discharge, indicates whether the effluent is likely to be harmful. These tests can be made under static conditions; if necessary the solutions can be gently aerated. The temperature need not be held constant but could be that of the receiving water at the time of the test. Fish mortalities can be recorded after either 24 h or 48 h and the LC_{50} calculated as described in section 2. Because such tests are likely to be carried out by unskilled personnel, the procedures adopted by any one effluent discharge need to be explicit to give maximum guidance, as, for example, in the proposals made by the Biological Water Quality Committee of the Ohio River Valley Water Sanitation Commission (ORSANCO) (*205*), for the effluent monitoring test to be used by dischargers to the Ohio River, USA.

The Carter bottle test may also be considered a valid method for assessing the toxicity of batches of effluent (see section 3.1.2).

5.1.3   *Fish species*

Since these are unstandardized tests, a particular fish species need not be specified; it would be desirable but not essential to use the most sensitive of the common species that are commercially or recreationally important and locally available in the receiving water. Conditions for the care of such wild species of fish before they are used for testing need to be similar to those outlined in section 4.2.3.

5.1.4   *Effluent investigational test*

With effluent discharges that are demonstrably toxic to fish, there is a need to determine the extent to which the toxicity can be explained in terms of the constituent effluent streams and known toxic components. For this purpose, tests similar to those described above are required to identify streams whose treatment would most effectively improve overall effluent quality because their constituent poisons were most amenable to reduction in con-centrations. Where the effluent streams include commonly occurring poisons, the species of fish used in the test should be those whose responses to these substances are well documented, so that the effect of the less well-known poisons can be assessed. In this case also, the test solutions should be analysed for those factors that influence the toxicity of the common poisons present.

6. LEGAL TESTS

6.1 General considerations

Where the quality standards set for those effluents described above need to be legally binding, a closely defined, reproducible test procedure is necessary to establish evidence in a court of law of a failure to comply with a toxicity standard. Such a test can be described as a *legal test*.

All effluents discharged to fresh waters should be subject to quality and quantity standards set by a regulating authority for pollution prevention. Wherever possible, the levels of toxic constituents should be controlled by chemical analysis, but there may be cases where a fish toxicity standard is essential because the toxic constituents are not readily determined by chemical analysis. Such a standard requires a test procedure that is simple yet reproducible and that is described in sufficient detail to enable the results to be defended in a court of law.

6.2 Procedure

The type of test required will, of course, depend on the way in which the standard is set. For the purposes of providing an example, the following standard will be considered: when the effluent is diluted X times with the specified dilution water and tested by the required procedure, no more than Y organisms shall die within the prescribed period of the test.

It will be seen that, with such a standard, only one dilution needs to be tested and the effluent either passes or fails the test; it is not essential to know to what degree the effluent passes or fails, although in some cases this might be advantageous. There has been little experience of this type of test and the procedure put forward is based on one used to a very limited extent in the United Kingdom (206); a similar test is used in the province of Milan, Italy.

Essentially, the tests should be simple and therefore static tests with fixed volumes of solutions are required. The dilutions of effluent should be prepared with a standard water as described in section 8.1.1.1; the solution should be gently aerated, if necessary, to maintain the dissolved oxygen concentration close to the air saturation value. Commercially available cultivated fish should be used and the size specified within close limits; they should be kept in the artificial dilution water for at least 7 days before use, and cared for as set out in section 2.6.1. The temperature should be conveniently above normal ambient room temperature and controlled to within $\pm 1°C$; the species of fish used should be such that this temperature is within its optimum range and it should be sensitive to toxic substances. Ten fish should be used in the test dilution, and a further 10 as a control in standard dilution water only. Mortalities in the control aquaria invalidate the test. The test should continue for at least 24 h and preferably for 48 h; shorter-term tests are less likely to give reproducible results. The effluent fails the test if more than 5 of the 10 fish die in the test concentration.

A basically similar test procedure has been proposed by the Working Group on Effluent Toxicity Requirements, Environment Canada, for the setting of effluent standards for the pulp and paper industry (J. S. Loch, personal communication). The effluents from these plants, when treated by biological methods, should not on average be acutely toxic to fish. A common standard is being proposed, therefore, whereby 50 rainbow trout (2–10 g) are exposed in batches of 10 to a 65% dilution of the effluent at 15°C, and a similar number are held in clean water as controls; the apparatus should be of a continuous flow type and the test continued for 96 hours. The sample fails the test if the number of fish mortalities in the effluent dilutions are statistically significantly greater than those in the controls.

6.3 Application of the test

It is first necessary to determine the minimum dilution that the effluent must receive if it is not to harm fisheries in the river or lake into which it is discharged. This can be achieved only by a series of lethal and sublethal tests, as described in section 4, although because pollution at a single site only is being considered the extent of the testing may be considerably less than that required for common and widespread pollutants. Then, if an effluent has to be diluted, say, Y times by the receiving water before it becomes harmless to fish, and if, with the maximum rate of discharge, the minimum dilution of the effluent in the receiving water is $2Y$ times, then the toxicity of the effluent could increase twofold before it becomes harmful. A series of dilutions of the effluent are then prepared to find the level at which 5 out of 10 fish only are killed using this legal test procedure; if this dilution was, say $\dfrac{Y}{10}$ times, then the standard may be set at a dilution of $\dfrac{Y}{5}$ times. Obviously, the actual standard set would depend upon other considerations, including local circumstances; the above procedure only indicates the general principle involved. It is clear, however, that the test conditions should be made as sensitive as possible, otherwise undiluted or very low dilutions of effluent may have to be tested.

It must be emphasized that the dilution of effluent specified for the fish toxicity test is not the same as the actual dilution of the effluent that is safe for the population of fish in a river. Furthermore, the legal test is an empirical procedure and is suitable for no other purpose than that given above.

6.4 Legal tests using organisms other than fish

Provided that the principles set out above are adhered to (e.g., reproducibility, production of an unequivocal response) it would be advantageous to carry out such tests on different organisms in a range of taxa to establish an overall toxicity to the community, as required by the methods of the Council for Mutual Economic Assistance (CMEA) (*141*).

7. RIVER MONITORING TESTS

7.1 General considerations

Rivers can be suddenly polluted from a variety of sources, giving rise to hazards for water-users downstream. In such cases, it may be of value to install a monitoring system whereby a continuous surveillance of a few test fish for signs of stress can provide an early warning of unfavourable conditions, and allow the water supply to, say, water treatment works or fish farms to be temporarily shut off. Such tests can be described as river monitoring tests, although they could also be used for monitoring lakes, if necessary, or even effluents.

The number and variety of chemicals being introduced each year rule out the use of any single analytical instrument or group of instruments being able continuously to monitor the quality of a river water. If, however, a number of animals could be exposed to the river water in apparatus capable of monitoring a variety of possible stress symptoms, and if a parallel physicochemical monitor was able to cancel alarms caused by irrelevant changes in water quality (e.g., pH, temperature upstream of a potable water intake), a useful facility would have been developed. However, the protection of a potable water supply is not guaranteed by the installation of a biological monitor because the chosen organism is unlikely to respond to every substance capable of causing harm or tainting.

Considerable advances have been made in this field recently. The objective of these tests is to provide a continuous monitoring of a river (or perhaps effluent) in such a way that action can be taken if the water quality becomes harmful to fish. Such action may include the diversion of an effluent to holding tanks, the taking of water samples for analysis, or the closing down of intakes to downstream potable water supply undertakings or fish farms. The basic apparatus consists of an aquarium through which the water to be monitored is pumped; fish are placed in this chamber and their reactions are recorded.

The detailed construction of the apparatus depends on the response chosen for measurement. Clearly, it is desirable to choose a response that gives the maximum early warning of a serious deterioration in water quality, but does not give rise to an excessive number of false alarms (the proportion of false alarms that can be tolerated depends upon the degree of risk presented by a deterioration in water quality). The retention time of water in the apparatus should be as short as possible to reduce the delay in measuring the response.

7.2   Methods using fish

7.2.1   *The measured response*

7.2.1.1   *Death*

Although death of the fish has been used as a measured response, it is of limited value in this context, and the least sensitive of the possible responses that can be measured.

7.2.1.2   *Inability to swim*

The most commonly monitored response is the inability of fish to maintain swimming activity in a water current. In such tests, the aquarium consists of a tube through which water is pumped; the fish is confined to the anterior part of the chamber by a screen, which may be either physical or electrical, or by shining a strong light into the posterior part of the chamber. Alternatively, the chamber can be narrowed toward the screen to provide an increased water velocity there. Loss of swimming ability by the fish brings it into contact with the physical screen or causes its passage through the electrical screen into the posterior chamber. The recording devices can monitor the frequency with which a fish touches a mechanical screen, its passive passage through a combined mechanical/electrical screen (composed of vertical wires attached to micro-switches), or its presence in the posterior chamber. Both optical and sonar detecting devices have been used, for which the latter has the advantage of being unaffected by changes in water turbidity (the use of a mechanical triggering screen requires a filtered water supply to avoid clogging with debris). It is usual to have several such units operating in parallel, or a single unit with several fish, and the alarm is only triggered if a significant number of fish demonstrate a sudden inability to swim.

Such a monitoring system would respond only to sudden changes in water quality, and a long-term deterioration, which may cause widely spaced responses in the fish, would not be so readily detected.

Details of such methods are given in (*207–210*).

7.2.1.3 *Alteration in behaviour pattern*

A more sensitive response is the changing activity patterns of a fish in a large aquarium into which water is pumped either horizontally or vertically or perhaps alternatively horizontally and vertically. Normal activity patterns are monitored by an array of photoreceptors and a change can be detected either as a direct abnormality (all fish at the surface) or a change in pattern from that obtained at the same time during previous days where there may have been a diel activity pattern. In such tests the normal pattern has to be established before any change can be monitored. An example of such a study is given in (*211*).

7.2.1.4 *Alteration in respiratory frequency*

Probably the most sensitive response measured so far is the change in respiratory frequency, in which the signals recorded are the nerve impulses to the opercular muscles. Again, the rates that are monitored on the first day (and that are slightly higher than normal) are taken as the control values and any subsequent rise above these values is taken as an indication of stress. Descriptions of apparatus are given in (*212*) & (*213*).

7.2.2 *Evaluation of methods*

None of these systems has been tested with a wide range of fish species and pollutants, so no detailed evaluation can be made. However, is is likely that for the purposes for which these tests are most commonly used, a simple, sensitive and reliable procedure will be required and, at the present time, the methods based on the loss of swimming ability seem to be superior to the remainder. The inability of a fish to avoid an electrical barrier, and subsequent interruption of a sonar beam, is likely to provide a very positive response. Maximum sensitivity can be achieved by an appropriate choice of fish species and water current (which may have to be varied in summer and winter), the latter providing a stress to which the pollutional stress would be added. More refined techniques of monitoring behaviour and respiratory patterns require more sophisticated apparatus, screened from all external stimuli except that of water quality, and are more liable to produce false alarms. There is a clear case here for a programme of rigorous comparative testing of techniques to evaluate their respective merits for a range of pollutional situations and needs.

7.2.3 *Care of fish*

As with previous tests, it is essential that the fish used should be healthy and free from disease, otherwise false alarms will occur. Normal feeding regimes can be followed for the stock fish, and fish used in those tests described in sections 6.2.1 and 6.2.2 may be fed during the test, if necessary with medicated food. Feeding of fish in those tests that monitor behaviour patterns can only be carried out if it does not cause anomalous results or if such results are taken into account. The length of time a fish is kept in the apparatus will vary with the species and techniques used, but 3–4 weeks would appear to be a satisfactory period if the fish are fed, and 3–5 days if they are starved.

7.2.4 Conclusions

It is clear that river monitoring tests have a considerable potential value, but they are still in the development stage. Comparative tests should be carried out to find a simple, reliable, sensitive test for different pollutional situations; increases in complexity to obtain a slight increase in sensitivity may not be warranted if, as a result, the technique becomes less reliable.

8. DETAILED DESCRIPTIONS OF SCREENING TESTS

8.1 Screening test using zebra fish *(Brachydanio rerio)*[a]

8.1.1 Materials

8.1.1.1 Dilution water, stock, and test solutions

The standard dilution water has a hardness of 100 mg·l^{-1} expressed as calcium carbonate and the following ionic composition in mg·l^{-1}:

Calcium	29.5
Magnesium	7.5
Sodium	56.5
Bicarbonate	100.0
Chloride	60.5
Sulfate	56.0
Nitrate	3.5

It is prepared by adding stock solutions of analytical reagents to deionized or distilled water whose conductivity does not exceed 5 conductivity units (10 μS·cm^{-2}).

Stock solution 1: Dissolve 320 g of $CaCl_2 . 6H_2O$, 29 g of NaCl and 9 g of $NaNO_3$ in deionized or distilled water and make up to 1 litre.

---

[a] Based on a procedure discussed by ISO (*185*).

Stock solution 2: Dissolve 151 g of $MgSO_4 . 7H_2O$ and 79 g of Na_2SO_4 in deionized or distilled water and make up to 1 litre.

Stock solution 3: Dissolve 27 g of $NaHCO_3$ in deionized or distilled water and make up to 1 litre.

For each 100 litres of standard water to be prepared, add 50 ml each of solutions 1 and 2 and 500 ml of solution 3.

The water shall have a pH of 7.8 ± 0.2.

In general, stock solutions of the test substances shall be prepared daily unless it is known that the material is stable in solution, in which case sufficient stock for 4 days may be made up.

Substances of low aqueous solubility may be first dissolved in a solvent of low toxicity to fish such as acetone, before preparing the stock solution. In such cases, the control (i.e., fish exposed to dilution water only) should contain the same solvent concentration as that of the highest test concentration.

Because of the problems that arise with test substances, which may be transformed or lost from stock solutions, no single procedure can be laid down for their preparation. It is therefore necessary to report the concentration of the stock solution and the method of preparation.

If the test substance is marketed as a formulation, both the designated active ingredient and the complete formulation shall be tested and the report shall state the specification of the material tested and whether the concentrations refer to the pure substance or formulation.

8.1.1.2 *Apparatus*

The test apparatus shall be constructed mainly of glass with the minimum of plastics materials. Ground glass joints shall be used as far as possible. It shall comprise the following components;

- Test flask. This is a 1 litre spherical glass flask with 3 necks (Fig. 51, a, b, and c). However, a gas wash-bottle head may be substituted in the neck (b) to replace (b) and (c) (*214*).

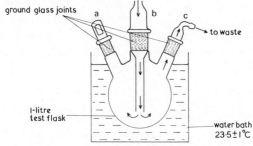

Fig. 51. Dosing apparatus with efficient mixing of dilution water and test material at $23.5 \pm 1°C$

• Water bath, capable of maintaining a temperature of 23.5 ± 1°C.

• Solution replacement equipment. This consists of peristaltic pumps or other metering devices that are capable of adequately mixing the stock solution of the test substance with the dilution to give the required concentration of the test substance before addition to each flask. The concentration in each test flask shall be maintained within ± 10% of the nominal value.

8.1.2 Species used and their pre-test maintenance

The test species to be used is *Brachydanio rerio* (Hamilton & Buchanan), commonly known as the zebra fish. Information about breeding is given below, and in *215–217*).

The stock population shall be maintained for a minium of two weeks in water of similar quality and temperature to those of the dilution water (section 8.1.1) and fed on a normal diet. The fish should be free from observable disease; if normal prophylactic treatment for the prevention of disease is used, including the use of medicated food, the fish should be left for at least two weeks after treatment before use in the test. Furthermore, if more than 10% of the stock fish become diseased then the whole population should be discarded. Fish alive at the end of a test should not be used in subsequent tests.

A representative sample of the fish population shall be measured in order to ensure compliance with the requirements set out in section 8.1.3.

8.1.2.1 Culture and maintenance of zebra fish

The species originates from the Coromandel coast of India where it inhabits fast flowing streams. It is a common aquarium fish, so that information about procedures for its care and culture can be found in standard reference books on tropical fish culture.

The fish rarely exceeds 45 mm in length. The body is cylindrical with 7–9 dark blue horizontal stripes on silver. These stripes run into the caudal and anal fins. The back is olive green. Males are slimmer than females and possess a golden sheen. Females are more silvery and the abdomen is distended, particularly prior to spawning.

8.1.2.2 Environmental parameters

The fish are capable of withstanding wide ranges of temperature, pH value, and hardness. Axelrod (*215*) states that the tolerable range of temperature is 15.5°C to 43.3°C, while for pH the range in 6.6–7.2. Fish may be bred, reared, and maintained in tap water with a total hardness of 300 mg·l^{-1} (as $CaCO_3$) and a pH of 7.7–8.2. The temperature is maintained at 26 ± 1°C to induce spawning.

8.1.2.3 Culture materials and methods

The fish may readily be spawned in glass tanks having a capacity of about 70 litres. Later the fry are transferred to a tank with a capacity of 200 litres.

Since the adult fish are avid egg eaters, a method of protecting newly laid eggs and young fish is necessary. One method, used successfully, is to confine the adult fish in mesh cages in the water so that as the female lays her eggs these fall through the mesh to the bottom of the tank out of reach of the adults.

The mesh cages, approximately 250 mm × 250 mm × 80 mm, are made of plastic netting with 3-mm mesh. They are clipped to the lips of the tank so that the whole of the upper edge of the cage is above water with the mesh dropping 60 mm into the water. An under-gravel filter system should not be used to cleanse the water because it is likely to damage the eggs. The tanks should be illuminated for 8 h per day.

8.1.2.4 Conditioning

This period lasts for approximately two weeks. Males and females are separated and fed on live food. This consists of white worms (enchytraeids), *Daphnia*, and brine shrimp (*Artemia*). The density of stocking during conditioning is kept below 30 fish per 70-litre tank.

At the end of the two weeks, the males possess a deep golden sheen and the females are greatly distended with ova.

8.1.2.5 Breeding stage

The spawning tank can be set up as follows:

An empty tank is filled with fresh tap water aged at 27°C for 48 hours and a plastic cage is placed inside the tank under the lip allowing the fish a swimming space of about 1 litre. Six females are placed in the basket in the morning and fed with freeze-dried brine shrimp. Nine males are added to the basket in the evening and fed once more with freeze-dried brine shrimp before the lights are switched off. Spawning is induced by the morning light and is completed after the lights have been switched on for approximately 4 hours.

The eggs, which are non-adhesive, fall through the mesh, out of reach of the adults. When the females are exhausted of eggs, the adults are removed and the eggs left to hatch.

8.1.2.6 *Development of fry*

The eggs hatch in 4–5 days. The fry or alevins adhere to the side of the tank and remain motionless for 24–48 hours. When the fry become free-swimming, they are fed on suitable proprietary fish food of small particle size. At 3 weeks, the fry can be fed newly hatched brine shrimp (*Artemia*) and then growth becomes more rapid. At 1 month, they can be transferred to a 200-litre tank and fed on a mixture of live and proprietary foods. The fish are sexually mature at 3 months and attain a length of 35 mm.

8.1.3 *Test procedures*

8.1.3.1 *Preliminary test*

This preliminary test, for establishing a suitable range of concentrations, can be carried out in 1-litre glass containers. A range of test solutions, which includes concentrations of 0.1, 1.0, 10, 100, 1000 and 10 000 mg·l^{-1}, and a control are prepared, using the dilution water described in section 8.1.1.1. The volume of each solution should be at least 1000 ml. Air is bubbled slowly through the solutions, which are maintained at 23.5°C.

Three zebra fish are placed in each solution and mortalities are recorded during the following 24 hours. If there are insufficient data for establishing the range of concentrations required for the definitive test, this preliminary procedure is repeated with either intermediate or extended ranges of concentrations.

8.1.3.2 *Definitive test*

Assemble sufficient sets of the apparatus as shown in Fig. 51 to carry out tests on at least 5 concentrations of the test substance and a control. Completely fill all but one of the flasks with one of a series of test solution concentrations of the test substance forming a geometric series, e.g., 0.5, 1.0, 2.0, 4.0 mg·l^{-1} and 8.0 mg·l^{-1}, as indicated in Fig. 45.

The concentrations shall be arranged so that all the fish are killed within a day in the highest concentration used and no deaths occur in the lowest concentration in the period of the test. A partial kill in at least 2 intermediate concentrations should be obtained within the test period. For some substances, a wide range of concentrations may be required to fulfil this conditions and for others a closer spacing of concentrations may be necessary.

The remaining flask, the control, shall be similarly filled with dilution water only, or dilution water and solvent only, and shall also be included in the test series; if more than one fish dies in this flask, the test shall be invalidated and shall be repeated.

When the contents of the flasks reach a temperature of $23.5 \pm 1°C$ introduce 10 fish into each. The fish shall be randomly selected from the stock population at individual fork lengths between 25 mm and 35 mm. The fish shall not be fed during the test period of 96 hours.

Set the apparatus to replace the test solutions at a rate of at least 25 litres per day, either continuously or by additions at short intervals. At this replacement rate, the dissolved oxygen content of incoming test solutions should be sufficient to meet the needs of the test fish without further aeration in the test flask; the dissolved oxygen content of the outgoing test solution should be greater than 70% of the air saturation value. The replacement solution shall be at the test temperature before it is added to the test flask.

Wherever possible chemical analysis of the concentration of the test substance shall be carried out, initially at regular intervals, and at least once per day on the overflow from each of the test flasks in order to measure the concentrations present. In addition, daily measurements shall be made of the pH value concentration of dissolved oxygen, and temperature of the overflow of each test flask.

Observe the fish in each test flask at fixed intervals, e.g., after at least 3 hours and after 6, 12, 24, 48 and 96 hours from the start of the test. Record the number of dead fish in each test flask. Any dead fish shall be removed from the flasks.

8.1.4 *Expression of results*

Plot the number of deaths at a specific time against the logarithm of the concentration as in Fig. 52. It would be desirable but not essential to use a probability (or probit) scale for the cumulative percentage mortality at different times. Interpolate from the graph the concentration that kills 5 fish

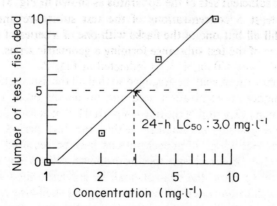

Fig. 52. Number of deaths of fish after 24 hours plotted against concentration of test substance

under the test conditions.   For the purpose of this test, this can be taken as the LC_{50}.

The report of the test shall contain the following information:

(*a*) The specification of the test substance and the method of preparing the test solution.

(*b*) All chemical, biological, and physical data pertaining to the test.

(*c*) The LC_{50} values for 24, 48, and 96 hours.   Although not essential for the purpose of the test, estimates of the 95% confidence limits of LC_{50} values could be made from the data above if a probability scale is used.

(*d*) Any unusual reactions by the fish under test and any visible external effects produced by the test substance.

(*e*) A reference to this book.

A specimen form for presenting data is given on pages 224 and 225.

8 . 1 . 5   *Interpretation and application of results*

The test procedure outlined above represents the minimum requirement for obtaining reproducible results for a wide range of substances likely to be screened for their toxicity to fish.   It should be stressed again, however, that the data obtained can only be used to place substances in an approximate order of acute toxicity: they cannot be used alone for the preparation of water quality objectives.

Laale (*218*) has reviewed the literature on the use of zebra fish in fisheries research.

8 . 2   Static screening test using zebra fish *(Brachydanio rerio)*[a]

The objective of the test is the determination of the concentration of a chemical that kills 50% of a sample of zebra fish in a 96-h test under defined conditions.

8 . 2 . 1   *Materials*

8 . 2 . 1 . 1   *Dilution water (see section* 8 . 1 . 1 . 1)

The water must have a pH of 7.8 $\pm$ 0.2 and a hardness of 100 mg·l^{-1} as $CaCO_3$.   It must be aerated immediately before use so that a dissolved oxygen concentration of at least 90% of the air saturation value (ASV) is achieved.

---

[a] Based on a procedure discussed by ISO (*185*).

8.2.1.2 *Apparatus*

- Test aquaria of at least 5 litres capacity, held at $23.5 \pm 1°C$.
- Stock aquaria held at $23.5 \pm 1°C$.

8.2.1.3 *Laboratory conditions*

Laboratories for the preparation of solutions and their storage, for the maintenance of fish stocks, and for the general preparation and performance of tests should be free of toxic dusts or vapours.

8.2.2 *Species used and its pretest maintenance*

Zebra fish of 30 ± 5 mm length are used, taken at random from a batch held for 14 days under the environmental conditions of the test and under the lighting conditions used in rearing the fish. The fish must be disease-free and fed normally until 24 hours before the start of the test.

8.2.3 *Test procedures*

8.2.3.1 *Preparation of solutions*

Stock solutions are obtained by dissolving a given weight of the test material in a given volume of dilution water (see section 8.1.1.1).

8.2.3.2 *Preliminary test*

From the stock solution, decimal dilutions are prepared using previously aerated dilution water (section 8.1.1.1), so that an adequate range of concentrations is covered, e.g., 1, 0.1, 0.01, 0.001, and 0.0001 $mg \cdot l^{-1}$. To each of 6 test aquaria (section 8.2.1.2), add either 5 litres of previously aerated dilution water (section 8.1.1.1) (the control) or 5 litres of one of the test concentrations.

Five fish are placed in each vessel. After 24 h the dissolved oxygen concentration in all vessels is measured, the number of dead fish in each vessel is counted, and the two concentrations bracketing a mortality of 50% are noted.

8.2.3.3 *Definitive test*

Into 7 test aquaria are added either 10 litres of previously aerated dilution water (control vessel) or 10 litres of concentrations of the test material. Alternatively, two 5-litre vessels can be used for each concentration and the control. The concentrations are chosen after the preliminary test data have

Specimen Form for Recording Results of Screening Test using Brachydanio rerio

Date: Sample: Sample No.:

Operator:

Concentration of Stock Solution:

Method of preparation of Stock Solution:

Flask No. (expected concentration of test material)	Flask (mg·l⁻¹)			Time (h)					Mean (range)
		3	6	12	24	48	96		
	(1) No. of dead fish								
	(2) Conc. measured (mg·l⁻¹)								
	(3) Temp. (°C)								
	(4) pH								
	(5) DO (mg·l⁻¹)								
	(6) Other information								

repeat for all test concentrations
(minimum: 5)

Control ($0\ \mathrm{mg\cdot l^{-1}}$)						
(1) No. of dead fish						
(2) Solvent conc. ($\mathrm{mg\cdot l^{-1}}$) (if applicable)						
(3) Temp. (°C)						
(4) pH						
(5) DO ($\mathrm{mg\cdot l^{-1}}$)						
(6) Other information						

$24\ \mathrm{h}\ LC_{50}$ .... $48\ \mathrm{h}\ LC_{50}$ .... $96\ \mathrm{h}\ LC_{50}$ ....

Size of fish:

Chemical analyses:

been inspected so that a range of concentrations is established from the highest not causing mortality to the lowest causing 100% mortality. It is desirable to obtain 3 or 4 concentrations causing mortalities between 10% and 90%. (The method illustrated in Fig. 45 may be used to determine the necessary geometric series of concentrations).

Ten fish are placed in each 10-litre vessel or 5 in each 5-litre vessel. After 24 h, the dissolved oxygen concentration in each vessel is measured, the control and test solutions are replaced and, after 96 h, the number of dead fish in each vessel is recorded.

Where practicable, each concentration of the test solutions should be analysed at the beginning and end of each test.

8.2.4   *Expression of results*

The percentage mortality for each concentration is plotted on a probit scale against concentration on a logarithmic scale. Only mortalities from 10% to 90% are plotted and a line is fitted to the points to estimate the 96-h LC_{50} (see section 2.7.1.2.1).

The results may be considered valid if

(*a*) the dissolved oxygen concentration measured at the end of every 24-h period is at least 70% of the air saturation value;

(*b*) no control fish die; and

(*c*) concentrations of test material remain preferably within 50% of the initial nominal values.

8.2.5   *Interpretation and application of results*

Although this static test is included in this Manual, note should be taken of the criticism of the validity of results of static tests as set out in section 2.2. The above test is applicable only to substances of low volatility that are readily soluble in water and have a low demand for dissolved oxygen and a low tendency to be absorbed to the test vessels or to be absorbed by the test fish.

8.3   The Carter bottle test

8.3.1   *Materials*

• Glass container, capacity 1–3 litres, capable of being entirely filled with the water to be tested

• Dissolved-oxygen meter

• Constant-temperature ($\pm 1°C$) water bath.

8.3.2   *Species used and their pretest maintenance*

Fingerling trout, about 100 mm fork-length and 11 g live weight, are used because in a 1-litre container a result should be obtained in one working day.   Other species and sizes of fish may be used, provided that the size of the test vessel is altered accordingly.

8.3.3   *Test procedures*

This test (*186*) is amenable to field as well as laboratory use.   An effluent or polluted river sample is placed in two containers, and the oxygen concentration in each is determined with a dissolved-oxygen meter.   One container is sealed so that no air is trapped.   Into the other container, one or more small fish are placed and the vessel is sealed, again without trapping air.   Both containers are placed in the constant-temperature water bath.   Immediately the last fish has died from the combined effects of asphyxiation and any toxicants in the water, the oxygen concentration in both vessels is again measured.   In the fish-free water, the fall in concentration of dissolved oxygen is a measure of the biochemical oxygen demand of the water; in the test with fish, their respiratory demand supplements the BOD and can be obtained by subtraction.

The results may be compared with those using fish in uncontaminated water, when, in principle, the final concentration of dissolved oxygen should be lower than that in contaminated water, since the fish would have died from asphyxiation alone.   In order to make this comparison, the volume of water, weight of fish, initial concentration of dissolved oxygen, and temperature should be as similar as can be conveniently arranged because the final dissolved oxygen concentration depends in part on the rate of oxygen removal from the water.   It is useful to carry out the tests in such a manner that the fish are equally stressed in each test.

The material may be tested in several different dilutions.

8.3.4   *Expression of results*

The results are expressed as the terminal, residual concentration of dissolved oxygen in each of the containers.

8.3.5   *Interpretation and application of results*

The results can be used to examine temporal and spatial changes in water quality.   In this way, the variability in the toxicity of a given effluent can be assessed, or the most toxic discharge to a river can be identified, both before and after dilution in the river.   The higher the final dissolved oxygen concentration, the more acutely toxic is the test material.

It should be noted that results obtained with this method are not necessarily comparable with those obtained under constant concentrations of dissolved oxygen and with periodic or continuous replacement of the test solution.

Comparisons of results obtained using the Carter bottle test with those obtained by toxicity tests in which an LC_{50} was defined have been published in (*170*) & (*219*), the former using the brown trout (*Salmo trutta*) and the harlequin (*Rasbora heteromorpha*), the latter a marine fish, *Ambassis safgha*.

The particular value of the Carter bottle test is that it is an inexpensive method for easily carrying out extensive surveys of water quality, especially where undiluted samples are not sufficiently toxic to kill a substantial proportion of a test batch of fish within 24 h in test solutions in which the dissolved oxygen concentration is maintained close to the air saturation value.

8.4   Screening tests using *Daphnia magna*[a]

8.4.1   *Materials*

8.4.1.1   *Dilution water*

The dilution water consists of dechlorinated tap water, groundwater, distilled water, or deionized water, to which suitable quantities of chemicals have been added to give a hardness of 250 ± 25 mg·l^{-1} (expressed as $CaCO_3$) and a pH of 7.8 ± 0.4.

The dissolved oxygen concentration must be above 80% of the air saturation value using aeration if necessary. Leave the dilution water to stabilize for 48 h. Check the pH of the water immediately before use and adjust if necessary using a concentrated hydrochloric acid or sodium hydroxide solution. The dilution water should ensure the survival of the *Daphnia* for at least 24 h and should not contain toxic concentrations of substances.

8.4.1.2   *Reagents and apparatus*

- Standard toxic agent: potassium dichromate ($K_2Cr_2O_7$) analytical grade
- Dissolved-oxygen meter
- Flat-bottomed glass test tubes (18 × 180 or 20 × 200 mm), calibrated at 8 and 10 ml, or 50-ml beakers
- Pipettes with smoothed openings, having an internal diameter of approximately 1 mm at the end
- Settling apparatus.

---

[a] Based on a procedure discussed by ISO (*185*).

Biological Examination 229

8.4.1.3 *Special precautions for sample handling*

Glass or new polyethylene bottles should be used for the collection, transport, and storage of waters to be tested for toxicity. The water should be tested as soon as possible, and no later than 6 h after collection, unless special precautions are taken, e.g., cooling or freezing. No preservatives must be added. Settling of the sample, if required, should be done before freezing.

In the case of chemical substances a stock solution will be prepared using the dilution water (see section 8.4.1.1).

8.4.1.4 *Laboratory conditions*

Preparation and storage of dilution water and all subsequent stages of the test must be carried out in the absence of vapours or dusts toxic to *Daphnia*. The temperature of the test medium must be $20 \pm 2°C$.

8.4.2 *Species used and its pretest maintenance*

Daphnia magna Straus 1820 (Crustacea, Cladocera), third generation at least, obtained by acyclical parthenogenesis under breeding conditions described in sections 8.4.2.1–8.4.2.3 and between 6 h and 48 h old must be used for the test.

The *Daphnia* can be obtained on application to the Institut National de Recherche Chimique Appliqée, Postbox 1, 91710, Vert-le-Petit, France.

Culture methods should yield populations that show a sensitivity to potassium dichromate within the limits set by the definitive test (see section 8.4.3.3), as compared with the preliminary test (see section 8.4.3.2). Examples of two suitable techniques are described in sections 8.4.2.1 and 8.4.2.2.

8.4.2.1 *Culture technique 1*

(a) *Principle*

Daphnia grow and reproduce by parthenogenesis in water enriched with microorganisms, illuminated and maintained at a constant temperature.

(b) *Materials*

• Round evaporating dishes, approximately 220 mm in diameter

• Normally lighted room at $20 \pm 3°C$

• Various sieves, including those having 560-μm and 800-μm square mesh, (plastic or stainless steel)

(c) Chemicals

• Breeding water: dechlorinated tap water or groundwater that satisfies the conditions laid down in section 8.4.1.1

• Pesticide-free fertile soil

• Glucose—analytical grade

• Meat extract (as used for bacteriology)

(d) Procedure

Add 200 g of soil to 2 litres of breeding water (see section 8.4.2.1(c)). Filter the mixture through a 1-mm mesh sieve. Pour the filtrate into an evaporating dish. Stabilize for 72 h in the breeding room. Add a few dozen *Daphnia* to each vessel. Prepare a nutrient solution containing 0.75-g meat extract and 0.75 g of glucose in 50 ml of water and store in a refrigerator. Add 0.5 ml of the nutrient solution to the content of the breeding vessel every 2 days, increasing the dose to 2 ml a day when the number of young *Daphnia* increases. If the contents of the vessel remain turbid, the quantity of nutrient solution added must be decreased or gentle aeration used.

Algal growth on the walls of the vessel is useful and should not be removed unless excessive. To compensate for loss of water by evaporation, top up the contents of the breeding vessel with distilled water. Every other week replace one-third of the water of the breeding vessels with stabilized fresh breeding water.

After a few weeks, remove the soil to simplify periodical collection of the *Daphnia* with the two sieves placed on top of each other. The filtrate, which is poured back into the breeding vessel, contains the very small individuals. Adults are retained on the 800-μm sieve and washed back into the breeding vessel.

The young *Daphnia* retained on the 560-μm sieve are washed into a beaker using a minimal amount of dilution water (see section 8.4.1.1). Their age (6–48 h) is determined by the time between two consecutive collections.

A part of the content of the beaker is poured into a suitable container and used as *Daphnia* stock for the toxicity test (see section 8.4.3). The test must be done immediately after collection. When necessary some of the young *Daphnia* retained on the 560-μm sieve are washed back into the breeding vessel to renew the adult stock. A steady state of the culture should be obtained before the beginning of the toxicity test. To maintain this steady state sieving should be done at least once a week, even when no toxicity tests are performed over a prolonged period. A minimum of two collections with an interval of 2–3 days must be made before *Daphnia* are collected for a subsequent toxicity test.

8.4.2.2   *Culture technique 2*

Several 2-litre beakers are each filled with 2 litres of dechlorinated tap water (see section 8.4.2.1(c)), which has been aerated for 24 hours.

Some small individuals from a strain of *Daphnia* are put into the 2-litre beakers, followed by the addition of 40–50 ml of suspended algal feed (see section 8.4.2.3). Then the culture is stored at $20 \pm 3°C$ in daylight, avoiding direct sunlight.

In order to avoid aging the culture, it is poured every 2–3 days through a set of 3 sieves (36, 100, and 400 mesh per cm^2) to separate young and old *Daphnia* and renew the culturing liquid.

Most of the detritus will pass through the finest sieve. The *Daphnia* are then carefully poured into freshly prepared 2-litre beakers and fed with algae as above, i.e., old, middle-aged, and young *Daphnia* are put into different beakers in order to guarantee good production.

No more than about 200 old individuals must be kept in any one 2-litre beaker, otherwise they will produce ephippia and stop reproduction. Beakers of larger volume may cause the same difficulties. Turbulence and temperature changes must also be avoided, as well as strong aeration, because the air bubbles may cause mechanical injury. It is important not to feed too much, otherwise lethal oxygen depletion may occur during the night; feeding is correct if after 12 hours there is no algal turbidity.

Young *Daphnia* aged between 6 h and 48 h obtained by sieving the culture twice at a time interval of 24 h are placed in a 2-litre beaker, fed with algae, and filtered again (400 mesh per cm^2) after a period of 6–24 h in order to concentrate them prior to the toxicity test.

Only about half of the young *Daphnia* are used for a test, the other half being used to replace old individuals in order to avoid an overaging of the culture.

8.4.2.3   *Culturing the algae*

Various green algae (e.g., *Chlorella* and *Scenedesmus*) are suitable as feed for *Daphnia*. They may be cultured by any appropriate method for algal mass production, but mass invasion by blue-green algae and diatoms is to be avoided. The following is a description of one method of culturing *Chlorella* in open beakers:

A nutrient solution is prepared by the addition to 10 litres of breeding water of 40 ml of a stock solution containing:

137.5 g $NaNO_3$
25.0 g $MgSO_4 . 7H_2O$
10.0 g KH_2PO_4
2.5 g citric acid, monohydrate
2.5 g ferric ammonium citrate

dissolved in 1 litre of distilled water and sterilized by heating to 100°C for half an hour.

1–2 litres of the nutrient solution are inoculated with *Chlorella vulgaris* and cultured at 20–22°C under artificial illumination (3000–4000 lx) comprising a 16-h day and an 8-h night. The beakers can be stored open under non-sterile conditions because of the very quick growth of *Chlorella*. Stir daily during the first 14 days to prevent permanent settling of the algae, after which the settled algae are separated by simple decantation. This reduces the culture volume which must be restored with fresh algae nutrient solution. The decanted, settled algae are used to feed the *Daphnia*.

8.4.3   Test procedures

8.4.3.1   Preparation of solutions

The test can be carried out in test tubes or beakers. A series of test tubes is filled with increasing quantities of the solutions or effluents to be tested and dilution water is added up to 8 ml. Five *Daphnia* are then placed in each tube and more dilution water added to make the volume up to 10 ml. The initial amounts of solution or effluent are chosen to ensure that when the volumes are diluted to 10 ml, the desired concentrations are achieved. A control tube containing only dilution water and 5 *Daphnia* is included in each test series.

When beakers are used, the procedure is the same, but the initial quantities of the solutions or effluents to be tested are diluted to 16 ml, 10 *Daphnia* are placed in each beaker, and the volume is made up to 20 ml with dilution water.

The test vessels are placed in the dark for 24 h at a temperature of $20 \pm 2°C$.

8.4.3.2   Preliminary test

A preliminary test is performed to determine the range of concentrations at which the definitive test (section 8.4.3.3) is carried out. To this end, use only a single series of geometrically spaced concentrations of test solution or effluent. An example is given in section 8.4.3.5.

After the 24-h exposure (see section 8.4.3.1), the numbers of motile *Daphnia* are recorded. Those that are not able to swim in the 15 seconds that follow a gentle agitation of the liquid are considered as immobilized, even if they can still move their antennae. The concentration range giving 0–100% immobilization is recorded.

Immediately after counting the immobilized *Daphnia*, the oxygen concentration is measured in the test tube or beaker that contains the lowest concentration at which all *Daphnia* have been immobilized.

8.4.3.3 *Definitive test*

This allows the determination of the percentages of *Daphnia* that are immobilized by different concentrations of the solution or effluent and the 24-h EC_{50} by interpolation.

The range of concentrations must be chosen in such a way that, if possible, 3 or 4 percentages of immobilization between 10% and 90% are obtained. Examples of choices of ranges of concentrations are given in section 8.4.3.5.

For each concentration, including a control, prepared as in section 8.4.3.1, there are 4 test tubes or 2 beakers each containing 5 or 10 *Daphnia* respectively. After a 24-h exposure, the numbers of motile *Daphnia* are determined and recorded as described in section 8.4.3.2 and the oxygen concentration is measured in the appropriate vessel.

8.4.3.4 *Check on the sensitivity of the* Daphnia *and conformity with the procedure*

The 24-h EC_{50} of potassium dichromate to *Daphnia* must be determined periodically in order to verify their sensitivity and the conformity with the procedure.

The check is performed in the manner described in section 8.4.3.3. When the 24-h EC_{50} falls outside the range of 0.9–1.5 mg $\cdot$ l^{-1}, it is advisable to verify that the test procedure has been strictly applied and the manner of breeding the *Daphnia* adhered to; if necessary a new strain of *Daphnia magna* should be obtained.

8.4.3.5 *Example of the determinations of the inhibition of motility of* Daphnia

The example is given for the procedure using test tubes and an effluent or a stock solution of a test chemical at 1000 mg $\cdot$ l^{-1}.

(a) *Results of preliminary test*

Concentration (%)	90	35	10	3.5	1	0.35	0.1	0.035	0.01
Motile *Daphnia* (No.)	0	0	0	0	0	5	5	5	5

The range of concentrations at which the definitive test is to be carried out is therefore 0.35–1%.

(b) *Results of definitive test*

Concentration	Motile *Daphnia* per tube				T	P
$(mg \cdot l^{-1})$	1	2	3	4		
0 (control)	5	5	5	5	20	0
3.5	5	5	3	4	17	15
4.8	2	3	4	3	12	40
6.2	3	1	1	2	7	65
8.0	1	0	2	1	4	80
10.0	0	1	0	0	1	95

T = total number of motile *Daphnia* at each concentration at the end of the test
P = percentage of immobilized *Daphnia* at each concentration.

(c) *Determination of the 24-h EC_{50} value*

The percentage immobilization of the *Daphnia* is plotted against the concentration on log-probit paper as shown in Fig. 53 and the 24-h EC_{50} read off.
For effluents the 24-h $EC_{50} = 5.4$ ml $\cdot l^{-1}$.
For the test chemical the 24-h $EC_{50} = 5.4$ mg $\cdot l^{-1}$.

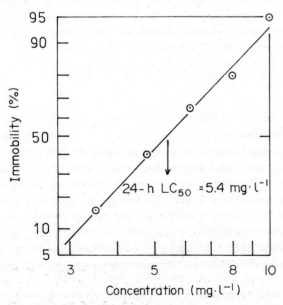

Fig. 53. Immobility of *Daphnia magna* in dilutions of a chemical

8.4.4 *Expression of results*

Record the percentages of immobilization between 10% and 90% on the basis of the total number of *Daphnia* per concentration as shown in section 8.4.3.5(b). These are then plotted as a function of the concentration on log-probit paper (Fig. 53). A straight line is fitted by eye and the 24-h EC_{50} is determined by the intersection of this line with the horizontal line corresponding to 50% immobilization.

The method of Litchfield & Wilcoxon (*167*) or a probit analysis can also be used to calculate the EC_{50} and the 95% confidence limits (*165*). If no reasonable estimation of the EC_{50} seems possible, the test must be repeated.

In cases where the log-probit plot is too steep to obtain sufficient points to apply statistical analysis, it may suffice to quote a concentration range within which the 24-h EC_{50} value falls. The results are valid if the following conditions are satisfied:

(*a*) the dissolved oxygen concentration at the end of the test (measured as indicated in section 8.4.3.2) is $\geqslant 2$ mg·l^{-1};

(*b*) The percentage immobilization of the controls is $\leqslant 10\%$; and

(*c*) the 24-h EC_{50} of the potassium dichromate falls between 0.9 and 1.5 mg·l^{-1}.

The 24-h EC_{50} and toxicity range are expressed as a dilution factor (ml·l^{-1}) in the case of effluents or solutions and in mg·l^{-1} in the case of chemical substances.

It must be stated that the procedure conforms to this standard. All the data used to obtain the 24-h EC_{50} value and to establish the validity of results, as well as the method of calculating the 24-h EC_{50} should be recorded.

Mention should be made of any unforeseen occurrences during the test that might have influenced the test result.

8.4.5 *Interpretation and application of results*

The sensitivity of organisms to the toxic properties of substances may vary considerably from one species to another, owing to differences in their metabolism and the nature of their habitat.

For example, the proposed method allows the acute effects of a substance on *Daphnia magna* to be assessed. The results obtained should not be extrapolated to other species or other responses.

For a more accurate prediction of the environmental toxicity of a substance or effluent a single test is not sufficient. To that end, further tests with species representative of different trophic levels (e.g., bacteria, algae, protozoa, metazoa) and metabolic characteristics are desirable.

Toxicity tests are conducted in the laboratory under arbitrarily defined conditions, which only imperfectly simulate environmental conditions. They enable interlaboratory comparisons to be made on possible toxic effects of substances or effluents obtained under such conditions. The results are intended to provide an approximate prediction of the acute toxic effects of substances or effluents in the environment, but many other environmental factors, e.g., the presence of organic and inorganic materials, hardness, pH, buffering capacity, may influence these effects. To obtain a closer approximation to the actual toxicity in a specific environmental situation, the result obtained by a standardized toxicity test should therefore be complemented by data determined in the field or under conditions including the period of exposure that simulate the environment more closely.

8.5   Screening tests using *Biomphalaria glabrata*[a]

8.5.1   *Materials*

8.5.1.1   *Dilution water*

The following formula for the dilution water, used also for the controls, is recommended:

$NaHCO_3$, 47 mg
$KHCO_3$, 10 mg
$CaCl_2 . 2H_2O$, 22 mg
$MgSO_4 . 7H_2O$, 31 mg
deionized tap water, 1000 ml

8.5.1.2   *Apparatus*

• Plastic vessels, approximately $500 \times 600 \times 100$ mm

• Pyrex beakers, low form, 1 litre and 100 ml

• Nylon net for covering 1-litre beakers

• Water bath $(22 \pm 1°C)$

• Low-power microscope

8.5.1.3   *Laboratory conditions*

Preparation and storage of dilution water and all stages of the experiment must occur in an atmosphere free of toxic dusts and vapours.

---

[a] Based on a test developed by O. Rivera (personal communication).

8.5.2   *Species used and its pretest maintenance*

The albino strain of *Biomphalaria glabrata* (*220*) can be used. Eggs and adults may be obtained from scientific institutions as well as from aquarist shops.

Adults are maintained in plastic vessels (approximately 500 × 600 × 100 mm) in dechlorinated tap water at a maximum density of 15 individuals per litre. The water is gently aerated, producing slight movement of the superficial layer. Temperature is maintained at about 22 ± 1°C all the year round. The light period is of 12 hours per day (about 1500 lux at the water surface). The water is renewed every 3 days and the egg-capsules attached to the container walls are collected. Containers are washed as needed with warm water without detergent. The snails feed on fresh lettuce leaves renewed every 2–3 days, an adult requiring about one leaf in 3 days.

To obtain individuals of the same age, all the egg-capsules attached to the walls of a container are collected 24 hours after the container has been cleaned. Damaged capsules are discarded and the rest are transferred to a Pyrex container (low form): 100 capsules per litre of water. On the fifth or sixth day, the water is renewed. Eggs generally hatch 8–10 days after laying. One day after hatching one lettuce leaf divided into 4–5 parts is placed in each container; the leaf should previously have been frozen and thawed to facilitate feeding by the young snails. After 3–4 days another leaf, treated in the same manner, is added. Ten days after hatching, the snails are transferred to the containers described for the adults and are reared using the same method.

During the first month of life the density will be of about 50 individuals per litre; in the second and third months about 25 individuals per litre.

8.5.3   *Test procedures*

8.5.3.1   *Acute test*

8.5.3.1.1   *Preparation of solutions*

Several 1-litre beakers, containing 1 litre of test solution and covered by a nylon net to prevent escape of the snails, are immersed in a water-bath maintained at 22 ± 1°C. Twenty adults of the same age (4 months) randomly selected are placed in each beaker. Every 24 hours the solutions are renewed. For each concentration of pollutant 3 experiments are carried out.

8.5.3.1.2   *Preliminary test*

A lower limit is determined as the highest concentration of pollutant producing after 72 hours a mortality[a] statistically equal to that of the

---

[a] Death is defined as the absence of any reaction to tactile stimulation of the snail tentacles.

control. An upper limit is determined as the lowest concentration producing 100% mortality after 72 hours. If no information exists on the sensitivity of the snail to a given pollutant (or mixture of pollutants), several tests may have to be carried out.

8.5.3.1.3 *Definitive test*

The definitive test, preferably using a continuous flow of solution, is carried out with 4 different concentrations (and a control) chosen between the upper and the lower limits determined as above. After 72 hours, the mortality in each concentration is noted and the data plotted against the logarithm of concentration; a best-fit line is then drawn and the LC_{50} interpolated.[a]

8.5.3.2 *10-day test with snail embryos*

Concentrations of pollutant that are lower than those taken for the acute test are used to examine responses that may be more relevant. The percentage viability[b] of embryos in test solutions is compared with that of the control. Both continuous flow and static methods may be used. The procedure is the same as that described in section 8.5.3.1, with the following modifications:

(*a*) Egg-capsules are collected within 6 hours after laying and are distributed randomly among the test vessels.

(*b*) Each egg-capsule is kept in a 100-ml Pyrex beaker (low form) and the total number of eggs recorded for each beaker.

(*c*) Five egg-capsules are exposed to each concentration.

(*d*) Test solutions and the control water must be renewed at 24-h intervals.

(*e*) Ten days after the beginning of the experiment, each capsule is examined to record the number of dead individuals. Examination of 100 egg-capsules requires no more than two hours using a low-powered microscope.

The treatment of the data is the same as that described in section 8.5.3.1.3.

This method can be improved by considering also the percentage of easily identified anomalous individuals.

---

[a] The LC_{50} is the concentration of pollutant producing 50% mortality in the treated group in excess of the percentage mortality of the control.

[b] Viability is expressed as the number of hatchings per 100 eggs.

8.5.3.3 "*Instantaneous*" *test* (*24 hours*)

The response measured in this test is the decrease in the rate of heart-beat in snails exposed to adverse conditions.

The test is carried out at 25°C on individuals 3 months old. For each concentration and the control, 5 randomly chosen individuals are kept for 24 hours in the solution to be tested, after which the heart rate of each snail (easily observed under a low-magnification dissection microscope) is determined at 20-minute intervals for 1 hour.

8.5.4 *Expression of results*

8.5.4.1 *Acute test*

The result reported is the 72-h median lethal concentration.

8.5.4.2 *10-day test with snail embryos*

The result may be reported as the 10-d median lethal concentration or the 10-d median effective concentration producing morphologically abnormal individuals.

8.5.4.3 "*Instantaneous*" *test* (*24 hours*)

The concentration reported is the lowest that causes a significant decrease in heart rate in test animals compared with the rate in the controls.

8.5.5 *Interpretation and application of results*

The 3 test methods outlined in section 8.5 may indicate the acute toxicity to a species of snail of water samples taken at different times or different places, as well as the effects of single or mixed test substances. The sensitivity of the species to heavy metals may be utilized in particular screening operations.

8.6 Screening test using an aquatic macrophyte, (*Elodea canadensis*)

8.6.1 *Materials*

8.6.1.1 *Dilution water*

An uncontaminated water to which the following volumes of nutrients, made up as $10 \text{ g} \cdot \text{l}^{-1}$ solutions in distilled water, are occasionally added:

KNO_3 solution, 10 ml
$MgSO_4$ solution, 1 ml
K_2PO_4 solution, 1 ml
$FeCl_3$ solution, 3 drops.

The mixture is made up to 1 litre with distilled water.

8.6.1.2   *Apparatus*

• Aquaria, minimum capacity 10 litres, containing unwashed sand to a depth of a few cm

• A source of diffuse illumination (e.g., a window avoiding direct sunlight).

8.6.1.3   *Laboratory conditions*

Laboratories for the preparation and performance of the tests should be free of toxic dusts and vapours.

8.6.2   *Species used and its pretest maintenance*

Laboratory cultures of Canadian pondweed (*Elodea canadensis*, also known as *Anacharis canadensis*) are prepared in the aquaria. After a suitable depth of the dilution water (see section 8.6.1.1) has been added to the sand layer and the water has stood for a few days, plants are planted in the sand and exposed to natural light. They require the occasional addition of nutrients (see section 8.6.1.1).

8.6.3   *Test procedures*

After the plants have been kept in the laboratory for several days, they can be used in tests. Lengths of stem (100 cm) are placed in a series of 100-ml graduated cylinders containing the chosen dilutions of the test material. The cylinders are placed in an illuminated box or beside a north-facing window to avoid direct sunlight. The state of the *Elodea* stem is inspected after 1, 2, 4, 8, 24, and 48 hours, and, if necessary after 5 days.

8.6.4   *Expression of results*

At a selected time the concentration causing half the test material to produce the chosen response (see section 3.3.1) is noted, or interpolated graphically, or calculated as indicated in section 2.7.

8.6.5   *Interpolation and application of results*

See sections 3.3 and 2.8.

8.7   Screening test using a terrestrial macrophyte, white mustard *(Sinapis alba)*

8.7.1   *Materials*

8.7.1.1   *Dilution water*

For the definitive procedure, distilled water is used; in the field, potable water from wells or the tap (which should be run for a few minutes before use) are suitable. If the water is chlorinated, boiling and subsequent aeration are necessary.

8.7.1.2 *Apparatus*

- Petri dishes 100 mm in diameter

- A 10-ml measuring cylinder

- A constant temperature cabinet adjusted to 20°C (not absolutely necessary)

- Silon or nylon textile fabrics cut off in the form of discs about 90 mm in diameter

- Seed of the cultivated white mustard (*Sinapis alba*)

- One pair of soft entomological forceps

- A millimetre-scale.

All glassware and textile fabrics must be sterilized before use.

8.7.1.3 *Laboratory conditions*

The preparations and performance of tests should be carried out in laboratories free of toxic dusts and vapours.

8.7.2 *Species used and its pretest maintenance*

The seed of the white mustard, *Sinapis alba*, may be stored in the dry until required.

8.7.3 *Test procedures*

The textile fabric must cover the bottom of the dish entirely. Thirty undamaged seeds of the plant are placed on the fabric in each dish (Fig. 54), preferably in a geometrical arrangement, 10 ml of the water for examination are added, and the dishes are covered and stored in the constant temperature cabinet; alternatively they can be left at room temperature (16–20°C), but in darkness. After 24 hours, the germinating seeds are counted and the length of the roots measured. After a further 24 hours, this procedure is repeated and the ratio of the length of the root to that of the hypocotyl calculated. (The hypocotyl is that part of the rootlet that lies under the cotyledons and shows no capillary fibres (root hairs) (Fig. 55). After another 24 hours the measurement is made again and the experiment concluded.

Fig. 54. Thirty mustard seeds arranged on fabric at start of toxicity test

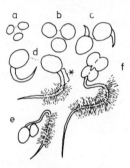

Fig. 55.   Mustard seeds during test. a—at start of test; b,c—on first day; d—second day; e,f—third day (end of test). * Indicates position of hypocotyl.

The toxicity test described above is the simplest procedure that can be applied easily. It is possible to refine this procedure, e.g., by including a large series of parallel tests, by determining the influence of ions leached from the glass and substrate, by determining the initial pH and its changes in the course of the experiment, or by determining the changes in the conductivity. The results of the bioassays/toxicity tests depend on various factors, several of which can be standardized. The influence of light must be excluded and the temperature maintained in the range 16–20°C. The seeds must be well ventilated using sterile air. Complete sterilization of all equipment should prevent interference by bacteria and moulds. The quality of the control water and the guaranteed success of germination of the cultivated seed are basic requirements for successful testing.

8.7.4   *Expression of results*

The average values of the root and hypocotyl measurements for the water examined and for the control water are tabulated, and the results can be expressed graphically.

8.7.5 *Interpretation and application of results*

If almost all seeds germinate in all dishes, including the control, and if the rootlets show a more rapid growth in comparison with that of the hypocotyls, the examined water can be considered as suitable for irrigation.

If the control seeds germinate and growth proceeds successfully, but the seeds in the test water do not germinate at all, or the rootlets grow slowly, the water cannot be applied for irrigation. In this case, the hypocotyls grow more rapidly than the rootlets, which may first turn brown, then black, and finally die.

If germination and growth are absent or poor, both in the water examined and in the control, the experiment should be repeated with new seed.

Growth in the test water can be more rapid than in the control, where the test water contains growth stimulating substances (e.g., phenols at concentrations of 20 mg·l^{-1} or more).

8.8 Screening tests using the algae *Selenastrum capricornutum*, *Microcystis aeruginosa* and *Anacystis cyanea*

8.8.1 *Materials*

8.8.1.1 *Dilution water and nutrient medium*

(a) *Synthetic algal nutrient medium.* This medium is prepared from stock solutions of macronutrients and micronutrients in glass-distilled water. Biological or reagent grade salts must be used. The final concentrations of the macronutrients are shown in the following table:

Compound	Concentration (mg·l^{-1})	Element	Concentration (mg·l^{-1})
NaNO$_3$	25.5	N	4.20
K$_2$HPO$_4$	1.04	P	0.186
MgCl$_2$	5.70	Mg	2.90
MgSO$_4$.7H$_2$O	14.7	S	1.91
CaCl$_2$.2H$_2$O	4.41	C	2.14
NaHCO$_3$	15.0	Ca	1.20
		Na	11.0
		K	0.469

Stock solutions of individual salts are made up at 1000 times the final concentrations.

For the micronutrients, the final concentrations are as shown below:

Compound	Concentration ($\mu g \cdot l^{-1}$)	Element	Concentration ($\mu \cdot l^{-1}$)
H_3BO_3	185	B	32.5
$MnCl_2$	264	Mn	115
$ZnCl_2$	32.7	Zn	15.7
$CoCl_2$	0.780	Co	0.354
$CuCl_2$	0.009	Cu	0.004
$Na_2MoO_4 . 2H_2O$	7.26	Mo	2.88
$FeCl_3$	96.0	Fe	33.1
$Na_2EDTA . 2H_2O$	300		

The trace metals, $FeCl_3$, and Na_2EDTA are combined in a single stock mixture at 1000 times the final concentrations.

To make up the medium, 1 ml of each of the stock solutions is added to glass-distilled water to give a final volume of 1 litre. The trace metal/$FeCl_3$/EDTA mixture is added after filtration.

(*b*) *Pretreatment of uninoculated reference medium.* For some work, sterilization may not be required for experiments to be carried out with freshly prepared culture media, since the recommended test species are not axenic and therefore contain an assortment of symbiotic and commensal (nonparasitic) bacteria. Stock cultures, however, should be maintained in previously sterilized culture media. It is recommended that uninoculated sterile reference medium be stored in the dark to avoid any possible photochemical changes.

(*c*) *Prolonged storage.* Reference medium for stock cultures may be filter-sterilized by suction through a membrane of 0.45 μm average pore size (previously washed by filtering at least 50 ml of distilled water). If necessary a glass-fibre prefilter, similarly washed, may be used. Alternatively the medium may be autoclaved at 1.1×10^5 Pa at 121°C. The length of time required for autoclaving will depend on the volume of the sample, e.g., 10 min $\cdot l^{-1}$ or at least 30 min. After the sample has been autoclaved and cooled, it should be allowed to equilibrate in an atmosphere of either air or carbon dioxide to restore the carbon dioxide lost during autoclaving and to lower the pH to its original value (it will generally rise on autoclaving).

8.8.1.2 *Apparatus*

(*a*) *Sampling and sample preparations*

- Water sampler, non-metallic

- Sample bottles, autoclavable (e.g., borosilicate glass, linear polyethylene, polycarbonate, or polypropylene).

- Membrane filter apparatus for use with 47-mm prefilter pads and a 0.45-μm average pore size filter

- Autoclave or pressure cooker capable of producing 1.1×10^5 Pa at 121°C.

(*b*) *Culturing and incubation*

- Erlenmeyer flasks of good quality borosilicate glass, such as Pyrex, should be used as culture vessels, the same brand of glass being used throughout. When trace nutrients are being studied, special glassware, such as Vycor, polycarbonate, or coated glassware should be used.

The flask size is not critical, but the surface-to-volume ratios are, because of carbon dioxide limitation. The recommended volumes are 40 ml, 60 ml, and 100 ml of sample in 125-ml, 250-ml, and 500-ml flasks, respectively.

It is desirable to number the test flasks permanently in order that any anomalous growth that appears to be related to specific flasks can be identified and those flasks eliminated from future tests.

Foam plugs, loose-fitting aluminium foil, or inverted beakers must be used as culture closures to permit good gas exchange (see section 8.8.3) and prevent contamination. Each laboratory must determine for each batch of closures purchased whether that batch has any significant effect on the maximum specific growth rate and the maximum standing crop.

There should be a constant-temperature room, or equivalent incubator, capable of providing temperature control at 24 ± 2°C.

Illumination should be cool white fluorescent lighting (see section 8.8.2). Several types of light meter may be used, but they must be calibrated against a standard light source or light meter.

(*c*) *General requirements*

- Analytical balance, capable of weighing 100 g with a precision of ± 0.1 mg

- Microscope, general purpose

- Microscope illuminator, general purpose

- Haemocytometer or plankton counting slide

- pH meter—scale of 0–14 pH units with accuracy of ± 0.1 pH unit

- Oven, dry heat capable of temperatures up to 120°C

- Centrifuge—capable of relative centrifugal force of at least $1000 \times g$

- Spectrophotometer or colorimeter—for use at 600–750 nm.

(d) *Optional requirements*

• Electronic cell counter

• Fluorometer

• Shaker table, capable of 100 oscillations per minute.

(e) *Storage of samples*

Although it is known that changes occur in water samples during storage, regardless of storage conditions, the extent and chemistry of these changes are not well defined; attempts should therefore be made to minimize the duration of storage. Changes in samples should be minimized by keeping samples cool, in the dark, using proper containers, and avoiding air spaces over the sample. Temporary storage prior to sample preparation should be in the dark at 0–4°C. If prolonged storage is anticipated the sample should be prepared first and then stored in the dark at 0–4°C.

8.8.2   *Species used and their pretest maintenance*

8.8.2.1   *Test algae*

Ankistrodesmus falcatus (Corda) Ralfs (*231*), *Selenastrum capricornutum* Printz, *Microcystis aeruginosa* Kütz. (*Anacystis cyanea* Drout and Daily), and *Anabaena flos-aquae* (Lyngb.) de Brébisson are the species recommended. A diatom has not yet been selected. If one is used add 10 mg of Si per litre (101.214 mg of Na_2SiO_3 . $9H_2O$ per litre) to the culture medium.

Test algae are available from the Culture Centre of Algae and Protozoa, 36 Storey's Way, Cambridge, CB3 0DT, England, or from the National Eutrophication Research Program, Pacific Northwest Water Laboratory, Environmental Protection Agency, 200 SW 35th Street, Corvallis, Oregon 97330, USA.

8.8.2.2   *Maintenance of stock cultures*

For preparation of the medium, see section 8.8.1.1.

Incubation conditions should be 24 ± 2°C under continuous, cool-white fluorescent lighting, 4304 lux $\pm 10\%$ for *S. capricornutum* and 2152 lux $\pm 10\%$ for *M. aeruginosa* and *A. flos-aquae*.

Upon receipt of the inoculum species, a portion should be transferred to the algal culture medium described in section 8.8.1.1 (e.g., 1 ml of inoculum in 100 ml of medium in a 500 ml Erlenmeyer flask). Subsequently, a new stock transfer using an aseptic technique should be made as the first operation upon opening a stock culture. The volume of the transfers is not critical so long as enough cells are included to overcome significant growth lag. A routine stock transfer schedule (weekly, for example) is recommended as a means of providing a continuing supply of healthy cells for experimental work.

Cultures 1–3 weeks old may be used as a source of inoculum. For *Selenastrum* a one-week incubation is often sufficient to provide enough cells. The blue-green species require a longer time to achieve maximum crop than does *Selenastrum*. This slower growth of the blue-green test species should be considered in planning for sufficient inoculum to carry out the required experimental work. Thus, 2–3 weeks may be required to provide inocula for tests with the blue-green species.

8.8.2.3 *Preparation of inoculum*

Cells from the stock culture should be centrifuged and the supernatant discarded. The sedimented cells should be resuspended in an appropriate volume of glass-distilled water containing 15 mg of $NaHCO_3$ per litre and again centrifuged. The sedimented algae should again be resuspended in the water-bicarbonate solution and used as the inoculum. The cells suspended in the bicarbonate solution should be counted and pipetted into the test water to give a starting cell concentration in the test waters as follows: *S. capricornutum* 10^3 cells per ml, *M. aeruginosa* and *A. flos-aquae* 50×10^3 cells per ml.

The volume of suspension transferred is calculated so that it results in the above concentrations in the test flasks (e.g., for *S. capricornutum* 5×10^5 cells per ml in the stock requires a 0.2-ml transfer per 100 ml of test water).

8.8.3 *Test procedures*

Temperature and illumination should be as during incubation (see section 8.8.2.2). Light intensity is measured adjacent to the flask at the liquid level.

8.8.3.1 *Preparation of glassware*

The recommended procedure is as follows: All cylinders, flasks, bottles, centrifuge tubes, and vials are washed with detergent or sodium carbonate and rinsed thoroughly with tap water. This is followed by a rinse with a 100 ml·l^{-1} solution of reagent quality hydrochloric acid; vials and centrifuge tubes are filled with the HCl solution and allowed to remain a few minutes; all larger containers are filled to about one-tenth capacity with HCl solution and swirled so that the entire inner surface is bathed. After the HCl rinse, the glassware is rinsed 5 times with tap water followed by 5 rinses with deionized water.

Pipettes are placed in 100 ml·1^{-1} HCl solution for 12 hours or longer and then rinsed at least 10 times with tap water in an automatic pipette washer, followed by a rinse with deionized water. Disposable pipettes may be used to eliminate the need for pipette washing and to minimize the possibility of contamination.

Cleaned glassware is dried at 105°C in an oven and is then stored either in closed cabinets or on open shelves with the tops covered with aluminium foil.

Before use, culture flasks are stoppered with plastic plugs or covered with aluminium foil and autoclaved at 1.1×10^5 Pa for 15 minutes. Following autoclaving the flasks are prerinsed with the type of medium to be used for subsequent culturing and placed for 20–30 minutes, inverted, on absorbent paper to drain.

8.8.3.2 *pH control*

In order to ensure the availability of carbon dioxide, the pH should be maintained below 8.5. This can be accomplished (1) by using optimum surface-to-volume ratios; (2) by continuously shaking the flask (approximately 100 oscillations per minute); (3) by ventilation with air or an air/carbon dioxide mixture; and, in extreme cases, (4) by bubbling an air/carbon dioxide mixture through the culture.

8.8.3.3 *Growth parameters*

Two parameters are used to describe the growth of a test alga in the EPA bottle test for algal assay (see section 3.4): maximum specific growth rate and maximum standing crop. Either or both of these parameters may be determined, depending on the objectives of any particular assay.

(a) *Maximum specific growth rate*

The maximum specific growth rate (μ_{max}) for an individual flask is the largest specific growth rate (μ) occurring at any time during incubation. The μ_{max} for a set of replicate flasks is determined by averaging μ_{max} of the individual flasks.

The specific growth rate, μ is defined by

$$\mu = \frac{\ln(X_2/X_1)}{t_2 - t_1} d^{-1}$$

where

X_2 = biomass concentration at the end of a selected time interval
X_1 = biomass concentration at the beginning of the selected time interval
$t_2 - t_1$ = elapsed time (in days) between selected determinations of biomass.

NOTE: If the biomass (dry weight) is determined indirectly, e.g., by cell counts, the specific growth rate may be computed directly from these determinations without conversion to biomass, provided the factor relating the indirect determination to biomass remains constant for the time period considered.

The maximum specific growth rate occurs during the logarithmic phase of growth—usually between day 0 and day 5—and therefore it is necessary that measurements of biomass be made at least daily during the first 5 days of incubation to determine this maximum rate. Indirect measurements of biomass, such as cell counts, will normally be required because of the difficulty in making accurate gravimetric measurements at low cell densities. The time at which measurements are made should be recorded for use in the computations.

The maximum specific growth rate (μ_{max}) can be determined by calculation using the above equation to determine the daily specific growth rate (μ) for each replicate flask and averaging the largest value for each flask. It may also be determined by preparing a semi-log plot of biomass concentration versus time for each replicate flask. Ideally, the exponential growth phase can be identified by 3 or 4 points that lie on a straight line on this plot. However, the data often deviate somewhat from a straight line, so a line judged to approximate most closely to the exponential growth phase is drawn on the plot. If it appears that the data describe two straight lines, the line of steeper slope should be used. A linear regression analysis of the data may also be used to determine the best fit straight line. The data points that most closely fit the line are selected and the specific growth rate (μ) is determined according to the equation given above.

The largest specific growth rates for the replicate flasks are averaged to obtain μ_{max}.

(b) *Maximum standing crop*

The maximum standing crop in any flask is defined as the maximum algal biomass achieved during incubation. For practical purposes, it may be assumed that the maximum standing crop has been achieved when the increase in biomass is less than 5% per day.

After the maximum standing crop has been achieved, the dry weight of algal biomass may be determined gravimetrically using either the aluminium-dish or filtration technique. If the biomass is determined indirectly, the results should be converted to an equivalent dry weight using appropriate conversion factors.

8.8.3.4 *Biomass monitoring*

Several methods may be used, but they must always be related to dry weight:

(a) Dry weight—gravimetrically.

(b) By direct microscopic counting (haemocytometer or plankton counting cell) or the use of an electronic particle counter. *A. flos-aquae*, which is filamentous, is not amenable to counting with an electronic particle counter. Microscopic counting can be facilitated by breaking up the algal filaments with a high-speed blender or by using ultrasonic vibration.

(c) Absorbance, using a spectrophotometer or colorimeter at a wavelength of 600–750 nm. In reporting the results, the instrument make or model, the geometry and path length of the cuvette, the wavelength used, and the equivalence to biomass should be reported.

(d) Chlorophyll—after extraction or by direct fluorometric determination. The equivalence between chlorophyll content and biomass should be reported.

(e) Total cell carbon—by carbon analyser. The equivalence between total cell carbon and biomass should be reported.

8.8.4 *Expression of results*

The fundamental measure used in the algal assay bottle test to describe algal growth is the amount of suspended solids (dry weight) produced and determined gravimetrically. Other biomass indicators, such as those indicated in section 8.8.3, may be used; however, all the results presented must include experimentally determined conversion factors between the indicator used and the dry weight of suspended solids. Several different biomass indicators should be used whenever possible because biomass indicators may respond differently to any given nutrient limiting conditions. The results of individual assays should be presented in the form of the maximum specific growth rate (with time of occurrence) and maximum standing crop (with time at which it was reached).

Both the maximum specific growth rate and the maximum standing crop should always be accompanied by an indication of the confidence interval. Calculation of the confidence interval for the average values presented should be based on at least 5 samples. Consequently, a minimum of 5 replicate determinations should be made the first time that an unfamiliar water source is analysed. The results of these 5 replicates are then used to calculate the standard deviation. Subsequent samples from the same source can be analysed using only 3 replicates and reported with the confidence interval established for that water source.

When replicate algal tests are conducted it is often observed that the growth rate in one of the flasks differs markedly from that in the remainder. Such outliers can be excluded from the results if they fall outside given limits. A laboratory should keep track of flasks that give outlying results and if they do so more than once they should not be used in further algal assays.

8.8.5 Interpretation and application of results

For the overall evaluation of assay results, it is necessary to determine (a) whether a given result is significant when considered as a laboratory measurement and (b) how well the laboratory assay results correlate with effects observed or predicted in the field. Several methods for determining statistical significance are available, such as the student's t-test and analysis of variance techniques. However, it must be emphasized that there is as yet no single method available for determining the significance of responses. The evaluation procedures must always be designed in accordance with the specific objectives of the experiments using valid statistical procedures.

8.9 Screening test using *Colpoda maupasi*

Where water containing toxic materials does not influence bacteria but affects the food intake of *Colpoda*, a receiving water influenced by toxicants will have a higher concentration of bacteria than uncontaminated receiving water at the end of the test period (*195*).

8.9.1 Materials

8.9.1.1 Physiological saline and nutrient media

- Physiological saline: Dissolve 8.5 g of NaCl (analytical reagent grade) in 1 litre of double-distilled water and sterilize 3 times for 60 min in a steam sterilizer on each of 3 successive days.

- Nutrient medium 1 (for bacterial stock cultures): Dissolve 10 g of meat extract, 10 g of peptone S (Brunnengräber) and 3 g of NaCl (analytical reagent grade) in 1 litre of distilled water. The solution is boiled for 1 h in a steam sterilizer and left to cool. After adding 10 ml of $1 \, mol \cdot l^{-1}$ NaOH and 30 g of agar–agar, it is boiled in the steam sterilizer until the agar–agar is dissolved. Still hot, the solution is adjusted to pH 7.3 by adding either $1 \, mol \cdot l^{-1}$ NaOH solution or $1 \, mol \cdot l^{-1}$ HCl, filtered through a fluted filter, and again boiled in the steam sterilizer for 1 hour. The final culture medium is distributed into Kapsenberg culture tubes in portions of 6 ml each. The culture tubes are then sterilized in a steam sterilizer for 30 min, after which the culture medium is allowed to solidify in the tubes, which are kept in an oblique position.

• Nutrient medium 2 (for preliminary bacterial cultures): Dissolve 10 g of peptone S (Brunnengräber) and 5 g of NaCl (analytical reagent grade) in 1 litre of distilled water. Boil the solution in the steam sterilizer for 1 h. Add 10 g of glucose to the hot solution, and filter through a duplex fluted filter. Distribute 100 ml of this solution into 300-ml Erlenmeyer flasks supplied with cotton stoppers and sterilize in the steam sterilizer for 30 min on each of 2 successive days.

8.9.1.2 *Apparatus*

See sections 8.9.2 and 8.9.3.

8.9.1.3 *Laboratory conditions*

Preparation and storage of all materials and the performance of all stages of the experiment must occur in an atmosphere free of toxic dusts and vapours.

8.9.2 *Species used and their pretest maintenance*

The protozoa can be obtained through the Culture Centre of Algae and Protozoa (see section 8.8.2.1).

8.9.2.1 *Stock cultures*

Stock cultures of *Escherichia coli* are kept available on nutrient medium 1. For maintenance of the bacterial strain, an adequate number of new cultures is prepared regularly, at intervals of about one month, by spreading cell material from a stock culture with a loop on culture medium 1 in Kapsenberg culture tubes. The freshly inoculated stock cultures are incubated at 37°C for 48 h and then stored at 25°C.

Stock cultures of the test strain of protozoa, *Colpoda maupasi*, are kept available in 10 ml of membrane-filtered, sterilized, uncontaminated dilution water, in 100-ml Erlenmeyer flasks stoppered with cotton-lined metal caps, at 27°C.

To maintain the test strain, an adequate number of new cultures is prepared regularly by inoculation; 2 ml of stock culture are mixed with 8 ml of membrane-filtered, sterilized, uncontaminated dilution water in 100-ml Erlenmeyer flasks stopped with cotton-lined metal caps. To each freshly prepared stock culture, 1 ml of bacterial suspension from the preliminary culture (below) is added and the cultures left at 27°C.

8.9.2.2 *Preliminary cultures*

An adequate number of preliminary cultures is prepared by inoculation (with a loop) of cell material from an *E. coli* stock culture into 100 ml of nutrient medium 2 (prepared as above). Following incubation at 37°C for 24 h, the cell suspensions of all preliminary cultures are centrifuged at 6000 r. min^{-1} (about 800 g) for 20 min. After decanting the nutrient solution, the centrifugate is suspended in physiological saline until the initial volume is reached again. This suspension is again centrifuged and decanted. The centrifugate is taken up by a volume of membrane-filtered, sterilized, uncontaminated dilution water; the volume of this suspension should be equal to one-tenth of the initial volume. The turbidity equivalent of the cell suspension is determined by photoelectric measurement of the extinction of the monochromatic radiation at 436 nm in the turbidimeter.

On the basis of this value, the final turbidity equivalent is adjusted to about 2000 mg of silica per litre by diluting the cell suspension with membrane-filtered, uncontaminated dilution water.

Preparation of preliminary cultures of *Colpoda maupasi* is as described for stock cultures (section 8.9.2.1). After culturing at 27°C for 48 h, the preliminary cultures are used for inoculation of the test cultures.

8.9.3 *Test procedures*

Prior to preparation of test cultures, the pH value of the sample to be examined and of the corresponding, uncontaminated, freshly sampled dilution water is determined.

Then, the pH value of 500 ml of the sample is adjusted to that of the dilution water using hydrochloric acid or sodium hydroxide solution. The acid or base concentration should be selected so as to keep the volume to be added as low as possible; the receiving water should have a pH value of about 7.5. The sample is filtered under nitrogen pressure (maximum 15×10^5 Pa) through membrane filters in a pressure filtering apparatus. The membrane-filtered dilution water is sterilized in the steam sterilizer for 30 min, to eliminate other protozoa.

From the sample and the dilution water prepared as described, 2 series of dilutions, with varying volume ratios are prepared. These dilutions ultimately contain 1 part by volume of sample in 2, 4, 8, 16, 32, 64, 100, 200, 400, and 800 parts by volume of mixture (sample plus dilution water). One of these parallel series serves as the *test dilution series*, the other as the *reference dilution series*.

The flasks of the test series are made up to their nominal value of 10 ml by adding 1 ml of bacterial suspension from the preliminary culture (turbidity equivalent 2000 mg·l^{-1}) and 1 ml of the preliminary protozoan culture; the flasks of the reference series are completed by adding 1 ml of bacterial suspension from the preliminary culture and 1 ml of membrane-filtered, sterilized dilution water. To prepare controls 8 ml of membrane-filtered, sterilized dilution water and 1 ml of bacterial suspension from the preliminary culture are each placed in 20 100 ml Erlenmeyer flasks stoppered with cotton-lined metal caps. In addition, 1 ml each of the preliminary protozoan culture is placed in 10 of these flasks, (*test control* cultures); to the remaining 10 flasks, 1 ml each of membrane-filtered, sterilized receiving water is added (*reference control* cultures). All cultures, from the test, reference, test control, and reference control series are left at 27°C for a minimum of 20 h. Beginning at the end of this period and then at 1 h intervals, the turbidity equivalent of one of the test control cultures is determined by photoelectric measurement of the extinction of the monochromatic radiation at 436 nm. As soon as the turbidity equivalent of one of these cultures has decreased to that corresponding to 70 mg of silica per litre, the test period for all cultures is terminated; the turbidity equivalent of all cultures is then determined.

8.9.4   *Expression of results*

There will be a clear difference between the turbidity equivalents of the reference and test control cultures, as in the example shown in Table 23. It

Table 23. Turbidity equivalents in mg of silica per litre

Dilution ratio: effluent/(receiving water + effluent)	Reference control cultures I 200 Reference series	Test control cultures II 70 Test series	Difference: I–II 130 Difference I–II
1/64	200	70	130
1/32	200	70	130
1/16	200	70	130
1/8	200	90	*110*
1/4	200	150	50
1/2	250	200	50

will be seen that this difference begins to diminish when the dilution ratio reaches a value of 1/8, indicating that the concentration of effluent is sufficient to inhibit the food uptake of the protozoa *Colpoda maupasi*. This threshold concentration is reported as the biologically harmful concentration.

8.9.5   *Interpretation and application of results*

See section 2.8.

8.10   Screening test using *Paramecium caudatum* Ehrenberg

Paramecium caudatum may be found in polysaprobic and α-mesosaprobic waters. Various responses to the test material may be utilized, as outlined in section 3.5.

8.10.1   *Materials*

See sections 8.10.2 and 8.10.3.

8.10.2   *Species used and its pretest maintenance*

The protozoa can be obtained through the Culture Centre of Algae and Protozoa (see section 8.8.2.1).

Stock cultures of *Paramecium caudatum* Ehrenberg are maintained in closed 10–100-ml Erlenmeyer (or similar) flasks on hay infusion. The hay infusion is prepared by boiling 10 g of hay for 20 min in 1 litre of tap water. The infusion is filtered, diluted with another litre of sterile tap water and stored under sterile conditions. The *Paramecium* culture must be renewed after 3–4 weeks.

8.10.3   *Test procedure*

Dilutions of the substance and an uncontaminated water are placed in Petri dishes (90–100 mm in diameter) with 50–100 *Paramecium*, so that the total volume in each dish is 10 ml.

After 1, 2, 4, 8, 24 and 48 h, the behaviour, mortality, and any morphological changes are noted, using a binocular microscope (× 30 to × 50).

8.10.4   *Expression of results*

The 48-h EC_{50} is determined and the maximum harmless concentration expressed as the appropriate ratio of test water to dilution water.

8.10.5   *Interpretation and application of results*

See section 2.8.

8.11   Screening test using *Pseudomonas fluorescens*

Dissolved toxic components of wastewater may inhibit the capability of *Pseudomonas fluorescens* to convert glucose into organic acids. Thus, after a certain time, in a receiving water not influenced by wastes, the action of the bacteria will result in a *lower* pH value than that of a sample of wastewater containing dissolved toxic substances and kept under identical conditions. To enable a quantitative determination of the inhibition of acid formation by pH measurement, the pH value and acid consumption of the sample of wastewater has to be adjusted to the corresponding values in the receiving water before the test is started. The potential of a toxic effluent for causing biological damage is expressed by the ratio of the volume of effluent to the total volume of the receiving water plus effluent at the dilution whose pH at the end of the test period deviates least from that of the sample of the receiving water.

8.11.1   *Materials*

8.11.1.2   *Physiological saline and nutrient media*

• Physiological saline: see section 8.9.1.1.

• Sodium bicarbonate solution, 0.5 mol·l^{-1}: Dissolve 21 g of $NaHCO_3$ (analytical reagent grade) in 500 ml of uncontaminated dilution water; introduce carbon dioxide through a fritted glass plate to adjust the pH value to 7.5.

• Stock solution: Dissolve 10 g of D($+$)-glucose (specified as suitable for bacteriological use) in 100 ml of uncontaminated dilution water. Sterilize by filtration through a 0.2-μm membrane filter.

• Culture medium (for stock cultures): Dissolve 40 g of bacteriological peptone, 20 g of glycerol (analytical reagent grade), 3 g of K_2HPO_4, anhydrous (purest grade), and 3 g of $MgSO_4$.$7H_2O$ (analytical reagent grade) in 1 litre of distilled water. Adjust the pH of the solution to 7.2 by adding either 1 mol·l^{-1} NaOH or 1 mol·l^{-1} HCl. Heat the solution to boiling point to dissolve the agar and dispense the culture medium in 6-ml portions to 18-mm × 180-mm culture tubes. Then sterilize the culture tubes in a steam sterilizer for 30 min and place the tubes in an inclined position until the medium has solidified.

• Nutrient solution (for preliminary cultures): Dissolve in 1 l of double-distilled water, 20 g of D($+$)-glucose (for bacteriological use), 2 g of KNO_3 (analytical reagent grade), 1 g of K_2HPO_4, anhydrous (purest grade), 0.05 g of $MgSO_4$.$7H_2O$ (analytical reagent grade), and 0.5 g of NaCl (analytical reagent grade). Adjust to pH 7.2 with 1 mol·l^{-1} HCl. Distribute 100 ml of this solution into each of ten 300-ml Erlenmeyer flasks, stoppered with cotton-wool plugs, and sterilize for 30 min on each of two successive days.

8.11.2 *Species used and their pretest maintenance*

Stock cultures of the test strain, *Pseudomonas fluorescens*, are kept on culture medium in 18-mm × 180-mm culture tubes. For maintenance of the test strain, an adequate number of new cultures is prepared regularly, at monthly intervals, by spreading cell material from a stock culture with a loop on culture medium in culture tubes. The freshly inoculated stock cultures are incubated at 25°C for 96 h and then stored in a refrigerator.

Preliminary cultures are prepared by suspension of one stock culture in each of a number of 6-ml portions of sterilized nutrient solution. An adequate number of preliminary cultures is prepared by inoculation of 2 ml of this suspension into 100-ml portions of nutrient solution. After incubation at 25°C for 96 h, the cell suspensions of all the preliminary cultures are centrifuged at 6000 r. $\min^{-1}$ (about 800 g) for 20 min and the supernatant decanted; the pellet is then suspended to its original volume in physiological saline and again centrifuged and decanted. Finally, the pellet is resuspended in a volume of membrane-filtered uncontaminated receiving water equal to that of the initial volume.

The turbidity equivalent of the cell suspension is determined by photo-electric measurement of the extinction of the monochromatic radiation at 436 nm in the turbidimeter.

On the basis of this determination, the final turbidity equivalent is adjusted to match that of a suspension of 2000 mg of silica per litre by diluting the cell suspension with membrane-filtered, uncontaminated receiving water.

8.11.3 *Test procedures*

Prior to preparation of *test cultures*, the pH values of the effluent and of the corresponding, uncontaminated, freshly sampled, filtered receiving water are determined. Then, the pH value of 500 ml of the effluent is adjusted to that of the receiving water with the aid of hydrochloric acid or sodium hydroxide solution. The acid or base concentration should be selected so as to keep the volume to be added as low as possible; the receiving water should have a pH of about 7.5.

Subsequently, the effluent is filtered under nitrogen pressure (maximum 15×10^5 Pa) through membrane filters in a pressure-filtering apparatus. The acid consumption of the effluent prepared in this way and of the non-contaminated receiving water is determined. Following this, the acid consumption of effluent is adjusted to that of the receiving water, in accordance with the result of the partial test.

If the acid consumption of the effluent exceeds that of the receiving water, the effluent is diluted with distilled water until the acid consumption values for effluent and receiving water become identical, the volume of distilled water required for this purpose being calculated from the difference in acid consumption between the effluent and the receiving water.

Example: If the acid consumption of the effluent after adjustment of the pH value to that of the receiving water is 4.5 mmol·l⁻¹ and that of the receiving water is 3.0 mmol·l⁻¹, 1.5 parts by volume of distilled water are to be added to 3 parts by volume of effluent. If the acid consumption of the effluent is lower than that of the receiving water, a freshly prepared sodium bicarbonate solution is added until the acid consumption values for the receiving water and the effluent become identical.

The volume of sodium bicarbonate solution required is calculated from the difference between the acid consumption of the receiving water and effluent and that of the sodium bicarbonate solution.

Example: If the acid consumption of the receiving water is 3 mmol·l⁻¹, and that of the effluent after adjustment of the pH value to that of the receiving water is 2 mmol·l⁻¹, then since a 0.5 mol·l⁻¹ sodium bicarbonate solution contains 500 mmol·l⁻¹, 1 part by volume of sodium bicarbonate solution is to be added to 498 parts by volume of effluent.

The effluent diluted in this way by the addition of distilled water or of sodium bicarbonate solution is diluted further with filtered receiving water to obtain a whole-number ratio between the volume of effluent and that of effluent plus dilution water.

Example:

(a) Predilution of effluent for adjustment of acid consumption to that of receiving water: 3 parts by volume of effluent diluted with 1.5 parts by volume of distilled water will result in a volume ratio between effluent and prediluted effluent of 1 to 1.5.

(b) Further dilution of this prediluted effluent using receiving water to obtain a whole-number dilution ratio: 4.5 parts by volume of prediluted effluent and 1.5 parts by volume of receiving water will result in a volume ratio between effluent and prediluted effluent of 1 to 2.

Subsequent measurements are performed to check whether the pH value and acid consumption of the prediluted effluent sample are identical with those for uncontaminated receiving water.

From the effluent prepared as described and the receiving water, a series of dilutions having varying volume ratios is made, taking into account the above-mentioned dilution ratio of the effluent.

These dilutions contain 1 part by volume of effluent in 2, 4, 8, 16, 32, 64, 100, 200, 400, and 800 parts by volume of diluted effluent (effluent plus receiving water). However, in preparing the test series of dilutions, the volume of diluent receiving water added to each of the culture tubes should be smaller by 2 ml than the amount calculated from the respective dilution ratio of effluent to receiving water; to begin with, each of the culture tubes should receive only 8 ml of culture medium.

Example: A nominal dilution of 1 to 4 corresponds to 2.5 ml effluent plus 7.5 ml of diluent receiving water, but the actual volumes used in preparing the medium are 2.5 ml of effluent and 5.5 ml of diluent receiving water.

To keep the volume of the medium in the culture tubes constant at the nominal value of 10 ml, additions of 1 ml of stock solution and 1 ml of bacterial suspension from the preliminary culture (turbidity equivalent 2000 mg of kieselguhr per litre) are necessary. At the same time, *control cultures* are prepared to verify that the reaction of the bacteria conforms to the appropriate biological standard, and to establish the period (in hours) required by the bacteria to reduce the pH value of the non-contaminated receiving water from its initial value to 6.0. For this purpose, 8 ml of receiving water, 1 ml of stock solution, and 1 ml of bacterial suspension from the preliminary culture are placed in each culture tube.

All samples (test and control cultures) are left unstoppered. They should be kept at 25°C for at least 16 h. After this period the pH value is determined in successive intervals of one hour using one of the control cultures each time. As soon as a pH value of 6.0 is reached in one of the control tubes, the reaction time for the test cultures is also terminated. For confirmation, the pH value is measured in the latter as well.

8.11.4 *Expression of results*

For determination of the biologically harmful effect of an effluent, it is diluted with different volumes of receiving water and the lowest concentration that, at the end of the test period, still has a pH value higher than 6.0 is selected. In the example shown in Table 24, this concentration (dilution ratio) is seen to be 1/16. This threshold concentration is reported as the minimum concentration of effluent that exhibits an inhibiting effect on the capacity of *Pseudomonas fluorescens* to convert glucose into acid.

Table 24. pH at the end of the test period related to dilution ratio

Dilution ratio: (effluent)/(effluent + receiving water)	pH value
1/64	6.0
1/32	6.0
1/16	*6.3*
1/8	6.5
1/4	7.0
1/2	7.5

8.11.5 *Interpretation and application of results*

See sections 3.6 and 2.8.

8.12 A laboratory-scale ecosystem test[a]

8.12.1 *Materials*

An unchlorinated water; salinity and dissolved solids content to be recorded.

---

[a] Based on a procedure described in (202).

Five aquaria are filled to a depth of 300–350 mm with 200 litres of water overlying 30–50 mm of bottom material obtained from a eutrophic field site. The temperature of the water should be maintained at about 20°C.

8.12.2 *Species used and their pretest maintenance*

Cultured algae (*Scenedesmus*, or another member of the Chlorophyceae) are introduced into the aquaria (1 ml per aquarium), together with filamentous algae and the following macrophytes: *Lemna gibba, Elodea nuttallii*, a *Potamogeton* (preferably *P. crispus*), and *Glycera maxima*. Other species may be added if available. The plants should be thoroughly cleaned before being placed in the aquaria and should initially cover 10–20% of the surface and 30–40% of the bottom materials; *Lemna gibba* should not be allowed to exceed 20% of the surface area during the experiment.

Into each aquarium, 20 roach (*Rutilus rutilus*) and 12 (4 male and 8 female) guppies (*Lebistes reticulatus*) are placed; they may be sparingly fed at regular intervals with commercially available dry fish food of the flake type.

The prepared aquaria should stand in an enclosed area, preferably a greenhouse, for one month before the test material is added.

8.12.3 *Test procedures*

The recommended dosages are then applied to 3 of the 5 aquaria which are then covered.

8.12.4 *Expression of results*

The following data should be collected, taking a herbicide as an example:

(*a*) *Herbicidal effect*
Initial fresh weight of the plants
Initial dry weight of the same volume of plants
Weekly estimate of the coverage of the sediment by submersible plants
Percentage of the surface covered by the floating plants
Dry weight of all vegetation after 4 months.

(*b*) *Persistence of herbicide*
A toxicity test is used to monitor herbicide residues in the water after 1 h and at intervals of 1, 3, 7, 15, 30, 60, and 120 d after application.

(*c*) *Accumulation*
Six roach are removed from each aquarium 2 and 4 months after herbicide application and residue analyses are conducted on muscle and whole-body samples.

(*d*) *Effect on fish*

Survival of roach is recorded; the number and weight of guppies is determined 4 months after herbicide application.

(*e*) *Effect on plankton*

The concentration of phytoplankton (assessed either by chlorophyll analysis or cell-counts per volume of water) is established 1 and 3 weeks before herbicide application and 1 week, 3 weeks, 2 months, and 4 months after application. At the same time, zooplankton estimates are made (number of organisms per volume of water).

A further series of tests and field trials may be required before the risks involved in the use of a herbicide can be fully evaluated.

REFERENCES

1. KOLKWITZ, R. Plankton and seston. *Ber. dtsch. bot. Ges.*, **30**: 334–346 (1912).

2. SCHWOERBEL, J. Methoden der Hydrobiologie, Stuttgart, Kosmos, 1966.

3. RAZUMOV, A. S. Mikrobialnyj plankton vody [Microbial plankton of water]. *Trud. vses. gidrobiol. Obšč.*, **12**: 1–60 (1962).

4. DAUBNER, I. Mikrobiologie des Wassers, Berlin, Akademie-Verlag, 1972.

5. DAUBNER, I. & PETER, H. Membranfilter in der Mikrobiologie des Wassers, Berlin, Walter de Gruyter, 1974.

6. LUMPKINS, E. D. & ARVESON, J. S. Improved technique for staining bacteria on membrane filters. *Appl. Microbiol.*, **16**: 433 (1968).

7. FJERDINGSTAD, E. Sulfur bacteria, Philadelphia, American Society for Testing and Materials, 1979 (ASTM Special Technical Publication 650).

8. RODINA, A. G. Methods in aquatic microbiology, Baltimore, University Park Press, 1972.

9. SLÁDEČEK, V., OTTOVÁ, V. & SLÁDEČKOVÁ, A. Návody k základnim pracim v technické hydrobiologii [Guide to basic procedures in technical hydrobiology], Praha, SNTL, 1973.

10. AMERICAN PUBLIC HEALTH ASSOCIATION, AMERICAN WATER WORKS ASSOCIATION & WATER POLLUTION CONTROL FEDERATION. Standard methods for the examination of water and wastewater, 13th ed., New York, APHA-AWWA-WPCF, 1971.

11. CLARKE, C. L. & BUMPUS, D. F. The plankton sampler—an instrument for quantitative plankton investigations, American Society of Limnology and Oceanography, 1950 (Special Publication No. 5), pp. 1–8.

12. WELCH, P. S. Limnological methods, New York, McGraw Hill, 1948.

13. LAGLER, K. F., BARDACH, J. E. & MILLER, R. R. Ichthyology. The study of fishes, New York, Wiley, 1962.

14. RICKER, W. E. Methods for the assessment of fish production in fresh water, Oxford, Blackwell, 1968 (IBP Handbook No. 3).

15. WHIPPLE, C. C., FAIR, G. M. & WHIPPLE, M. C. Microscopy of drinking water, 4th ed., New York, Wiley, 1927.

262   *Biological, Bacteriological and Virological Examination*

16. MOLLER PILLOT, H. W. M. Faunistische beoordeling van de verontreiniging in laaglandbeken [Faunistic assessment of pollution in low-land brooks], Tilburg, Pillot-Standaardboekhandel, 1971 [with English summary].

17. FJERDINGSTAD, E. Pollution of streams estimated by benthal phytomicroorganisms. I. A saprobic system based on communities of organisms and ecological factors. *Int. Rev. ges Hydrobiol.*, **49**: 63–131 (1964).

18. ELLIOT, J. M. & TULLET, P. A. Samplers for benthic invertebrates, Ambleside, Freshwater Biological Association, 1978 (Occasional Publication No. 4).

19. SURBER, W. E. Rainbow trout and bottom fauna production in one mile of stream. *Trans. Amer. Fish Soc.*, **66**: 192 (1937).

20. BARNES, H. Sampling bottom sediments and their fauna. *In*: Oceanography and marine biology, New York, Macmillan, 1959.

21. USINGER, R. L. & NEEDHAM, P. R. A drag-type riffle bottom sampler. *Progr. Fish.-Cult.*, **18**: 42–44 (1956).

22. ELLIOT, J. M. Some methods for the statistical analysis of samples of benthic invertebrates, Ambleside, Freshwater Biological Association, 1971 (Scientific Publication No. 25).

23. ELLIOTT, J. M. Methods for sampling invertebrate drift in running waters. *Ann. Limnol.*, **6** (2): 133–159 (1970).

24. KOLKWITZ, R. & MARSSON, M. Oekologie der pflanzlichen Saprobien. *Ber. dtsch. bot. Ges.*, **26A**: 505 (1908).

25. HASLAM, S. M. River plants, London, Cambridge University Press, 1977.

26. HASLAM, S. M., SINKER, C. A. & WOLSELEY, P. A. British water plants. *Field studies*, **4**: 243–351 (1975).

27. MCARTHUR, R. H. Fluctuations of animal populations as a measure of community stability. *Ecology*, **36**: 533–536 (1955).

28. ODUM, E. P. Fundamentals of ecology, 3rd ed., Philadelphia, Saunders, 1971.

29. LINDEMAN, R. L. The trophic-dynamic aspect of ecology. *Ecology*, **23**: 399–418 (1942).

30. CASPERS, H. & KARBE, L. Trophie und Saprobität als stoffwechseldynamischer Komplex. Gesichtspunkte für die Definition der Saprobitätsstufen. *Arch. Hydrobiol.*, **61**: 453–470 (1966).

31. ODUM, H. T. Primary production in flowing waters. *Limnol. Oceanogr.*, **1**: 102–117 (1956).

32. ODUM, H. T. Trophic structure and productivity of Silver Springs. *Ecol. Monogr.*, **27**: 55–112 (1957).

33. ODUM, H. T. & ODUM, E. P. Trophic structure and productivity of a windward coral reef community on Eniwetok Atoll. *Ecol. Monogr.*, **25**: 291–320 (1955).

34. OHLE, W. Bioactivity, production and energy utilization of lakes. *Limnol. Oceanogr.*, **1**: 139–149 (1956).

35. OHLE, W. Typologische Kennzeichnung der Gewässer auf Grund ihrer Bioaktivität. *Verh. int. Verein. theor. angew. Limnol.*, **13**: 196–211 (1958).

36. OHLE, W. Tagesrhythmus der Photosynthese von Planktonbiozönosen. *Verh. int. Verein. theor. angew. Limnol.*, **14**: 113–119 (1961).

37. PATTEN, B. C. An introduction to the cybernetics of the ecosystem. The trophic dynamic aspect. *Ecology*, **40**: 221–231 (1959).

38. DARNELL, R. M. Trophic spectrum of an estuarine community based on studies of Lake Ponchartrain, Louisiana. *Ecology*, **42**: 553–568 (1961).

39. DARNELL, R. M. Organic detritus in relation to secondary production in aquatic communities. *Verh. int. Verein. theor. angew. Limnol.*, **15**: 462–470 (1964).

40. DARNELL, R. M. Animal nutrition in relation to secondary production. *Amer. Zoologist*, **8**: 83–93 (1968).

41. NAUWERCK, A. Die Beziehungen zwischen Zooplankton und Phytoplankton im See Erken. *Symbol. bot. upsal.*, **17** (5): 1–163 (1963).

42. VAN NIEL, C. B. The bacterial photosyntheses and their importance for the general problem of photosynthesis. *Adv. Enzymol.*, **1**: 263–329 (1941).

43. GAARDER, T. & GRAN, H. H. Investigations of the production of plankton in the Oslo Fjord. *Rapp. P.-v. Réun. Cons. perm. int. Explor. Mer.*, **42**: 1–48 (1927).

44. STEEMAN-NIELSEN, E. The use of radioactive carbon (C-14) for measuring organic production in the sea. *J. Cons. perm. int. Explor. Mer.*, **18**: 117–140 (1952).

45. VOLLENWEIDER, R. A. A manual on methods for measuring primary production in aquatic environments, 2nd ed., Oxford, Blackwell, 1974 (IBP Handbook No. 12).

46. DOTY, M. S. & OGURI, M. The carbon-14-techniques for determining primary plankton productivity. *Publ. Staz. Zool. Napoli*, **31**, Suppl. (1959).

47. WOOD, K. G. Effect of beta spectrum on self-absorption of beta radiation from ^{14}C. *Int. J. appl. Rad. Isotopes*, **2**: 581–586 (1970).

48. WOOD, K. G. Self-absorption corrections for the ^{14}C-method with $BaCO_3$ for measurement of primary productivity. *Ecology*, **52**: 491–498 (1971).

49. HENDLER, R. W. Self-absorption correction for carbon-14. *Science*, **130**: 772–777.

50. SOROKIN, Y. I. & KADOTA, H. Techniques for the assessment of microbial production and decomposition in fresh waters, Oxford, Blackwell, 1972 (IBP Handbook No. 23).

51. JITTS, H. R. & SCOTT, B. D. The determination of zero thickness activity in Geiger counting of ^{14}C-solutions used in marine productivity studies. *Limnol. Oceanogr.*, **6**: 116–123 (1961).

52. SOROKIN, Y. I. The estimation of correction coefficients of the self-absorption of the radiation C-14 in the determinations of photosynthesis and chemosynthesis production in water basins. *Microbiologica*, **31**: 121 (1962).

53. STEEMAN-NIELSEN, E. On the determination of the activity in C-14 ampoules for measuring primary production. *Limnol. Oceanogr.*, **10**: 247–252 (1965).

54. EGLE, K. & SCHENK, W. Untersuchungen über die Reassimilation der Atmungs-kohlensäure bei der Photosynthese der Pflanzen. *Beitr. Biol. Pflanz.*, **29**: 75–105 (1952).

55. GOLDMAN, C. R. The use of absolute activity for eliminating serious errors in the measurement of primary productivity with ^{14}C. *J. Cons. perm. int. Explor. Mer.*, **32**: 172–179 (1968).

56. JITTS, H. R. The standardization and comparison of measurements of the ^{14}C-technique. *In:* Doty, M. S., ed. Proceedings of a Conference on Primary Productivity Measurements in Marine and Freshwater, Washington DC, US Atomic Energy Commission, 1963, pp. 114–120.

57. FINDENEGG, I. Standardisierung von $Na^{14}CO_3$-Lösungen für Produktions-messungen in Gewässern. *Wasser- u. Abwasserforschung*, **1**: 7 (1971).

58. LIND, O. T. & CAMPBELL, R. Comments on the use of liquid scintillation for routine determination of ^{14}C-activity in production studies. *Limnol. Oceanogr.*, **14**: 787–789 (1969).

59. SCHINDLER, D. W. & HOLMGREN, S. K. Primary production and phytoplankton in the Experimental Lake Area (ELA), northwestern Ontario, and other low carbonate waters, and a liquid scintillation method for determining ^{14}C-activity in photosynthesis. *J. Fish. Res. Board Can.*, **28**: 189–201 (1971).

60. SHAMOO, A. E. An improved toluene-based scintillator for estimating radioactivity in aqueous samples. *Analyt. Biochem.*, **39**: 311–318 (1971).

61. PUGH, P. R. Liquid scintillation counting of ^{14}C-diatom material on filter papers for use in productivity studies. *Limnol. Oceanogr.*, **15**: 652–655 (1970).

62. SCHINDLER, D. W. A liquid scintillation method for measuring carbon-14 uptake in photosynthesis. *Nature (Lond.)*, **211**: 844–845 (1966).

63. ARMSTRONG, F. A., WILLIAMS, P. M. & STRICKLAND, J. D. H. Photo-oxidation of organic matter in sea water by ultra-violet radiation: analytical and other applications. *Nature (Lond.)*, **211**: 481–483 (1966).

64. THOMAS, E. A. Nährstoffexperimente in Plankton-Test-Loten (1958). *Verh. int. Verein. Limnol.*, **15**: 342–351 (1964).

65. JOYET, G. Méthodes de travail biologique à l'aide d'isotopes radioactifs. Le dosage relatif dans les centres de tissus. *Bull. Acad. Suisse Sci. méd.*, **5** (5/6): 361–404 (1949).

66. DOTY, M. S. & OGURI, M. Selected features of the isotopic carbon primary productivity techniques. *Rapp. P.-v. Réun Cons. perm int. Explor. Mer.*, **144**: 47–55 (1958).

67. STEEMAN-NIELSEN, E. Experimental methods for measuring organic production in the sea. *Rapp. P.-v. Réun Cons. perm. int. Explor. Mer.*, **144**: 38–45 (1958).

68. SOROKIN, Y. I. Primary organic production in the Atlantic Ocean. *Hydrobiologia*, **22**: 306–316 (1963).

69. ARTHUR, C. R. & RIGLER, F. H. A possible source of error in the ^{14}C-method of measuring primary productivity. *Limnol. Oceanogr.*, **12**: 121–124 (1967).

70. SAKAMOTO, M. The chlorophyll amount in the euphotic zone in some Japanese lakes and its significance in the photosynthetic production of the phytoplankton community. *Bot. Mag. Tokyo*, **79**: 77–78 (1966).

71. TALLING, J. F. Photosynthesis under natural conditions. *Ann. Rev. Plant Physiol.*, **12**: 133–154 (1961).

72. GOLTERMAN, H. L. & CLYMO, R. S., ED. Methods for chemical analysis of fresh-waters, 2nd ed., Oxford, Blackwell, 1969 (IBP Handbook No. 8).

73. YENTSCH, C. S. & MENZEL, D. W. A method for the determination of phytoplankton chlorophyll and phaeophytin by fluorescence. *Deep-Sea Res.*, **10**: 221–231 (1963).

74. HOLM-HANSEN, O. ET AL. Fluorometric determination of chlorophyll. *J. Cons. perm. int. Explor. Mer.*, **30**: 3–15 (1965).

75. STRICKLAND, J. D. H. & PARSONS, T. R. A practical handbook of seawater analysis. *Bull. Fish Res. Board Can.*, **167**: 1–311 (1968).

76. TALLING, J. F. & DRIVER, D. Some problems in the estimation of chlorophyll *a* in phytoplankton. *In:* Doty, M. S., ed. Proceedings of a Conference on Primary Productivity Measurements in Marine and Freshwater, Washington DC, US Atomic Energy Commission, 1963, pp. 142–146.

77. MOSS, B. A spectrophotometric method for the estimation of percentage degradation of chlorophylls to pheopigments in extracts of algae. *Limnol. Oceanogr.*, **11**, 307–311 (1967).

78. MOSS, B. A note on the estimation of chlorophyll *a* in freshwater algal communities. *Limnol. Oceanogr.*, **12**: 340–342 (1967).

79. YENTSCH, C. S. The relationship between chlorophyll and photosynthetic carbon production with reference to the measurement of decomposition products of chloroplastic pigments. *Mem. Ist. Ital. Idriobiol.*, Suppl. 18, pp. 323–346 (1966).

80. LORENZEN, C. J. Determination of chlorophyll and pheopigments: spectrophotometric equations. *Limnol. Oceanogr.*, **12**: 343–346 (1967).

81. RICHARDS, F. A. & THOMPSON, T. G. The estimation and characterisation of plankton populations by pigment analyses. II. A spectrophotometric method for the estimation of plankton pigments. *J. mar. Res.*, **11**: 156–172 (1952).

82. PARSONS, T. R. & STRICKLAND, J. D. H. Discussion of spectrophotometric determination of marine plant pigments, with revised equations for ascertaining chlorophylls and carotenoids. *J. mar. Res.*, **21**: 155–163 (1963).

83. HOLM-HANSEN, O. & BOOTH, C. R. The measurement of adenosine triphosphate in the ocean and its ecological significance. *Limnol. Oceanogr.*, **11**: 510–519 (1966).

84. LEHNINGER, A. L. Bioenergetics, New York, Benjamin, 1965.

85. HAMILTON, R. D. & HOLM-HANSEN, O. Adenosine triphosphate content of marine bacteria. *Limnol. Oceanogr.*, **12**: 319–324 (1967).

86. HOLM-HANSEN, O. ATP-levels in algal cells as influenced by environmental conditions. *Plant Cell Physiol.*, **11**: 689–700 (1970).

87. COOMBS, J. ET AL. Studies on the biochemistry and fine structure of silica shell formation in diatoms. *Exp. Cell Res.*, **47**: 315–328 (1967).

88. STEWART, W. O. & ALEXANDER, G. Phosphorus availability and nitrogenase activity in aquatic blue-green algae. *Freshwater Biol.*, **1**: 389–404 (1971).

89. LEE, C. C. ET AL. Adenosine triphosphate in lake sediments (I, II). *Soil Sci. Soc. Amer. Proc.*, **35**: 82–96 (1971).

90. PATTERSON, J. W., BREZONIK, P. L. & PUTNAM, H. D. Measurement of significance of adenosine triphosphate in activated sludge. *Environm. Sci. Technol.*, **4**: 569–575 (1970).

91. MCELROY, W. D., SELIGER, H. H. & WHITE, E. H. Mechanism of bioluminescence, chemoluminescence and enzyme function in the oxidation of firefly luciferin. *Photochem. Photobiol.*, **10**: 153–170 (1969).

92. MCLEOD, N. H., CHAPPELLE, E. W. & CRAWFORD, A. M. ATP assay of terrestrial soils: a test of an exobiological experiment. *Nature (Lond.)*, **223**: 267–268 (1969).

93. HOLMS, W. H., HAMILTON, I. D. & ROBERTSON, A. G. The rate of turnover of the adenosine triphosphate pool of *Escherichia coli* growing aerobically in simple defined media. *Arch. Mikrobiol.*, **83**: 95–109 (1972).

94. TAL, R., DICKSTEIN, B. & SUHLMAN, F. G. *Experientia*, **20**: 652 (1964).

95. BREZONIK, P. L. & PATTERSON, J. W. Activated sludge ATP: effects of environmental stress. *J. san. Engng Div. Amer. Soc. Civil Engrs*, **97**: 813–824 (1971).

96. ST JOHN, J. B. Determination of ATP in *Chlorella* with the luciferine-luciferase enzyme system. *Analyt. Biochem.* **37**: 409–416 (1970).

97. ROMANENKO, W. I. & ROMANENKO, V. A. [The destruction of the organic matter in the bottom sediments of the Rybinsk reservoir]. *Trans. Inst. Inland Waters, Acad. Sci. USSR*, **19** (22): 24–31 (1969) (in Russian).

98. HAYES, F. R. & ANTHONY, E. H. Lake water and sediment: VI. The standing crop of bacteria in lake sediments and its place in the classification of lakes. *Limnol. Oceanogr.*, **4**: 299–315 (1959).

99. GAMBARJAN, On the method of estimation of intensity of the destruction of organic matter in the bottom sediments of the deep water bodies. *Mikrobiologia*, **31** (5): 895–898 (1962).

100. EDMONDSON, W. T. & WINBERG, G. G. A manual of methods for the assessment of secondary productivity in fresh waters, Oxford, Blackwell, 1971 (IBP Handbook No. 17).

101. LIEBMANN, H., ED. Müncher Beiträge zur Abwasser-, Fischerei- und Flussbiologie, vol. 19, München, Oldenbourg, 1971.

102. WUHRMANN, K. Stream purification. *In:* Mitchell, R., ed. Pollution microbiology, New York, Wiley-Interscience, 1972.

103. BRUJEWITSCH, S. W. Die Bestimmung der Produktion von organischer Substanz im Meer. Quoted by Alekin, O. A. Grundlagen der Wasserchemie, Leipzig, VEB Deutscher Verlag für Grundstoffindustrie, 1962.

104. MCCONNELL, W. J. Productivity relations in carbon microcosms. *Limnol. Oceanogr.*, **7**: 335–343 (1962).

105. MÜLLER, D. & KNÖPP, H. Zur Messung der Primärproduktion und der biogenen Belüftung in Fliessgewässern. 1. Ein Laborvergleich der Messmethoden. *Int. Rev. ges. Hydrobiol.*, **56**: 49–67 (1971).

106. KNÖPP, H. Untersuchungen über das Sauerstoff-Produktionspotential von Flussplankton. *Schweiz. Z. Hydrol.*, **22**: 152–166 (1960).

107. KNÖPP, H. Stoffwechseldynamische Untersuchungsverfahren für die biologische Wasseranalyse. *Int. Rev. ges. Hydrobiol.*, **53**: 409–441 (1968).

108. MENHINICK, E. F. A comparison of some species diversity indices applied to samples of field insects. *Ecology*, **45**: 859–861 (1964).

109. MARGALEF, R. Diversity of species in natural communities. *Publ. Inst. Biol. aplicada*, **9**: 5 (1951).

110. WILHM, J. L. & DORRIS, T. C. Biological parameters for water quality criteria. *BioScience*, **18**: 477–481 (1968).

111. SLÁDEČEK, V. Saprobic successions. *Verh. Int. Ver. Limnol.*, **18**, 896–902 (1972).

112. CASPERS, H. & KARBE, L. Vorschläge für eine saprobiologische Typisierung der Gewässer. *Int. Rev. ges. Hydrobiol.*, **52**: 145–162 (1967).

113. SLÁDEČEK, V. The ecological and physiological trends in the saprobiology. *Hydrobiologia*, **30**: 513–526 (1967).

114. PANTLE, R. & BUCK, H. Die biologische Überwachung der Gewässer und die Darstellung der Ergebnisse. *Gas- und Wasserfach*, **96**: 604 (1955).

115. SLÁDEČEK, V. The measures of saprobity. *Verh. Int. Ver. Limnol.*, **17**: 546–559 (1969).

116. HAMM, A. ET AL. Die Bewertung der Gewässergüte nach dem Sauerstoffhaus-halt im fliessenden Gewässer. *Wasserwirtschaft*, **55** (9): 20–23 (1965).

117. ZELINKA, M., MARVAN, P. & KUBÍČEK, F. [Surface water purity evaluation]. Opava, Slezsky ustav, 1959, p. 155 (in Czech).

118. DITTMAR, H. Reicht das bisherige Saprobiensystem für die Gütebeurteilung eines Gewässers aus? *Forsch. Berat.*, A (8): 263–265 (1959).

119. SLÁDEČEK, V. Zur Ermittlung des Indikations-Gewichtes in der Gewässer-untersuchung. *Arch. Hydrobiol.*, **60**: 241–243 (1964).

120. SLÁDEČEK, V. The reality of three British biotic indices. *Water Res.*, **7**: 995–1002 (1973).

121. SLÁDEČEK, V. & TUCEK, F. Relation of the saprobic index to BOD_5. *Water Res.*, **9**: 791–794 (1975).

122. KOLKWITZ, R. & MARSSON, M. Grundsätze für die biologische Beurteilung des Wassers nach seiner Flora und Fauna. *Mitt. Prüfungsanst. Wasserversorg. Abwasserbeseit.*, 1: 33–72 (1902).

123. KOLKWITZ, R & MARSSON, M. Ökologie der pflanzlichen Saprobien. *Ber. dtsch. bot. Ges.*, 26A: 505–515 (1908).

124. KOLKWITZ, R. & MARSSON, M. Ökologie der tierischen Saprobien. *Int. Rev. ges. Hydrobiol.*, 2: 126–152 (1909).

125. DRESSCHER, T. G. N. & VAN DER MARK, H. A simplified method for the biological assessment of the quality of fresh and slightly brackish water. *Hydrobiologia*, 48 (3): 199–201 (1976).

126. LIEBMANN, H. Handbuch der Frischwasser- und Abwasserbiologie, 2nd ed., vol. 1, Jena, 1962, p. 588.

127. ŽADIN, V. I. & RODINA, A. G. [Biological fundamentals of the water supply and wastewater treatment.] *In:* Pavlovskij & Žadin [Life in freshwaters of the USSR], vol. 3, Moskva-Leningrad, 1950, pp. 779–818 (in Russian).

128. KOLKWITZ, R. Pflanzenphysiologie, 3rd., Jena, 1935, p. 310.

129. KOLKWITZ, R. Ökologie der Saprobien. *Schr.-R. Ver. Wasser-, Boden- und Lufthygiene*, 4: 1–64 (1950).

130. ZELINKA, M. & MARVAN, P. Zur Präzisierung der biologischen Klassification der Reinheit fliessender Gewässer. *Arch. Hydrobiol.*, 57: 389–407 (1961).

131. FJERDINGSTAD, E. Pollution of streams estimated by benthal phytomicroorganisms. I. A saprobic system based on communities of organisms and ecological factors. *Int. Rev. ges. Hydrobiol.*, 49: 63–131 (1964).

132. FJERDINGSTAD, E. Taxonomy and saprobic valency of benthic phytomicro-organisms. *Int. Rev. ges. Hydrobiol.*, 50: 475–604 (1965).

133. SCHMITZ, W. Biologische und chemische Kriterien zur Beurteilung des Güterzustandes von Fliessgewässern. *Wasserwirtschaft in Baden-Württemberg*, pp. 92–103.

134. BESCH, W. K. Cartographie écologique des eaux courantes de Bade-Wurtemberg. *Ann. Hydrobiol.*, 1: 1–9 (1973).

135. ZIMMERMANN, P. Experimentelle Untersuchung über die ökologische Wirkung der Strömungsgeschwindigkeit auf die Lebensgemeinschaften des fliessenden Wassers. *Schweiz. Z. Hydrol.*, 23: 1–81 (1961).

136. WOODIWISS, F. S. The biological system of stream classification used by the Trent River Board. *Chem. Ind.*, 443–447 (1964).

137. TUFFERY, G. & VERNEAUX, J. Méthode de détermination de la qualité biologique des eaux courantes. *In:* Travaux de le Section technique de Pêche det de Pisciculture, C.E.R.A.F.E.F., Paris, Ministère de l'Agriculture, 1967.

138. CHANDLER, J. R. A biological approach to water quality management. *J. Water Poll. Contr. (Lond.)*, 69: 415–422 (1970).

139. SLÁDEČEK, V. Water quality system. *Verh. Int. Ver. Limnol.*, 16: 809–816 (1966).

140. COMMISSION FOR THE CARE OF WATER PURITY. [Frame instructions for sampling and unified analysis of water and wastes], Prague, Scientific and Technical Publishing House, 1950, pp. 1–23 (in Czech).

141. COUNCIL FOR MUTUAL ECONOMIC ASSISTANCE. Standard methods for water quality examination, 2nd ed., Moscow, CMEA, 1974 (in Russian).

268   Biological, Bacteriological and Virological Examination

142. ŠRÁMEK-HUŠEK, R. Die Rolle der Ciliantenanalyse bei der biologischen Kontrolle von Flussverunreinigungen. *Verh. Int. Ver. Limnol.*, **13**: 636–645 (1958).

143. ZELINKA, M. The nymphs of Ephemeroptera from the river basin of Moravice and their relation to the water purity. *Práce mor.-slez. akad. věd. přír.*, **25**: 181–200 (1953) (in Czech).

144. ROTHSCHEIN, J. Saprobiologische Charakteristik der fliessenden Gewässer im Einzugsgebiet des Flusses Bodrog auf der Basis von Zoobenthosanalysen. *Sci. Pap. Inst. Chem. Technol., Prague, Technol. Water*, **6** (2): 227–277 (1962).

145. FRIČ, A. Die Wirbelthiere Böhmens. *Arch. Landesdurchforsch. Böhmens*, **2** (4): 1–152 (1873).

146. HUET, M. La pollution des eaux courantes. *Bull. Centre Belge Doc. Eaux*, **15**: 68–76 (1952).

147. ILLIES, J. Versuch einer allgemeinen biozönotischen Gliederung der Fliessgewässer. *Int. Rev. ges. Hydrobiol.*, **46**: 205–213 (1961).

148. SLÁDEČEK, V. Zur biologischen Gliederung der höheren Saprobitätsstufen. *Arch. Hydrobiol.*, **58**: 103–121 (1961).

149. LANDNER, L. The eutrophication of lakes, Copenhagen, WHO Regional Office for Europe, 1976 (document ICP/CEP 210).

150. SLÁDEČEK, V. Relation of saprobic to trophic levels. *Verh. Int. Ver. Limnol.*, **20**: 1885–1889 (1978).

151. SLÁDEČEK, V. Zum Verhältnis Saprobität: Trophie. *Ergebn. Limnol.*, **9**: 79–93 (1977).

152. VOLLENWEIDER, R. A. Scientific fundamentals of the eutrophication of lakes and flowing water, with particular reference to nitrogen and phosphorus as factors in eutrophication. Technical Report on Water Management Research, OECD, DAS/CSI, No. 68.27, 1968, pp. 1–159.

153. DILLON, P. J. & RIGLER, F. H. The phosphorus-chlorophyll relationship in lakes. *Limnol. Oceanogr.*, **19**: 767–773 (1974).

154. Symposium: Experimental use of algal cultures in Limnology. *Mitt. Int. Ver. Limnol.*, **21**: (1978).

155. BUCH, K. Kolsyrejämvikten i Baltiskahavet [Carbonic acid equilibrium in the Baltic sea]. *Fennina*, **68** (5): 1–208 (1945).

156. Report on fish toxicity procedures. *In:* Alabaster, J. S. & Lloyd, R., ed. Water quality criteria for freshwater fish, Sevenoaks, Butterworth, 1980.

157. DUTHIE, J. R. The importance of sequential assessment in test programs for estimating hazard to aquatic life. *In:* Mayer, F. L. & Hamelink, J. L., ed. Aquatic toxicology and hazard evaluation, Philadelphia, American Society for Testing and Materials, 1977 (Publication STP 634), pp. 17–35.

158. AMERICAN PUBLIC HEALTH ASSOCIATION, AMERICAN WATER WORKS ASSOCIATION & WATER POLLUTION CONTROL FEDERATION. Standard methods for the examination of water and wastewater, 14th ed., New York, APHA-AWWA-WPCF, 1976.

159. BROWN, V. M. Concepts and outlooks in testing the toxicity of substances to fish. Bioassay techniques and environmental chemistry, Ann Arbor, Ann Arbor Science Publishers, 1973, pp. 73–95.

160. MARCHETTI, R. Biologia e tossicologia delle acque usate, Milano, Editrice Technica Artistica Scientifica, 1962.

161. SPRAGUE, J. B. Measurement of pollutant toxicity to fish—I. Bioassay methods for acute toxicity. *Water Res.*, **3**, 793–821 (1969).

162. STARK, G. T. C. An automatic dosing apparatus made with standard laboratory ware. *Lab. Pract.*, **16**, 594–595 (1967).

163. ABRAM, F. S. H. An automatic dosage apparatus. *Lab. Pract.*, **9**, 796–797 (1960).

164. GRENIER, F. A constant flow apparatus for toxicity experiments on fish. *J. Water Pollut. Contr. Fed.*, **32**, 1117–1119 (1960).

165. FINNEY, D. J. Probit analysis, 3rd ed., London & New York, Cambridge University Press, 1971.

166. LITCHFIELD, J. T. A method for rapid graphic solution of time per cent effect curves. *Pharmacol. exp. Ther.* **97**: 399–408 (1949).

167. LITCHFIELD, J. T. & WILCOXON, F. A simple method of evaluating dose-effect experiments. *Pharmacol. exp. Ther.*, **96**: 99–113 (1949).

168. HAMILTON, M. A., RUSSO, R. C. & THURSTON, R. V. Trimmed Spearman-Karber Method for estimating median lethal concentrations in toxicity bioassays. *Environm. Sci. Technol.*, **11** (7): 714–719 (1977).

169. LLOYD, R. & TOOBY, T. New terminology required for short-term static fish bioassays; LC (I) 50. *Bull. environm. Contam. Toxicol.*, **22** (1/2): 1–3 (1979).

170. ALABASTER, J. S. Testing the toxicity of effluents to fish. *Chem. Ind.*, 759–764 (1970).

171. BRETT, J. R. Swimming performance of sockeye salmon (*Oncorhynchus nerka*) in relation to fatigue time and temperature. *J. Fish Res. Board Can.*, **24**: 1731–1741 (1967).

172. SPRAGUE, J. B. Avoidance reactions of rainbow trout to zinc sulphate solutions. *Water Res.*, **2**: 367–372 (1968).

173. DIXON, W. J., ED. BMD biomedical computer programs. *In:* Automatic computation series No. 2, 2nd ed., Los Angeles, University of California Press, 1970.

174. BERKSON, J. A statistically precise and relatively simple method of estimating the bioassay with quantal response based on the logistic function. *J. Amer. Statist. Assoc.*, **48**: 565–599 (1953).

175. PICKERING, O. J. & VIGOR, W. N. The acute toxicity of zinc to eggs and fry of the fathead minnow. *Progr. Fish Cult.*, **27**: 153–157 (1965).

176. ALDERDICE, D. F. Factor combinations. Responses of marine poikilotherms to environmental factors acting in concert. *In:* Kinne, O., ed. Marine ecology, vol. 1, part 3, London, Wiley-Interscience, 1972, pp. 1659–1722.

177. TATTERSFIELD, F. & MORRIS, H. M. An apparatus for testing the toxic values of contact insecticides under controlled conditions. *Bull. ent. Res.*, **14**: 223–233 (1924).

178. KEULS, M. The use of the "studentized range" in connection with an analysis of variance. *Euphytica*, **1**: 112–122 (1952).

179. DUNCAN, D. B. Multiple range and multiple F tests. *Biometrics*, **11**: 1–42 (1955).

180. DUNNETT, C. W. A multiple comparison procedure for comparing several treatments with a control. *J. Amer. Statist. Assoc.*, **50**: 1096–1121 (1955).

181. ALABASTER, J. S. ET AL. An approach to the problem of pollution and fisheries. *Symp. zool. Soc. Lond.*, No. 29, 87–114 (1972).

182. MOUNT, D. I. & STEPHAN, C. A method for establishing acceptable toxicant limits for fish—Malathion and the butoxyethanol ester of 2,4-D. *Trans. Amer. Fish. Soc.*, **96** (2): 185–193 (1967).

183. MOUNT, D. I. Chronic toxicity of copper to fathead minnows, *Pimephales promelas* (Rafinesque). *Water Res.*, **2**: 215–223 (1968).

184. McKim, J. M. Evaluation tests with the early life stages of fish for predicting long-term toxicity. *J. Fish. Res. Board Can.*, **34**: 1148–1154 (1977).

185. International Organization for Standardization. Final (revised) proposal for screening chemicals and products for acute toxicity to freshwater fish, 1976 (ISO/TC 147/SC5/WG3 (sec-6)18).

186. Carter, L. Bioassay of trade wastes. *Nature (Lond.)*, **196**: 4861, 1304 (1962).

187. Buikema, A. L. J., Lee, D. R., & Cairns, J. jr. A screening bioassay using *Daphnia pulex* for refinery wastes discharged into freshwater. *J. Test Eval.*, **4** (2): 119–125 (1976).

188. Alabaster, J. S. Estimating the effect of herbicides on fish. European Weed Research Council Symposium, 1967.

189. Maki, A. W. Modifications of continuous-flow toxicity test methods for small aquatic organisms. *Progr. Fish Cult.*, **39** (4): 172–174 (1977).

190. Stebbing, A. R. D. The effects of low metal levels on a clonal hydroid. *J. Mar. Biol. Ass. U.K.*, **56**: 977–994 (1976).

191. Parker, C. Research Note—A rapid bioassay method for the detection of herbicides which inhibit photosynthesis. *Weed Res.*, **5**: 181–184 (1965).

192. US Environmental Protection Agency. Algal assay procedure: bottle test, Corvallis, Oregon, EPA—National Environmental Research Center, 1971.

193. Nordforsk Secretariat of Environmental Sciences. Algal assays in water pollution research. Proceedings from a Nordic Symposium, Oslo, 25–26 October 1972, Oslo, 1973.

194. Hall, R. H. An algal toxicity test used in the safety assessment of detergent components. Paper presented before the 36th Annual Meeting of the American Society of Limnology and Oceanography, Salt Lake City, Utah—June 12, 1973.

195. Bringmann, G. & Meinck, F. Wassertoxikologische Beurteilung von Industrieabwassern. *Ges.-Ing.*, **85**: 229–236 (1964).

196. Lee, G. F. Chemical aspects of bioassay techniques for establishing water quality criteria. *Water Res.*, **7**: 1525–46 (1973).

197. Sprague, J. B. The ABC's of pollutant bioassay using fish. *In:* Cairns, J. & Dickson, K. L., ed. Biological methods for the assessment of water quality, Philadelphia, American Society for Testing and Materials, 1973 (Publication ASTM STP 528), pp. 6–30.

198. Sprague, J. B. Measurement of pollutant toxicity to fish. III. Sublethal effects and "safe" concentrations. *Water Res.*, **5**: 245–66 (1971).

199. Ottaway, E. M. & Simkiss, K. "Instantaneous" growth rates of fish scales and their use in studies of fish populations. *J. Zool. Lond.*, **181**: 407–419 (1977).

200. US Environmental Protection Agency. Biological field and laboratory methods for measuring the quality of surface waters and effluents. EPA, 1973 (publication EPA-670/4-73-001).

201. Water quality criteria for European freshwater fish. Report on monohydric phenols and inland fisheries. Technical Paper No. 15 of the European Inland Fisheries Advisory Commission of the Food and Agriculture Organization of the United Nations, Rome, 1972.

202. Van Zon, J. C. J. & Zonderwijk, P. Bijdrage tot de normstelling t.a.v. het gebruik van herbiciden in water. [Contribution to standardization with regard to the use of herbicides in water]. Coördinatie-commissie Onkruidonderzoek Werkgroep Watergangen, 1974.

203. Hemens, J. & Warwick, R. J. The effects of fluoride on estuarine organisms. *Water Res.*, **6**: 1301–1308 (1972).

204. Warren, C. E. Biology and water pollution control, Philadelphia, Saunders, 1971.

205. OHIO RIVER VALLEY WATER SANITATION COMMISSION. Biological Water Quality Committee 24 hour bioassay. Orsanco, 1973.

206. UNITED KINGDOM, MINISTRY OF HOUSING AND LOCAL GOVERNMENT. Fish toxicity tests: Report of the Technical Committee, London, HM Stationery Office, 1969.

207. BESCH, VON W. K. ET AL. Warntest zum Nachweis akut toxischer Konzentrationen von Wasserinhaltsstoffen. *Arch. Hydrobiol.*, **74** (4): 551–765 (1974).

208. HALL, J. W. ET AL. A procedure for the detection of pollution by fish movements. *Biometrics*, **31** (1): 11–18 (1975).

209. WESTLAKE, G. F. ET AL. The use of fish to continuously monitor an industrial effluent, The Institute of Electrical and Electronics Engineers, Inc., 1976 (Annals No. 735 CH 1004-1 18-4).

210. POELS, C. L. M. Continuous automatic monitoring of surface water with fish. *J. Soc. Water Treatm. Exam.*, **24** (1): 46–56 (1974).

211. WARNER, R. E., PETERSEN, K. & BORGMAN, L. Behavioural pathology in fish: a quantitative study of sublethal pesticide toxication. *J. appl. Ecol.*, **3** (Suppl.): 223–247 (1966).

212. SPOOR, W. A., NEIHEISEL, T. W. & DRUMMOND, R. A. An electrode chamber for recording respiratory and other movements of free-swimming animals. *Trans. Amer. Fish. Soc.*, **100**: 22–28 (1971).

213. MILLER, W. F., SANDWELL, F. W. & GORTON, P. A. A monitoring chamber for trout behaviour and physiology. *In:* Amlaner, C. J. & Macdonald, D. W., ed. A handbook on biotelemetry and radio tracking, Oxford, Pergamon, 1979, pp. 307–311.

214. ALABASTER, J. S. & ABRAM, F. S. H. Estimating the toxicity of pesticides to fish. *Pest Articles and News Summaries, Section C*, **11**: 91–97 (1965).

215. AXELROD, H. R. Breeding aquarium fishes, Book 1. T. F. H. Publications, Inc., 1967.

216. NIIMI, A. J. & LAHAM, Q. N. Influence of breeding time interval on egg number, mortality and hatching of the zebra fish (*Brachydanio rerio*). *Can. J. Zool.*, **52**: 515–517 (1974).

217. MERTENS, J. Year-round controlled mass reproduction of the zebra fish. *Aquaculture*, **2**: 245–249 (1973).

218. LAALE, H. W. The biology and use of zebra fish *Brachydanio rerio* in fisheries research. A literature review. *J. Fish Biol.*, **10** (2): 121–173 (1977).

219. BALLARD, J. A. & OLIFF, W. D. A rapid method for measuring the acute toxicity of dissolved materials to marine fishes. *Water Res.*, **3**: 313–333 (1969).

220. NEWTON, W. L. The establishment of a strain of *Australorbis glabratus* which combines albinism and high susceptibility to infection with *Schistosoma mansoni*. *J. Parasitol.*, **41**: 526–528 (1955).

221. WALLEN, D. G. & GEEN, G. H. Loss of radioactivity during storage of ^{14}C-labelled phytoplankton on membrane filters. *J. Fish. Board Can.*, **25**: 2219–2224 (1968).

222. BRAY, G. A. A simple efficient liquid scintillator for counting aqueous solutions in a liquid scintillation counter. *Anal. Biochem.*, **1**: 279–285 (1960).

223. STEEMAN-NIELSEN, E. Experimental methods for measuring organic production in the sea. *Rapp. P.-v. Réun. Cons. perm. int. Explor. Mer.*, **144**: 38–45 (1957).

224. ZSCHEILE, F. P. A quantitative spectro-photoelectric analytical method applied to solutions of chlorophylls *a* and *b*. *J. phys. colloid. Chem.*, **38**: 95–102 (1934).

225. ZSCHEILE, F. P. An improved method for the purification of chlorophylls *a* and *b*; the quantitative measurement of their absorption spectra; evidence for the existence of a third component of chlorophyll. *Botan. Gaz.*, **95**: 529–562 (1934).

226. MacKinney, G. Criteria for purity of chlorophyll preparation. *J. biol. Chem.,* **132**: 91–109 (1940).

227. MacKinney, G. Absorption of light by chlorophyll solutions. *J. biol. Chem.,* **140**: 315–322 (1941).

228. Zscheile, F. P., Comar, C. L. & MacKinney, G. Interlaboratory comparison of absorption spectra by the photoelectric spectrophotometric method. Determinations on chlorophyll and Weigert's solutions. *Plant Physiol.,* **17**: 666–670 (1942).

229. Vernon, L. P. Spectrophotometric determinations of chlorophylls and phaeophytins in plant extracts. *Analyt. Chem.,* **32** (9): 1144–1150 (1960).

230. McElroy, W. D. The energy source for bioluminescence in an isolated system. *Proc. nat. Acad. Sci.* (*Wash*)., **33**: 342–346 (1947).

231. Breitig, G. & Von Tümpling, W., ed. Ausgewählte Methoden der Wasseruntersuchung, vol. 2: Biologische, Mikrobiologische und Toxikologische Methoden, Jena, Fischer, 1975.

CHAPTER 2

BACTERIOLOGICAL EXAMINATION

K. Ormerod,[a] G. J. Bonde[b] & K. K. Kristensen[c]

CONTENTS

[a] Head, Biological Laboratory Section, Norwegian Institute of Water Research, Oslo, Norway.
[b] Professor, Institute of Hygiene, University of Aarhus, Aarhus, Denmark.
[c] Lecturer, Veterinary Faculty for FAO Fellows and Scholars, Copenhagen, Denmark.

273

1. INTRODUCTION

The greatest dangers associated with water are due to direct and indirect contamination by the excrements of warm-blooded animals, including man. Human faeces contain 20–30% of undigested food residues, the remainder consisting of water and bacteria. In the healthy individual these bacteria consist of the normal inhabitants of the intestine, of which *Escherichia coli* is regarded as the most characteristic. The number of these organisms is of the order of 10^9 per g of faeces (*1*). In acute intestinal disease and in the carrier state, these inhabitants of the intestine may be replaced by pathogenic organisms. Usually the sick, convalescent, and chronic carriers form only a small portion of the community, and the excreta of any one person are suspended in a large volume of water. In the sewage from a cess pit or septic tank, however, the excreta are suspended in a very small volume of water and the number of pathogenic bacteria in the effluent may reach many millions per ml. A large proportion of epidemic outbreaks have been traced back to such effluents (*1*).

The greatest risk to human and animal health arises directly from the ingestion of pathogenic organisms in sewage-polluted water or from the consumption of food that has become contaminated by sewage or sewage-polluted water during growth or preparation. The possible hazards of bathing in sewage-contaminated water and of other recreational uses of water have been the subject of active discussion in many countries for several years. However, there are still great differences of opinion among health authorities with regard to establishing restrictions on recreational uses of water. One complicating factor is that the health hazards will depend upon which diseases are prevalent in the population in question; another difficulty is that the term "bathing" may not have the same significance as regards exposure time, total submergence, etc., in countries with warm climates as in countries with colder climates. Therefore, caution is required in extrapolating epidemiological findings from one country to another (*2*).

The bacteriology of the bottom sediment and the sand in the beach zone washed over by waves may be an important aspect in assessing the water quality of a lake, river, or estuarine area assigned for swimming, particularly where there is a great variability in the bacterial quality of the water (*3, 4*). Sediments may also prove to be of critical significance in waters used for cultivating shellfish (*3*).

The use of sewage-polluted water for irrigation of agricultural land and the use of sewage or sewage sludge as fertilizer have also been shown to be hazardous to human and animal health. The maximum permissible density of faecal indicator organisms or pathogens will here again be dependent on which diseases are prevalent in the population, as well as on the kinds of crop cultivated and how these products are prepared before eating. Thus, the same caution is required in the extrapolation of epidemiological findings as for recreational uses of water.

In sewage treatment the removal of organic matter is accompanied by the removal of faecal organisms. The total number of faecal organisms is thus diminished, but all the varieties originally present may still be found in the same proportions. After discharge to natural waters, the faecal organisms do not usually multiply, although exceptions have been reported. The faecal organisms are normally reduced in numbers, owing to exposure to light and low temperatures, to predation by water animals, to starvation through lack of nutriment, and to sedimentation. Survival of some pathogenic bacteria has, however, been shown to be favoured by water temperatures less than 10°C.

In fresh water, the time of survival of faecal bacteria may be measured in weeks, depending largely on the initial numbers discharged ; in sea water the period is measured in hours (*1*). Faecal bacteria may survive for long periods in sewage sludge, in marine and freshwater mud, and when adsorbed to water plants (*5*).

For routine control purposes the direct search for the presence of specific pathogenic agents in water is impracticable. Therefore, water bacteriologists have evolved simple and rapid tests for the detection of intestinal organisms that are easier to isolate and identify (e.g., coliform bacteria, faecal streptococci and anaerobic, sulfite-reducing spore-formers). The presence of such faecal bacteria in a water sample indicates that pathogens could be present. When designating reference methods for the detection and estimation of microorganisms indicative of faecal pollution, the main problem is to choose one method for each organism from all the more or less equally good methods in use in different countries today.

In the *WHO International Standards for Drinking-Water* (*6*), the chapter " Recommended methods for the detection and estimation of organisms indicative of pollution " recommends several methods for each indicator organism. The indicator organisms listed are coliform bacteria, *E. coli*, faecal streptococci, and anaerobic spore-forming organisms, and the methods recommended are some of those most commonly used in different countries. One of the reasons for this approach is that the quality criteria for drinking water in each country are based on the number of organisms detected by the specific method used in that country. Another reason is that it is always difficult to break old traditions.

In the field of water pollution control, another approach may be taken. When monitoring water courses for bacteria of faecal origin, the aim is not to be able to detect the few organisms that may have survived some treatment processes, but to give a reliable estimate of the concentration level of true faecal organisms. Thus, other techniques and methods than those chosen for drinking water control may be considered. A laboratory working in the field of water pollution control must also be prepared to perform bacteriological analyses on sewage, sewage sludge, beach sand, and sediment deposits as well as on water samples. The optimum choice of method would be one that could be applied to all the different types of sample and still be practical for routine use. The multiple-tube technique with most probable number (MPN) evaluation of the data is one such technique applicable to all these kinds of sample, and methods applying this technique have been developed for all the faecal indicator bacteria in question. The procedures are, however, demanding in both time and incubator space.

Another approach could be to combine membrane filter procedures—as used for filterable samples with low concentration of bacteria—with direct plating on the same or a similar culture medium, as used for samples with high concentration of bacteria. Methods applying this technique are also available for all the faecal indicator bacteria in question ; they are less demanding in incubator space and time and thus more practical for routine use than the multiple-tube methods, although often of less specificity in diagnosis.

The colony count methods for faecal coliform bacteria and faecal streptococci are of more recent date and not yet so widely used as the multiple-tube methods. For filterable water, the membrane filter methods offer such great practical advantages that it would be unrealistic to exclude them from the recommended methods. For this reason there are no recommended reference methods for faecal coliform bacteria or faecal streptococci. One multiple-tube method and one colony count method have been chosen as alternative methods for each of these indicator organisms, without allocating priority. The methods for faecal indicators recommended in this chapter were selected from among those commonly used in Europe, USA, and other parts of the world. A review and comparison study on media and methods in use for faecal indicators (7) was sent to experts in different countries, together with a questionnaire designed to ascertain their views on which methods could be used as reference methods. The selection of the recommended methods (8) was based on the answers to this questionnaire.

In manuals on standard methods for drinking water analysis, the recommended methods may change with each new edition because a more selective medium with a higher recovery rate has been developed. In water pollution control, it might be better to stick to methods already widely used and to concentrate on finding relationships between the bacterial levels determined by these methods and the possible health hazards in question. Although new methods should be considered when they represent scientific or practical improvements, one should bear in mind that changes in reference or standard methods may necessitate reconsideration of established bacterial density limits.

A method for the detection and estimation of microorganisms indicative of pollution with easily degradable organic matter is also included in this chapter. The use of other microbial indicators is briefly discussed, but no methods are described.

The pathogenic bacteria for which methods are given in this manual represent only those bacteria that are more likely to be of epidemiological significance. Often it may be a matter of interpretation whether one or another bacterium causes disease of epidemic or endemic significance. In this connexion, it must be mentioned that during the last few years *Yersinia enterocolitica* has been accepted as a bacterium of endemic or epidemic importance in relation to water. Parasites, too, may often be spread by water but good methods are still needed for their isolation and standardization.

The methods for isolation of pathogenic bacteria described in this book have been selected in accordance with the need for reliable, selective, and relatively simple methods. Two alternative methods for the determination of pathogenic bacteria are described. Where the results of comparative investigations were available, they have been used for the selection of the two alternative methods.

The increasing need for reuse of water has enlarged the number of pathogenic organisms that may need to be considered in any studies on the hygienic quality of water. Direct and indirect reuse of water—including reuse for drinking, recreation, the culture of fish, oysters, or algae, agriculture and industry—will be influenced by urbanization, population density, etc. Reuse for agricultural purposes (watering, irrigation) will increase in many countries and call for microbiological examination of the water used for edible crops.

New trends in aquaculture suggest that there will be an increasing use of treated sewage water for this purpose. Whenever treated sewage water or polluted surface water is used for the production of food or feeding stuffs, a microbiological examination of the water used is needed. Often disinfection will be necessary to obtain the quality of water recommended. These developments may cause situations where the indicator bacteria normally used in monitoring will not always bring to light the hygienic problems, but may have to be supplemented by extended monitoring, including that of selected pathogenic organisms.

In order to cover all the microbiological problems that may relate to water and the reuse of water, some notes on pathogenic agents that may be transmitted by water are given in section 6.2. A section on sampling equipment and methods (section 2) and a section on microbiological techniques (section 3) are also included in this chapter. The latter section also covers the mathematical background to the different techniques. This may be of help for choosing between MPN and colony count methods, especially when a certain precision is wanted. Presenting these techniques in a separate section will also minimize the need to repeat the details in all the methods described. In the descriptions of the methods, only the details of procedure specific to each method are included.

The section on statistical methods (section 4) is intended to give guidance on the treatment of bacteriological data and is not meant to be a "cookbook" applicable in all situations. Just as some basic training in bacteriology and virology is necessary to apply the methods described in the bacteriological and virological chapters, some knowledge of statistical methods and fundamental terms must be envisaged. A proper evaluation of the results obtained will, in most cases, require a statistical treatment, or at least an understanding of statistical principles.

The programmable desk computer can handle large amounts of data in a short time and compute basic parameters such as means, standard deviations, and correlation coefficients, but it cannot choose the right statistical model, which must be based upon a knowledge of distribution functions. In addition to the well known type I and type II errors, it is necessary to take account of errors due to a faulty model, for instance, the application of those computational techniques that are permissible only when the data follow a normal distribution.

2. SAMPLING FOR QUANTITATIVE ESTIMATION OF BACTERIAL POPULATIONS IN THE AQUATIC ENVIRONMENT

2.1 Sampling equipment

2.1.1 *Introduction*

A variety of equipment has been devised and described for collecting samples of both the water column and the bottom deposits. The type of apparatus used will, to a certain extent, be determined by the sampling location and conditions and also by the information sought as a result of the sampling.

In general, the collecting apparatus should meet the following requirements (*9*):

(*a*) It should be robust so as to withstand the rough handling normal on board ship and the high pressures to which it will be subjected at great depths.

(*b*) It should be capable of being sterilized, although it is not agreed that this is essential.

(*c*) It should be constructed of an inert material, i.e., it should not exert any bacteriostatic or bactericidal effect as can happen with some metals or certain types of rubber.

(*d*) It should be capable of collecting a sufficient volume of material for analysis.

2.1.2 *Equipment for sampling from taps*

For sampling from taps or with the aid of pumps, sampling bottles similar to those commonly used for potable water may be used. The bottle should have a capacity of a least 250 ml and be fitted with a large screw cap or a ground glass or sterilizable rubber stopper covered with thin aluminium foil. Silicone rubber liners, which will withstand repeated sterilization at 160°C or autoclaving at 121°C, should be used inside the screw cap.

Some metal or plastic screw caps are equipped with liners that produce toxic or bacteriostatic compounds on sterilization; these should not be used. Plastic sample bottles made of polypropylene may be autoclaved repeatedly. For those plastic bottles that distort on autoclaving, low-temperature ethylene oxide gas sterilization should be used. If sample bottles with glass stoppers are used, a strip of paper about 75 mm by 10 mm should be inserted between the stopper and the neck of the bottle before sterilization. This prevents jamming of the stopper and cracking of the glass on cooling. At least half the strip should be outside the bottle so that when the stopper is taken out of the bottle the paper can be removed without danger of the fingers coming into contact with the rim. The stopper and neck of the bottle should be covered with paper or aluminium foil.

2.1.3 *Equipment for sampling from shallow waters, surface water layers, sewage, and sewage sludge*

The same type of sampling bottle as described in section 2.1.2 may be used. To avoid contact by the hand with the water to be sampled and to facilitate sampling from steep banks, boats, etc., a metal string or a wooden pole may be fastened to the bottle neck. During sampling, the bottle is lowered into the water and the bottle neck held below the surface by means of this pole or string. A practical sampler of this type is shown in Fig. 1.

2.1.4 *Equipment for sampling from lakes and large rivers*

A number of instruments for aquatic sampling have been constructed and described in scientific books and journals. Some have mechanical devices for removing the stopper at the desired depth and replacing it when the vessel has filled with water. Other arrangements make use of glass tubes, which are broken off at the desired depth by a messenger-triggered device; in this way a water sample is drawn into the sterile collecting container.

Another type of sampler, which is the main type used for samples subjected to chemical analysis, is an open-ended metal cylinder, which closes after it reaches the required depth. This sampler has the advantages of being able to withstand high pressures (sampling of oceans and deep lakes) and of having a simple mechanism for closing a top and bottom lid. This

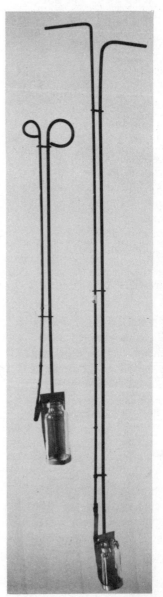

GENERAL DETAILS

SAMPLE BOTTLE IN
POSITION TO BE
LOWERED INTO WATER

SAMPLE BOTTLE IN POSITION
AND COLLECTING SAMPLE

SAMPLE BOTTLE IN
RETRIEVAL POSITION

ensures minimum disturbance of the water layer to be sampled and also makes it possible to take a sample of water of known dimensions at a known depth.

The use of this type of sampler has been criticized on the grounds that contamination of the water samples occurs by the carry down of bacteria from water layers above to subsequent depths in a profile of sampling series, and therefore the apparatus may not be suitable for bacteriological sampling. However, several investigators using this type of sampler in stratified lakes and in oceans (*9–13*) have not found this a problem. Another criticism is that the metal might have a bactericidal effect on the bacteria in the sample. Some investigators find that this is no problem, provided that the water sample is transferred to glass bottles immediately after reaching the surface (*13*), while others do not advocate the use of metal containers for sampling *sea water* for microbiological analysis. Examples of this type of sampler : The Nansen water sampler (brass), the Friedinger sampler (stainless steel), and the Ruttner sampler (made of glass or Plexiglass). The last-mentioned sampler is slightly different from the other two, having a closing mechanism that produces a turbulent flow-in to suction. The manufacturers of some of these samplers are given in ref. *9*.

Samplers with mechanical devices for removing the stopper at the desired depth and replacing it when the sample bottle is filled with water require two cables. One lowers the entire instrument, the second raises and lowers the stopper. Such samplers, however, can only be used successfully in relatively shallow water. At greater depths the cables often become twisted, and it is then impossible to open the bottle. An example of this type of sampler is given in the book by Rodina (*14*). Another simple type is the " rat-trap bottle " (*9*). For depths of up to 10 m, autoclaved, corked 500-ml medicinal flat bottles are screwed to a triggered rat- or mouse-trap so that when the trap is released, the cork jerks out of the bottle. When this is done under-water, the bottle fills with water and is automatically sealed by a second closure cork within the bottle, which floats up on the surface of the incoming water. When in use the bottles are clamped to a weighted support, lowered from the boat to the required depth and the rat-trap is released by a mes-senger. For depths of up to 15 m, more robust 500-ml blood plasma bottles may be fitted to similarly triggered rat-traps. These bottles can be sterilized, are inexpensive, and the sample is ready for examination without further transfer. Their main limitation is that the depth that can be sampled is restricted to 15 m or less by hydrostatic pressure. The rat-trap bottle is illustrated in Fig. 2.

A type of sampler based on the breaking of a glass tube by a messenger at the desired depth, resulting in the filling of a container, exists in a large number of variations. The containers may be made of glass or rubber, and even plastic bags are used. With some samplers, the filling of the container through the broken glass tube is dependent on the creation of a partial

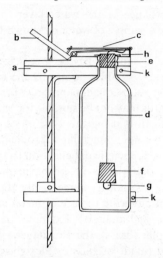

Fig. 2. The rat-trap bottle

a, rat-trap ; b, trigger platform ; c, trigger arm ; d, cord attached to upper greased bung, e, and to lower greased bung, f, which carries a glass weight, g, to ensure that it remains in the correct position to close the neck of the bottle ; h, anti-pressure pin to prevent bung, e, being forced into the bottle ; k, clamps for attaching apparatus to the cable.

vacuum inside the container as it cools after sterilization. The volume of water collected does not usually exceed half the capacity of such bottles. This disadvantage may be overcome by using a stopper with two glass tubes, one long and one short, leading into the bottle, and connecting these with rubber tubing to a short piece of glass tube, which in turn is broken by a messenger. Examples of this type of sampler : J-Z sampler, Mortimer sampler, Stolbunov-Ryabov sampler (plastic bag), the Sieburth sampler (compressed rubber bulb as container), and for sampling at great depths, the Isachenko sampler. All these samplers are described in detail in the books by Rodina (*14*) and by Collins et al. (*9*).

Since few of the samplers mentioned are sold commercially, arrangements must be made to have most of them specially made. Constructional details can be found in the literature cited. To show the general principles of the last-mentioned type of sampler, an illustration of a simple and inexpensive water sampler developed at the Norwegian Institute for Water Research (NIVA), for the sampling of rivers, lakes and fjords, is shown in Fig. 3 and 4. Any commercially available, wide-necked, sterilizable glass bottle from 300 ml to 1 litre capacity may be used as the sample bottle. Thick-walled, small-volume cylindrical bottles can be used at greater depths than thin-walled, large-volume bottles. Older types of thick-walled 300-ml Norwegian milk bottles have been used down to a depth of 250 m in lakes, and modern, thin-walled bottles of 500 ml size have been used successfully at depths of 100 m.

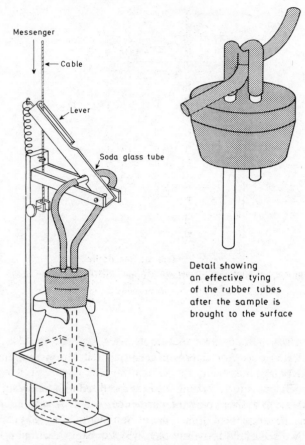

Messenger

Cable

Lever

Soda glass tube

Detail showing
an effective tying
of the rubber tubes
after the sample is
brought to the surface

Fig. 3. The NIVA sampler for shallow and deep water samples

Close-fitting stoppers of Neoprene or other sterilizable rubber must be especially made for the bottles (Fig. 4). The stoppers are made with two holes to take tubes of borosilicate glass. One of the tubes is long and intended for the inflowing water, the other is short and intended for letting the air out during filling. Care must be taken not to make the stopper too tight-fitting, otherwise it will be difficult to remove it without breaking the glass tubes when the sample is to be analysed. The glass tubes are fitted with suitable lengths of a specially made, thick-walled Neoprene rubber tubing; both this and the stoppers are able to withstand repeated auto-claving without becoming stiff or sticky. At the free end of one of the pieces of rubber tubing, a short tube of soda glass is inserted. Immediately after steaming or autoclaving, the rubber tubes are connected by the soda glass tube and a partial vacuum is created inside the bottle as it cools. This

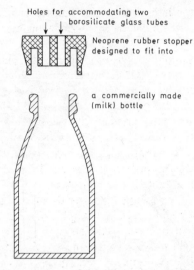

Holes for accommodating two
borosilicate glass tubes

Neoprene rubber stopper
designed to fit into

a commercially made
(milk) bottle

Fig. 4. Design of the rubber stopper for the NIVA sampler

helps to keep the stopper tightly fastened, but it is not essential for the filling of the bottle.

When a sample is to be taken, the bottle is fitted to a heavy metal frame (brass, weight 1.2 kg) which is then attached to a hydrographic cable and lowered to the required depth. When in position, a heavy messenger released down the cable hits the lever, which moves down and causes the soda glass tube to break. The rubber tubes straighten and water is collected some distance away from the cable and frame. A device for keeping the inlet tube well away from the frame may be fitted. The sampler is shown in Fig. 3. Decreased hydrostatic pressure prevents contamination from the intervening water column on raising the apparatus to the surface. After the collection of a sample, the bottle is taken out of the frame, and the rubber tubes are tied as shown in Fig. 3 to prevent contamination during transport to the laboratory. By regulating the length of the shorter glass tube, an ample air space is obtained within the bottle to facilitate mixing prior to examination.

After the examination, the remains of the broken soda glass tube are removed, the bottle and stopper washed and a new soda glass tube is inserted. After sterilization, the bottle is again ready for use. Neoprene stoppers and tubing can easily be made to special order by rubber manufacturing industries, and the use of commercially available bottles makes this sampler very cheap. Thus, a large number of sample bottles can be prepared and stored for later use, as for surface sampling bottles. The sampler described is very similar to the J-Z-, Mortimer-, and Stolbunov-Ryabov samplers (*14*).

One more type of sampling device for deep water may be mentioned— the Williams filter apparatus. This is a membrane filter apparatus, which can be used at great depths (*15*). After lowering to the required depth, a messenger breaks a seal allowing water to enter a cylinder through a filter membrane. A non-return valve prevents the water from flooding the membrane as the apparatus is raised. This apparatus eliminates the need for much of the immediate handling work on board ship, which is necessary with samplers of the Nansen bottle type. All that is necessary is the transfer of the membrane to a suitable growth medium and the measurement (at atmospheric pressure) of the volume of water that has been filtered through the membrane into the cylinder. This sampler has the disadvantage that only one microbiological operation can be performed on any individual sample. However, if field techniques for analysis are considered, this type of sampler may become very useful.

2.1.5 *Equipment for sampling from lake and river sediments*

Surface sediment samples from exposed (not covered with water) sediments may be collected directly into sterilized containers (jars or plastic bags) using a sterilized spatula or spoon. Sediments covered by water require special sampling equipment.

Owing to the lack of special equipment for sampling sediments aseptically, aquatic bacteriologists have been using equipment constructed for other purposes, such as enumeration of benthic fauna, study of the microzonal composition of sediment, or detecting animal remains. Therefore, the discussion of such instruments may be found in handbooks on sampling sediments for studying benthos, sediment formation, and so forth, or in oceanography manuals and journals (marine geology).

During the last few years there have, however, been some attempts at constructing special equipment to permit aseptic sampling of sediments.

The choice of apparatus for microbiological sampling of sediments will be determined by the purposes of the investigation as well as by the depth of the water mass and the character of the sediment. Because the topmost layer of the sediment is the site of the most intensive microbiological activity, it is important always to sample sediment without stirring it or causing changes in the sediment layers. This is the first requirement for full effectiveness of the sampler. Hence, the sampler must not create a pressure wave that might displace the softest surface sediments. For most analyses of faecal indicator bacteria the top layer is also the most important. However, deeper layers must be sampled if one wishes to estimate how long the influence of pollution has lasted by comparing the concentration of spores from the faecal bacterium *Clostridium perfringens* at increasing depths of the sediments. The sampler must penetrate far enough into the sediments to include the layers one wishes to examine, but must not sink in so far that sediment spills out at the top. Further, the sample must not be subject to washout on the way up.

Sediment samplers are of two types: the grab sampler, which scoops up sediment from the bottom, and the core sampler, which is driven into the sediment and takes a core of sediment with or without overlying water. Recent literature shows a distinct trend away from grab samplers towards tube-type core samplers. If grab samplers are used, the only suitable equipment is that in which the cover of the grab can be opened from above (*14, 16*).

The essential element of core-type samplers is a tube, which is pushed into the sediment. It is helpful to use tubes made of transparent plastic to permit observation of the sample and selection of any part of it for sub-sampling. It is very important that the flow of water through the tube be quite free during penetration or an incomplete sample will be taken. It cannot be assumed that a complete sample has been taken simply because the interface is well retained. Studies of X-ray photographs of cores in plastic tubes 3-5 cm in diameter show that if the flow of water is impeded even slightly, the tube will push aside loose sediment after it has sampled the interface until it reaches sediment that is stiff enough to enter the tube (*16*). To prevent the material from washing out, a valve or rubber stopper should close the top after penetration. For very soft sediments, a valve at the bottom is required as well.

For shallow waters, a Plexiglass tube of diameter about 5 cm or more and a length of at least 50 cm is suitable for sampling. This tube can be pushed down into the sediment by hand and the upper end closed by a rubber stopper before the tube is brought to the surface. A rubber stopper may also be used to close the bottom end before the tube is taken out of the water, to prevent the sediment from spilling out.

For deeper waters, the Plexiglass tube may be fitted to a frame with a pole of appropriate length to permit the sampler to be driven into the sediment, and also with an arrangement to close the upper end of the tube before bringing it to the surface. The Lastockin-Ulomski sampler is one such sampler, and the top closure is sufficiently tight for sampling areas of about 1–20 cm². This sampler may also be lowered on a rope (*16*).

Two samplers for aseptic sampling of sediments are the Emery bacterial bottom sampler (*17*) and the bacterial bottom sampler of Van Donsel and Geldreich (*18*). The last-mentioned sampler may be fitted with a weight and a lowering device for use in deep water. Other core samplers designed with frames for use in deep lakes are: the Jenkin sampler, the Craib sampler, the Kajak sampler, the Perfilyev stratometer, and the Baranov sampler (*14, 16*).

The Jenkin sampler is very good but complicated; it is suitable for obtaining samples of surface mud together with the overlying water *in situ*

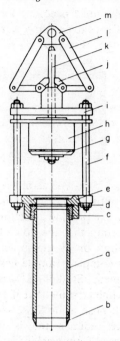

Fig. 5. The sampler of Kajak et al.

a, transparent plastic tube ; b, brass strengthening ring ; c, threaded frame of tube ; d, rubber gasket ; e, lower part of head ; f, rod connecting the upper and lower part of the head ; g, rubber part of cover ; h, weighting of cover ; i, upper part of head ; j, tightening jaw ; k, pin ; l, arm ; m, handle. In operation the cover drops down to the top of the tube when the corer has penetrated far enough to take the weight off the lowering line ; the handle, m, moves down releasing the jaws, j, from the pin that holds the cover, h. There is a commercially available model operated by a messenger.

in a relatively undisturbed state. The cores can be put to a variety of experimental uses. (This sampler is commercially available, see ref. *9*.) The Baranov sampler is also designed for the same purpose.

The Craib sampler (*19*) is designed for collecting undisturbed cores of marine sediments. It is suitable for taking samples where it is desired to examine the microbial population at various depths within the sediments.

The Kajak sampler (Fig. 5) is similar to the Lastockin-Ulomski sampler, but the lid has a rubber packing and is pressed down by means of special levers operated by the total weight of the sampler. This corer functions well with a sampling area up to 50 cm². It works on a rope without a messenger at any depth. A modified version operated by messenger has been tested by Brinkhurst (*20*) and is available commercially as the K-B sediment sampler (*16*).

None of these instruments is designed for aseptic collection of samples. However, by using tubes of diameter 5 cm or more, one may be able to avoid analysing material that has been in contact with the inside wall of

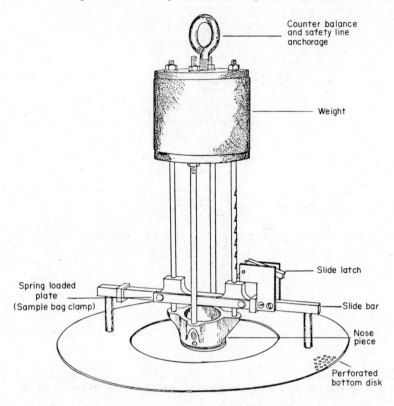

Counter balance
and safety line
anchorage

Weight

Slide latch

Spring loaded
plate
(Sample bag clamp)

Slide bar

Nose
piece

Perforated
bottom disk

Fig. 6. The bacterial bottom sampler of van Donsel & Geldreich (*18*)

the tube simply by pushing the core up the tube, cutting off appropriate layers for examination, and taking out material for analysis from the centre of the cut-off layer.

The Emery bacterial bottom sampler does collect samples aseptically, but may not perform satisfactorily on gritty substrates, and the sample size is too small for multiple testing procedures (*19*). The bacterial bottom sampler of van Donsel & Geldreich (*18*) consists of a " nosepiece " for holding an American-produced Whirl-pak-type plastic bag (180 ml size), a slide bar and a plate for keeping the sterile sample bag shut before sampling and for opening upon sampling, a perforated bottom disk that regulates the opening of the sample bag, and Nylon ropes for cutting the core and shutting the sample bag after the sampling is completed. The sampler is shown in Fig. 6 with a weight and an eye bolt attached to the top plate of the sampler.

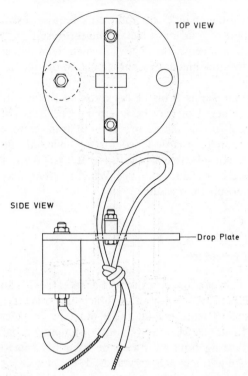

Fig. 7. The dropping plate of the bacterial bottom sampler shown in Fig. 6

A counterbalanced dropping plate, shown in Fig. 7, is attached to the eye bolt when lowering the sampler from a boat on deep water. As soon as the sampler touches bottom, tension is removed from the dropping plate, permitting disengagement of the hook and eye. This release then permits the sampler to penetrate the bottom sediment by the force of its own weight. Adjustment of the line length from the screw hook on the dropping plate to the sampler eye bolt will influence the free fall force, the depth of core collected, and the speed of sample bag closure. The initial motion of retrieving the sampler via the line attachment to the eye bolt will simultaneously pull the closing cords to cut off the bottom sample and close the plastic bag.

Special precautions must be taken in choosing material for the bottom disk if the sampler is going to be used for repeated operation from a boat. In such cases, the sampler must be lowered slowly to prevent water resistance from lifting the bottom plate and causing it to slide upward, thus permitting the bag to fill with water. A small plate or one with large perforations will allow quicker descent than one with small perforations or of solid sheet metal. On the other hand, soft sediments require disks with small perforations or made of solid sheet metal, and this results in an extremely slow descent. In soft sediments, the depth to which the nosepiece penetrates can be limited by the attachment of a tubing clamp on one of the solid rods as a slide stop.

When the sampler is brought back to the surface, the plastic bag is removed, and a new bag may be inserted. The bags containing samples are brought back to the laboratory without transfer to other containers. Although the sampler was designed for use in relatively shallow waters, it will operate at considerable depths (up to at least 60 m). At depths greater than 15 m there is a chance that the Whirl-pak bag may rupture as it is returned to atmospheric pressure.

2.2 Sampling procedures

The selection of sampling locations in a water mass is an important task, which must be performed with all possible care. Each type of water mass has its own special features and these must be considered in designing experiments. In studies of water pollution, sampling programmes designed for chemical investigations may also be used for bacteriological investigations. This subject is treated in volume 1, chapter 2.

Containers for bacteriological samples should be capable of being sterilized, and should as a rule be sterilized to avoid misjudgements about whether or not sterile containers are necessary. Some deep-water samplers are not sterilizable, and if these are used, the water sample should be transferred to a sterile container immediately after the sampler reaches the surface. Containers for samples with residual chlorine should contain an ample amount of sodium thiosulfate to neutralize the effect of the disinfectant on the microorganisms during transport and storage (see section 2.3).

To avoid contamination of the sample from the outer surface of a sampling bottle, the bottle may be wrapped in paper before sterilization and the paper kept on until the moment of sampling. A sterilized sampling bottle should be kept unopened until the moment it is required for filling, and should never be rinsed out before the sample is taken.

When sampling from taps or by pumps with tubing, the water should be allowed to run to waste for several minutes until the water coming out can be said to be representative of the water body one wishes to sample. The flow of water should then be reduced so that the sampling bottle may be filled without splashing, and it should be left to run for about one minute before filling the bottle.

When sampling from shallow or surface waters, the cover and stopper of the bottle should be removed and retained in one hand, and the bottle, held by the base with the other hand, should be plunged neck downwards below the surface. The bottle should then be tilted till the neck points slightly upwards, the mouth being directed towards the current. Where no current exists, the bottle should be pushed forward horizontally until filled. When completely full, the bottle should be brought rapidly above the surface, a small portion of the water poured out to leave ample air space to facilitate mixing of the sample prior to examination, and then restoppered. Throughout the procedure care should be taken that water entering the bottle does not come into contact with the hand.

Sampling of sewage and liquid sewage sludge may be performed by means of a surface-water bottle with a wooden pole or metal string fastened around the bottle neck, as described in section 2.1.3.

Sampling of different kinds of treated sewage sludge, such as sludge from fermentation tanks, aerobic stabilization sludge, sludge from drying beds, etc., has to be done by other means. The aim is to obtain a sample that is representative of the sludge masses one wishes to examine. In this case, several subsamples should be taken at different places in the sludge masses and mixed for the final sample, rather than taking just one large sample. The subsamples can be collected directly into sterilized containers using a sterilized spatula or spoon.

For sampling with special equipment designed for deep waters or sediments, the sampling instructions for each type of sampler should be followed.

2.3 Sample transportation, preservation, and storage

2.3.1 *Transportation and storage*

This subject is well covered in volume 1, chapter 2, section 3.3. However, since there is no way of keeping the bacterial concentration constant during transportation and storage, some general rules are laid down:

If samples cannot be processed within 1 hour following collection, the temperature should be held below 10°C by the use of iced coolers during a maximum transport time of 6 hours. Such samples should be refrigerated upon receipt in the laboratory and processed within 2 hours. When local conditions necessitate delays in delivery of samples longer than 6 hours, consideration should be given to field examination techniques (see section 3.9) or to a delayed-incubation procedure for the analysis of coliform bacteria. If this is not possible, the time elapsing between collection and examination should in no case exceed 30 hours and the samples should be held below 10°C and preferably placed in a refrigerator at 3–5°C as soon as possible after sampling. The time and temperature of storage of all samples should be recorded and should be considered in the interpretation of data.

2.3.2   *Preservation of viable bacteria by neutralizing residual disinfectants in the sample*

If the water to be sampled contains—or is likely to contain—traces of chlorine or chloramine (swimming pool waters, chlorinated sewage effluents), it is necessary to add to the sampling bottles, before sterilization, a sufficient quantity of sodium thiosulfate to neutralize these substances. It has been shown that a concentration of approximately 18 mg·l⁻¹ has no significant effect on the coliform, faecal coliform, faecal streptococci and staphylococci content of unchlorinated water on storage. This concentration of sodium thiosulfate is said to be enough to neutralize up to 5 mg·l⁻¹ of residual chlorine (*21, 22*). However, the higher concentration of 100 mg·l⁻¹ is recommended by other literature on standard methods for drinking water, and this concentration is said to be enough to neutralize up to about 15 mg of residual chlorine per litre (*23*).

In water pollution investigations, chlorine residuals may be higher than in drinking water, and the content of oxidizable substances may also be expected to be higher. Therefore, the highest concentration—100 mg of sodium thiosulfate per litre—is recommended. This can be accomplished by adding 0.2 ml of a 100 g·l⁻¹ solution of sodium thiosulfate to a 250-ml bottle before sterilization by either dry or moist heat.

3. TECHNIQUES FOR QUANTITATIVE ESTIMATION OF MICROORGANISMS

3.1 Mathematical background to the different techniques

The choice of technique for quantitative estimation of a particular type of bacterium may depend partly on which technique is suitable for the laboratory sample (water, sludge, sediments) and the bacterium in question (aerobic or anaerobic, detection of acid, gas, or other criteria), and partly on which technique is preferred by the laboratory or research worker. The membrane filter technique may be superior for waters of low bacterial densities, while the plate counts are easy to perform and give results in a short time, but require higher bacterial densities than the membrane filter technique.

Liquid media in tubes may be used with the MPN technique, which is designed to give the results with a defined and relatively good precision, but requires a large number of tubes and incubator space. Liquid media may also be used with a titre technique, which requires fewer tubes and less incubator space, but gives less precise results. Each technique has advantages and disadvantages, and the choice of technique should be given careful consideration when designing research experiments, pollution control investigations, or quality criteria monitoring.

All the techniques described in this manual rely on the assumption that the bacteria appear as single individuals in the test sample. If they appear in chains or are particle bound, each chain or particle containing several individuals will be estimated as one unit. Some techniques, such as the MPN-tube technique, also rely on the assumption that the bacteria are evenly distributed in the test sample. In colony count techniques, the number of test portions to be examined in order to give a fair estimate of the bacterial density of the laboratory sample may be reduced to one if even distribution is achieved. Thus, even distribution of bacteria in the test sample is considered imperative, and measures must be taken to achieve this.

The laboratory sample may also contain bacterial densities too high for direct use as a test sample. In such cases, the laboratory sample will have to be diluted with a suitable diluent.

3.1.1 *Multiple tube technique (MPN method) (23, 24, 25)*

In the multiple tube method of estimating bacterial densities, measured volumes of the laboratory sample to be tested, or of one or more dilutions of it, are added to tubes containing a liquid differential medium. It is assumed that on incubation each tube that received one or more viable organisms in the inoculum will show growth and the differential reaction appropriate to the organism sought and the medium used. By adding a certain volume of sample to a given number of tubes, and repeating this series with certain submultiples of the volume for a given number of series, it is possible to estimate a " most probable number " (MPN-value) of viable organisms in a given volume of sample. This estimate is based on certain probability formulae. Theoretical considerations and large-scale replicate determinations indicate that this estimate tends to be greater than the actual number, and that the error tends to diminish with increasing numbers of tubes in each dilution examined (*25*).

All the MPN-methods in this chapter are based on the combination of 5 tubes per dilution level and a minimum of 3 subsequent, decimal dilution levels. After incubation under the conditions prescribed for each type of organism, the tubes are checked for growth and for differential reaction, and the number of positive tubes recorded. The MPN-value corresponding to the found combination of positive tubes is read off from Table 1. Included in this table are the 95% confidence limits for each MPN-value.

The MPN for combinations not appearing in the table, or for other combinations of tubes or dilutions, may be estimated by Thomas's simple formula (*23*) :

$$\text{MPN per 100 ml} = \frac{\text{No. of positive tubes} \times 100}{\sqrt{\left(\begin{array}{c}\text{ml sample in}\\\text{negative tubes}\end{array}\right) \times \left(\begin{array}{c}\text{ml sample}\\\text{in all tubes}\end{array}\right)}}$$

Table 1. MPN and 95% confidence limits within which it can lie,
for various combinations of positive and negative results when five 10-ml portions,
five 1-ml portions and five 0.1-ml portions are used (6)

Number of tubes giving positive reaction out of			MPN	95% confidence limits	
5 of 10 ml each	5 of 1 ml each	5 of 0.1 ml each		Lower limit	Upper limit
0	0	1	2	< 0.5	7
0	1	0	2	< 0.5	7
0	2	0	4	< 0.5	11
1	0	0	2	< 0.5	7
1	0	1	4	< 0.5	11
1	1	0	4	< 0.5	11
1	1	1	6	< 0.5	15
1	2	0	6	< 0.5	15
2	0	0	5	< 0.5	13
2	0	1	7	1	17
2	1	0	7	1	17
2	1	1	9	2	21
2	2	0	9	2	21
2	3	0	12	3	28
3	0	0	8	1	19
3	0	1	11	2	25
3	1	0	11	2	25
3	1	1	14	4	34
3	2	0	14	4	34
3	2	1	17	5	46
3	3	0	17	5	46
4	0	0	13	3	31
4	0	1	17	5	46
4	1	0	17	5	46
4	1	1	21	7	63
4	1	2	26	9	78
4	2	0	22	7	67
4	2	1	26	9	78
4	3	0	27	9	80
4	3	1	33	11	93
4	4	0	34	12	96
5	0	0	23	7	70
5	0	1	31	11	89
5	0	2	43	15	114
5	1	0	33	11	93
5	1	1	46	16	120
5	1	2	63	21	154
5	2	0	49	17	126
5	2	1	70	23	168
5	2	2	94	28	219
5	3	0	79	25	187
5	3	1	109	31	253
5	3	2	141	37	343
5	3	3	175	44	503
5	4	0	130	35	302
5	4	1	172	43	486
5	4	2	221	57	698
5	4	3	278	90	849
5	4	4	345	117	999
5	5	0	240	68	754
5	5	1	348	118	1 005
5	5	2	542	160	1 405
5	5	3	918	303	3 222
5	5	4	1 609	635	5 805

For samples with unknown bacterial densities, more than 3 subsequent decimal dilutions may be necessary for the test. The results from only 3 of these dilutions should, however, be used in computing the MPN.

If the analysis is performed to investigate whether or not the bacterial density is in agreement with some water quality criterion, another approach may be taken. Water quality criteria are usually based on an upper number of a certain type of bacterium per standard volume. In such cases, the standard volume may be used as a test portion, and there is then no need to analyse other amounts of test portion. Then, the MPN-evaluation does not necessarily have to be employed. The analysis may simply be performed to determine the presence or absence of the specified bacterial type in the standard volume or a number of subvolumes adding up to the standard volume.

3.1.2 Colony count techniques

There are several different methods in use for estimating the level of viable organisms by colony counting. The principle of this technique is to separate the organisms in the sample, keep them separated while they are subjected to nutrients and incubation conditions encouraging growth, and finally to count the visible colonies developing from each organism capable of growth under the given conditions.

The separation is carried out by shaking or by mechanical homogenization of the sample, and the organisms are kept separated either by trapping on a membrane filter or solid medium surface, or by mixing the sample with a liquid medium that solidifies upon cooling. The growth medium may be composed with the aim of being selective for certain organisms, and the incubation conditions may also be chosen to enhance the selectivity. However, it has been shown that, even if the growth medium is made non-selective and the incubation conditions optimized for the growth of most types of organism, colony counts give lower results than direct counts of " viable " organisms in a sample. The colony count technique has the advantage over the direct count technique that it permits selective enumeration of the sought organism in a relatively simple way.

Different colony count techniques may differ in the maximum volume of sample per unit that it is permissible to analyse under standard conditions, and sometimes there are also restrictions given for the minimum volume of sample to be analysed. The latter limit is not necessary, because if organisms as small as bacteria are evenly distributed in the sample, only the accuracy of measuring and delivering the sample volume and the number of bacteria in that volume will affect the results.

Tables 2 and 3 illustrate the number of colonies that will have to be counted in order to achieve different degrees of precision. Whether the colony counts are made on plates, on filters or in tubes, there will be an upper limit for the acceptable number of colonies per unit (plate, filter,

Table 2. Relative precision of colony counts for different numbers counted (26)

Accuracy [a] (% of mean value)	Number of colonies counted
± 5	1 537
± 10	386
± 15	173
± 20	98
± 25	64
± 30	45
± 35	34
±40	25

[a] The relationship between accuracy at 95% confidence limits (two times standard deviation) and the total number of colonies counted assumes Poisson distribution of the bacteria in the sample.

Table 3. 95% confidence limits for low colony numbers [a]

Total number of colonies counted, C	95% confidence limits [b]	
	Upper limit	Lower limit
1	5.6	0.025
5	11.7	1.6
10	18.4	4.8
>20	$\approx C + 2\,(2 + \sqrt{C})$	$\approx C - 2\,(1 + \sqrt{C})$

[a] After UK report No. 71 (24).
[b] The standard deviation is often differently expressed by different statisticians, e.g.:

$$\pm \sqrt{C} \qquad \pm \sqrt{C + \tfrac{1}{2}} \qquad \frac{+2 + \sqrt{C}}{-1 + \sqrt{C}}$$

This is of practical value for low colony counts only.

etc.). This number may be limited by " crowding " of colonies (nutritional competition between different types of bacteria), or by the inability to count colonies in the higher ranges. The count may also be influenced by increasing difficulties in distinguishing colonies of a certain appearance when they decrease in size owing to increasing nutritional competition. Spreading zones of colony metabolites may also affect the colour of neighbouring colonies on filters with high colony density. Antagonism between different bacteria may also affect the upper limit for acceptable number of colonies per filter, plate or tube, but no general rules can be worked out to eliminate this effect.

With selective media resulting in predominantly one kind of colony, as in the colony count methods for faecal coliforms, faecal streptococci and anaerobic, sulfite-reducing spore-formers described in this chapter, there is no scientific reason for an upper limit as long as separate colonies are discernible (27). The colonies, however, decrease in size owing to increasing competition for nutrients, and the practical upper limit will be governed by the available counting equipment. Automatic counting devices, or magnification and automatic recording of manual counts, will increase the range above what is practically possible without such aids. The general upper limit for an " average " laboratory, as stated in this work, is based on manual counting and low magnification (hand lens). The higher the counts, the higher the precision, but the counting may be laborious and time-consuming. This will have to be considered in designing experiments— higher precision may be more practically achieved by increasing the number of plates, tubes or membranes per sample than by increasing the sample volume per unit.

If the analysis yields only plates with colony numbers higher than 300 the colony number may be estimated by counting part of the plate only. Special counting devices with magnification and illumination usually do have a counting background subdivided into segments of a circle or squares that may be used as subdivisions of an appropriate area for counting. Without such counting equipment, the plate may be subdivided into 2–8 segments, one of which is counted. An area large enough to cover at least 100 colonies, but preferably 200 colonies (standard deviation $\pm 10\%$ and $\pm 7.5\%$ respectively), should be counted for the estimation of the total colony number on the plate. This estimated colony number is calculated as follows :

$$\text{Number of colonies counted} \times \frac{\text{Total area of the plate}}{\text{Segment area counted}} \text{ or } C \times \frac{TA}{SA}$$

If the smallest volume of laboratory sample or dilutions thereof have given colony numbers too numerous to count (TNTC), the results may be expressed as such (see section 3.10.6).

The colony count technique does not differ from other particle count techniques with regard to precision. To obtain a 95% confidence limit of $\pm 10\%$ or better, a minimum of 386 colonies will have to be counted from one sample. The volume used to obtain this count may be analysed in one or more portions, but to obtain the final result with this precision, the calculation has to be made as given in section 3.10.3.

If the bacterial density region of the laboratory sample is unknown, one will have to use several test portions of different volume to obtain an acceptable estimate of this density.

If the analysis is performed to investigate whether or not the bacterial density is in agreement with some water quality criterion, the standard unit may be used as test portion, and there will be no need to analyse other amounts of test portion (see section 3.1.1). This approach, with either the colony count or the liquid media tube technique, involves less work than the optimal precision technique, and is recommended for monitoring aquatic environments in conformity with established quality criteria.

In this technique, the volume is standardized, but rules must also be worked out on how to interpret the resulting data. These rules must cover details of how often samples are to be analysed, how often and/or how much the critical bacterial density may be exceeded before action is taken, and what action to take in such circumstances.

At present, the majority of countries with municipal water supplies have such bacterial quality criteria for drinking-water. In the field of water pollution, however, few countries have established bacterial quality criteria, although some do have such criteria for bathing water. Therefore, the methods described in this manual are based on the optimal precision techniques.

3.2 Pretreatment of laboratory samples

3.2.1 Water samples

For ordinary water samples, even distribution of bacteria may be accomplished by thorough mixing of the content in the bottle (e.g., by shaking approximately 20 times in a not completely filled sampling bottle) immediately before drawing the test portion for direct estimation or dilution. Water containing visible particles should be homogenized as described for semisolid samples.

3.2.2 Semisolid and solid samples

Using normal techniques, solid samples will have to be suspended in a liquid in order to be analysed. Then, care must be taken both to draw a test portion representative of the laboratory sample and to prepare a suspension with even distribution of the bacteria contained in the test portion. For such samples, the results will have to be calculated by weight rather than by volume of the laboratory sample, and dry weight determinations will be necessary. A sample that may be homogenized as stated in the following without addition of liquid is considered semisolid. Even though such samples may be volumetrically measured (with a graduated cylinder), the bacterial density should not be calculated by volume but rather by dry weight of the sample.

It is recommended that the homogenization procedure be optimized with the type of homogenizer available in each laboratory for the most common types of sample to be analysed. Homogenization time should be regulated to yield the maximum number of organisms (*28*), but care must be taken not to let the temperature rise above approximately 40°C during homogenization. Example : Using a rod-shaped homogenizer with knives rotating at a speed of 20 000 r·min^{-1}, 2 minutes homogenization time for 100–150-ml samples in 250–300 ml containers has been found optimal for raw sewage and sewage sludge.

For solid laboratory samples, mix as well as possible according to the consistency of the sample (stirring, grinding, cutting, etc.). Weigh 2 approximately equal portions of sample, 1 for preparation of diluted sample, and 1 for the determination of dry weight. Normally, portions of approximately 1 g are sufficient for sewage sludge, while lake and river sediments may require larger portions in order to obtain the optimal count of organisms with the methods used. Weigh to the nearest 0.001 g, and transfer quantitatively 1 of the weighed portions (WW_1) to a container for homogenization. Add sterile diluent (see section 3.3) up to a suitable volume, depending on the kind of homogenizer used, and homogenize. Measure and record the total volume (TV) with a precision of 2.5 % or better.

Further dilution of the homogenized solid or semisolid sample before analysing is dependent on the expected bacterial density and the methods to be employed. It will usually be necessary to analyse more than one dilution level to secure optimal results.

The weight determination is performed as follows : The portion of solid laboratory sample intended for dry weight determination is weighed directly in a dish preweighed for this purpose. Record the weight to the nearest 0.001 g (WW_2). Dry this weighed sample to constant weight at 103–105°C. " Constant weight " is obtained when weighings after repeated drying reveal no deviation from the nearest 0.001 g. Record the final weight (DW_2). For semisolid laboratory samples, measure a portion of homogenized sample with a graduated cylinder and transfer quantitatively to a preweighed dish for dry weight determination. A volume of 50 ml is normally sufficient for semisolid sewage sludge. Record the volume to the nearest millilitre (HS). Dry the measured portion of sample to constant weight at 103–105°C. Record the final weight to the nearest 0.001 g (DW_1).

3.3 Dilution of laboratory samples or suspension of laboratory samples

I. DILUENT

Dilutions should always be made with the following diluent :

KH_2PO_4	0.04 g
$MgSO_4 \cdot 7H_2O$	0.25 g
NaOH to pH 7.0 $\pm$ 0.1	
Distilled water	1 litre

The addition of magnesium sulfate to phosphate buffer diluent improves the recovery of metabolically injured bacteria (23).

Prepare stock solutions :

A. Phosphate stock solution :

   KH_2PO_4 :   20.0 g in 500 ml distilled water

B. Magnesium sulfate solution :

   $MgSO_4 \cdot 7H_2O$:   25.0 g in 500 ml distilled water

C. Sodium hydroxide solution :

   NaOH : 4.0 g in 500 ml distilled water, or
   NaOH solution, 1 mol $\cdot$ l^{-1}: 100 ml, diluted to 500 ml with distilled water.

Do not mix the stock solutions because the resulting mixture may support the growth of microorganisms and thus the shelf life will be shortened.

Prepare the diluent as follows :

To approximately 900 ml of distilled water, add 1 ml of solution A and 5 ml of solution B.

Then add approximately 1 ml of solution C to a pH value of 7 ± 0.1. Fill up to 1 litre with distilled water.

For each new batch of solutions A and C prepared, the exact volume of solution C to bring the pH value to 6.9–7.1 may be determined, thus avoiding the necessity of adjusting the pH-value every time new diluent is prepared from these solutions.

Sterilize by autoclaving in suitable portions in screw-cap bottles to prevent evaporation during storage.

II. APPARATUS

- Sterile dilution tubes or bottles.
- Sterile bacteriological pipettes or sterile dispensers suitable for measuring the volume of diluent with a precision of 2.5% or better.
- Sterile bacteriological pipettes for measuring samples and test portions with a precision of 2.5% or better.

   Optional : A whirl-mixer for efficient mixing of the sample and diluent.

III. PROCEDURE

Measure the appropriate quantities of diluent and add to the dilution tubes or bottles.

Shake the laboratory sample or suspension to obtain even distribution of the bacteria (see section 3.2), immediately draw off the required volume and add to the dilution vessel.

Mix to obtain even distribution of the bacteria either by the same procedure as in section 3.2, by the aid of a whirl-mixer, or by filling and emptying the pipette to be used in the subsequent withdrawing of the diluted sample at least 3 times.

Continue the dilution series by each time withdrawing a fixed volume of the last dilution and adding this to a fixed volume of diluent.

Some or all of the dilutions may be used as test samples.

Record the dilution factor F of the test sample (dilution 1 → F, see Example). A significant change in bacterial density may be expected if the diluted sample is left at room temperature too long before use. At room temperatures of 20–25°C, a holding time of up to 60 minutes may be acceptable (see Table 1 in Geldreich (*29*)), but higher room temperatures may accelerate bacterial change.

Dilution step recommended : 10-fold dilution, see Table 4.

Table 4. Preparation of 10-fold dilutions

Dilution step 1, 1 → 10			
Laboratory sample or suspension, ml	1	2	10
Diluent volume in ml	9	18	90
Resulting dilution step 1, total volume, ml	10	20	100
Dilution step 2, 1 → 100			
Dilution from step 1, ml	1	2	10
Diluent volume in ml	9	18	90
Resulting dilution step 2, total volume, ml	10	20	100
Dilution step 3, 1 → 1000			
Dilution from step 2, ml	1	2	10
Diluent volume in ml	9	18	90
Resulting dilution step 3, total volume, ml	10	20	100
Continue to dilution step 4 and on, if necessary			

Example :

Withdraw 1 ml of laboratory sample and add to a dilution vessel containing 9 ml of diluent. The resulting 10-ml dilution contains 0.1 ml of laboratory sample per ml, and the dilution (test sample) is described as dilution 1 → 10, with dilution factor $F = 10$.

Then withdraw 1 ml from this dilution and add to a second dilution vessel containing 9 ml of diluent, resulting in 10 ml of dilution 2, or 1 → 100.

Continue the dilution to step 1 → 1000 and on, if necessary.

Some advice about the volume of test sample to be prepared for use in the MPN-techniques : All the calculation methods for estimation of bacterial density in the MPN-dilution series are based on the assumption that a certain volume of water is taken directly from the original sample (usually 10, 1 and 0.1 ml). When dilutions of the original (laboratory) sample are used as test samples, a stochastic error will be introduced unless the dilution volumes are at least 3 times as large as the minimum required (*30*).

Example :

For a 10-fold dilution with a final volume of 10 ml, only 3 ml may be used as a test portion, and 5 ml of test portion require at least 15 ml of test sample.

Thus, test samples for inoculation of MPN-series as described in this manual should be prepared in minimum volumes of 15 ml. If only one MPN-series is to be prepared from a laboratory sample, by tradition 1 ml to 10 ml final volume is commonly used both in the USA and in Europe. Therefore, the MPN-procedures described in section 4 are "traditional" rather than mathematically correct. Using dilution 2 → 20 as shown in Table 4, second column, would reduce the stochastic error.

3.4 Multiple tube technique (MPN method)

I. FIELD OF APPLICATION

The multiple tube technique is applicable to all kinds of sample : clean and turbid water, sewage and sewage sludge, muds and other sediments, provided the bacteria may be evenly distributed in the prepared test samples. Theoretically, the technique may cover samples with very low bacterial densities if large containers are used as culture vessels, but in water pollution studies, 10 ml is usually the largest sample volume used. The technique then covers densities of 0.02 bacteria per ml (2 per 100 ml) and above.

II. APPARATUS

- Culture containers with metal or plastic caps or cotton plugs, minimum 3×5 containers per sample. When 10 ml is the largest volume of test sample to be withdrawn, 16- $\times$ 160-mm or 18- $\times$ 180-mm test tubes may be used as containers.
  If gas is to be detected, each test tube should contain a small glass vial, or Durham tube, 2- $\times$ 15-mm.
- Test tube racks, preferably capable of holding 15 tubes or multiples of 5 tubes.
- Sterile bacteriological pipettes of suitable size for withdrawing test portions of 10, 1 and 0.1 ml with a precision of $\pm 2.5\%$ or better.
- Sterile bacteriological pipettes, graduated measuring cylinder, or a sterile dispenser suitable for measuring 9 or 90 ml of diluent with a precision of $\pm 2.5\%$ or better.

- Sterile containers for dilution of sample. For 10 ml of diluted sample test tubes of 18×180 mm may be used, for dilution volumes of 20 ml or more, larger containers are recommended.
- Sterile wooden applicators or an inoculating needle with loop of diameter 3 mm for inoculation of confirmatory tubes, if used.

III. PREPARATION OF CULTURE MEDIUM

The growth media may be prepared beforehand and sterilized. Double-strength medium in volumes of 10 ml per tube should be used for sample volumes of 10 ml, to keep the nutrient concentration at the same level as in the 1-ml and 0.1-ml sample series.

If tubes with gas vials are stored at temperatures lower than 20–25°C, incubation overnight in the incubator in question is recommended (*23*), and all tubes showing an air bubble in the inverted vial should be discarded (see section 5.6.9).

IV. PROCEDURE

IV.1 *Identity marking of culture tubes*

For safe performance of methods that imply presumptive and confirmative tests, each of the culture tubes should be given an identity mark.

This may be done by marking each tube with a laboratory sample code (for example a letter), and a number indicating the dilution level to which the tube belongs. The latter may be accomplished by simply marking each set of 15 or more tubes with figures 1 to 15 or further :

Identity marking of tubes	Sample code	A A A A A	A A A A A	A
	Tube no.	1 2 3 4 5	6 7 8 9 10	11

Upon transfer of the sample for a confirmative test, each confirmatory tube is given the identity mark of the corresponding presumptive tube, in order that no interchange will be possible.

IV.2 *Test portion*

Test portions of 10, 1 and 0.1 ml will cover laboratory samples with bacterial densities between 0.02 and 16 bacteria per ml, or as normally expressed, 2–1600 bacteria per 100 ml.

Laboratory samples with higher bacterial densities will have to be diluted in 10-fold dilutions (see section 3.3), and 5×1-ml test portions should be withdrawn from each dilution.

IV.3 *Inoculation and incubation of the culture tubes*

After thorough mixing of the laboratory sample (see section 3.2), immediately withdraw the required test portions for each of the 5 tubes in each dilution series :

> 10 ml to each of 5 tubes with 10 ml of double-strength medium, 1 ml to each of 5 tubes with single-strength medium, and 0.1 ml to each of another 5 tubes with single-strength medium.

If 1 ml is chosen as the largest test portion of laboratory sample, dilution may be done either beforehand or simultaneously with inoculating the tubes, as here described:

> Add 1 ml of laboratory sample (or lowest dilution considered) to each of 5 tubes with single-strength medium, and to a dilution vessel containing 9 ml of sterile diluent. Mix the latter thoroughly, at once withdraw test portions of 1 ml and add to each of 5 other tubes with single-strength medium. Withdraw a 1-ml test portion and add to a dilution vessel with 9 ml of diluent. Mix, and continue as described with the last 5 tubes, or continue the dilution series as far as thought necessary (see section 3.3, III).

Record the volume of test portion, V, and, if dilution is employed, also the dilution factor, F, for each dilution step.
Incubate as prescribed for each organism.
A schematic illustration of the MPN-tube technique is shown in Fig. 8.

IV.4 *Recording of results*

At the end of the incubation period, record the number of positive tubes in each series of 5 tubes. If more than 3 series have been employed, locate the highest dilution with all 5 tubes showing a positive reaction, no tubes in the series of lower dilution being negative. Record the volume of the test portion, V, and, where appropriate, the dilution factor, F, for this series of 5 tubes, and record the number of positive tubes in this and the two subsequent series of higher dilution. Locate, in Table 1, the MPN-value corresponding to the combination of positive tubes found in the 3 subsequent dilutions. Record this MPN-value and 95% confidence limits. An example of a practical laboratory form is shown in Fig. 7A.

In this example, 5 steps have been employed. From the resulting data, 3 possible combinations for locating the MPN-value in Table 1 exist :
By choosing step 1 as the lowest dilution step, the combination would be 5–5–3, with corresponding MPN-value 303–918–3222.
By choosing step 2 as the lowest dilution level (the highest dilution with all 5 tubes showing positive results), the combination would be 5–3–1 with corresponding MPN-value 31–109–253.

Fig. 7A. A suggested laboratory form for recording results from the MPN-method

SAMPLE CODE : A

M P N — TECHNIQUE FOR ESTIMATION OF BACTERIAL DENSITIES IN LIQUID SAMPLES

Test dilutions	Step 1					Step 2					Step 3					Step 4					Step 5				
Test portions, V ml	10					1					1					1					1				
Dilution factor, F	1					1					10					100					1000				
Tube number	1	2	3	4	5	6	7	8	9	10	11	12	13	14	15	16	17	18	19	20	21	22	23	24	25
Positive reaction at end of incubation	+	+	+	+	+	+	+	+	+	+	+		+	+			+								
Number of positive tubes per set	5					5					3					1					0				

Corresponding M P N-value from table ; and 95% confidence limits : 31 – 109 – 253

V / F in lowest dilution step applied, Step : ___2___ V : ___1___ F : ___1___

Result : M P N-value × $\frac{10}{V}$ × F = $\frac{110 \cdot 10}{110 \cdot 10}$ bacteria per 100 ml laboratory sample[a]

[a] For solid samples, per 100 ml of basic suspension

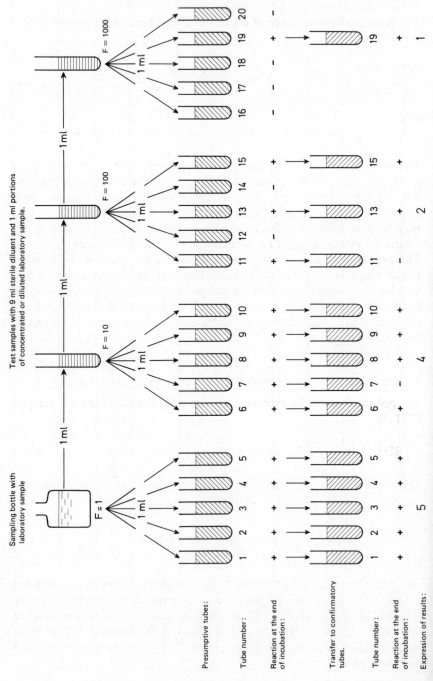

Schematic illustration of the MPN-tube technique

By choosing step 3 as the lowest dilution level, the combination would be 3-1-0 with corresponding MPN-value 2-11-25. The most probable number of organisms in the laboratory sample or suspension would be :

Start from step	MPN-value from Table 1	Dilution factor F	Test portion V	MPN in lab. sample	Range of 95% confidence limits
1	303–918–3222	1	10	303–918–3222	2919
2	31–109–253	1	1	310–1090–2530	2220
3	2–11–25	10	1	200–1100–2500	2300

The combination giving the narrowest range for the 95% confidence limits is the optimal choice. Most often, the combination with step 2 as the lowest dilution level (see p. 306) will give optimal results. A combination of positive tubes from different dilution steps is sometimes used (*23*). This may be done for extra safety in drinking water examination, but is mathematically incorrect and is not recommended for polluted water.

The procedure described covers methods where the analysis can be completed with this one series per sample. However, this is mostly only a first step—a presumptive test—and the positive tubes from this will have to be confirmed by another test ; the final MPN is calculated from the results of this confirmative test. Details of such methods are described in section 5, but the main performance and calculation of the results are as described in this section.

V. EXPRESSION OF THE BACTERIAL DENSITY OF THE TEST SAMPLE

The general formula for expressing the bacterial density of the test sample, BDT, is :

$$\text{BDT} = \frac{10}{V} \times \text{MPN-value from Table 1}$$

This expression for BDT and the dilution factor, F, are used to calculate the bacterial density of the laboratory sample, BDL, see section 3.10.

3.5 Standing tube technique for anaerobic bacteria

I. FIELD OF APPLICATION

This technique is used for the enumeration of anaerobic bacteria, which are oxygen-tolerant and thus do not require an oxygen-free atmosphere during preparation and incubation. Otherwise, the principles of the method are the same as for pour-plate counts (see section 3.6). Bacteria that are inactivated by short exposure to temperatures of 43–45°C may not be enumerated by this technique.

The minimum bacterial density in a laboratory sample to be analysed by this technique is dependent on the size of tubes used.

With 25- ×250-mm (large) tubes, test portions up to 50 ml may be used. To obtain colony counts with 2 × standard deviations of 40% or better (25 colonies per tube), the test portion must contain at least 0.5 bacteria per ml.

With 16- ×160-mm or 18- ×180-mm tubes, test portions up to 10 ml may be used, limiting the lowest possible density to 2.5 bacteria per ml. More than one tube per test sample is recommended for laboratory samples with lower bacterial densities.

II. APPARATUS

- Sterile bacteriological pipettes or graduated measuring cylinders suitable for measuring the test portion with a precision of 2.5% or better.

- Sterile test tubes of size 16×160 mm, 18×180 mm, or 25×250 mm, for culture tubes, with screw caps or other stoppers to facilitate mixing of the liquefied agar medium and the test portion.

- Screw-cap bottles (tubes) of suitable size to hold 50 ml, 200 ml and 350 ml of agar-base.

- Screw-cap tubes of size 16×160 mm or 18×180 mm to hold 10 ml of agar-base.

- Test tube racks for holding the tubes in an upright position.

- A water bath set to 43–45°C for tempering the liquefied single-strength agar medium, diluent, and test sample.

- A 5–6 times magnification lens as counting aid.

Optional : A water bath set to 45–55°C for tempering the liquefied double-strength agar medium. If double-strength medium is used routinely, this water bath is recommended as standard equipment.

III. PREPARATION OF CULTURE MEDIUM

Since this technique is to be used for bacteria that grow without oxygen, it is important to keep atmospheric oxygen out of the growth medium. This may be accomplished by preventing the culture medium from becoming saturated with oxygen during preparation. For this reason, the liquefied medium should be kept in the tempering bath for as short a time as possible. If sterile, pre-prepared media are used, air is driven out when they are heated in boiling water to remelt the agar.

In freshly prepared media, air is driven out during autoclaving. After this, single-strength medium is tempered in a water bath at 43–45°C for as short a time as possible before use, taking care that the column of medium is completely immersed in the water.

For double-strength medium, a temperature of 43–45°C may be too low to keep the agar medium in a liquid state. Containers with this type of medium may instead be cooled in a container of hot water until the water temperature has reached 45–55°C before pouring into tubes or on to plates. If reducing agents are used to ensure low redox potential in the medium at the onset of growth, these should be added after tempering, immediately before pouring.

IV. PROCEDURE

IV.1 *Test portion*

Volumes of 0.1–1 ml in the smaller size tubes and 0.1–10 ml in the large tubes may be used with single-strength medium, and volumes up to 10 ml and 50 ml respectively, with double-strength medium.

The practical maximum number of countable colonies inside a tube is dependent on the size and appearance of the colonies, but may be expected to be lower than for pour- and spread-plates. Therefore, decimal quantities of the test sample are not recommended as test portions; half quantities may be a better choice.

IV.2 *Preparation of the colony count culture*

Mix the test sample (see section 3.2), immediately withdraw the required test portion and add to a growth tube. Record the volume of the test portion, V, and if diluted, the dilution factor of the test sample, F (see section 3.3). Proceed with the next portion or test sample.

Dilution of the laboratory sample may conveniently be performed simultaneously with preparing the tubes, as described for pour-plates (see section 3.6, IV).

When large test portions requiring double-strength medium are used, the test samples or test portions in the tubes should be brought up to a temperature of 43–45°C before mixing with the double-strength agar. Organisms growing readily at 44°C may be tempered in the water bath used for tempering agar media, while other bacteria should be exposed to this temperature for as short a time as possible.

Remove a growth medium container from the tempering bath, wipe water off the outside, and pour aseptically into the growth tubes, which should be completely filled when stoppered. Mix carefully without letting air bubbles into the medium, and cool quickly. If screw-caps are used, these may be loosened during cooling but should later be closed unless gas-

producing bacteria are cultivated. The aim is to keep oxygen out of the growth medium.
Incubate in an ordinary aerobic incubator as prescribed for the organism being sought.

V. COUNTING

Count the colonies appearing in the tubes according to what are described as positive criteria for the organism being sought. If necessary, use the magnifying lens. Record the count for each tube, C_i.
Tubes with colonies too numerous to count should be reported as TNTC, and if there is growth without well defined colonies, the report should be " confluent growth ".

VI. EXPRESSION OF THE BACTERIAL DENSITY OF THE TEST SAMPLE

Express the bacterial density of the test sample, BDT, as follows :

$$ \text{BDT} = \frac{\Sigma C_i}{\Sigma V_i} $$

where C_i is the number of colonies counted per tube and V_i is the volume of the test portion per tube.
Do not calculate the BDT. The calculation of the bacterial density of the laboratory sample, BDL, is described in section 3.10.

3.6 Pour-plate technique

I. FIELD OF APPLICATION

Pour-plates may be used for all kinds of bacteria that grow in laboratory media if the colour of the agar medium is not too dark for the colonies to be seen inside the solidified medium.
With standard performance, using test portions preferably of 1 ml, but with possible test portions of 0.1–5 ml for Petri dishes of diameter 90–95 mm, the technique may be used for waters with bacterial densities as low as 5 bacteria per ml. For lower densities, the number of plates per sample may be increased to obtain the lower limit of 25 colonies counted per sample. This technique cannot be used for bacteria that are inactivated by exposure to temperatures of 43–45°C.

II. APPARATUS

- Suitable containers for the growth medium : screw-cap bottles or test tubes with metal or plastic caps, or screw-caps.

• Water bath or heating block set to hold a temperature of 43–45°C, for cooling and tempering the culture medium after autoclaving or after boiling to remelt the agar. The heating block or the water level in the bath should be of sufficient height to cover completely the column of medium in the tubes or bottles.

• Sterile glass or plastic Petri dishes : These are of diameter 90–95 mm for standard technique ; larger or smaller dishes may be used for special techniques.

• Sterile bacteriological pipettes, suitable for measuring the test portion with a precision of 2.5% or better. The size may vary between 5 ml and 0.1 ml, 1-ml pipettes being the normal size for standard technique.

• Equipment for dilution of the laboratory sample, if necessary, as described in section 3.3.

• Incubator : the temperature is stated for each method.

• Colony counting aid : The colonies should be counted under 5–6 times magnification (hand magnification lens). A counting aid with magnification, illumination, and a pressure-sensitive or electronic marking pen for automatic recording of counts is, however, preferable.

III. PREPARATION OF CULTURE MEDIA

Liquify sterile, pre-prepared medium in portions of 13–15 ml in test tubes, or in other suitable containers for larger volumes, by immersion in boiling water. Then, place these containers, or similar containers taken directly from the autoclave, in a water bath (or heating block) set at 43–45°C. Temper test tubes for a minimum time of 20 minutes (*31*). Larger containers may need a longer time.

IV. PROCEDURE

IV.1 *Test portion*

Test portions of 0.1–5 ml may be used for pour-plates of diameter 90–95 mm, but 1 ml is the test portion most commonly used. Since the practical counting limit is set to about 300 colonies per plate, the optimum test portion will be one containing 100-300 bacteria (Table 2).
Guidance for the withdrawal of suitable test portions is given in Table 5.

IV.2 *Preparation of the colony count culture*

Mix the test sample thoroughly (see section 3.2) and withdraw at once the required test portion with a sterile pipette. Add the test portion to a sterile Petri dish. With dilution performed simultaneously, withdraw one test portion and add to a dilution tube with sterile diluent, then withdraw another portion and add to a sterile Petri dish (section 3.3).

Table 5. Selection of test portions for plate counts

Expected bacterial density of laboratory sample or suspension, bacteria per ml	Test portion V ml	Dilution factor F	Range covered with one plate containing 25–300 colonies, expressed as bacteria per ml laboratory sample	Comments
	1	1	Less than 25 colonies on plate.	Use more than one plate per laboratory
Less than 25	2.5	1	Plate may contain 25–50 colonies, covers density range down to 10 bacteria per ml.	sample until total number of colonies counted exceeds 25, or use membrane
	5	1	Plate may contain 25–125 colonies, covers density range down to 5 bacteria per ml.	filtration.
25– 3 000	1	1	25– 300	
	0.5	1	50– 600	
	0.1	1	250– 3 000	
	1	10	250– 3 000	
3 000– 30 000	0.1	10	2 500– 30 000	
	1	100	2 500– 30 000	
30 000– 300 000	0.1	100	25 000– 300 000	
	1	1 000	25 000– 300 000	
300 000–3 000 000	0.1	1 000	250 000–3 000 000	
	1	10 000	250 000–3 000 000	

Record the volume of test portion (V) and the dilution factor (F) for each plate.

Remove the medium tubes one by one from the heating block or water bath—in the latter case wipe off water from the outside of the tube—, flame the opening after removing the cap, and pour the medium into the dish. Mix immediately by a combination of rapid to-and-fro and circular movements for a period of 5–15 seconds, the plate being kept flat on the bench throughout.

In special circumstances, i.e., when reagents have to be added aseptically after remelting the medium, small portions of medium distributed in tubes may not be practical. The medium may then be distributed in larger portions in bottles, and volumes of approximately 15 ml poured into each Petri dish after plating the test portions.

Not more than 20 minutes should elapse between plating and pouring. The plates should be left undisturbed until the agar has set, and then transferred as quickly as possible to the appropriate incubator. Water vapour usually condenses inside the upper half of the dish when the plate is left to solidify; drops of water may then fall down during incubation and cause spreading of the colonies. To prevent this, pour-plates should always be incubated in an inverted position. A schematic illustration of the pour-plate technique is shown in Fig. 9.

V. COUNTING

Counting should be done with the aid of the magnification lens, unless the plate contains few colonies or all are large enough to be seen clearly. Without other kinds of counting aid, the optimum practical number is between 100 and 300 counts per plate.

From a dilution series, select plates with colony numbers in the region 25–300 for counting.

Count the colonies on the plates and record the results, C_i. If there are more than 300 colonies on all plates, select one and count an area large enough to cover 100–200 counted colonies (see section 3.1.2). Plates with colonies too numerous to count should be reported as TNTC, and if there is growth without well defined colonies, the report should be " confluent growth ".

VI. EXPRESSION OF THE BACTERIAL DENSITY OF THE TEST SAMPLE

Terms occurring in the calculation :

C_i : Number of colonies counted per individual plate

V_i : Volume of test portion per individual plate

BDT : Bacterial density of the test sample

SA : Sector area or size of the counted area on a plate with colony numbers exceeding 300

TA : Total area of the plate

Add the results of the individual counts for test portions from each test sample :

$$C_1 + C_2 + \ldots C_n = \Sigma C_i.$$

Add the individual volumes analysed of each test sample :

$$V_1 + V_2 + \ldots V_n = \Sigma V_i$$

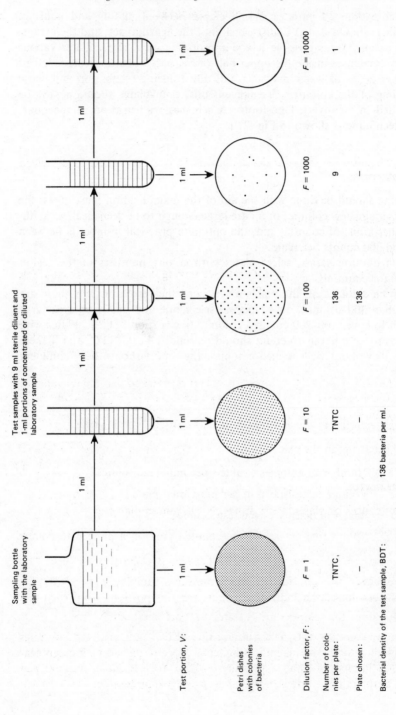

Fig. 9. Schematic illustration of plate count technique

Express the bacterial density of the test sample as :

$$\text{BDT} = \frac{\Sigma C_i}{\Sigma V_i}$$

Do not calculate the BDT.

If only a part of one plate is counted (section 3.1.2, p. 299), express as follows:

$$\text{BDT} = C \times \frac{\text{TA}}{\text{SA}} \times \frac{1}{V}$$

The calculation of bacterial density in the laboratory sample is described in section 3.10.

3.7 Spread-plate technique

I. FIELD OF APPLICATION

This technique is well suited for methods relying on colony differentiation, because all colonies will grow on the surface of the agar medium.

With standard performance, using portions preferably of 0.1 ml, this technique may only be used for waters with bacterial density higher than 250 bacteria per ml. Test portions up to 1 ml have, however, been reported to work successfully on plates predried until they have lost approximately 2 g of water (see section IV.1). This technique may also be applied for enumerating psycrophilic bacteria and other bacteria that are inactivated by short exposure to temperatures of 43–45°C.

Because most of the items necessary may be prepared in advance, this technique is recommended for field use.

II. APPARATUS

- Sterile glass or plastic Petri dishes, 90–95 mm in diameter.

- Sterile bacteriological pipettes of full volume 0.1 ml, precise to 0.002 ml, for withdrawing the test portion. Pipettes of full volume up to 1 ml may be considered for test portions between 0.1 and 1 ml.

- Equipment for dilution of the laboratory sample, if necessary, as described in section 3.3.

- Incubator : the temperature is stated for each method.

- Colony counting aid : The colonies should be counted under 5–6 times magnification (hand magnification lens). A counting aid with magnification, illumination, and a pressure-sensitive or electronic marking pen for automatic recording of counts is, however, preferable.

Optional : Water bath of 45–50°C for tempering agar medium.
Turntable for sample spreading.

III. PREPARATION OF CULTURE MEDIA

Sterile, pre-prepared medium in tubes or bottles, remelted by heating in
boiling water until the agar is liquefied, or in similar bottles or tubes
directly from the autoclave, is left at room temperature in a container
of hot water until the water temperature has cooled to 45–50°C before
pouring the plates. A thermometer should be used to follow the decrease
in water temperature. A water bath at 43–45°C intended for pour-plates may
be used, but the slightly higher temperature range of 45–50°C is preferable
because this will secure complete liquidity of the agar medium, so that after
setting it will form a completely flat surface ; this is important for even
distribution of the test portion on the agar surface. Pouring plates when
the medium is still hot will result in much water condensing inside the lid.
Pour plates to a thickness of 2–5 mm on a flat surface and leave undisturbed
until the agar has set. Air bubbles on the surface may be removed by a
quick touch of the flame of a gas burner. Store plates under refrigeration.

IV. PROCEDURE

IV.1 *Drying of plates*

Plates intended for surface counts must have a dry surface in order to
absorb the sample. A substantial amount of condensation may be formed
inside plates stored at low temperature, and this must be removed before
use. Therefore, this type of plate should always be dried prior to use.
Plates should be dried inverted with lids on over night (16–18 hours) at
37°C, or inverted with lids off for 1–2 hours at 44°C.

IV.2 *Test portion*

Volumes of 0.1–0.5 ml are commonly used for spread-plates of diameter
90–95 mm, but volumes up to 1.0 ml may be used.
On the surface of 90–95-mm diameter agar plates, up to about 300 colonies
may be counted without special counting aid. See Table 5 for suitable test
portions from samples with different bacterial densities.
These general rules do not apply to methods where special colony criteria,
such as colour due to acid production, are used to distinguish between
different types of bacteria on the plate. For such methods, the optimum
colony number must be determined separately.

IV.3 *Preparation of the colony count culture*

Great controversy exists in the literature on how to spread the sample over the agar surface. Some microbiologists report losses of 10–20% of the population when using a bent glass rod for sample spreading, while others report excellent agreement between results using a glass rod and those using other means of spreading. Theoretically, spreading with a glass rod might easily lead to considerable losses through some of the sample sticking to the glass ; therefore, the use of a glass rod is not recommended.

The sample may be added dropwise with a pipette to cover as much as possible of the surface, taking great care not to get any of the sample between the agar and the side of the Petri dish. If the plate is placed on a turntable, this procedure may—after some experience—be found quick and easy to perform. Using round-tipped " blow out " pipettes, the sample may also be spread over the agar surface by quick zig-zag movements of the pipette, which is allowed to be slightly in contact with the agar surface. Record the volume (V) of the test portion, and if the test sample was prepared by dilution, also the dilution factor (F) (see section 3.3). After spreading the sample, the plates should be placed in an appropriate incubator. The plates should not be inverted until the sample is completely absorbed.

V. COUNTING

Counting should be done with the aid of the magnification lens, unless the plate contains few colonies, or unless all colonies are large enough to be seen clearly. Without other kinds of counting aid, the optimum practical number is between 100 and 300 counts per plate (see section 3.1.2).

From a dilution series, select plates with colony numbers in the region of 25–300 for counting.

Count the colonies on the plates and record the results (C_i). If there are more than 300 colonies on all plates, select one and count an area large enough to cover 100–200 counted colonies (see section 3.1.2). Plates with colonies too numerous to count should be reported as TNTC, and if there is growth without well defined colonies, the report should be " confluent growth ".

VI. EXPRESSION OF THE BACTERIAL DENSITY OF THE TEST SAMPLE

Express the bacterial density of the test sample, BDT, as :

$$\text{BDT} = \frac{\Sigma C_i}{\Sigma V_i} \text{ bacteria per ml,}$$

or if only a part of one plate is actually counted :

$$\text{BDT} = C \times \frac{\text{TA}}{\text{SA}} \times \frac{1}{V}$$

as explained in section 3.1.2 (p. 299).
Do not calculate the BDT at this stage.
The calculation of bacterial density in the laboratory sample, BDL, is described in section 3.10.

3.8 Membrane filter technique

I. Field of application

Concentration of bacteria on membrane filters is a practical way of analysing waters with low bacterial density. Large amounts of water may be filtered through a membrane filter, but particles other than bacteria will also be kept back on the filter surface, and may interfere in the formation of clearly defined colonies. This is the main drawback of this method—it cannot be used for waters of low bacterial density compared with the density of other particles.

The practical optimum number of colonies on a membrane filter of diameter 45–50 mm is about 100 colonies. Thus, the membrane filter technique may be used without dilution of the laboratory sample for waters with a bacterial density less than 1000 per ml, and it is highly recommended for bacterial densities less than 10 bacteria per ml.

II. Apparatus

- Sterile membrane filtration apparatus.
- Vacuum source (vacuum pump or water pump attached to a tap).
- A stopcock, which should be interposed between the filtering apparatus and the vacuum source.
- Forceps, which should be round-tipped without grooves on the inner sides of the tips. They may be sterilized before use by dipping in 95% ethanol or absolute methanol and then igniting the fluid.
- Sterile culture dishes : Glass or plastic dishes of the Petri dish type may be used, preferably of diameter 50–60 mm. When available, sterilizable plastic dishes (e.g., ointment containers) with close-fitting lids are recommended. The bottom of the dish should be flat so that the absorbent pad for the culture nutrient will lie flat.
- Membrane filters of diameter 47–50 mm and pores small enough to trap the organism being sought. The membrane filters may be pre-sterilized or sterilized by placing in boiling water immediately before use.

• Sterile absorbent pads of diameter 48–55 mm. These are necessary if liquid growth media are used. Absorbent pads may be sterilized either separately, together with the membrane filters, or inside sterilizable culture dishes.

• Sterile equipment for withdrawing the test portion : Suitable pipettes or graduated measuring cylinders for measuring the test portion with a precision of ±2.5% or better. Some filtering apparatus have a graduated upper container that can measure larger volumes of test portion.

• Colony counting aid : A magnification lens (5–6×). A pressure-sensitive or electronic counting device for automatic recording of counts may facilitate counting. If available, a low-power (10–15×) binocular wide-field dissecting microscope is preferable to the magnification lens.

• Incubator with humidity control to keep the humidity inside the incubator at 90–100%. This precaution must be taken to prevent change in the medium concentration by evaporation if the Petri dish type of culture dish is used. It is not necessary for culture dishes with tight-fitting lids.

Optional : An additional flask between the filtering flask and the water pump to trap carry-over water.
A water bath set to 45–50°C for tempering liquefied agar media before pouring plates.

III. PREPARATION OF CULTURE MEDIA

III.1 *Solid media*

Prepare the growth medium as described for each group of organisms. Pour the sterile liquefied agar medium into the culture dishes forming a layer of depth 2–4 mm (5–10 ml in 50–60-mm dishes). Remove any air bubbles with a quick touch of a gas burner flame.
If the dishes are prepared beforehand and stored under refrigeration, remove drops of water condensate from the lid and agar surface before use.

III.2 *Liquid media*

Prepare the growth medium as described for each group of organisms. To a sterile absorbent pad in a sterile container, add 1.8–2.5 ml of medium aseptically. The correct amount must be established for each type of absorbent pad. The culture medium may conveniently be added some time before analysing, so that the absorbent pads may have time to swell and become completely saturated with the medium. If the pads are too dry, the membranes will not make even contact ; if too wet, spreading of colonies is encouraged.
Remove excess medium from the dish prior to use.

IV. PROCEDURE

IV.1   *Test portion*

The volume of sample to be examined must receive careful consideration before filtration is started. When the bacterial density of the laboratory sample is totally unknown, it is necessary to filter several decimal quantities of sample to establish the true bacterial density. The best method is to estimate the ideal quantity expected to yield a countable membrane and select two additional quantities representing one-tenth and 10 times this quantity, respectively. Sample quantities that will yield counts between 25 and 100 " positive " colonies result in optimum accuracy of the density determination. Higher precision will be obtained with higher counts per membrane, but the practical counting limit for this size of membrane lies around 100 colonies when mainly one colony type is present.

Larger density regions may be covered with membranes having a gridded surface (see V. COUNTING). When applying this way of widening the density region, the restrictions on colony criteria given in section 3.7 (p. 319) should be observed.

IV.2   *Preparation of the colony count culture*

Homogenize the laboratory sample by vigorous shaking and, if necessary, prepare appropriate dilutions with the dilution water prescribed in section 3.3.

Using sterile forceps, place a sterile filter over the base of the sterile filter apparatus, grid side up. Carefully place the matched funnel unit over the receptacle and lock it in place.

Close the stopcock. Add a known quantity of the laboratory or prepared test sample, either by means of the graduation marks on the funnel, by filling a funnel of known volume one or more times, or by measuring the test portion with the aid of a sterile graduated cylinder or pipette. Record the volume used (V), and if diluted, the dilution factor, F. When less than 20 ml of test portion is to be filtered, a small amount (minimum 20 ml) of sterile diluent should be added to the funnel before filtration. This increase in water volume aids in uniform dispersion of the bacterial suspension over the entire effective filtering surface.

Filtration is then accomplished by opening the stopcock and passing the sample through the filter under partial vaccum. The funnel and filter may be rinsed by the filtration of three 20–30-ml portions of sterile diluent. Unlock and remove the funnel, remove the filter with sterile forceps, and place it on the sterile nutrient pad or agar medium with a rolling motion to avoid entrapment of air. Carefully remove any surplus liquid from the dish before the membrane is placed on the absorbent pad.

Sterilization of the filter apparatus is not necessary between filtrations of equal or different volumes of the same test sample. Between filtrations of different test samples, the filtering apparatus should be sterilized using one of the methods described in VII.1.

Incubate the filters as prescribed for each method. Usually, there is no tendency to interference from water condensate forming in the upper half of the dish during incubation; thus, the dishes do not usually need to be inverted.

V. COUNTING

When few colonies appear on the filter, and when there is a great difference between " positive " and " negative " colonies, the counts may be performed without magnification. Otherwise, the count should be made with a counting aid.

Select membranes with 25–100 colonies for counting. Count and record the number of colonies on each membrane, C_i.

If all test portions have yielded membranes with more than 100 colonies, and mainly one (the " positive ") colony type appears on the membranes, select one membrane and count enough grid squares to cover 80–100 colonies. Record the number of colonies (C) and the number of grid squares (n) counted.

Membranes with colonies too numerous to count should be reported as TNTC, and if there is growth without well defined colonies, the report should be " confluent growth ".

VI. EXPRESSION OF THE BACTERIAL DENSITY OF THE TEST SAMPLE

For membranes with optimum counts, express the results as for the pour-plate technique (section 3.6.VI).

$$BDT = \frac{\Sigma C_i}{\Sigma V_i} \text{ bacteria per ml.}$$

When only the colonies in a certain number of squares are counted on a membrane, the results should be expressed as follows:

$$BDT = \frac{C}{V} \times \frac{TA}{n \cdot Sq} \text{ bacteria per ml,}$$

where n is the number of squares counted,
   Sq is the area of one square, and
   TA is the total filtration area of the membrane filter.

Filter apparatus for filters of diameter 47 mm and 50 mm usually has a total filtration area of 9.6 cm^2 and 12.5 cm^2, respectively, and one square

with sides of 3.1 mm is 1/100 and 1/130, respectively, of the total filtration area. This information is usually supplied by the manufacturers of membrane filters.
The calculation of bacterial density in the laboratory sample is described in section 3.10.

VII. STERILIZATION OF AND SPECIAL REQUIREMENTS FOR EQUIPMENT
FOR MEMBRANE FILTER TECHNIQUE

VII.1 *Filtration apparatus*

Several types of filtration apparatus designed for use in membrane filter technique are commercially available. The filter-holding assembly should consist of a seamless funnel, which fastens to a receptacle bearing a porous plate or a fritted stainless steel screen for support of the filter membrane. Assembly parts should be so designed that the funnel unit can be attached to the receptacle by means of a convenient locking device. The construction should be such that the membrane filter will be securely held on the plate of the receptacle without mechanical damage and all the fluid will pass through the membrane during filtration of the sample. The filter-holding assembly may be constructed of glass, porcelain, or any noncorrosive, bacteriologically inert metal.

Sterilization may be done by autoclaving, immersion in boiling water, or ultraviolet (UV) irradiation, and metal apparatus may also be sterilized by dry heat. Between samples, a metal apparatus may be sterilized by thorough flaming with a laboratory gas burner followed by cooling with sterile distilled water or diluent. Rapid decontamination of all types of apparatus may also be accomplished by the use of boiling water (23).

In the UV sterilization procedure, a 2-minute exposure of the filtration unit to UV radiation is sufficient. Do not subject membrane-filter culture preparations to any random UV radiation leaks that might emanate from the sterilization cabinet. Some form of eye protection is recommended. Either safety glasses or prescription-ground glasses afford adequate eye protection against stray radiation from a UV sterilization cabinet that is not light-tight during the exposure interval.

VII.2 *Culture dishes*

Sterilizable glass or disposable plastic dishes of the Petri dish type may be used, preferably of diameter 60 mm. The bottom of the dish should be flat so that the absorbent pad for the culture nutrient will lie flat.
Sterilizable plastic ointment containers with tight-fitting lids are available in some countries, and may be used successfully as culture dishes.
If reuse of disposable plastic dishes is wanted, the open culture dishes should

be treated by immersion in 70% ethanol for 30 minutes, air-dried on a sterile towel protected from dust, and reassembled. Ultraviolet radiation or other appropriate chemical or physical agents may be used for sterilization purposes. Choice of the means of sterilization should be governed not only by convenience but also by actual tests demonstrating the effectiveness of such methods. Freedom of the culture containers from residual growth-suppressive effects of the particular method used must be demonstrated. After sterilization and removal of the sterilizing agent, the containers should be closed, employing sterile techniques, and stored in a dustproof container until needed.

Metal containers should be avoided. They are usually quickly corroded, especially by media containing salt, and this may interfere in several ways in the analysis (inhibiting zones or change of colour around the corrosion spots, etc.).

VII.3 *Absorbent pads*

Absorbent pads for nutrients should consist of disks of filter paper or other material known to be of high quality and free of sulfites or other substances that could inhibit bacterial growth. Presterilized absorbent pads or pads subsequently sterilized in the laboratory should release less than 1 milligram of total acidity (calculated as $CaCO_3$) when titrated to the phenolphthalein end point, pH 8.3, using 0.02 mol $\cdot$ l^{-1} NaOH (*23*). The pads should be 44–60 mm in diameter and of a thickness sufficient to absorb 1.8–2.5 ml of nutrient. The pads may be simultaneously sterilized with membrane filters, available in resealable Kraft envelopes, or separately in other suitable containers. They must be free of visible moisture prior to use.

VII.4 *Membrane filters*

These are porous membranes composed of biologically inert materials, such as cellulose esters, acetates, or nitrate, alfa-cellulose, polyvinylchloride, polyethylene, or fluorocarbon. There are also non-porous polycarbonate membranes that have been exposed to charged particles in a nuclear reactor, and the tracks left by these particles then etched into uniform cylindrical pores.

The filters recommended for use in bacterial analysis are, however, those composed of cellulose nitrate or mixed cellulose esters. Membrane filters are manufactured in different pore sizes; the pore size commonly used in analysis of coliform bacteria and other bacteria of the same size is 0.45 μm. When fluids pass through these filters, all particles larger than the pore size of the filter are retained on the filter surface and lie in a plane where they can readily be examined and counted. With appropriate nutrients, bacteria retained on the filter surface can be grown directly into visible colonies, provided the membranes do not exhibit bactericidal or bacteriostatic properties.

Only those filter membranes may be employed that have been found, through complete laboratory tests certified by the manufacturer, to provide full bacterial retention, stability in use, freedom from chemicals harmful to the growth and development of bacteria, and satisfactory speed of filtration. They should preferably be grid-marked in such a manner that bacterial growth is neither inhibited nor stimulated along the grid lines. Several different brands of membrane filter meeting these specifications can be obtained from manufacturers and suppliers of laboratory equipment. However, recent literature (32, 33) shows that most certified membranes in common use exhibit inhibiting properties in various degrees, apparently both from the filter material and from traces of the chemical (ethylene oxide) used for sterilization. This leads to lower counts with the membrane filter technique than with the pour-plate technique for the same sample.

The surface structure of the membrane may have similar effects (34), and some manufacturers are now producing membranes the surface structure of which has been optimized for bacterial growth.

The speed of filtration may also have an effect on the results : rapid filtration may lead to lower counts than those obtained when the test portion is allowed to drip through quickly.

In the light of this new information, it is recommended that before the membrane filter technique is adopted for routine analysis, each laboratory should perform tests to determine the toxicity of the membranes and absorbent pads to be used and to detect faults in the technique employed (VII.5).

Membrane filters must be sterilized prior to use, preferably by autoclave. The paper separators should be removed from the packaged filters and replaced by absorbent pads. The filters should be divided into groups of 10–12, or other convenient units, and placed in 90-mm Petri dishes or wrapped in heavy wrapping paper. The membranes are then autoclaved for 10 minutes at 121°C (23). The temperature is critical and if exceeded will result in interference with filtration.

Some types of filter, however, withstand this temperature for longer periods than others. At the end of the sterilization period, the steam is allowed to escape rapidly to minimize the accumulation of water condensate on the filters.

Suitable packaged filters designed for autoclave sterilization—or if desired, presterilized—can be purchased in most countries. Sterilization by boiling in distilled water may also be used provided the membranes do not curl in the process. After the water and filters have been brought to the boil, the filters are used direct from the container. Do not subject filters to prolonged boiling. Some types of filter curl in this process ; they may sometimes be prevented from curling by special treatment before the boiling (35, 36).

The literature also gives advice on reuse of membrane filters if this is wanted for economical reasons. However, reuse is recommendable only if performed under strict control of an experienced bacteriologist.

VII.5 Comparison test between plate counts and membrane filter counts

At least 5 membrane filters, or absorbent pads, should be randomly selected from the packages of membranes or pads to be tested. The membranes should be tested by comparing membrane counts with plate counts on the same agar medium (pour-plate or surface-plate counts). The absorbent pads should be tested with non-toxic membranes by comparing membrane counts on liquid medium in absorbent pads with membrane counts on the same medium with 1.5% agar added. For the membranes (pads) to be considered non-toxic, the arithmetic mean of the count on 5 or more filters (pads) must be at least 90% of the arithmetic mean of the count on the same number of agar plates. The total number of colonies counted by the *plate count* technique should not be lower than 200. If the membrane filter technique yields results lower than 90% of the plate counts, this may be due not only to toxicity of the membranes or adsorbent pads, but also to faults in the performance of the technique. The reason should be carefully looked into before the membranes or pads are graded as toxic.

3.9 Field techniques

Samples that can be kept cool, transported to a laboratory and analysed within 30 hours from the time of sampling as described in section 2.3, should preferably be analysed by laboratory techniques.

Field techniques should be considered when surveys of water courses lasting several days are made in districts without microbiological laboratories. Whether the expedition travels by car or by boat, there will usually be a limited space for laboratory equipment, which then must be reduced to a minimum.

Membrane filter methods with approved delayed incubation alternatives require filtering devices, presterilized filters, nutrient pads, holding medium, pipettes, dilution bottles, and sturdy containers for sending the samples by mail to the laboratory where the final analysis will be performed.

If methods other than the aforementioned are to be performed, the incubation will have to take place in the field. Limited space calls for as few incubators and as short an incubation time as possible. A short incubation time will allow a maximum number of analyses to be performed during the expedition.

The multiple tube method for faecal coliforms requires two incubation temperatures and a long combined incubation time, and MPN-evaluation requires 15 tubes per sample, thus occupying a relatively large amount of incubator space.

The membrane filter and agar plate colony count methods for faecal indicator bacteria all require an incubation temperature of 44°C. Thus, only one incubator, which is able accurately to control the temperature to the region 44.0–44.5°C, will be necessary. The Petri dishes or membrane containers occupy little space and are kept in the incubator for a maximum of 2 days. However, these analyses require more equipment for preparing the final colony count cultures than do the multiple tube methods. These factors must be considered before deciding which technique should be chosen for field use.

The multiple tube technique should be performed without modification, as described in section 3.4.

The membrane filter technique may also be performed without modification, as described in section 3.8. For the field technique, however, a stainless steel laboratory filtration unit in a vacuum flask operated by a hand pump, and sterilized with the aid of a gas torch, may be preferable. Special syringes with three-way valves and fittings for autoclavable filter holders are commercially available in many countries, as well as special field kits for the membrane filter technique. Filtration of small volumes (0.5–1 ml) of sample may also be accomplished by placing a sterile, wet filter on top of a sterile absorbent pad, and adding the sample with a pipette as small drops evenly distributed over the filter surface. The sample will be sucked through the filter and into the absorbent pad by capillary forces, and the filter may be transferred to the growth or holding medium. Without a filtering device, this absorption of 1 ml of sample will usually take 1 minute (*37*).

The plate count field technique is best accomplished with the spread-plate technique described in section 3.7, using the pipette both for withdrawing the test portion and for spreading the sample over the surface.

With the use of identical growth media, the membrane filter and plate colony counts may be considered as one method, membrane filters being used only when concentration of bacteria from the water sample is considered necessary. The applicability of this combined membrane filter/spread plate technique must, however, be tested for each growth medium considered. Selective absorption of nutrients, indicators, dyes, etc. by membrane filters may change the growth conditions on the membrane surface compared with those on the agar medium surface (and if pour-plates are used, the growth conditions inside the agar medium).

3.10 Calculation of the bacterial density of the laboratory sample

3.10.1 *Complete list of abbreviations and symbols used in the calculations*

BDL   Bacterial density of laboratory sample

BDT	Bacterial density of test sample
MPN value	Most probable number of organisms per 100 ml of a defined test sample, taken from Table 1
V	Volume of test portion
V_i	Volume of test portion per individual plate, membrane filter or tube, as explained in section 3.6, p. 315
C	Number of colonies counted
C_i	Number of colonies counted per individual plate, membrane filter or tube, as explained in section 3.6, p. 315
TNTC	Colonies too numerous to count
TA	Total surface area of an agar plate, or total filtration area of a membrane filter
SA	Area of sector or square counted on an agar plate
Sq	Area of one square on a gridded membrane filter
n	Number of squares counted on a membrane filter
F	Dilution factor, $1 \rightarrow F$ as explained in section 3.3, p. 303
F_i	Individual dilution factors for different dilutions of one laboratory sample
V_s	Standard volume, established by tradition for each method
V_h	Volume of homogenized, semisolid sample withdrawn for dry weight determination
DW_1	Dry weight of V_h
DWL_1	Dry weight per standard volume of semisolid laboratory sample
TV	Total volume of homogenized laboratory sample suspension
WW_1	Wet weight of solid laboratory sample withdrawn for preparation of homogenized suspension
WW_2	Wet weight of solid laboratory sample withdrawn for dry weight determination
DW_2	Dry weight of WW_2
DWL_2	Dry weight per gram wet weight of solid laboratory sample
Σ	Symbol that indicates " sum of ", as explained in section 3.6

3.10.2 *Complete list of formulae used for calculating the bacterial density of the laboratory sample, BDL*

For undiluted water samples :

A. $\quad \text{BDL} = \text{MPN value} \times \dfrac{10}{V}$ 　　Multiple tube technique, bacteria per 100 ml.

B. $\quad \text{BDL} = \dfrac{\Sigma C_i}{\Sigma V_i} \times V_s$ 　　Colony count techniques, bacteria per standard volume.

For diluted water samples :

C. $BDL = MPN \text{ value} \times \dfrac{10}{V} \times F$

Multiple tube technique, bacteria per 100 ml.

D. $BDL = \Sigma C_i \times \dfrac{1}{\Sigma \dfrac{V_i}{F_i}} \times V_s$

General formula for colony count technique, bacteria per standard volume.

E. $BDL = \dfrac{\Sigma C_i}{\Sigma V_i} \times F \times V_s$

Normally used formula for colony counts, bacteria per standard volume.

For semisolid samples :

F. $BDL = MPN \text{ value} \times \dfrac{F \times V_h}{10 \times V \times DW_1}$

Multiple tube technique, bacteria per gram dry weight.

G. $BDL = \dfrac{\Sigma C_i}{\Sigma V_i} \times \dfrac{F \times V_h}{DW_1}$

Colony counts, bacteria per gram dry weight.

For solid samples :

H. $BDL = MPN \text{ value} \times \dfrac{TV \times F \times WW_2}{10 \times V \times DW_2 \times WW_1}$

Multiple tube technique, bacteria per gram dry weight.

I. $BDL = \dfrac{\Sigma C_i}{\Sigma V_i} \times \dfrac{TV \times F \times WW_2}{DW_2 \times WW_1}$

Colony counts, bacteria per gram dry weight.

For undiluted water samples the laboratory sample and test sample are identical. For solid laboratory samples the test sample will be a suspension of the laboratory sample or dilutions of this suspension. For heavily polluted water and semisolid samples, the test sample may be one or more dilutions of the laboratory sample.

For practical reasons, the calculations of bacterial densities in different types of laboratory sample are described separately.

3.10.3 *Water samples*

For MPN multiple tube technique : $BDT = MPN \text{ value} \times \dfrac{10}{V}$

For colony count technique : $BDT = \dfrac{\Sigma C_i}{\Sigma V_i}$

I. Undiluted laboratory samples

If the test sample is identical with the laboratory sample, the calculated BDT will also express the bacterial density in the laboratory sample. The formula for colony count techniques gives the density as bacteria per ml, whereas the formula for multiple tube technique gives the density per 100 ml laboratory sample. By tradition, the density of bacteria indicative of faecal pollution is expressed as bacteria per 100 ml sample, while such parameters as the heterotrophic plate count are expressed as bacteria per ml. For this reason, the standard volume V_s is introduced into the formula for the colony count technique.

Thus, for the cases when the test portions are drawn directly from the laboratory sample :

For multiple tube technique : $\text{BDL} = \text{BDT} = \text{MPN value} \times \dfrac{10}{V}$ . . (A)

For colony count technique : $\text{BDL} = \text{BDT} \times V_s = \dfrac{\Sigma C_i}{\Sigma V_i} \times V_s$ . . . . . (B)

If preservation of the information about the 95%-confidence limits is wanted, express the BDL as described in section 3.10.7.

II. Diluted laboratory samples

When the test sample is a dilution of the laboratory sample, another factor, the dilution factor F, is introduced into the formulae for BDL.

For multiple tube technique : $\text{BDL} = \text{MPN value} \times \dfrac{10}{V} \times F$ . . . . (C)

For the multiple tube technique, the MPN value is expressed as number of bacteria per 100 ml sample, and V_s does not enter into the formula as long as the standard volume of the method is 100 ml.

For the colony count technique, F enters into the formula in the term

expressed as $\dfrac{1}{\Sigma V_i}$. Instead of adding all volumes of test portion, the ratios

V_i/F_i should be added :

Colony count technique, general formula : $\text{BDL} = \Sigma C_i \times \dfrac{1}{\Sigma \dfrac{V_i}{F_i}} \times V_s$. (D)

If all the test portions are drawn from the same dilution of the laboratory sample, F_i will be the same for all individual volumes, and the term

$\dfrac{1}{\Sigma \dfrac{V_i}{F_i}}$ may be expressed as $\dfrac{F}{\Sigma V_i}$.

When results from different dilutions are within the optimum range (for plate counts, 25–300 colonies per plate), all results may be used if calculated according to the general formula D.

Example : 1 ml of dilution 1→2 giving 105 colonies
1 ml of dilution 1→4 giving 39 colonies
Standard volume : 1 ml

$$\text{BDL} = (105 + 39)\,\frac{1}{\frac{1}{2} + \frac{1}{4}} \times 1 = 192 \text{ bacteria per ml.}$$

However, in most cases optimum results will be obtained from one dilution only. Therefore, the formula normally used will be :

Colony count technique, formula normally used :

$$\text{BDL} = \Sigma C_i \times \frac{F}{\Sigma V_i} \times V_s \quad \ldots \ldots \ldots \quad (E)$$

The calculated value for BDL should not include more than two significant figures.

Example, colony counts :

$$\text{BDL} = (158 + 135)\,\frac{100}{1 + 1} \times 1 = 14\,650 \text{ bacteria per ml.}$$

This value should be expressed as 15 000 bacteria per ml (two significant figures only).

MPN-technique :

The found MPN is 31–109–253 if the volume V = 1 ml. If V = 10 ml, the values would be correct as given.

$$\text{BDL} = 109 \times \frac{10}{1} \times 1 = 1090 \text{ bacteria per 100 ml.}$$

With two significant figures only :

1100 bacteria/100 ml, or 310–1100–2500 bacteria/100 ml.

If preservation of the information about the 95%-confidence limits is wanted, express the BDL as described in section 3.10.7.

3.10.4 *Semisolid samples*

The formulae for calculating the bacterial density of the homogenized, semisolid sample are the same as described under section 3.10.3.

The bacterial density may be expressed per standard volume, but the dry weight per standard volume should also be stated in order to give information about the content of non-valatile substances in the laboratory sample.

Dry weight determination :

$$DWL_1 = DW_1 \times \frac{V_s}{V_h} \text{ grams per standard volume}$$

The results may also be expressed as bacterial density per gram dry weight of the laboratory sample, and the formulae will then be :

For multiple tube technique : $BDL = MPN \text{ value} \times \dfrac{F \times V_h}{10 \times V \times DW_1}$. (F)

For MPN values taken from Table 1, the standard volume V_s is always 100 ml, thus the formula is reduced to the expression shown above.

For colony count techniques : $BDL = \Sigma C_i \times \dfrac{F \times V_h}{\Sigma V_i \times DW_1}$ . . . . . (G)

Express the value of BDL to two significant figures only.
If preservation of the 95% confidence limits is wanted, express the BDL as described in section 3.10.7.

3.10.5 *Solid samples*

For solid laboratory samples, the bacterial density should be calculated per gram dry weight.
The formulae for calculating the bacterial density of homogenized, solid samples prepared as described under section 3.2.2, are the formulae C, D and E described for diluted laboratory samples in section 3.10.3.II.

The amount of laboratory sample in the homogenized suspension is :

$$\frac{WW_1}{TV} \text{ gram wet weight per ml suspension}$$

The dry weight of the laboratory sample is :

$$DWL_2 = \frac{DW_2}{WW_2} \text{ gram dry weight per gram wet weight}$$

Thus, the dry weight of laboratory sample in the homogenized suspension is :

$$\frac{WW_1}{TV} \times \frac{DW_2}{WW_2} \text{ gram dry weight per ml}$$

For MPN values taken from Table 1, the standard volume is always 100 ml. To express the bacterial density per ml of homogenized suspension, the expression in formula C will have to be divided by 100, resulting in the

expression : $BDL = MPN \text{ value} \times \dfrac{F}{10 \times V}.$

The bacterial density per ml divided by gram dry weight per ml will give the results as bacterial density per gram dry weight :

For multiple tube technique :

$$\text{BDL} = \text{MPN value} \times \frac{TV \times F \times WW_2}{10 \times V \times DW_2 \times WW_1} \quad \cdots \cdots \cdots \quad \text{(H)}$$

For colony count techniques : $\text{BDL} = \dfrac{\Sigma C_i}{\Sigma V_i} \times \dfrac{TV \times F \times WW_2}{DW_2 \times WW_2} \quad \cdots \quad \text{(I)}$

Express the value of BDL to two significant figures only (section 3.10.3). If preservation of the information about the 95% confidence limits is wanted, express the BDL as described in section 3.10.7.

3.10.6 Special calculation for estimated colony counts

I. *No colonies appearing on the plate, on the membrane filter, or in the tube*

Unless the test portion is identical with the standard volume of laboratory sample, the BDL should not be reported as zero bacteria per standard volume. In such cases, perform the calculation of BDL by using <1 (less than one) instead of zero as the value for C.

Example : 1 ml of 1 → 100 dilution giving 0 colonies.

$$\text{BDL} = <1 \times \frac{100}{1} \times 100 = <1 \times 10^4 \text{ bacteria per 100 ml.}$$

II. *Colony numbers higher than the practical upper limit*

When all the test portions have yielded counts above the practical counting range, a part of the plate or membrane filter may be counted and the total number of colonies on the plate or membrane calculated, as described in sections 3.1.2 and 3.8, V.
The formulae for the calculated total number of bacteria per plate or membrane filter are :

For plate count technique : $\qquad C \times \dfrac{TA}{SA} \quad \cdots \cdots \cdots \cdots \cdots \quad \text{(J)}$

For membrane filter technique : $\quad C \times \dfrac{TA}{n \times Sq} \quad \cdots \cdots \cdots \cdots \quad \text{(K)}$

The expressions J and K then replace the term ΣC_i in the formulae B–I for the calculation of BDL.
If the smallest volume of laboratory sample or dilutions thereof has given colonies too numerous to count, the expression TNTC may be used instead of ΣC_i in the formulas B–I to give an estimate of the order of magnitude of the bacterial density of the laboratory sample.

Example : 1 ml of dilution 1 → 1000, giving results TNTC.
BDL = TNTC × 10^3, or colonies too numerous to count from 0.001 ml laboratory sample.

If wanted, the term TNTC may be replaced by " $>N$ ", where N is a number considered to be the highest number of colonies that may be counted in a smaller area of a plate or filter :

Example : The highest possible counting limit is considered to be 300 colonies in 1/10 of an agar plate ; that makes 300 × 10 colonies per plate as the upper limit. The term TNTC could then be replaced in the calculations by >3000.

3.10.7 Expression of data to preserve information about the 95% confidence limits

The information about the precision of the data is contained in the total number of colonies counted for the colony count technique, and in the MPN-value for the multiple tube technique.

Example : A count of 300 bacteria per ml could have been achieved by counting 3 colonies from 0.01 ml of sample, 30 colonies from 0.1 ml of sample, or 300 colonies from 1 ml of sample. In the first case, the 95% confidence limits would be 50–800, in the second 190–410, and in the third 265–335 bacteria per ml.

For MPN-values, the 95% confidence limits are stated in Table 1. The results from the MPN-evaluation may also be presented with the 95% confidence limits included (*38*).

Example : Bacterial density estimated as 2–9–21 organisms per 100 ml. The two extreme values indicate the upper and lower confidence limits, and the middle one the most probable number of organisms per 100 ml.

For colony counts, the 95% confidence limits are given in Tables 2 and 3. For counts (*C*) above 25, the confidence limits may be expressed as :

$$\frac{\Sigma C_i \pm 2 \sqrt{\Sigma C_i}}{\Sigma V_i}$$

If the 95% confidence limits are not calculated at the same time as the BDL, this information will be lost. However, by expressing the results as the product of the MPN-value or colony count and the calculated value for the rest of the terms occurring in the formula, this information will be preserved.
The MPN-value will be a number of maximum 4 figures, and the colony count value will usually be a number of maximum 3 figures.

The other factor may be expressed as a single figure (i.e., below 10), followed by one or more decimals, multiplied by a power of 10.

Example :

1 ml of 1 → 100 dilution giving 160 colonies :

$$BDL = 160 \times \frac{100}{1} \times 1 = 160 \times 10^2 \text{ bacteria per ml}$$

1 ml of 1 → 100 dilution giving 160 colonies and another
1 ml of 1 → 100 dilution giving 175 colonies :

$$BDL = (160 + 175) \times \frac{100}{1 + 1} \times 1 \doteq 335 \times 5 \times 10 \text{ bacteria per ml}$$

This information on the precision is of value both in judging the results and in evaluating data to be used in later calculations, especially when statistical treatment in an electronic computer is considered.

However, for direct comparison of BDL-values, as in tables etc., expressions like $335 \times 5 \times 10$ are not practical. To arrive at comparable values, and still preserve some information about the order of magnitude of the 95% confidence limits, the colony number may be expressed as a calculated average per largest analysed volume of laboratory sample or lowest dilution thereof giving results within the optimum range.

Example :

The foregoing BDL = $335 \times 5 \times 10$ would then be expressed as :

$$BDL = 335 \times \frac{1}{1 + 1} \times 10^2 = 168 \times 10^2$$

Rounding up to two significant figures, this would be expressed as 170×10^2 bacteria per ml. In this case, both test portions are 1 ml of 1 → 100 dilution.
However, if the data are :
1 ml of dilution 1 → 100 giving 285 colonies and
1 ml of dilution 1 → 1000 giving 45 colonies,
the calculated BDL using equation D will be :

$$BDL = (285 + 45) \times \frac{1}{^1/_{100} + ^1/_{1000}} \times 1 = 330 \times \frac{100}{1 + 0.1} =$$

$$\frac{330}{1.1} \times 10^2 = 300 \times 10^2 \text{ bacteria per ml}$$

because 1 → 100 is the lowest dilution with counts within the optimum range.

The 95% confidence limits for C-values above 100 counts are $C \pm 20\%$ of C or less (Table 2).
For colony counts between 25 and 100, the confidence limits lie between $C \pm 40\%$ C and $C \pm 20\%$ C, and for counts lower than 25, $C \pm$ more than 40% of C.
This practical approximation of confidence limits may not be performed for the MPN-values taken from Table 1.

The formula $\dfrac{\Sigma C_i \pm 2\sqrt{\Sigma C_i}}{\Sigma V_i}$ for 95% confidence limits of colony counts

relies on the assumption that the special case of binomial distribution, the Poisson distribution, is applicable. A Poisson distribution may be assumed in bacterial suspensions with up to 1000 bacteria per ml, because the volume of a single bacterium is so small that if a volume of that size could be removed from the suspension, the probability that it would be a bacterium is very small compared with the probability that it would be water. In actual practice, however, it has been found that the observed variations are usually greater than one would expect from a Poisson distribution, because of variations due to factors like crowding of colonies on plates, clumping of bacteria in the suspension, and personal errors of measurement.

The discrepancy between the deviations one would expect from Poisson's equations and those that occur in practice increase with an increase in the number of colonies counted per plate, tube or membrane filter. With only 50 colonies per unit there is virtual agreement between theory and experimental results, while when the counts get up to 300, the actual standard deviation as determined from a *series* of counts will be about twice that predicted by Poisson's equations (*39*).

Therefore, the given formula for calculation of the standard deviation and 95% confidence limits should be applied as a guidance to the precision of the data only in cases where not more than one or two replicate test portions are used per dilution step.

For 6 or more replicate test portions giving counts within the acceptable range for colony numbers per unit (plate, filter, tube), the results should be calculated as follows :

$$\text{BDL} = \frac{\Sigma C_i/n}{V} \text{ bacteria per ml}$$

where ΣC_i is the sum of individual counts, n the number of replicate test portions, and V the volume of test portion in ml.

The standard deviation, σ, may then be calculated from the following formula :

$$\sigma = \sqrt{\frac{\Sigma(C_i{}^2) - (\Sigma C_i)^2/n}{n-1}}$$

The 95% confidence limits are :

$$\frac{\Sigma C_i/n \pm 2\sigma}{V}$$

4. STATISTICAL PROBLEMS CONCERNING COUNTS OF BACTERIA AND VIRUSES IN WATER, SEWAGE, AND SEDIMENTS

4.1 Distribution problems

A prerequisite for the application of statistical methods to the estimation of numbers of microorganisms is a knowledge of their distribution in the materials. Of particular importance is the final distribution of viable microorganisms found in the laboratory experiments as, for example, in relation to the appearance of visible colonies or when using the growth no-growth technique in fluid media.

The working out of applicable statistical models is consequently very controversial, the difficulties being already inherent in the state of the microorganisms in the basic materials. Microorganisms always form a part of some structure (cf. Fig. 10) or are subject to attraction from other particles (cf. Fig. 11). In suspension in the counting chamber they have a highly uneven distribution.

During sampling, transportation, and the laboratory procedures, the initial states will be changed in an unpredictable way. Laboratory examination may be performed by solid media methods, such as pour-plates or

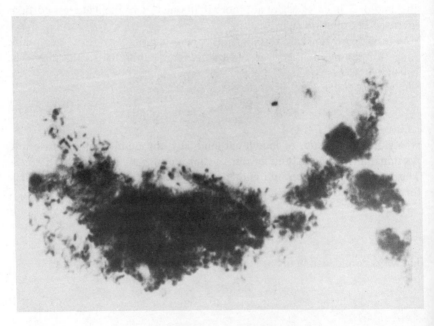

Fig. 10.   Clumps in underground water

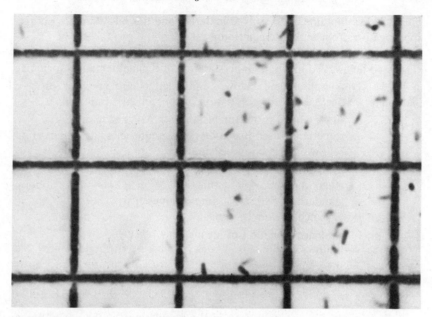

Fig. 11. Suspension in counting chamber with highly uneven distribution

tubes, roll tubes, membrane filtration, or spread plates, or by fluid media as applied in the multiple tube method.

During pipetting, homogenization and mixing with hot agar media, or on impact with membrane filters, clumps and other structures will generally be broken up but they will practically never be reduced to single elements. In other cases, flocculation may take place. Incubation in fluid media is a less complicated and therefore probably more gentle method (cf. the discussion in reference *40*).

Many investigations have been conducted on the distribution functions pertaining to counts of microorganisms and some kind of exponential distribution has been found by all authors. Some authors have found the simple Poisson distribution but most have found more complicated distributions, such as the negative binomial, the Polya distribution, (cf. reference *40*), or the log normal distribution. From almost 15 000 counts of plates and deep agar cultures, Bonde found the following relationship of the variance (σ^2) to the mean (μ) :

$$\sigma^2 \approx \gamma \, \mu^\beta$$

both γ and β being close to 1, thus not excluding the possibility of a simple Poisson law.

Counts of microorganisms have so far proved more complicated than chemical examinations of dissolved material, and this has often discouraged investigators from making bacteriological counts.

In practical work these difficulties may be avoided in several ways, as discussed below. To facilitate understanding of the mathematical formulae, a list of terms is presented below. Latin letters are used for observed parameters, Greek letters for population or theoretical parameters :

x = single observation (for instance an MPN reading)

a = sometimes used for observed frequencies or observations following a Poisson distribution

y = transformed observation, e.g., $y = \sqrt{x}$ or $y = \log x$

$\bar{x}$ = mean of observations (sometimes $= m$ in Poisson distribution)

s = standard deviation of sample values

s^2 = variance of sample values

s.e.m. = standard deviation of means $(\bar{x})$ $(= s/\sqrt{n})$

L = limiting values

v^2 = the variance ratio

u = a standardized variable $\dfrac{x - \xi}{\sigma}$, which measures the deviation of the observation from the population (or theoretical) mean with the theoretical standard deviation as unit

t = the standard variable $\dfrac{x - \bar{x}}{s}$ measuring the deviations of the sample values from the sample (empirical) mean with the sample standard deviation as unit

f = no. of degrees of freedom

n = no. of observations or total volume observed

ξ = population (theoretical) mean

σ, σ^2 = population (theoretical) standard deviation and variance

λ = population mean and variance in Poisson distribution

θ = probability of an event or observation

4.2 Means of avoiding difficulties caused by the uneven distribution of microorganisms in practical work

4.2.1 *Transformations*

In quite a few instances the Poisson distribution gives a good description of the relation and it may be applied as a reasonable approximation in many others. This is the case whether pour-plates, deep agar cultures, or membrane filtration are employed, depending more upon the material for investigation and the method of handling than on the kind of microorganism or the medium. The spread-plate method and the multiple-tube method raise special problems.

The Poisson distribution has several convenient properties for practical work :

(*a*) A square root transformation of the observations is applicable, the transformed values $y = \sqrt{x + \frac{1}{2}}$ having approximately a constant standard deviation of $\frac{1}{2}$ and a variance of $\frac{1}{4}$.

(*b*) When the individual observations have a Poisson distribution, their sum is also Poissonian.

(*c*) The variance is identical with the mean and so the standard deviation $= \sqrt{m}$, and the confidence limits of m are $m \pm 1.96 \sqrt{m}$ at the 95% level.

The rationale of applying a Poisson type of distribution is the small total volume of the microorganisms compared with the bulk of medium (water, sediment) in which they are suspended (see reference *40*, p. 107). So the chance of catching a microorganism on sampling is therefore small compared with the chance of catching a " particle " of water of the same size. The sample volume is here designated n, the probability of obtaining growth of colonies in unit volume of the sample is designated θ, and so the expected number of colonies in the sample n_i will be $n_i\theta = \lambda_i$. The number of colonies counted, a_i, provides an estimate of the parameter λ_i. A close approximation to the probability that the number of colonies will be a_i is therefore given by the Poisson equation :

$$p\{a_i | n_i\} = e^{-\lambda_i} (\lambda_i{}^{a_i}/a_i!)$$

Two Poisson counts a_1 and a_2 representing counts of two volumes of equal size $n_1 = n_2$ may be compared after transformation by a u-test (sometimes named z-test, see reference *41*, p. 159). Further examples will be found in reference *40*, p. 135, including cases with a proportionality factor. The test aims at demonstrating whether two observations might belong to the same distribution (the null hypothesis)

$$u = \frac{\sqrt{a_1 + \frac{1}{2}} - \sqrt{a_2 + \frac{1}{2}}}{\frac{1}{2}}$$

Several Poisson counts that all represent the same volume may also be compared, in order to demonstrate whether they are equal, i.e., belong to the same distribution with standard error $\frac{1}{2}$. The test has to demonstrate [a] whether

$$s^2/\sigma^2 \approx \chi^2/f$$

or in this case $\qquad s^2/\frac{1}{4} \approx \chi^2/f$

---

[a] See references *40*, p. 134 and *41*, p. 374 and Table VI in reference *42*.

Thus $4s^2$, where s is the standard deviation of the individual, transformed observations, should be distributed as χ^2/f if the individual, observed counts come from the same population.

Example

Four undiluted samples of lake water from August, September, November, and March at the same station give *C. perfringens* counts 184, 88, 42, 53, each estimate being a sum of counts in 10 individual tubes. The transformed values $y_1 \ldots y_4 = \sqrt{a_1 + \frac{1}{2}}, \ldots \sqrt{a_4 + \frac{1}{2}}$ are 13.58, 941, 6.52 and 7.31, $f = 3$. $\text{SSD}^a = 29.999$, $s^2 = \text{SSD}/f = 9.999$. $4s^2 \approx 40$, which is considerably outside the fractiles of χ^2/f, $f = 3$ (*42*, Table VI).

The transformed values, assumed to be normally distributed, can be applied in analyses of variance of observations which are stochastically independent.

For estimations by the multiple tube method special conditions apply. From the combination of tubes with a positive reaction (formation of acid and gas) a most probable number of organisms (MPN) is computed by a maximum likelihood estimate, based upon the assumption that the distribution of microorganisms in the sample is a simple Poisson distribution. A table for computing MPN values is presented as Table 1 in section 3 of this chapter. The MPN values are skew estimates of the " true values " generating the combinations of positives and negatives found by experiment. Therefore, log MPNs, which are more symmetrical estimates, should be applied in any kind of computation (*40*).

The log-transformed values also have a constant standard deviation depending only upon the number of tubes in each dilution and the dilution ratio. For 5-fold tubes in 1 : 10 dilutions the standard deviation is $0.58/\sqrt{n} = 0.259$, where n is the number of tubes.

The log MPNs could be regarded as approximately normally distributed values and for groups of these a standard deviation could be computed by the ordinary technique, and analyses of variance could be performed between groups of such log-transformed results.

Example

Two stations A and B in the open sea give the following estimates in June, July, August, and September (log-transformed MPNs) :

A 0.90, 2.97, 1.00, 1.30, 1.11
B 1.48, 2.52, 1.72, 2.20, 2.18
Sum A =   7.28, SSD = 2.954, s^2 = 0.738
Sum B = 10.10, SSD = 0.688, s^2 = 0.172
$f = 4 + 4 = 8$

$$v^2 \,(4,4) = 4.290 \;^b$$

$90\% < p\,\{\; v^2\,(4,4) < 4.290 \;\} < 95\%$ (cf. reference *41*, p. 294), i.e., the probability

---

[a] SSD = sum of squared deviations from the mean.
[b] v^2 is named F by some authors.

of obtaining the observed value of v^2 is between 0.05 and 0.1. Thus, it may be assumed that the two variances do not differ significantly.

A common estimate of variance can then be computed, $s^2 = 0.910/2 = 0.455$

Mean A $= 1.456$, mean B $= 2.020$

$d =$ mean B $-$ mean A $= 0.564$

The standard error of the difference between the means $= s\sqrt{^1/_5 + ^1/_5} = 0.427$ and

$$t_{f=8} = \frac{0.564}{0.427} = 1.32.$$

This value is less than the tabulated value of t (2.306) at the 0.05 probability level and 8 degrees of freedom. Thus, no difference can be demonstrated between the two stations.

4.2.2 *The problem of dilutions*

Making dilutions is very often necessary to obtain a countable number of colonies or to enable the sample to pass through a membrane filter. During the process of dilution, however, there are several possible sources of variation : (*a*) breaking up of clumps by pipetting and shaking, (*b*) loss of microorganisms clinging to the walls of pipettes or test tubes, (*c*) dying off in the diluent.

In fact, such drastic changes may be introduced as to change the distribution function itself, but this cannot of course be controlled in practical work. Of course, the dilution factor enters into the estimates of variance, but the increased variation hardly makes allowance for the error added by the dilution itself. For an observed count a_i in a $^1/_{10}$ dilution the number per unit volume of the original sample $= 10a_i$ and the standard deviation $= \sqrt{10a_i}$.

It is thus of great utility if all comparisons can be carried through on the undiluted sample, or on identical dilutions. One way of overcoming these difficulties is described in section 4.3.

4.2.3 *Application of the central limit theorem*

According to this theorem, the distribution of the sum of n independent random variables tends to the normal distribution for $n \to \infty$ under fairly general conditions (see reference *41*, p. 188). In the special case where the variables all have the same distribution, this theorem is valid if only the mean and the variance of this common distribution exist.

The application of this theorem has been envisaged in the preparation for the Danish method for counting *C. perfringens* in which the same sample or the same dilutions of a sample are incubated in 10 tubes. The means a and the empirical variances s^2 can be computed from these 10 observations (see reference *41*, p. 394).

Example

Two 1 : 100 dilutions of samples A and B of raw sewage give the following counts in each of the two series of 10 tubes of sulfite-alum medium incubated at 48°C for 24 hours :

A : 31, 22, 19, 28, 36, 30, 34, 32, 30, 29, sum 291

B : 36, 24, 27, 31, 27, 33, 26, 32, 42, 34, sum 312

Mean A $= 29.1$, SSD $= 238.90$, $s^2 = 26.54$, $f = 9$

Mean B $= 31.2$, SSD $= 265.60$, $s^2 = 29.51$, $f = 9$

$v^2 (9,9) = 1.111$

$50\% < p \{ v^2 (9,9) < 1.111 \} < 70\%$ (cf. reference *41*, p. 398)

i.e., the two empirical s^2 can be considered identical and a common s^2 computed from $(SSD_A + SSD_B)/(f_A + f_B) = 28.027$, and a common $s = 5.294$,

$$s\sqrt{1/n_1 + 1/n_2} = 2.368, \quad d = \text{mean B} - \text{mean A} = 2.100$$

$$t = 2.100/2.358 = 0.887, f = 18.$$

The two samples do not differ significantly.

In case of significantly differing variances $s^2_A + s^2_B$, the degrees of freedom are not the sum of $f_A + f_B$ but lie between the smaller of f_A and f_B and the sum $f_A + f_B$, and can be computed from the formula (*41*, p. 398) :

$$\frac{1}{f} = \frac{c^2}{f_A} + \frac{(1 - c^2)}{f_B}, \text{ where } c = \frac{s^2_A/n_A}{s^2_A/n_A + s^2_B/n_B}$$

The square root transformations of the sums A and B of the counts are 17.073 and 17.677, with a difference of 0.604, which is also in accordance with the null hypothesis

$$u = \frac{0.604}{\frac{1}{2}} < 1.96.$$

When two sets of results are to be compared and there is some connexion between pairs of results, each pair comprising one result from each of two sets (e.g., if a series of samples received two different kinds of treatment), an alternative method of calculation is generally preferable (cf. reference *41*, p. 402).

According to the test hypothesis corresponding counts are assumed to have the same value apart from random variations, from which it follows that the differences $d_i = x_{i1} - x_{i2}$ all have the true value zero. These differences are furthermore assumed to be normally distributed with variance σ_d^2. The mean difference $\bar{d} = \frac{1}{n} \sum_{i=1}^{n} d_i$ is normally distributed with parameters 0, σ^2_d/n, and $u = \frac{\bar{d}}{\sigma_d/\sqrt{n}}$ is normally distributed with parameters 0,1.

Example

Let the estimates from the previous example signify the results of an experiment with two different brands of peptone A and B in the sulfite-alum agar medium. Ten samples of sewage are divided into two parts ; after drawing lots one portion is incubated in the peptone A medium, the other in peptone B medium.

The mean $\bar{d} = 2.1$, $f = 9$, $s^2_d = 42.3222$, $s_d/\sqrt{10} = 2.057$. Hence, $t = 2.1/2.057 = 1.02$ and no difference can be demonstrated between the two peptones.

This paired test may be more discriminating than that of the preceding example because of the positive correlation between the two treatments leading to a smaller variance, which more than balances the smaller numbers of degrees of freedom.

The assumptions underlying this test can be checked by plotting the paired estimates against each other.

Where basically different distribution functions govern the two estimates of two kinds of treatment, this test can be applied only after transformations. This will be the case when MPNs of fluid media are compared with counts of solid media (see section 4.2.4) or when pasteurized and non-pasteurized samples are compared (cf. reference *40*, p. 135).

4.2.4 Non-parametric methods

Uncertainty of the nature of the distribution of results and the trouble involved in transforming many estimates are often an incentive to apply non-parametric tests. As these are generally less discriminating they will more often lead to acceptance of null-hypotheses and prompt (more careful) repetition of the experiment.

Among useful tests of this kind may be mentioned the sign test (see reference *40*, p. 252 and reference *43*).

Example

Two media are compared by multiple the tube methods in altogether 689 sets of samples ; 64 give similar MPNs and are discarded. Medium A gives the greater value in 258, medium B in 367 of the samples ; as the frequency $258/625 = 0.41$ differs significantly from $\frac{1}{2}$ (cf. also reference *42*, Table XI) the hypothesis of similar performance of the two media cannot be maintained.

Group correlation can be applied (reference *40*, p. 253) for a more detailed investigation of the relationships.

Example

By a comparison of the multiple tube method and membrane filtration the results were graded in groups (*a*)–(*d*) according to magnitude.
(*a*) $\geqslant$ 10 000, (*b*) 9 999–1 000, (*c*) 999–100, (*d*) 99–0 and the results distributed in these groups as below :

Membrane filter

	a	b	c	d
a	18	2	0	0
b	6	24	2	3
c	0	10	7	2
d	0	2	0	24

Multiple tube (row labels a, b, c, d)

Most of the estimates from the two methods fall in the same groups (the diagonal). This leaves 9 membrane filter and 18 multiple tube estimates, which is compatible with a binomial distribution of parameter ½ (*42*, Table XI). However, the comparison shows the interesting feature that a number of samples put in group (*b*) by membrane filtration (1000–9999) are assigned to group (*c*) by the multiple tube method.

In particular when large groups of MPNs are to be compared it is very tempting to avoid transformations and apply some rank test (e.g., Wilcoxon's matched pairs, reference *43*, p. 75 ; or Mann-Whitney's U test, reference *43*, p. 116).

4.3 Comparison of results on two single samples

Very often in the laboratory it will be of interest to compare two estimates, whether on two samples or on a single sample treated by two methods. This is a difficult problem. For colony counts it can be solved in the following manner (cf. reference *40*, p. 108). The two volumes to be compared are designated n_1 and n_2 with sum

$$n_1 + n_2 = n.$$

The hypothesis to be tested (H_o) is that the probability of colony growth in unit volume is the same in both counts, say θ, and the corresponding number of colonies will be

$$n_1\theta = \lambda_1 \text{ and } n_2\theta = \lambda_2$$

The observed numbers of colonies, a_1 and a_2, and their sum, $a_1 + a_2 = a.$, both follow the Poisson law with parameter λ, as above

$$\lambda_1 + \lambda_2 = \lambda.$$

The conditional probability

$$p\{a_1 \mid a.\} = \binom{a.}{a_1}\left(\frac{\lambda_1}{\lambda.}\right)^{a_1}\left(\frac{\lambda_2}{\lambda.}\right)^{a_2}$$

is thus expressed by a binomial law with known parameters. The null hypothesis is a common θ in both counts and so

$$\frac{\lambda_1}{\lambda.} = \frac{n_1}{n.},$$

and the test is performed by simply examining if the ratio $a_1 \mid a.$ can be accepted as an estimate of the ratio $n_1 \mid n$. This is done by computing the double sided 95% confidence limits of the ratio $a_1 \mid a.$ found by experiment (e.g., Table XI in reference *42*) and comparing this with the ratio n_1/n. For another application of this procedure see reference *42*, p. 20.

Example

This procedure is particularly useful in a situation such as the following. A technician filters 100 ml of a sample A, but finds this too tedious, so of the sample B only 50 ml is run through. From sample A 26 colonies are counted. From sample B 10 colonies. Does this apparent difference reflect a real difference between the two samples?

$$a_1 = 26 \qquad a. = 26 + 10 = 36$$

$$n_1 = 100 \qquad n. = 150 \qquad \frac{n_1}{n.} = 0.666$$

The ratio $n_1/n.$ is inside the two-sided 95% limits of $a_1/a.$, i.e., 0.548 and 0.858, so the two results are not significantly different.

For single estimates of colony counts the two-sided 95% confidence limit may be applied (with caution because of the unknown type of distribution in such cases). Thus, if the counts on two pour plates are 342 and 200 colonies, the standard deviations of these two counts are $\sqrt{342}$ and $\sqrt{200}$, respectively, and

$$u = \frac{342 - 200 - 1}{\sqrt{342 + 200}} = \frac{141}{23.3} = 6.1 > 1.96 \text{ (see reference } 41, \text{ p. 725).}$$

Another possibility is of course to make use of transformations with a constant standard deviation of $^1/_2$:

$$u = \frac{\sqrt{a_1 + \frac{1}{2}} - \sqrt{a_2 + \frac{1}{2}}}{\frac{1}{2}} \quad (42, \text{ p. 20})$$

For MPN values the log transformation must always be applied (40, p. 32) :

$$u = \frac{\log \text{MPN}_1 - \log \text{MPN}_2}{0.259}$$

(Care should be taken not to regard the two MPNs as some kind of average of n samples each. The application of a t test on such provisions would have only 1 degree of freedom (i.e., $t = 12.7$) and would be extremely insensitive.

The two-sided confidence limits of log MPN are given in many handbooks and standards of water examination and are shown in Table 1. They are quite in agreement with the standard deviation given above, log MPN $\pm 1.96 \times 0.259$, or about 10-fold differences between the upper and lower confidence limits of the MPN.

Example

Lower limit	MPN	Upper limit
2	9	21
28	94	219
303	918	3222

These considerations are based upon the error of method for a single sample, and the test is intended to confirm or reject the null hypothesis that the two results, a_1 and a_2, come from populations with identical means. If the two single estimates are of different origin, other sources of variation will most likely be added to the error of method and the hypothesis also rejected, but when only two estimates are available it is not possible to compute a more realistic, probably bigger, standard deviation, as is possible when more samples are available (cf. the second example given in section 4.2.1 and the first example in section 4.2.3).

4.4 Statistical evaluation of bathing water

Although a dose-response relationship between occurrence of infectious diseases and pollution of the sea is difficult to establish, sufficient convincing cases exist to justify the maintenance of a bathing beach control. However, the limiting values and control procedures must be flexible and technically feasible.

The control is preferably carried out as a monitoring procedure, using simple methods and frequent examinations. The taking of *E.coli* counts by the multiple tube method is a time-honoured practice of reasonable precision and acceptable cost.

Bacteria in water occur in clumps, and one clump may well contain an infective dose. There is general agreement that water visibly polluted with faecal matter is obnoxious and harmful. For practical purposes this will generally correspond to values of about 2000 or more *E.coli* per 100 ml, corresponding to a dilution of raw sewage of only 1 : 50–1 : 100. For practical purposes an upper value should then be fixed near this figure.

The error of the method and the variation due to external factors, such as wind, current, temperature, and sunshine, are certainly considerable and must be taken into consideration by fixing limits and sampling programmes.

A control of quality by means of " proportion defective ", i.e., the frequency or percentage excess of a fixed limit of *E.coli* counts must be based upon 4 assumptions (cf. also reference *41*, p. 303–307) :

1. There exist areas with a homogeneous distribution of *E.coli* (MPNs).

2. Log MPN is normally distributed, but with an unknown population mean and unknown variance.

3. On the basis of a finite sample of n observations (e.g., $n = 20$) it is possible to decide whether for instance more than 5% of all possible samples taken in such areas exceed the limiting value L ($L = 3 = $ log MPN 1000, or other values).

4. The *E.coli* count is applicable as a quality control parameter.

The theoretical means and variances need not be known.

What is needed is a statement of the type : The probability that not more than 5% of all possible water samples from the area in one year give $L \leqslant 3$ is 95%.

Procedure : n water samples are examined ; for each sample logs are taken and mean and standard deviations, $\bar{y}$ and s, are computed.

If the area, i.e., the whole batch of samples, is of this standard quality the equation :

$$\xi + u\sigma = L \ (u = 1.65 \text{ for one-sided 5\% probability})$$

must be satisfied in theory, or in practice $\bar{x} + ts = L$.

The control is effected by computing the t values of individual stations in the area and comparing these t values with the theoretical two-sided limits, i.e., $t_{0.975}$ and $t_{0.025}$. These limits depend upon the percentage excess, or proportion defective, θ, aimed at (here = 5%) and the probability of obtaining such a proportion defective, P (= 95%) ; they also depend on the number of observations available. The formula for computing the limiting t values (often named $t_{P\theta}$) is :

$$t_P \left(\theta \right) \simeq \frac{u_{1-\theta} + u_P \sqrt{\dfrac{1}{n}\left(1 - \dfrac{u_P^2}{2f}\right) + \dfrac{u_{1-\theta}^2}{2f}}}{1 - \dfrac{u_P^2}{2f}}$$

Example

If 20 observations are available for each station in an area and a 95 % security (P) is needed that 1000 ($L = 3.00$) should not be exceeded in more than 5% (θ) of samples the two-sided $t_{P\theta}$ values are

$$t_{0.025} = 1.0 \text{ (lower limit)}$$

and

$$t_{0.975} = 2.6 \text{ (upper limit)}$$

For example, the computation of $t_{0.975}$ is :

$$t_{P\theta} = t_{95\%, \ 5\%} = \frac{1.65 + 1.96 \sqrt{\dfrac{1}{20}\left(1 - \dfrac{1.96^2}{38}\right) + \dfrac{1.65^2}{38}}}{1 - \dfrac{1.96^2}{38}}$$

From each of 5 locations 1–5 in an area 20 samples are taken in a bathing season. The means of 20 samples, their standard deviations, and the t values are computed A graphical control is possible by drawing a line for each of the two limiting values and plotting the observed t values.

Location	$\bar{x}$	s	t
1	1.92	0.9	1.2 [a]
2	1.70	1.3	1.0 [a]
3	2.34	3.8	0.17
4	3.11	5.3	0.02
5	1.54	2.1	0.95

[a] Within limits

Station No. 4 is clearly defective as the mean exceeds L and the standard deviation is enormous (but not unrealistic) ; 3 and 5 have high standard deviations and only 1 and 2 are within the limits. A station can be condemned because of both high means and high standard deviations, i.e., widely varying results within the year ; this is also an indication that the distribution of bacteria within that area during the time of observation is not homogeneous (cf. condition 1), which may be due to the fact that these areas may be polluted to a varying degree from more than one source.

5. INDICATOR ORGANISMS

5.1 The use of microbial indicator organisms in the abatement of water pollution

5.1.1 *Microorganisms in common use as indicators of faecal pollution*

The organisms most commonly used as indicators of faecal pollution are the coliform group as a whole, and particularly *Escherichia coli*. Coliform bacteria are normal inhabitants of faeces, where they occur in high numbers (cf. section 1. Introduction). Various studies have been made to develop methods selective for the coliform bacteria of undoubted faecal origin. Results obtained with these " faecal-coliform " methods have shown that this group of bacteria is a better indicator of pollution by warm-blooded animals than the traditional total coliform procedure when applied to stream pollution investigations, sewage treatment systems, and bathing water quality. For this reason, procedures for total coliform bacteria are not considered in the present Manual.

The term " coliform bacteria " refers to a certain group of bacteria belonging to the family Enterobacteriaceae and distinguished by being able to ferment lactose. Some of the faecal pathogenic bacteria also belong to this family. All members of the family Enterobacteriaceae may be expected to show more or less the same ability to survive in sewage, water, and mud environments, but exceptions do occur. Other faecal organisms may show a lower or higher ability to survive. Coliform bacteria have a low resistance towards chlorine. Faecal micro-organisms or microorganisms that may enter sewerage systems from other sources than faeces have been shown to have a higher resistance (for example the mycobacteria and certain yeasts, *44*). Thus, the coliform bacteria are not well suited as microbiological indicators of wastewater chlorination efficiency.

Another widely used indicator of faecal pollution is the bacterial group called " faecal streptococci ". These bacteria belong to the family Strepto-coccaceae. The faecal streptococci may survive for a longer time in the aquatic environment than the faecal coliform bacteria, but they are not as numerous as the latter in human faeces.

Intensive studies on the occurrence of faecal streptococci in domestic wastes, storm water, the faecal discharge from man and farm animals, wild life, freshwater fish, vegetation, and insects have yielded new data for a reappraisal of the sanitary significance of a faecal coliform—faecal streptococci indicator system (45). These data have demonstrated that faecal streptococci were present in greater numbers than coliform bacteria in faecal discharges from farm animals, dogs, cats, and various wild animals. Storm water also contained higher levels of faecal streptococci than of faecal coliforms. In contrast, the faeces from man and the wastes in domestic wastewaters contained at least 4 times as many faecal coliforms as faecal streptococci.

The ratio of faecal coliforms to faecal streptococci typical of the different types of pollution may be summarized as follows : Faecal discharges from farm animals, dogs, cats, various wild animals : less than 1 : 1 ; faecal discharges from man : equal to or greater than 4 : 1 ; domestic wastewater : equal to or greater than 4 : 1 ; storm water : less than 1 : 1.

In these investigations—made by Geldreich & Kenner (45)—the faecal coliform method was the Alternative 1 method described in section 5.2.2. and the faecal streptococci method was the plate count on KF-streptococcus agar, as described in reference 23.

The faecal coliform to faecal streptococcus ratios given above must be applied carefully. Correlations are most meaningful when developed from bacterial densities in water samples taken at waste outfalls into a stream, and will be valid only during the initial 24-hour travel downstream from the point of pollution discharge into the receiving river.

In special circumstances the use of *S. bovis* and *S. equinus* as a specific indicator group for non-human pollution may be useful in studies involving livestock pollution from cattle and dairy farm feed-lots, meat packing and dairy plant wastes, duck farms and duck processing wastes, and pollution from wild bird refuges. These two faecal streptococci strains are the most sensitive indicator organisms within the faecal streptococcus group because of their rapid die-off outside the animal intestinal tract (46).

The increasing use of chemical treatment of domestic sewage in some countries has led to increased interest in the faecal streptococcus test. Flocculation by lime or other strong bases may lead to pH-values higher than 9 in the treated sewage. If the coliform test is used as the only test for estimating the effectiveness of the process in removing faecal organisms the process will be graded as excellent. Faecal streptococci, however, being able to *grow* at pH 9.6, will not be reduced to the same extent and may therefore be used as indicator organisms for pathogenic organisms with similar pH-resistance.

The third group of microorganisms in common use as indicators of faecal pollution is the " anaerobic, sulfite-reducing spore-formers ", belonging to the family Bacillaceae. The value of these bacteria as indicators of faecal pollution lies in their ability to form spores. The organism of primary interest is *Clostridium perfringens*. By means of special methods,

C. perfringens has been shown to amount to more than 95 % of the anaerobic, sulfite-reducing spore-formers in the intestine of man.

The number of anaerobic, sulfite-reducing spore-formers in the intestinal canal is usually smaller than that of faecal coliforms, and the same applies to sewage. Analysis for such spore-formers has therefore little place in the examination of recently polluted water, for when the spore-formers are detectable in 100 ml of such a water, faecal coliforms are usually present in large numbers. The spores of these spore-formers can, however, survive in water for a long time and persist when all the other faecal bacteria have disappeared. Therefore, this test may be used for demonstrating remote or intermittent pollution.

These spore-formers may also be used as indicators of the survival of pathogenic spore-formers in different sewage treatment processes and sewage sludge stabilization.

In recent years there has been an increased interest in these organisms as indicators of the influence of faecal pollution in fjords, lakes, and slow-flowing rivers. Whereas the water may show great fluctuations in the concentration of faecal indicator organisms, owing to the action of currents (tidal, wind, natural flow of rivers, etc.), the sedimented bacteria in the mud may serve as a concentrated and stable index of the quality of the overlying water. Bacterial spores survive for a long time in muds and may be of importance in the estimation of long-term effects, by comparing the concentration of spores from faecal spore-formers at increasing depths of a sediment core.

The region of influence from domestic sewage outlets in recipient waters has been studied by analysing the surface layer of sediments for anaerobic, sulfite-reducing spore-formers. The results showed that the ratio of spores to vegetative cells increased with increasing distance from the source of pollution (4).

In the last-mentioned investigation, both spores and vegetative cells of anaerobic, sulfite-reducing spore-formers were enumerated. The usual method is to enumerate the total counts of vegetative cells and spores and then to enumerate the spores separately in a pasteurized sample ; the number of vegetative cells is obtained by subtraction.

It is, however, a well-recognized phenomenon in all sporing organisms, both aerobic and anaerobic, that heating may induce germination in some spores that would otherwise have remained dormant. Some strains of *C. perfringens* have been shown to require heating before germinating (47). In such cases, more spores will be able to germinate and grow into visible colonies from heated than from unheated samples. Thus, a " total count " of spore-formers may give low values owing to lack of activation of spores that require heat treatment to stimulate their germination.

The method mentioned above for enumeration of vegetative cells must therefore be regarded as an unreliable procedure. The ratio of spores to vegetative cells may still be used in the way described (*4*) and the increasing ratio of spores to vegetative cells with increasing distance from the source of pollution may still be regarded as a general phenomenon, but the actual values of the ratio may be dependent on the strain of sulfite-reducing anaerobic spore-former predominant in each location.

The aim of the investigation will govern whether the enumeration of spores only or of spores and total counts should be the method of choice. If only one faecal indicator is wanted for special investigations, the ratio of spores to vegetative cells of the anaerobic, sulfite-reducing spore-formers in the sediments may prove to be the best choice.

5.1.2 *Indicators of pollution with easily degradable organic matter*

In water pollution studies one often encounters conditions that are not of danger to human or animal health, but that still present a problem to man.

Contamination of water with organic matter may lead to different kinds of problem, such as sludge formation in pipes carrying the water, heavy growth of microorganisms on all surfaces in contact with flowing water (river beds, boats, fishing nets, etc.), or foam formation on rivers due to slowly degradable synthetic detergents. Easily degradable organic matter also leads to problems because it allows profuse multiplication of the heterotrophic microorganisms natural to the water.

In flowing waters some of these heterotrophic microorganisms may appear in great masses and are relatively easy to identify. The filamentous bacterium *Sphaerotilus natans* is thus often found as grey-coloured slime in flowing water polluted with easily degradable organic matter, such as sewage and spent sulfite liquor from the cellulose industry (Plate 1). In fast-flowing rivers with slightly acidic water, the last-mentioned pollutant may also lead to the formation of a thick, orange-to-red-coloured " carpet " of the fungus *Fusarium aquaeductuum* on the river bed (Plate 2). The fungus *Leptomitus lacteus* may similarly be found in running water polluted with low-molecular weight organic substances, such as drainage from grass ensilage, garbage dumps, etc. (Plate 3). Effluents from oil refineries may contain dihydrogen sulfide, which enhances the development of similar growth of the sulfur bacterium *Thiothrix* on surfaces in contact with flowing effluent. These types of biological slime formation are natural in the cause of self-purification of the water, but may create problems both for man and for other organisms natural to the water. When such slime formations are encountered, and the source of pollution is not evident, it may be of some help to examine the slime under the microscope in order to establish which organisms are present. Any type of fungus suggests organic matter as the causative agent, and there is usually no need for further identification. Slime dominated by thread-forming bacteria may need investigation into the type of organism present. *Sphaerotilus*, which indicates the presence of organic matter, grows inside a sheath, which may be demonstrated by passing oxalic acid reagent (5% oxalic acid in 1 mol·l⁻¹ HCl) between the slide and the cover slip (*48, 49*). After this acidification, the sheath usually separates from the bacterial cells and becomes clearly visible outside them. This is demonstrated in Plates 5 and 6. The sulfur bacterium *Thiothrix* also grows as long threads, but does not grow as separate cells inside a sheath, and thus no sheath becomes visible after acid treatment. Further descriptions of these organisms may be found in textbooks on bacteriology.

Greyish-white slime on river bottoms does not always indicate growth of heterotrophic organisms. The diatoms *Gomphonema*, *Didymosphenia geminata*, and *Cymbella affinis*, which grow attached to stones, etc. and may form slime on river beds, may easily be mistaken for slime formed by fungi. Again, microscopic examination will reveal which type of organism is present. The diatoms are not indicators of organic pollution. Some of these diatoms are shown in Plates 7–9.

Brown-coloured slime may be formed by an alga (Chrysophyceae), *Hydrurus foetidus* (Plate 10). Brown slime may also be formed by " iron bacteria ", some of which oxidize both iron and manganese, and some iron only (Plate 4). The iron-oxidizing bacteria are indicators of ferrous iron. Some of these, belonging to the genus *Leptothrix*, may be mistaken for *Sphaerotilus*, which also has the ability to precipitate iron on its sheath if iron is present in the water. Addition of oxalic acid reagent under the microscope will again help to reveal which organism is present : *Sphaerotilus* will be clearly visible once the brown colour is removed, while this special type of iron bacterium has cells that migrate out of the sheath and no cells will be seen after the treatment. When no cells remain, the cause of slime formation is ferrous iron. When the sludge is dark brown, and cells are visible after treatment, reduced manganese, iron, and small amounts of organic matter may play a role in the slime formation. However, if the sludge is " rust coloured " and cells are visible inside a sheath (*Sphaerotilus*), organic matter is most likely the cause of the slime formation. To prevent heterotrophic slime formation, the primary source of pollution must be localized, and the effluent given proper treatment before discharge to the recipient water.

In slow-flowing waters and in lakes, growth of heterotrophic micro-organisms may lead to oxygen deficiency in the water. Both dissolved and particulate organic matter may have this effect, providing it is biologically degradable. Particulate organic matter undergoing degradation is usually found at the bottom of lakes, and the oxygen deficiency of the water will be dependent on the load of organic matter undergoing degradation and the rate of oxygen diffusion from the water masses above.

The bacteria living on easily degradable organic matter in water may also cause problems when the water is used by man. Some such problems are spoilage of food in food industry and spoilage of washed agricultural

Plates 1–3. Heterotrophic organisms that form "biological slime" on river bottoms

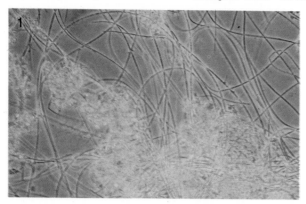

Plate 1. Biological slime containing *Sphaerotilus natans*
Thicker threads : *Sphaerotilus natans.*
Thinner threads : Flexible bacterium often found together with *Sphaerotilus* and *Fusarium*
in biological slime.

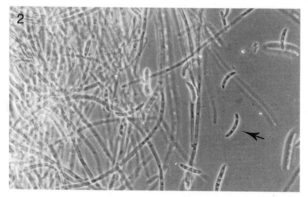

Plate 2. *Fusarium aquaeductuum*
Characteristics : Spore form. Fungi imperfecti.

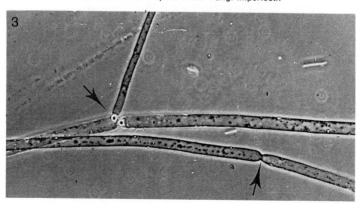

Plate 3. *Leptomitus lacteus*
Characteristics : Celluline plugs, constrictions instead of septate mycelium. Aquatic *Phycomycetes.*

Plates 4–6. Organisms that may form brown-coloured slime in flowing waters

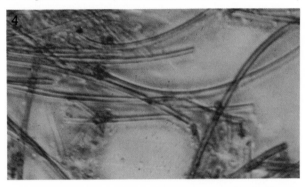

Plate 4. Threads of an iron-oxidizing bacterium of the genus *Leptothrix*
Threads of *Sphaerotilus natans* may show a similar appearance in water containing ferrous iron.

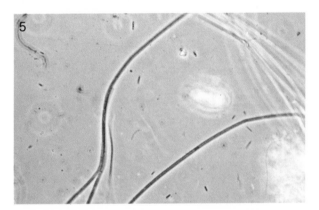

Plate 5. Threads of *Sphaerotilus natans* without iron deposits

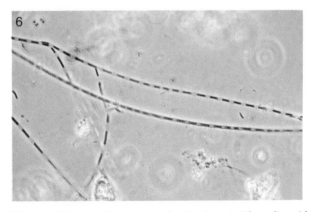

Plate 6. Threads of *Sphaerotilius natans* after treatment with oxalic acid reagent

Plates 7–10. Benthic algae that may form white to gray-coloured slime

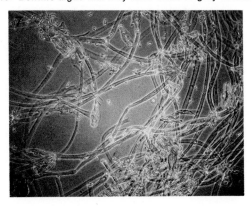

Plate 7. Threads (mucilage stalks) and cells of the diatom *Didymosphenia geminata*

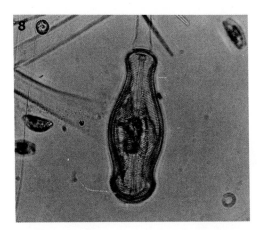

Plate 8. Cell of *Didymosphenia geminata*, enlarged

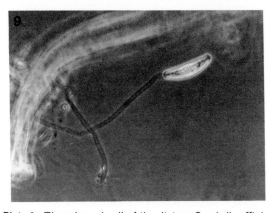

Plate 9. Threads and cell of the diatom *Cymbella affinis*

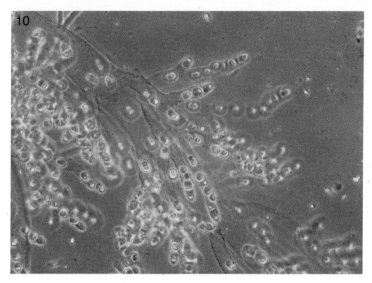

Plate 10. Microscopic appearance of *Hydrurus foetidus* (*Chrysophyceae*)

This alga may be found as brown-coloured slime strands attached to the bottom and banks of cold-water rivers. When crushed between the fingers, the slime will give off a strong, fishy smell. This may help to indicate which organism is present.

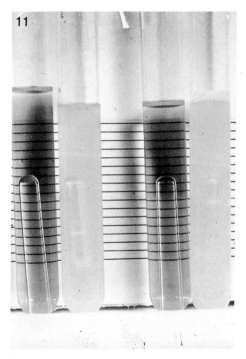

Plate 11. Positive and negative reactions in the presumptive and the confirmatory tests for faecal coliform bacteria

Left : presumptive tubes.   Right : confirmatory tubes.
Part of the turbidity is due to bile precipitated by the acid produced. Precipitated bile may prevent gas from entering the inverted vial. The tubes should therefore be gently shaken and left for a while before being reported as negative for gas production.

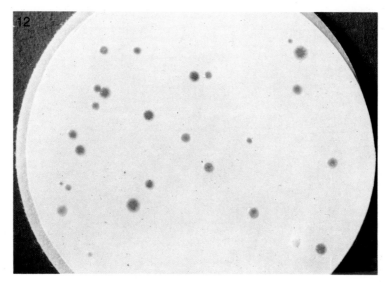

Plate 12. Colonies of faecal coliform bacteria on a membrane filter.
The blue colonies are faecal coliforms

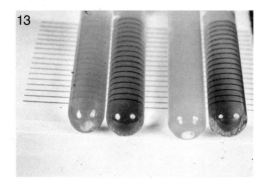

Plate 13. MPN multiple tube test for faecal streptococci

Right : presumptive test. No turbidity indicates a negative reaction.
Turbidity (growth, here with a white "button") indicates a positive reaction.
Left : confirmatory test. No turbidity indicates a negative reaction.
Turbidity with a "violet button" indicates a positive reaction.

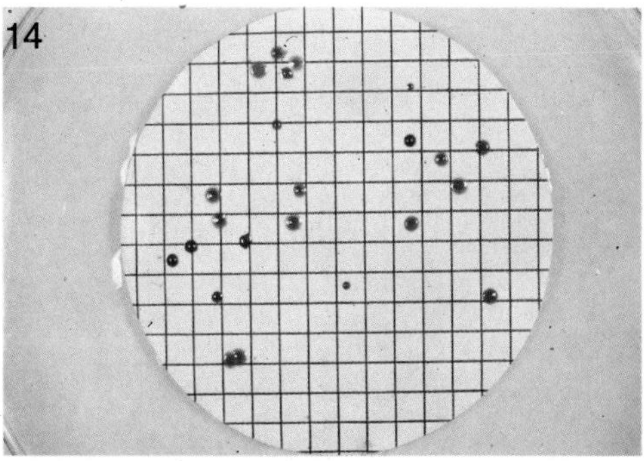

Plate 14. Colonies of faecal streptococci on a membrane filter

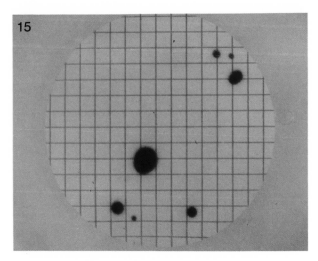

Plate 15. Colonies of anaerobic, sulfite-reducing spore-formers on a membrane filter

Plate 16. Colonies of anaerobic, sulfite-reducing spore-formers on pour-plates

Plate 17. Salmonella on brilliant green-lactose-saccharose agar (BLSF agar)
after 24 hours (salmonella colonies in red and coli colonies in yellow)

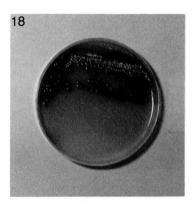

Plate 18. Salmonella on bismuth sulfite agar after 24 hours.
Note blackening and metallic lustre

Plate 19. Salmonella on desoxycholate-citrate agar (Hynes's modification)
after 24 hours. Note the small, colourless colonies

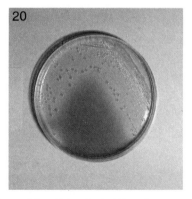

Plate 20. NAG vibrio on thiosulfate-citrate-bile salt-sucrose agar (TCBS agar)
after 24 hours. *Vibrio cholerae* and NAG vibrios appear as rather small, yellow colonies

Plate 21. NAG vibrio on taurocholate-tellurite-gelatine agar (TTGA agar) after 24 hours. *Vibrio cholerae* and NAG vibrios appear as rather small colonies. When viewed against a white background, the centre of the colony may appear to be somewhat black

Plate 22. *Vibrio parahaemolyticus* on thiosulfate-citrate-bile salt-sucrose agar (TCBS agar) after 24 hours. Note the greenish centres of the colonies

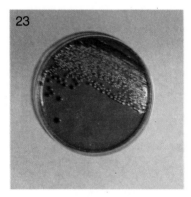

Plate 23. *Vibrio parahaemolyticus* on bromothymol blue-Teepol-salt agar (BTB agar) after 24 hours.
Note that the colonies are already rather large and have greenish centres

products during storage. Some saprophytic bacteria potentially pathogenic to man, animals, and plants may also multiply in such polluted water and may cause problems if the water is used for irrigation or recreational purposes. A method of estimating the degree of pollution with easily degradable organic matter would therefore be of importance for certain uses of water. The biochemical oxygen demand (BOD) analysis may detect such pollution directly if the pollution is recent or continuous and if the concentration of organic matter is high enough to be detected by this analysis. However, the bacterial population arising from organic pollution could also serve as an indicator of such pollution. For this reason, methods for estimating the number of heterotrophic microorganisms present in water have been developed and are in use in several countries. A reference method for making a heterotrophic plate count is also included in this chapter (see section 5.5).

5.1.3 Other microbial indicators of use in water pollution control

Research is continuously going on to find new methods that may be of use in abating water pollution. Some methods involving the use of micro-organisms have been applied for several years in certain countries, while other methods must still be considered as being in the research stage. A few such methods will be mentioned in the following.

Instead of, or in addition to the heterotrophic plate count, enumeration of fluorescing bacteria on King's agar B (*Pseudomonas fluorescens*) and other pseudomonads (*50–54*) may be carried out to evaluate the risks of spoilage of food in the food industry or during storage of washed agricultural products.

In this connexion, it might also be of interest to know the level of spores and vegetative cells of fungi and actinomycetes present in the water. General methods that include all types of fungi or Actinomycetes are not likely to be developed. Different investigators have their own favourite methods; some are described as " general " and some are developed for special purposes. Some of these methods are summarized in Tables 6 and 7. The details may be found in the literature references.

A nocardioform actinomycete, *Rhodococcus coprophilus*, may also be used as an indicator of faecal pollution from farm animal effluents. In unpolluted lakes and rivers there are usually more *Micromonospora* and *Streptomyces* than nocardioform actinomycetes, but in streams enriched with farm effluents the nocardioforms, especially *R. coprophilus*, can be present in high numbers (500 to over 1000 per ml). This organism is present on pasture grasses and hay; it survives ingestion and passage through the cow and is excreted in the faeces where growth occurs (*55*). The dung of other herbivores, such as horses, sheep and goats, also contains *R. coprophilus* (*149*). There was a significant correlation between the numbers of faecal streptococci and *R. coprophilus* in river water samples but no relation-

Table 6.   Some media for the isolation and enumeration of actinomycetes from lake and river water and sediments and wastewater

Concentration in grams per litre unless otherwise stated

Ingredients	Glycerol-arginine agar, Porter et al. (59)	Glycerol-asparagine agar (14)	Starch-casein agar, Küster & Williams (59)	Starch-casein agar (23)	Starch agar (14, agar A.) (37)	Starch agar B (14)	Chitin agar (36)	Krassilnikov 2 medium (14, 37)	Krassilnikov 3 medium (14)	Czapek agar (14)	Propionate-malachite green agar (58)	Propionate-thiamine agar (55)
Na₂HPO₄	—	—	2.0	2.0	—	0.5	0.7	5.7	—	—	2.5	0.732
K₂HPO₄	—	2.5	—	—	—	—	—	—	1	1	—	—
KH₂PO₄	—	—	—	—	0.3	—	0.3	2.4	—	—	1	0.466
CaCO₃	0.1	—	0.02	0.02	—	—	—	—	—	3	—	0.02
CaCl₂	0.1	—	—	—	—	—	—	—	—	—	0.5 mg	—
CaCl₂·6 H₂O	—	0.1	—	—	—	0.05	—	—	0.2	—	—	—
MgCO₃	—	—	—	—	1.0	—	—	—	—	—	—	—
MgCl·6 H₂O	—	—	—	—	—	—	—	—	—	—	—	—
MgSO₄·7 H₂O	0.1	0.3	0.05	0.05	—	0.2	0.5	1.2	0.5	0.5	0.05	0.10
FeSO₄·7 H₂O	0.1	—	0.01	0.1	—	—	0.01	0.01	0.0002	0.01	—	0.20 mg
Fe₂(SO₄)₃·9 H₂O	—	—	—	—	—	—	—	—	—	—	—	—
Ferric ammonium citrate	—	—	—	—	—	trace	—	—	—	—	0.04	—
MnCl₂·6 H₂O	—	—	—	—	—	—	—	0.008	—	—	—	0.02 mg
MnSO₄·4 H₂O	—	—	—	—	—	—	—	—	—	—	—	—
ZnSO₄·7 H₂O	—	—	—	—	—	—	0.001	0.01	0.01	—	0.001	0.18 mg
CuSO₄·5 H₂O	—	—	—	—	—	—	—	0.006	—	—	0.001	—
NaCl	1.0	1	2.0	2.0	0.5	—	—	—	2	0.5	0.85	0.30
KCl	—	—	—	—	—	—	—	—	—	—	—	—
NaNO₃	—	—	—	—	1.0	0.05	—	—	—	2	—	0.10
KNO₃	—	—	2.0	2.0	—	—	—	—	—	—	—	—
(NH₄)₂HPO₄	—	—	—	—	—	—	—	—	—	—	—	—
(NH₄)₂SO₄	—	—	—	—	—	—	—	2.6	2	—	0.5	—
Casein (vitamin-free)	—	—	0.3	0.3	—	—	—	—	—	—	—	—
L-Arginine	2.5	—	—	—	—	—	—	—	—	—	—	—
L-Glutamic acid (Na⁺)	—	—	—	—	—	0.05	—	—	—	—	0.5	—

	1	2	3	4	5	6	7	8	9	10	11	12
propionate	—	—	—	—	—	—	—	—	—	—	1	0.2
Sodium lactate	—	—	—	—	—	—	—	—	—	—	—	—
Sodium citrate	—	—	—	—	—	—	—	—	—	—	—	0.1
Ammonium lactate	—	6.5	—	—	—	—	—	—	—	—	—	—
Glucose	—	—	10	10	10	2	10	11	10	10	30 or 30	2
Sucrose	—	—	—	—	—	—	—	—	—	—	—	—
Water-soluble starch	—	—	—	—	—	—	—	—	—	—	—	—
Chitin, dry	—	—	—	—	—	2.5	—	—	—	—	—	2
Oleic acid	—	—	—	—	—	—	—	—	—	—	0.05[a]	0.05[a]
Albumin fraction V, bovine	—	—	—	—	—	—	—	—	—	—	5[a]	—
Biotin	—	—	—	—	—	—	—	—	—	—	0.5 mg	—
Pyridoxine	—	—	—	—	—	—	—	—	—	—	0.001	—
Thiamine HCl	—	—	—	—	—	—	—	—	—	—	—	0.004
Catalase	—	—	—	—	—	—	—	—	—	—	0.004	—
Malachite green	—	—	—	—	—	—	—	—	—	—	0.001	—
Agar	20	20	20	15	15	20	8 Oxoid 20 Japan.	—	15	15	15	18
Antifunga agents:												
Cycloheximide (actidione)	—	—	—	—	—	—	0.05	—	—	—	—	0.05
Nystatin	—	—	—	—	—	—	0.05	—	—	—	—	—
Antibacterial agents	—	—	—	—	—	Heating	—	—	—	—	Acid treatm.	Heating
pH-value	not stated	7.0	not stated	7.0	7.4	7.4	7.0	7.0	not stated	7.0–7.3	not stated	7.0
Technique	not stated	Plate count	Isolation from soil	Pour pl. double	Plate count	Plate count	Inverted membrane	Titre	not stated	not stated	Membrane filter	Spread plate
Purpose	Isolation from soil	For streptomycetes	Isolation from soil	For taste & odour & actinomycetes	For streptomycetes	For streptomycetes	For actinomycetes from unpolluted water & sediment	For actinomycetes (i.e., streptomycetes)	For streptomycetes	For streptomycetes	For acidfast bacteria	For nocardioform Lspi from polluted water & sediment

[a] Included as OADC-oleic acid albumin dextrose catalase.

Table 7. Some media for the isolation and enumeration of fungi from lake and

Ingredients	Purpose of selective agent	Concentration in grams			
		Peptone-glucose agar, Goos et al.	Peptone-glucose-rose bengal agar, Cooke	Martin's rose bengal agar	Martin's rose bengal agar modified for membrane filter
		(60)	*(60)*	*(36)*	*(56)*
K_2HPO_4		—	—	—	—
KH_2PO_4		0.5	(1)	1	1
$MgSO_4 \cdot 7 H_2O$		0.5	(0.5)	0.5	0.5
Magnesium glycerophosphate		—	—	—	—
$FeSO_4 \cdot 7 H_2O$		—	—	—	—
K_2SO_4		—	—	—	—
KCl		—	—	—	—
NaCl		—	—	—	—
$NH_4H_2PO_4$		—	—	—	—
KNO_3, $NaNO_3$		—	—	—	—
$Ca(NO_3)_2$		—	—	—	—
Peptone		2	5	5	5
Yeast broth		—	—	—	—
Yeast autolysate		—	—	—	—
Yeast extract		—	—	—	—
Malt extract		—	—	—	—
Meat extract		—	—	—	—
Na-K-tartrate		—	—	—	—
Glycerol		—	—	—	—
Glucose		10	10	10	10
Sucrose		—	—	—	—
Agar		15	20	10	10
Rose bengal	Suppression of rapidly growing and spreading fungi	—	0.035	0.35	0.7
Ox bile, dehydrated	Suppression of spreading fungi, and of bacteria	—	—	—	—
Crystal violet	Antibacterial agent	—	—	—	—
Chloramphenicol	" "	0.05	—	—	—
Kanamycin	" "	—	—	0.1 and/	0.1
Streptomycin	" "	—	—	or 0.1	
Penicillin, units/l	" "	20 000	—	—	—
Actinomycin	" "	—	—	—	—
Chlortetracycline (Aureomycin)	" "	—	0.035	—	—
para-aminobenzoic acid	" "	—	—	—	—
10% lactic acid, approx. 10 ml per litre medium of pH-value 7	Acidification to pH-value 3.5 to inhibit acid-sensitive bacteria	yes	—	—	—
pH-value (without addn. of lactic acid)		4.0 or 4.8		5.4	not stated
Technique		Spread plate		Plate count, membrane filter	Membrane filter
Incubation		15, 25 and 37°C, 5–15 d.		22°C for 7 days	
Purpose		General fungi		General fungi	

---

a Also used for sewage yeasts and moulds in the CMEA-standards *(53)* : Incubation of spread plate 15–20°C. After 48 ± 2 hours yeast colonies are counted, after 7–10 days mould colonies are counted.

river water and sediments and from wastewater

per litre unless otherwise stated

Czapek Original a	Dox agar Modified b	Littman's bile agar			Yeast extr.-malt extr.-glucose-rose bengal agar	Yeast extract agar	Glucose-yeast-tap water agar	Vitéz medium
(60, 61)	(62)	(60)	(61)	(63)	(58)	(37)	(14, 37)	(37, 54)
1	—	—	—	—	—	—	0.1	—
—	—	—	—	—	—	—	1	1.0
0.5	—	—	—	—	—	0.25	0.7	0.2
—	0.5	—	—	—	—	—	—	—
0.01	0.01	—	—	—	—	0.01	—	c
—	0.35	—	—	—	—	—	—	—
0.5	0.5	—	—	—	—	—	—	—
—	—	—	—	—	—	1	0.5	3.0
—	—	—	—	—	—	—	—	1.0
Na : 2 ; 3	2	—	—	—	—	—	—	K : 1.0
—	—	—	—	—	—	—	0.4	—
—	—	10	10	10	5	—	—	15
—	—	—	—	—	—	—	50.0 ml	—
—	—	—	—	—	—	—	50.0 ml	—
—	—	—	—	—	3	10	—	—
—	—	—	—	—	3	—	—	—
—	—	—	—	—	—	—	—	2.0
—	—	—	—	—	—	—	—	1.0
—	—	—	—	—	—	—	—	5.0 ml
—	—	10	10	10	10	10	60	30
30	30	—	—	—	—	—	—	—
20 ; 10	12	12	15	20	15	15	20	20–25
—	—	—	—	—	0.2	—	—	—
—	—	15	15	15	—	—	—	—
—	—	0.001	0.001	0.001	—	—	—	—
—	—	0.005	—	—	5	—	—	—
—	—	—	—	—	—	—	—	—
—	—	0.003	0.03	0.03	—	—	100 000 units }	—
—	—	—	—	—	1 g/l	—	50 000 } or	—
—	—	—	—	—	—	—	0.002)	—
—	—	—	—	—	—	—	0.050) ←	—
—	—	—	—	—	—	—	d ←	—
—	—	—	—	—	—	—	—	0.05
ʔs ; —	—	—	—	—	—	—	—	—
4 ; 7.3	6.8	7.0 ± 0.2			3.6–3.7	not stated	4.0	5.9–6.3
Spread plate		Spread plate			Inverted black membrane filter	Pour plate	Pour plate	Membrane filter
2 weeks at 25 °C		4–8 days at 30–32 °C			37 °C, 20 h	22 °C ; 5, 10 d.	22 °C ; 5, 10 d.	37 °C ; 2–5 d.
eneral ngi	Candida chlamydospores	General, and dermatophytes ; not saprolegiaceous fungi			Yeasts in wastewater	General fungi	Water fungi	Candida in swimming pools

b Modified to prevent precipitation of magnesium phosphate.
c Traces of Fe, Co, Mn, Zn, Cu are also added.
d Or streptomycin : 0.02 g/l, chlortetracycline : 0.10 g/l and chloramphenicol : 0.02 g/l.

ship between the actinomycete and *E. coli* (*150*). The propionate-thiamine agar used for counting actinomycetes in these investigations is included in Table 6.

Actinomycetes, especially species of the genus *Streptomyces*, and also various fungi are a common source of earthy smells or musty tastes and odours. Actinomycetes are washed in from the soil and may grow in surface waters on vegetable matter such as algae, higher plants or plant remains, and sometimes animal and fish remains, especially on exposed river mud flats, reservoir banks or algal concentrations in sewage treatment plants if the surroundings reach temperatures of 20°C or higher (*56*). Thus, counts of actinomycetes and fungi may also be wanted in connexion with sudden outbreaks of tastes and odours in drinking water. Some such enumeration methods are included in Tables 6 and 7. In such investigations, the search is for the most probable causative organism, and the microorganisms do not serve as *indicators* of pollution.

Actinomycetes and fungi may also be of use in disinfectant efficiency studies : In chlorinated swimming pools, the presence of yeasts may indicate that the residual chlorine is not high enough for efficient disinfection. The presence of *Candida albicans* has been demonstrated in such swimming pools (*53*), and in this case the indicator of nonefficient chlorination is also a human pathogen (cf. list in section 6.2). A method for enumeration of this organism is included in Table 7 (Vitéz medium, references *37* and *54*).

In order to assess the efficiency of wastewater chlorination in terms of destruction of pathogens, there is a need for a reliable bio-indicator that is at least as resistant to chlorine as the most chlorine-resistant pathogens. The bio-indicator should also be rapidly and unambiguously quantifiable in chlorinated effluents by simple and easily applied techniques. The group of bio-indicators most often used, the faecal coliforms, does not meet the criterion of being as resistant to chlorine as the most resistant pathogens, and is thus not suited for judging the efficiency of wastewater chlorination. Other types of microorganism, such as acid-fast bacteria and yeasts appearing in human faeces and sewage, have been seriously considered as suitable bio-indicators.

Some investigators (*44*) who found such promising bio-indicators to be present in sewage and human faeces did further studies to evaluate the resistance to chlorine of the different isolates (*57, 58*). The most promising isolates were found to be two bacterial strains and one yeast : *Mycobacterium fortuitum* and *Mycobacterium phlei*, and *Candida parapsilosis*. The bacteria showed the highest resistance to chlorine, but the yeast was found to be more numerous in human faeces than the mycobacteria. However, the approach taken by these investigators was to consider groups of micro-organism as potential indicators rather than focusing attention on any one particular species, just as faecal coliforms are used rather than the single species *Escherichia coli*.

5.1.4 *The choice of microbial indicator parameters for monitoring of water courses*

When working in the field of water pollution research, it may often be of interest to analyse for several of the microbiological indicator organisms mentioned in the foregoing. For the purposes of water pollution control, frequent analysis may be of great importance, and the number of parameters may have to be reduced to a minimum for both financial and practical reasons. In most cases one indicator of faecal pollution and the heterotrophic plate count (section 5.5) will be sufficient to give a fair estimate of the faecal and non-faecal organic pollution. For the sake of comparison, one of the faecal indicators should be chosen as the standard parameter, and the parameter designated " faecal coliform bacteria " is recommended for this purpose. Some kinds of pollutant may change the water quality to such an extent that the use of other faecal indicators may have to be considered in order to give a fair estimate of the faecal influence. However, in most cases the faecal coliform bacteria and the heterotrophic plate count may be regarded as the basic parameters in monitoring of water courses. On the basis of the results of these analyses, further actions should be considered, taking into account all available information on the different human, animal, and plant diseases prevailing in the community and the different kinds of pollution entering the water course. The need to analyse for several faecal indicator organisms or for direct analysis of human, animal, or plant pathogens should then be judged accordingly.

5.2 Methods for enumeration of faecal coliform bacteria

5.2.1 *Definition and general considerations*

The term " coliform bacteria " usually refers to Gram-negative, oxidase-negative, non-sporing rods capable of growing aerobically on an agar medium containing lactose with the production of acid and aldehyde, or capable of fermenting lactose with the production of both acid and gas within 48 hours at 35–37°C.

The group of coliform bacteria fermenting lactose at 30°C is fairly widespread in nature and is not considered to be of any particular epidemiological importance in the examination of waters.

Escherichia coli is a coliform organism, as defined above, which is capable of fermenting lactose in broth with the production of acid and gas both at 35–37°C and at 44°C in less than 48 hours, which produces indole in peptone water containing tryptophane, which is incapable of producing acetylmethylcarbinol, and which gives a positive result in the methyl red test (22, 24).

E. coli is undoubtedly of faecal origin, but as other coliform organisms are widespread in nature, the significance of their presence in water has been much debated. However, all the members of the coliform group (as here defined) may be of faecal origin.

The perfect practical procedure to distinguish between *E. coli* and the other coliform strains from faecal and non-faecal environments has not yet been discovered. Even as here defined, the analysis for *E. coli* would require cultivation in lactose broth at both 35–37 and 44°C for detection of acid and gas production, isolation of pure culture from positive tubes, and the subjecting of each culture suspected of being *E. coli* to Gram stain test, spore test (oxidase test, aldehyde test), and IMViC tests.[a] Discriminatory tests not including all the tests described above may, however, be used in the practical solution of pollution problems.

If one accepts *faecal* bacteria other than *E. coli* IMViC type + + − − being regarded as positive in the test, the distinction can be made by using the IMViC tests on pure cultures isolated from confirmed fermentation tubes, and interpreting the results according to the Parr classification of faecal coliform bacteria (Table 8). This procedure then includes more strains than *E. coli*, and is called a " faecal coliform " test.

Table 8.   The Parr interpretation of IMViC reactions [a]

Origin of bacteria	Bacteria of genus	I	M	Vi	C
Faecal	*Escherichia*	+	+	−	−
		+	−	−	−
		−	+	−	−
Soil	*Aerobacter* [b]*-Klebsiella*	−	−	+	+
		−	−	+	−
		−	−	−	+
"Intermediate" group		Remaining 10 possibe combinations			

[a] After Geldreich (*67*).
[b] According to Bergey's Manual of Determinative Bacteriology, 8th ed., *Enterobacter* (*66*).

Since IMViC classification should be applied only to a pure culture of coliform bacteria that has been found positive by the completed test, generally about 1 week of considerable labour in the laboratory is involved. For this reason, attempts have been made to modify the procedure without significant loss in sensitivity. The American Standard Methods (*23*) include two such faecal coliform methods, one being a multiple tube (MPN) and

---

[a] IMViC tests is a collective term for the 4 tests : indole, methyl red, Voges-Proskauer, and sodium citrate.

the other a membrane filter (MF) method, where the selectivity to a large extent is based on the elevation of the incubation temperature from 44°C to 44.5°C. In the MF procedure, lactose fermentation is measured by the production of acids, whereas in the MPN-test, gas production is positive evidence of fermentation. Comparison of these two techniques indicated that the two procedures were measuring predominantly the same group of organisms : the faecal coliform bacteria (67).

The WHO International Standards for Drinking Water (6) recognizes confirmatory faecal coliform tests utilizing a choice of brilliant green-bile-lactose broth (BGBL), formate-ricinoleate broth, or MacConkey broth in the multiple tube procedure. Faecal coliforms are considered to be present if gas production occurs within 6 to 24 hours of incubation at 44°C. Preliminary studies (68) comparing the use of one of the American standard confirmatory broths (EC-broth) and the other mentioned broths in the elevated temperature test (44.5°C) indicated that the BGBL and ricinoleate broths gave lower recoveries, whereas the MacConkey broth could give some false positive reactions owing to growth of spore-forming anaerobic bacteria.

With respect to membrane filter procedures, the American faecal coliform method was preferred by a majority of the reviewers of the questionnaire (7) referred to in the Introduction (section 1, p. 278). Preincubation at a lower temperature than 44°C was considered unpractical for general use, since this would hold laboratories to a very limited and rigid schedule that would severely restrict time for processing samples during working hours ; alternatively, the laboratories would have to acquire a dependable series of automatic incubators capable of programmed temperature changes.

All these considerations led to the choice of the multiple tube and the membrane filter faecal coliform tests from the American Standard Methods (23) as the two alternative methods to be presented in this chapter. The specificity of these faecal coliform tests is directly related to the incubation temperature, which is $44.5 \pm 0.2°C$ (23). However, the restrictions on creating a demand for a multitude of incubators of different temperature settings rule out the general use of 44.5°C as a selective procedure. Laboratories that do not have a separate water bath incubator set at 44.5°C may therefore use the general 44°C incubator, provided that the temperature is regulated to be within 44.0–44.5°C.

5.2.2 *Alternative method 1 — Multiple tube method for faecal coliform bacteria*

I. Scope

This method has been developed for the quantitative analysis of " faecal coliform " bacteria, as defined in section 5.2.1, in polluted lake and river waters and sediments, raw sewage, sewage sludge, and sewage effluents.

II. FIELD OF APPLICATION

This method may be used for all types of sample, but for samples containing mainly metabolically injured bacteria the modification described in XII.1 may be a better choice.

III. DEFINITIONS

All sample volumes capable of producing bacterial growth with gas production in lactose-lauryl sulfate broth within 48 hours at 35–37°C, and growth with gas production within 24 ± 2 hours at 44.0–44.5°C after transfer to lactose-bile broth, are considered as having contained at least one viable faecal coliform bacterium.

IV. PRINCIPLE

The principle of the multiple tube technique is described in detail in section 3.4.

In general, one series of multiple tubes is used in the presumptive test, and one confirmatory tube is used for each positive tube from the presumptive test, for each laboratory sample.

Bacterial growth with gas production is the indicator of a positive reaction in both tests.

The number of confirmed positive tubes in 3 chosen subsequent dilutions of the laboratory sample is recorded.

This combination of positive tubes is used to find the most probable number of faecal coliforms in the laboratory sample by using a statistical table worked out for this purpose, taking into consideration also the dilution factor of the test samples for the calculation of the MPN-value for the laboratory sample.

V. REACTIONS

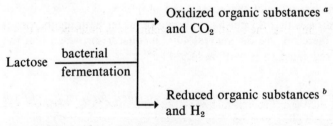

For coliform bacteria: [a] Organic acids
                        [b] Alcohol, butylene glycol

For inhibition of Gram-positive lactose fermenters, including aerobic and anaerobic spore-forming bacteria, the synthetic surfactant (wetting agent) lauryl sulfate is used in the presumptive medium. This surfactant inhibits the interfering organisms at concentrations that permit good growth of faecal coliform bacteria. Bile salts are used in the confirmatory medium for the same purpose. Gas production ($CO_2 + H_2$) at 44.0–44.5°C is indicative of the presence of faecal coliform bacteria (*69, 70*).

VI. REAGENTS

Lactose-lauryl sulfate broth, LL-broth, as described in section 5.6.10, single and double strength in fermentation tubes.
Lactose-bile broth, LB-broth, as described in section 5.6.10, in fermentation tubes.
Diluent as described in section 3.3.

VII. APPARATUS

• In general as described for the multiple tube technique in section 3.4, II.
• Test tubes with inverted vials (fermentation tubes); the vials (or Durham tubes) are for detection of gas production during fermentation. Presumptive test : A series of [5×minimum 3] fermentation tubes per laboratory sample. Confirmatory test : Normally, a maximum of 5×3 fermentation tubes per laboratory sample.
• An incubator at 35–37°C.
• An incubator at 44.0–44.5°C.

VIII. SAMPLING AND SAMPLES

The taking of laboratory samples is described in section 2.
The preparation of test samples is described in section 3.2, and their dilution in section 3.3.

IX. PROCEDURE

The general procedure for the multiple tube technique is described in detail in section 3.4, IV.

IX.1. *Check test*

If pre-prepared media are stored at temperatures below 25°C, perform air-check test as described in section 5.6.9, p. 413.

IX.2. *Test portion*

The choosing of suitable test portions is discussed in section 3.4, IV.2. Table 9 may also be used for guidance.

IX.3. *Determinations*

First day :

Mark the fermentation tubes with the laboratory sample code and dilution identity mark as described in section 3.4, IV.1.

(a) No dilution of laboratory sample or suspension :

Use 10 ml of double-strength LL-broth in tubes 1–5, and single-strength LL-broth in the other tubes.

Pipette test portions of 10 ml into tubes 1–5, test portions of 1 ml into tubes 6–10, and test portions of 0.1 ml into tubes 11–15.

Record the largest volume of test portion used, $V = 10$ ml.

Table 9. Suggested starting dilution for multiple tube coliform examinations of various laboratory sample qualities [a]

Sample source	Starting dilutions (ml) for a three-dilution multiple tube test				
	10	1	0.1	0.01	0.001
Wells	x [b]				
Lakes	x - - - - - -x				
Bathing beaches	x - - - - - -x				
Creeks		x - - - - - -x			
Rivers		x - - - - - -x			
Sewages					
chlorinated		x - - - - - -x			
secondary treatment		x - - - - - -x			
primary treatment			x - - - - - -x		
raw, municipal				x - - - - - -x	

[a] After Geldreich (29).
[b] x = starting dilution ; x - - -x = alternative choices.

(b) Dilution of the laboratory sample or suspension :

Dilute the laboratory sample or suspension as described in section 3.3, or section 3.4, IV.3.

Pipette test portions of 1 ml from each of at least 3 subsequent 10-fold dilutions into 5 fermentation tubes with LL-broth.

Record the dilution factors applied, $F_1, F_2, \ldots F_n$.

If both diluted and undiluted laboratory sample or suspension are used as test samples, record both volume V and dilution factor F for all test samples employed. For the laboratory sample or suspension, the dilution factor is equal to 1, i.e., $F = 1$.

Incubate at 35–37°C

Second day :

At the end of 24 ± 2 hours' incubation, gently shake or rotate the tubes and examine for growth with gas in the inverted vial.

Return tubes without gas to the incubator.

Record all tubes with growth and gas as positive in the presumptive test. Normally, the lactose-lauryl sulfate broth gives rise to few " false positive " cultures, that is positive presumptive tubes that are not confirmed as positive in the confirmatory test. Therefore, if more than 3 series of 5 tubes have been employed, locate the highest dilution with all 5 tubes showing gas ; all tubes in the series of lower dilution should show gas.

Confirm all tubes in this series and all positive tubes in the two subsequent series of higher dilution. Before inoculation of confirmatory tubes, gently shake or rotate the presumptive tubes to suspend the bacteria. Transfer one loopful (or use sterile, disposable, wooden applicators) of culture from each presumptive tube to one fermentation tube with LB-broth. Mark the confirmatory tube with the identity mark of the presumptive tube. Incubate at 44.0–44.5°C.

Third day :

Examine the remaining presumptive tubes for growth and gas. Record tubes without growth as negative in the presumptive test. Discard these tubes.

Record tubes with growth but without gas as doubtful negative. Record tubes with growth and gas as positive in the presumptive test. Inoculate one confirmatory tube from each positive and doubtful negative tube in the presumptive test.

Mark the confirmatory tubes with the identity marks of the presumptive tubes. Discard the presumptive tubes.

Incubate the confirmatory tubes at 44.0–44.5°C.

Examine the confirmatory tubes from second day's transfer for growth and gas after 24 ± 2 hours incubation. Record tubes with gas as positive in the confirmatory test. Discard all these tubes.

Fourth day :

Examine confirmatory tubes from the third day's transfer for growth and gas after 24 ± 2 hours incubation. Record the tubes with gas as positive in the confirmatory test. Discard the tubes.

Positive and negative reactions in the presumptive and confirmatory tests are shown in Plate 11.

A suggested laboratory form for recording the results is shown in Fig. 12.

X. EXPRESSION OF RESULTS

Express the results as the number of positive tubes in each series of 5 tubes.

Example :   Presumptive test :   5–5–3–1
            Confirmatory test :   5–2–0

Use the results from the confirmatory test to find the corresponding MPN-value in Table 1.

Fig. 12. A suggested laboratory form for recording results from the MPN-method for faecal coliform bacteria

MPN-TECHNIQUE FOR FAECAL COLIFORM BACTERIA

LABORATORY SAMPLE CODE :____

	Step 1					Step 2					Step 3					Step 4					Step 5				
Test dilutions																									
Test portion, V ml																									
Dilution factor, F																									
Tube number	1	2	3	4	5	6	7	8	9	10	11	12	13	14	15	16	17	18	19	20	21	22	23	24	25
24 h presumptive test: Growth and gas																									
24 h confirmed tubes: Growth and gas																									
24–48 h presumptive test: Growth and gas																									
Growth only																									
24 h confirmed tubes: Growth and gas																									
Number of confirmed tubes per step:																									

Corresponding MPN-value from table, and 95% confidence limits :

V/F in lowest dilution step applied ; Step :

V :

F :

Result : MPN-value $\times \dfrac{10}{V} \times F =$ Faecal coliform bacteria per 100 ml of laboratory sample [a]

[a] For solid samples, per 100 ml of basic suspension

Space for other important information, such as date of sampling, may be added according to the wishes of the different laboratories.

XI. Schematic Representation of the Procedure

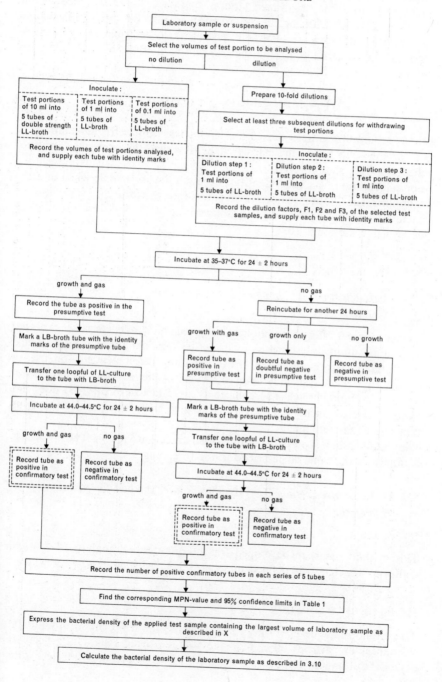

Locate and record the test portion of the laboratory sample V, or the dilution factor F of the diluted laboratory sample, used to inoculate the series of 5 tubes with the highest number of positive tubes but smallest volume of laboratory sample (the basic series), as described in section 3.4. Express the bacterial density in the test sample used to inoculate the basic series of tubes, as follows :

$$BDT = MPN\text{-value} \times \frac{10}{V} \text{ bacteria per 100 ml.}$$

If the laboratory sample is used directly as test sample for inoculating the basic series of 5 tubes, the calculated BDT is also the bacterial density of the laboratory sample, BDL.

For calculation of bacterial density of the laboratory sample when dilution is applied, the dilution factor F also enters into the formula. Calculate the bacterial density of water, semi-solid or solid laboratory samples as described in section 3.10.

XII. SPECIAL CASES

XII.1 *Modification for samples containing mainly metabolically injured bacteria (24, 61, 71).*

Higher recovery rates of metabolically injured coliform bacteria are expected when a presumptive test medium without bactericidal agents is used. Thus, the formate-lactose-glutamate (FLG-)medium recommended for use in drinking water analysis may be used instead of lactose-lauryl sulfate broth in the presumptive test. The commonly used lactose broth (23) does not contain selective agents but is expected to give more false positive reactions than the FLG-medium.

The FLG-medium is prepared as described in section 5.6.10. The procedure is otherwise the same as described in the foregoing.

5.2.3 *Alternative method 2 — Membrane filter method for faecal coliform bacteria*

I. SCOPE

This method has been developed for the quantitative analysis of " faecal coliform " bacteria, as defined in section 5.2.1, in lake and river waters.

II. FIELD OF APPLICATION

This method may be used only for samples with a low content of colloidal substances or particles other than the bacteria being sought. Particles or colloidal substances trapped on the membrane surface may interfere with the development of colonies (see section 3.8), and large numbers of bacteria other than the faecal coliforms may grow on the surface and interfere with the indicator system for faecal coliform bacteria. In these cases, the MPN-technique should be used. For samples containing mainly metabolically injured bacteria (i.e., chlorinated samples), the modification described in XII.1 (p. 374) should be used.

In cases when sample transport may be too long to permit analysis within 30 hours of sampling, consideration should be given to the delayed incubation technique described in XII.2 (p. 375).

Modified methods for completion in the field are described in XII.3.

III. DEFINITIONS

All bacteria capable of growing on lactose-bile-rosolic acid medium into visible colonies with blue or blue-green colour within 24 ± 2 hours at 44.0–44.5°C are considered as faecal coliform bacteria.

IV. PRINCIPLE

Bacteria in the sample are trapped on the membrane filter surface during filtration; the membrane is then placed on a growth medium, which enters the membrane pores from below and supplies the bacteria on the surface with the nutrients necessary for growth. The growth medium is of neutral reaction, and contains an acid-base indicator which turns blue in acid; thus colonies that are acid as a result of lactose fermentation cause the indicator to turn blue.

V. REACTIONS

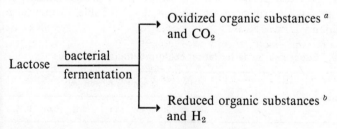

For coliform bacteria : [a] Organic acids
                          [b] Alcohol, butylene glycol

Bile salts inhibit most Gram-positive bacteria, including aerobic spore-formers, as does rosolic acid, but they permit the growth of Gram-negative rod-shaped bacteria. Anaerobic spore-formers do not grow on the membrane surface in an atmosphere of air. Of the remaining bacteria capable of growth on this medium, few but the faecal coliforms are able to grow at a temperature of 44.0–44.5°C.

Thus, the acid may be assumed to be produced by Gram-negative, lactose-fermenting, non-spore-forming, rod-shaped bacteria : the faecal coliforms (*69, 72*).

VI. Reagents

Lactose-bile-rosolic acid broth or agar, as described in section 5.6.10 (LBR-medium).
Diluent, if necessary, as described in section 3.3.

VII. Apparatus

- In general, as described for the membrane filter technique, section 3.8, II.
- White, gridded membrane filters of pore size 0.45 μm.
- Incubator at 44.0–44.5°C.

VIII. Sampling and samples

The taking of laboratory samples is described in section 2. The preparation of test samples is described in section 3.2.

IX. Procedure

The general procedure for the membrane filter technique is described in detail in section 3.8, IV.

IX.1 *Test portion*

Select the volume of test portion that will result in the growth of 25–100 colonies per filter, as described in section 3.8, IV.1. Table 10 may also be used for guidance.

Table 10. Suggested guide for faecal coliform filtration quantities [a]

Water source	Quantities filtered (ml)						
	100	50	10	1	0.1	0.01	0.001
Lakes, reservoirs	x	x					
Wells, springs	x	x	x				
Water supply, surface intake			x	x	x		
Natural bathing waters			x	x	x		
Sewage treatment plant secondary effluent				x	x	x	
Farm ponds, rivers				x	x	x	
Storm water runoff				x	x	x	
Raw municipal sewage					x	x	x
Feedlot runoff					x	x	x

[a] After Geldreich (*29*).

IX.2 *Preparation of colony count culture*

Prepare the LBR-medium as described in section 5.6.10. Pour plates of agar medium of at least 2 mm thickness, or add 2.2–2.5 ml liquid medium per culture dish containing an absorbent pad. Prepare all the culture dishes before starting the analysis of samples.

Shake the test sample (see section 3.2), measure the chosen volume, and filter through the membrane filter as described for the membrane filter technique, section 3.8, IV.2. Record the test volume filtered, V.

Roll the filter, grid side up, on to the agar medium or nutrient pad in the dish. Remove excess liquid medium from the latter before rolling on membrane.

Proceed with the next sample, observing the rule that no more than 30 minutes should elapse between filtering and placing the culture dishes in the incubator.

IX.3 *Incubation*

Incubate at 44.0–44.5°C for 24 ± 2 hours.

IX.4 *Counting*

Colonies produced by faecal coliform bacteria are blue or greenish blue in colour. The non-faecal coliform colonies are grey to cream-coloured or yellow. The background colour on the membrane filter will vary from yellowish cream to faint blue, depending on the age of the rosolic acid reagent. Normally, few non-faecal coliform colonies will be observed on this medium because of the selective action of the elevated temperature and addition of rosolic acid.

Count the blue and blue-green colonies and record the count, C.

An illustration of faecal coliform colonies is shown in Plate 12.

X. EXPRESSION OF RESULTS

Express the bacterial density of the test sample, BDT, as described for the membrane filter technique in section 3.8 :

$$\text{BDT} = \frac{\Sigma C_i}{\Sigma V_i} V_s$$

The standard volume, V_s, is 100 ml.

Calculate the bacterial density in the laboratory sample, BDL, as described in section 3.10.

XI. SCHEMATIC REPRESENTATION OF THE PROCEDURE

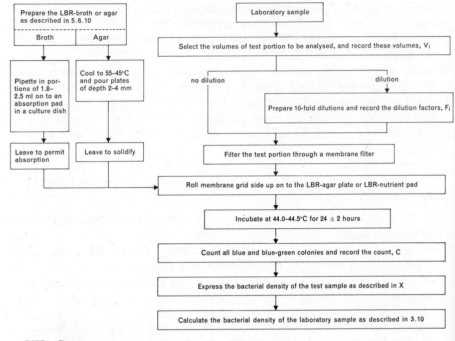

XII. SPECIAL CASES

XII.1 *Modification for samples containing mainly metabolically injured bacteria (29, 73).*

Instead of placing the membrane filter directly on the LBR-medium, the membrane is placed on top of a layer of lactose agar without any bactericidal agents and left to incubate at 35–37°C for 2 hours. The lactose agar is freshly layered on top of a dish with LBR-agar. The selective agents and indicator of the latter medium will diffuse towards the membrane on top, and after some time the selective action will start to work.

Additional reagent : Lactose agar, prepared as described in section 5.6.10, is required in addition to LBR-agar.

Procedure : Prepare the LBR-agar plates as described in IX.2. Not more than 1 hour before use, pour a 1-mm thick layer (2–3 ml in a 50–60-mm or 6–7 ml in a 90–95-mm dish) of lactose agar on top of the LBR-plate. Allow to solidify. Continue as described in IX.2 from " Shake the test sample ... ". The subsequent incubation is performed at 35–37°C for 2 hours, followed by 44.0–44.5°C for 22–24 hours. The counting procedure is identical with that described in IX.4.

An illustration of a two-layered agar plate for metabolically injured bacteria is shown in Fig. 13.

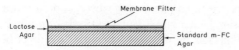

Fig. 13. The two-layered agar plate for metabolically injured bacteria [a]

[a] The agar designated m–FC Agar is identical to the LBR-Agar mentioned in the text.

XII.2 *Delayed incubation (23, 29, 74)*

When the distance between the place of sampling and the laboratory is too great to permit analysis within 30 hours of sampling, delayed incubation may be used. In this case, the sample is filtered in the field and placed on a pad saturated with a " holding medium " that will keep the bacteria viable but arrest visible growth for up to 72 hours. If placed in sturdy containers, the filters may be sent to the laboratory by mail or other transport. Both extreme heat and cold should be avoided during transport. Visible growth occasionally occurs on the transport medium when high temperatures are encountered.

Additional reagent : Vitamin-free peptone holding medium, VFH-medium, as described in section 5.6.10, in addition to LBR-medium.

Procedure : Pipette sterile VFH-medium into a culture dish containing a sterile pad, using 2.2–2.5 ml of medium per pad of approx. 50 mm diameter. Leave until the pad is thoroughly soaked and discard excess medium in the dish. Filter as described for the membrane filter technique in section 3.8 or the field technique in section 3.9.

Roll the filter, grid side up, on to the holding pad, place the holding dish in an appropriate shipping container and send to the laboratory for completion of the examination.

Upon arrival in the laboratory, transfer the membrane to a container with LBR-medium and proceed as described in the original method.

To check the validity of the delayed incubation method, selected colonies are inoculated into fermentation tubes containing lactose-lauryl sulfate broth. The tubes are checked for growth with gas production at 24 and 48 hours of incubation at 35–37°C. Culture from each tube showing gas is inoculated into fermentation tubes containing lactose-bile broth and the tubes checked for gas production after 24 hours at 44°C.

This check on the validity of delayed test results is recommended as an initial control check for the examination of waters on a continual basis.

XII.3 *Methods modified for completion in the field*

If the analysis is to be completed in the field, the combination of membrane filter and spread plate techniques with pre-prepared agar plates of LBR-medium (see section 5.6.10) is recommended.

Membrane filters are used for water where concentration of bacteria is considered necessary, otherwise 0.1 ml of sample or diluted sample is spread directly on the surface of the agar medium, as described for the field technique in section 3.9.

After incubation at 44.0–44.5°C for 24 ± 2 hours, count all blue and greenish blue colonies as faecal coliform colonies.

5.2.4 *Further identification of coliform bacteria*

In countries with a tropical climate or in water polluted with effluents from certain types of industry, the membrane filter faecal coliform method may take account of bacteria that are not of immediate faecal origin (*68*). Some investigators state that the true faecal coliforms usually give rise to blue colonies with a crystalline deposit on the surface, whereas the non-faecal variety appear blue but lack the crystalline deposit, which is probably precipitated bile salts (*68, 75*).

One such interfering organism is *Klebsiella pneumoniae*. Recent investigations into the differentiation of *K. pneumoniae* from the other members of the *Enterobacteriaceae* have led to the development of a selective agar medium for this organism (*76*).

Other media that may show good differentiation between *Escherichia* and *Klebsiella* strains are the Tergitol 7 agar (*61, 63*) and lactose TTT 7 agar (*77, 78*). These media may be used with the membrane filter and spread plate techniques. Incubation at 44°C and low colony density on the filter or plate are recommended for optimum differentiation.

Tests that may be used to identify an isolated strain of coliform bacteria as belonging to one of the 4 recognized genera *Escherichia*, *Citrobacter*, *Klebsiella* and *Enterobacter*, are shown in Table 11. The commonly used IMViC-tests are included. The exact procedures may be found in textbooks on bacteriology.

To test for interfering, non-coliform organisms, such as *Aeromonas*, *Xanthomonas*, and *Pseudomonas*, a cytochrome oxidase test is recommended. One such test, with stabilized test reagent, is described in references *54* and *79*.

5.3 Methods for the enumeration of faecal streptococci

5.3.1 *Definition and general considerations*

Species of streptococci occurring in human and animal faeces are likely to be found in polluted water. These faecal streprococci include species such as *Streptococcus faecalis*, *S. faecium*, *S. durans*, *S. bovis* and *S. equinus*.

The distinctive characteristics of faecal streptococci are their ability to grow at 45°C and to grow in the presence of 40% bile and in concentrations

Table 11. Characters of the coliform bacteria (56)

Test	Esche-richia	Citro-bacter	Kleb-siella	Enterobacter clo-aceae	Enterobacter aero-genes	Enterobacter hafniae	Enterobacter lique-faciens
Mannitol	A	A	A	A	A	A	A
Adonitol	O	O	A	A	A	A	A
Dulcitol	d	d	d	O	O	O	O
Inositol (gas)	O	O	O	O	+	O	+
Sucrose	d	d	A	A	A	A	A
Indole	+	O	O	O	O	O	O
Gelatin	O	O	O	(+)	X	O	X
H₂S	O	+	O	O	O	O	O
NH₄-citrate	O	+	+	+	+	+	+
Voges-Proskauer	O	O	+	+	+	+	+
Methyl red	+	+	O	O	O	O	d
Urease	O	O or X	+	O	O	O	d
Malonate	O	O	+	+	+	+	O
KCN	O	+	+	+	+	+	O
Phenylalanine	O	O	O	O	O	O	+
Motility	+	+	O	+	+	+	O
Lysine decarboxylase	+	O	+	O	+	+	(+)
Arginine dihydrolase	d	+	O	+	O	O	O
Ornithine decarboxylase	d	+	O	+	+	+	+

A = acid, gas may or may not be produced.
d = differing strains, some with positive and some with negative reaction.
+ = positive within 2 days. (+) = delayed positive.
X = late irregular positive.
O = negative reaction of test.

of sodium azide that are inhibitory to coliform organisms and most other Gram-negative bacteria. Some species resist heating at 60°C for 30 minutes and will grow at pH 9.6 and in media containing 6.5% sodium chloride.

Recent increases in the sensitivity of the cultivation media for faecal streptococci have not been achieved without compromising to some extent the suppression of other organisms present in the water environment. Strains of *Corynebacterium* and *Pediococcus*, *Streptococcus lactis*, and other bacteria common to irrigation water, sugar beet plant effluents, and other food processing wastes can develop substantial growth in either the liquid media or selective agar media now available. Maximum suppression of interfering bacteria can, in part, be achieved through careful media preparation (46).

Although it is recognized that for the colony count methods, preincubation at 35–37°C and final incubation at 44°C are optimal for scientific reasons, this procedure has been found impractical for routine use. Instead, direct incubation at 44°C is chosen on the advice of some European laboratories.

5.3.2 *Alternative method 1 — Multiple tube method for faecal streptococci*
I. SCOPE
This method has been developed for the quantitative analysis of "faecal

streptococci " as defined in section 5.3.1, in polluted lake and river waters
and sediments, raw sewage, sewage sludge, and sewage effluents.

II. FIELD OF APPLICATION
This method may be used for all types of laboratory sample.

III. DEFINITIONS
All sample volumes capable of producing bacterial growth within 48 hours
after inoculation into glucose-azide broth and incubation at 35–37°C, and
growth within 24 ± 2 hours at 35–37°C after transfer to glucose-azide-ethyl
violet broth, are considered as having contained at least one viable faecal
streptococcus.

IV. PRINCIPLE
The principle of this method is described in detail in section 3.4. In
short, one series of multiple tubes is used in the presumptive test and one
confirmatory tube is used for each positive tube from the presumptive test,
for each laboratory sample. Bacterial growth is the indicator of a positive
reaction in both tests.
The number of confirmed positive tubes in 3 chosen subsequent dilutions
of the laboratory sample is recorded.
This combination of positive tubes is used to find the most probable number
of faecal streptococci in the laboratory sample by using a statistical table
worked out for this purpose, taking into consideration also the dilution
factor of the test samples for the calculation of the MPN-value of the
laboratory sample.

V. REACTIONS
Presumptive test :

Glucose-azide broth $\xrightarrow{\text{azide-tolerant bacteria}}$ Growth at 35–37°C within 48 hours of incubation

Confirmatory test :

Glucose-azide-ethyl violet broth $\xrightarrow{\text{azide- and ethyl violet-tolerant bacteria}}$ Growth at 35–37°C in 24 ± 2 hours

Sodium azide is added to inhibit Gram-negative bacteria.
Ethyl violet is added because of its inhibitory effect upon the growth of
Gram-positive spore-formers and cocci other than the faecal streptococci.

VI. REAGENTS
Glucose-azide broth, GA-broth, as described in section 5.6.10, single and
double strength in test tubes.

Glucose-azide-ethyl violet broth, GAE-broth, as described in section 5.6.10, in test tubes.
Diluent as described in section 3.3.

CAUTION : Sodium azide, NaN₃, is a hypotensive agent. Any contact with mucous membranes (nose, mouth) should be avoided, since this may bring about unconsciousness. Avoid draughts when weighing and do not pipette solutions containing NaN₃ using mouth suction. Antidote : Levarterenol bitartrate (80).

VII. APPARATUS
- In general, as described for the multiple tube technique in section 3.4, II.
- Medium tubes per laboratory sample :
  A series of minimum 3×5 tubes for the presumptive test.
  A series of 5 tubes with confirmatory medium for each series of 5 tubes in the presumptive test.
- An incubator at 35–37°C.

VIII. SAMPLING AND SAMPLES
The taking of laboratory samples is described in section 2. Preparation of test samples is described in section 3.2, dilution in section 3.3.

IX. PROCEDURE
The general procedure of the multiple tube technique is described in detail in section 3.4, IV.

IX.1 *Test portion*
The choosing of suitable test portions is discussed in section 3.4, p. 305.

IX.2 *Determinations*
First day :

Mark the GA-broth tubes with the laboratory sample code and dilution identity mark as described in section 3.4, IV.1.

(*a*) No dilution of laboratory sample or suspension :
Use 10 ml of double-strength GA-broth in tubes 1–5, and single-strength GA-broth in the other tubes.
Pipette test portions of 10 ml into tubes 1–5, test portions of 1 ml into tubes 6–10, and test portions of 0.1 ml into tubes 11–15.
Record the largest volume of test portion used, $V = 10$ ml.

(*b*) Dilution of the laboratory sample or suspension :
Dilute the laboratory sample or suspension as described in section 3.3 or section 3.4, IV.3.

EMbC3 - Σ

Pipette test portions of 1 ml from each of at least 3 subsequent 10-fold dilutions into 5 tubes with GA-broth.

Record the dilution factors applied, F_1, F_2, ... F_n.

If both diluted and undiluted laboratory sample or suspension are used as test samples, record both volume V and dilution factor F for all test samples employed. For the laboratory sample or suspension, the dilution factor is equal to 1, i.e. $F = 1$.

Incubate at 35–37°C.

Second day :

At the end of 24 ± 2 hours' incubation, examine for growth. Return tubes without growth to the incubator.

Record all tubes with growth as positive in the presumptive test.

The GA-broth usually supports growth of many more types of bacteria than does the GAE-broth. Therefore, there may be many positive presumptive tubes that are not confirmed, and as a general rule all positive presumptive tubes should be confirmed.

Before inoculation of confirmatory tubes, gently shake or rotate the presumptive tubes to suspend the bacteria.

Transfer 3 loopfuls of culture from each presumptive tube to one tube with GAE-broth.

Mark the confirmatory tube with the identity marks of the presumptive tube. Incubate at 35–37°C. Also return positive presumptive tubes to the incubator.

Third day :

Presumptive tubes that were negative on the second day are re-examined for growth. Record tubes without growth as negative in the presumptive test, and discard these tubes.

Record tubes with growth as positive in the presumptive test, and inoculate a confirmatory tube from each positive presumptive tube and incubate as described for second day.

Examine second day's confirmatory tubes for growth after 24 ± 2 hours. Growth usually appears as a violet button at the bottom (when the tube is viewed from the bottom, see Plate 13.

Record tubes with growth as positive in the confirmatory test. Discard both GAE-tubes and corresponding GA-tubes.

Reinoculate tubes without growth and return to the incubator for another 24 hours. Discard corresponding GA-tubes.

Positive and negative reactions in the presumptive and confirmatory tests are shown in Plate 13.

Fourth day :

Examine reinoculated tubes from second day's transfer for growth. Record tubes with growth as positive in the confirmatory test, and tubes without growth as negative. Discard all these tubes.
Examine GAE-tubes inoculated on the third day. Record tubes with growth as positive in the confirmatory test, and discard these GAE-tubes and corresponding GA-tubes. Reinoculate tubes without growth and return to the incubator for another 24 hours. Discard corresponding GA-tubes.

Fifth day :

Examine reinoculated tubes from third day's transfer. Record tubes with growth as positive in the confirmatory test, and tubes without growth as negative. Discard all these tubes.
Doubtful confirmatory tubes (slight turbidity only) may be finally confirmed by streaking on citrate-azide-bile-esculin agar, the formula for which is given in section 5.6.10.
A suggested laboratory form for recording the results is shown in Fig. 14.

X. EXPRESSION OF RESULTS

Express the results as the number of positive tubes in each series of 5 tubes.

Example : Presumptive test : 5–5–5–3–1
Confirmatory test : 5–4–3–1–0

Use the results from the confirmatory test to find the corresponding MPN-value in Table 1 as described in section 3.4, IV.4. Locate and record the test portion of laboratory sample, V, or dilution factor, F, of the diluted laboratory sample, used to inoculate the series of 5 tubes with the highest number of positive tubes but smallest volume of laboratory sample (the basic series). In the example above, the combination of positive tubes for finding the MPN-value would be 5–4–3.
Express the bacterial density of the laboratory sample or the test sample used to inoculate the basic series of tubes as follows :

$$\text{BDT} = \text{MPN-value} \times \frac{10}{V} \text{ bacteria per 100 ml}$$

If the laboratory sample is used directly as test sample for inoculating the basic series of 5 tubes, the calculated BDT is also the bacterial density of the laboratory sample, BDL.
For calculation of the bacterial density of the laboratory sample when dilution is applied, the dilution factor F also enters into the formula.
Calculate the bacterial density of water, semi-solid, or solid laboratory samples as described in section 3.10.

Fig. 14. A suggested laboratory form for recording the results from the MPN-method for faecal streptococci

MPN-TECHNIQUE FOR FAECAL STREPTOCOCCI

LABORATORY SAMPLE CODE :

Test dilutions	Step 1					Step 2					Step 3					Step 4					Step 5				
Test portions, V ml																									
Dilution factor, F																									
Tube number	1	2	3	4	5	6	7	8	9	10	11	12	13	14	15	16	17	18	19	20	21	22	23	24	25
24 h presumptive test: Growth																									
24 h confirmed tubes : Growth																									
24 h reinoculated confirmatory tubes : Growth																									
24–48 h presumptive : Growth																									
24 h confirmed tubes : Growth																									
24 h reinoculated confirmatory tubes : Growth																									
Number of confirmed tubes per step :																									

Corresponding MPN-value from table, and 95% confidence limits :

V/F in lowest dilution step applied ; step :   V :

Result :   MPN-value $\times \dfrac{10}{V} \times F =$ F :   Faecal streptococci per 100 ml laboratory sample or suspension

Space for other important information, such as date of sampling, may be added according to the wishes of the different laboratories.

XI. SCHEMATIC REPRESENTATION OF THE PROCEDURE

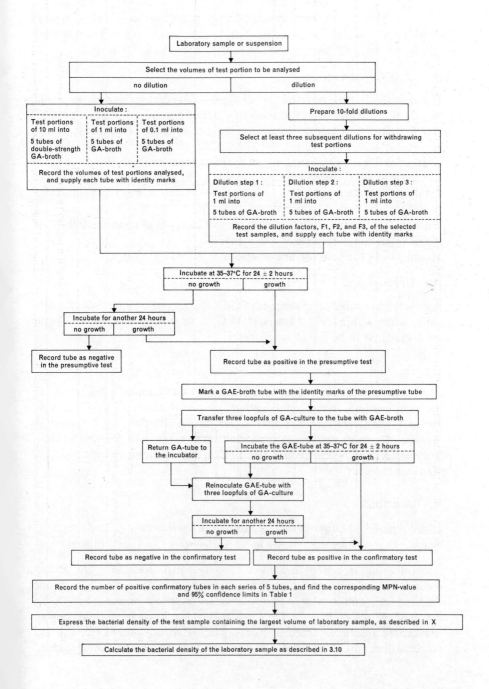

5.3.3   *Alternative methods 2 : Colony count methods for faecal streptococci*

I. SCOPE

These methods have been developed for the quantitative analysis of "faecal streptococci " as defined in section 5.3.1, in polluted lake and river waters and sediments, raw sewage, sewage sludge, and sewage effluents.

II. FIELD OF APPLICATION

These methods may be used for all types of laboratory sample provided they do not contain mainly metabolically injured bacteria. For water samples with low density of faecal streptococci the membrane filter technique should be chosen, observing the normal restrictions on the use of this technique (see section 3.8). For other samples, the plate count methods should be used. For samples likely to contain mainly metabolically injured bacteria, as in disinfection efficiency studies, use the modification described in XII.1 (p. 388).

If detection of recent pollution with animal faeces is of special interest, use the modification described in XII.2 (p. 388).

Modifications for field use are described in XII.3 (p. 389).

III. DEFINITIONS

All bacteria capable of growing into visible, dark red to pink colonies with entire edges within 48 ± 3 hours at 44°C on or in glucose-azide TTC agar are considered to be faecal streptococci.

IV. PRINCIPLE

The bacteria in the laboratory sample are trapped in one of 3 places : inside the agar medium upon solidification, on the surface of solidified agar medium, or on the membrane filter surface during filtration. Each bacterium capable of growth on the selective medium develops into a visible colony. The faecal streptococci reduce the TTC in the medium, resulting in red-coloured colonies.

V. REACTIONS

$$\text{Glucose-azide agar} \xrightarrow{\text{azide-tolerant bacteria}} \text{Growth at 44°C} \xrightarrow{\text{TTC-reducing bacteria}} \text{Red colonies}$$

Sodium azide is added to inhibit Gram-negative bacteria. The redox-indicator 2,3,5-triphenyltetrazolium chloride, TTC, is colourless in the oxidized form and is reduced to insoluble, red triphenylformazan by suitable bacterial reducing systems. The formation of the insoluble formazan is an irreversible reaction. Once a microorganism reduces the TTC, the red colour will persist. The faecal streptococci all possess this reducing system.

VI. REAGENTS

Glucose-azide TTC agar (GA-TTC-agar) as described in section 5.6.10. Diluent as described in section 3.3. For the membrane filter and spread plate techniques, the medium may be prepared beforehand in culture dishes and stored under refrigeration. For the pour plate technique, the medium should be freshly prepared.

CAUTION : Sodium azide, NaN₃, is a hypotensive agent. Any contact with mucous membranes (nose, mouth) should be avoided, since this may bring about unconsciousness. Avoid draughts when weighing and do not pipette solutions containing NaN₃ using mouth suction. Antidote : Levarterenol bitartrate (80).

VII. APPARATUS

- In general as described in sections 3.6, II for the pour plate technique, 3.7, II for the spread plate technique, or 3.8, II for the membrane filter technique.
- White, gridded membrane filters of pore size 0.45 µm.
- Incubator at $44 \pm 0.5°C$.

VIII. SAMPLING AND SAMPLES

The taking of laboratory samples is described in section 2. Preparation of test samples is described in section 3.2, dilution in section 3.3.

IX. PROCEDURE

IX.1 *Test portion*

The choosing of suitable test portions is discussed in sections 3.6, IV.1 for the pour-plate technique, 3.7, IV.2 for the spread-plate technique, and 3.8, IV.1 for the membrane filter technique.

IX.2 *Preparation of the colony count cultures*

A. *Membrane filter technique*

Filter the test portion as usual for the membrane filter technique (see section 3.8, IV.2) and roll the filter, grid side up, on to the agar plate surface.

B. *Spread-plate technique*

Spread the test portion over the surface of an agar plate as described in section 3.7, IV.3.

C. *Pour-plate technique*

Prepare the agar medium in 200-ml portions as described in section 5.6.10. Keep the medium in a water bath at 43–45°C for a maximum of 4 hours before pouring plates. Do not remelt solidified medium. Withdraw the test portion and add to a sterile Petri dish. Proceed with the next test portion. Do not plate more test portions at a time than will permit observance of the limitation of not allowing more than 20 minutes to elapse between plating and pouring. Remove a medium bottle from the tempering bath, wipe off any water on the outside, add the TTC-solution and mix without introducing air bubbles. Pour layers of approximately 4–6 mm depth and mix as described for this technique. Allow the plates to solidify. Proceed with the remaining samples.

For all techniques :

Record the volume of test portion (V) and dilution factor (F) for the test samples used. Place the prepared plates in the incubator as quickly as possible to prevent deterioration of the light-sensitive TTC.

IX.3   *Incubation*

Incubate for 48 ± 3 hours at 44 ± 0.5°C.

IX.4   *Counting*

Select the plates for counting according to the rules given in sections 3.6, 3.7, and 3.8.
Count the colonies according to the criteria given in III. Faecal streptococci occurring as sub-surface colonies are frequently lens-shaped. Normally, few non-faecal streptococcus colonies will be observed because of the selectivity of the medium and incubation temperature. However, occasional samples may contain Gram-positive soil organisms, such as *Pediococcus*, *Corynebacteria* and *Micrococcus*, which may develop on this medium as tiny, pinpoint, red, yellow, or orange colonies. Infrequently, *Bacillus* species may produce fuzzy, white colonies, with or without minute red-dot centres. An illustration of colonies of faecal streptococci on a membrane filter is shown in Plate 14.

X.   EXPRESSION OF RESULTS

Express the bacterial density in the test sample as described for each technique in sections 3.6, 3.7 and 3.8.

The general formula is :

$$\text{BDL} = \frac{\Sigma C_i}{\Sigma V_i} \times V_s, \text{ bacteria per standard volume}$$

The standard volume, V_s, is 100 ml.
Calculate the bacterial density of the laboratory sample as described in section 3.10.

XI. SCHEMATIC REPRESENTATION OF THE PROCEDURE

XI.1 *Membrane filter and spread plate techniques*

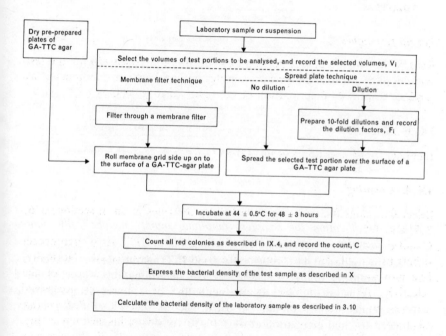

XI.2 *Pour plate technique*

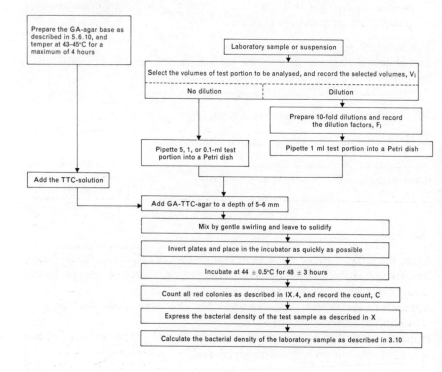

XII. SPECIAL CASES

XII.1 *Modification for samples containing mainly metabolically injured bacteria*

Direct incubation at 44°C on glucose-azide TTC agar may give low recovery of metabolically injured bacteria. If the determination of such injured bacteria is especially desired, preincubation at a lower temperature is recommended. This should be performed at 35–37°C for 2–4 hours, followed by final incubation at 44 ± 0.5°C for 46–44 hours.

XII.2 *Detection of faecal streptococci in animal faeces*

Alterations :

Field of application : The present formula of the citrate-azide-bile-esculin agar is not recommended for use with the membrane filter technique.

Definitions : All bacteria capable of growing into visible, brownish-black colonies with brown halos within 24 ± 2 hours at 35–37°C on or in citrate-azide-bile-esculin agar are considered to be faecal streptococci (*23*, *29*).

Reactions : The CABE-agar is a selective and differential medium that inhibits the proliferation of Gram-negative bacteria. The only Gram-positive cocci that will grow and exhibit esculin hydrolysis are the group D streptococci (see Table 12).

Table 12. Colony characteristics

Organisms	Growth at 35–37°C for :	
	24 hours	48 hours
Faecal streptococci, Group D	Brownish black colonies with brown halos	
Listeria monocytogenes	Pinpoint colonies	Small (0.5 mm) brownish black colonies with brownish halos

Thus, the recommended incubation conditions are : 35–37°C for 24 hours.
Reagents : Diluent as described in section 3.3. Citrate-azide-bile-esculin agar (CABE-agar), as described in section 5.6.10.
Apparatus : In general, as described for the pour plate technique in section 3.6. Incubator at 35–37°C.
Preparation of the colony count cultures : Use C, pour plate technique. Spread plate technique, B, may also be used.

XII.3 *Methods modified for field performance*

No delayed incubation method has been developed for faecal streptococci. However, the GA-TTC agar is very selective and these indicator organisms are slow growing on this medium. Therefore, the membrane filter or spread plate technique may be performed in the field using pre-prepared plates of GA-TTC agar, and the plates brought back to the laboratory cooled on ice. If a 44°C incubator is available, the analyses may also be completed in the field. Membrane filtration may be accomplished as usual in the laboratory or by a special field technique (see section 3.9). It is important to keep the agar plates protected from light because of the light-sensitive TTC-reagent.

5.3.4 *Further identification of faecal streptococci*

Normally there is no need for species identification of faecal streptococci in water pollution studies. If such identification should, however, be wanted in special studies, the schematic identification outlined in Fig. 15 may be useful. The exact procedures may be found in textbooks on bacteriology.

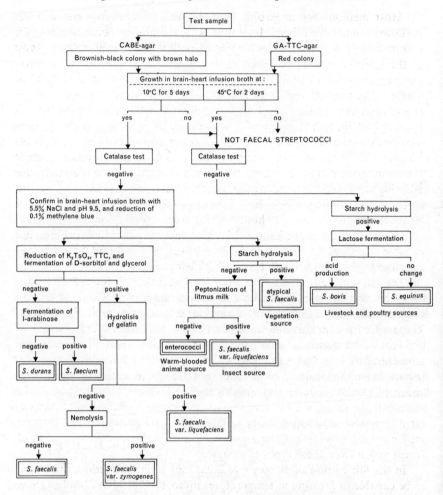

Fig. 15.　Schematic outline for identification of faecal streptococci
(after Geldreich, *29*)

5.4　Reference method for enumeration of anaerobic sulfite-reducing spore-formers

5.4.1　*Definition and general considerations*

The organism of primary interest is *Clostridium perfringens*. This is a Gram-positive anaerobic spore-forming rod, but spores are normally not formed in laboratory media. Distinctive characteristics: Stormy fermentation of milk, non-motile, optimum temperature 45°C, and growth occurs between 20°C and 50°C.

Most methods for anaerobic, sulfite-reducing spore-formers in water pollution studies have been developed with the aim of being selective for *Clostridium perfringens* in aerobic waters polluted by faecal matter. Most of the selective media are based on the ability of *C. perfringens* to grow and reduce sulfite to sulfide in simple media at a temperature of 45°C or above. The method that appeared to give optimum conditions, both as regards recovery and colony size, was chosen as reference method for this manual (*40, 50, 51*). The use of a nutrient medium without carbohydrates narrows the number of different clostridia capable of growing into visible colonies in 24 hours. Furthermore, the black halo of ferrous sulfide surrounding each colony will not be as wide as when glucose is added, thus allowing more colonies to be counted per tube, plate, or filter before confluent halos make counting impossible. Likewise, the incubation time need not be shortened to less than 24 hours, as for some glucose-containing media.

However, there is also a possibility that bacteria not reducing sulfite, but capable of producing hydrogen sulfide from sulfur-containing proteins, may interfere by forming black halos around their colonies.

The chosen method has also been used successfully for selective enumeration of *C. perfringens* from marine sediments (*4*). However, in this original method a selective incubation temperature of 48°C was employed. The restrictions on creating a demand for a multitude of incubators of different temperature settings rule out use of this selective incubation temperature. This loss of selectivity is expected to have little effect on results from the analysis of aerobic waters, where naturally occurring, anaerobic, sulfite-reducing spore-formers are less likely to be found. In sediments, however, such organisms would most likely be present ; particularly in marine sediments rich in sulfate. Thus, the recommended method may not be able to select the anaerobic, sulfite-reducing spore-formers of faecal origin from these types of sample.

In the 8th edition of Bergey's Manual (*66*) several clostridia are stated to be capable of growing at temperatures up to 45°C or above, and to show slight, moderate, or abundant growth on nutrient agar without carbohydrates added. Some of these are capable of producing H_2S from proteins. The ability to reduce sulfite to sulfide is not recorded for clostridia in this edi-edition of Bergey's Manual, and some of the species reported in the 7th edition (*65*) as having this ability are no longer listed in the 8th edition. However, one organism that might interfere is the former *C. nigrificans*, now named *Desulfotomaculum nigrificans;* others are *C. acetobutylicum* and *C. sporogenes*. The first is a common inhabitant of soil and fresh water, and, in contrast to clostridia, is also capable of reducing sulfate. The second is found in soil ; the third occurs in soil and faeces and may thus be rightfully included among the other faecal sulfite reducers.

A few bacteria belonging to the genus *Bacillus* have been found to interfere on plates with Wilson & Blair (glucose-peptone-sulfite) agar and cover agar ; i.e., *B. megaterium* and *B. cereus*. When used with the membrane filter technique, sulfide media may give rise to surface growth of these aerobic spore-formers if the membranes are placed grid (face) side up and covered with liquefied agar medium.

Marshall et al. (*81*) report that the following bacteria may interfere in methods for the enumeration of *C. perfringens*, based on sulfite reduction : *C. bifermentans*, *C. sporogenes*, *C. pasteurianum*, *C. subterminale*, *C. butyricum*, *C. novyi*, *C. lactoacetophilum*, *C. aerofoetidum*, and *C. butylicum*. Facultative anaerobic sulfite reducers include : *Salmonella paratyphi B*, *S. enteriditis*, *S. typhimurium*, *Proteus vulgaris*, *P. mirabilis*, *Streptococcus faecalis* var. *liquefaciens*, and *Strep. faecalis* var. *zymogenes*. Methods more selective for *Clostridium perfringens* than the chosen reference method are in use in some countries. One such method employs the MPN-technique with D.R.C.M. (differential, reinforced, clostridial medium) in the presumptive test, detecting all anaerobic sulfite reducers (*24*). The confirmatory test relies on " stormy fermentation " of milk as an indication of the presence of *C. perfringens*. However, several other clostridia bring about " stormy fermentation " of milk (*C. butyricum*, *C. plagarum*, *C. acetobutylicum*, *C. aurantibutyricum*), so that this second step is not enough to ascertain the presence of *C. perfringens*.

When the sample is incubated at 44°C instead of at 48°C, the methods discussed here are not selective enough for enumeration of vegetative cells of sulfite reducing spore-formers, since there is no assurance that the sulfite reducers are spore-formers unless the sample has been pasteurized. Other growth media designed for selective enumeration of *C. perfringens* from food, employing plate count technique, rely on selective agents that inhibit growth of other bacteria producing sulfide from inorganic or organic sulfur sources. Some of these methods are described in references *81*, *82*, and *83*.

When performed as described in the following, the different techniques for colony counting are presumed to give equivalent results. Each laboratory may choose the technique of its preference, perhaps taking into account what is expected to be the optimum technique for the expected bacterial density of the laboratory sample.

5.4.2   *Colony count methods for anaerobic sulfite-reducing spore-formers*

I. Scope

These colony count methods have been developed for the quantitative analysis of anaerobic, sulfite-reducing spore-formers of faecal origin in polluted lake and river waters and sediments, raw sewage, sewage sludge, and sewage effluents.

II. Field of application

These methods may be used for all types of sample observing the normal restrictions on the use of the membrane filter method.

III. Definitions

All bacteria that survive pasteurization and produce black colonies in peptone-iron sulfite agar with the described techniques in 24 ± 2 hours at $44 \pm 0.5°C$ are considered to be anaerobic, sulfite-reducing spore-formers. Hydrogen sulfide producers natural to lake and river sediments may interfere in the method.

IV. Principle

This method is based on colony counts in peptone-iron sulfite agar with the use of the standing tube, pour plate, or membrane filter technique, described in sections 3.5, 3.6 and 3.8, respectively.

The particular technique used may be chosen according to preference by each laboratory, but the membrane filter technique is recommended for water with low bacterial density.

V. Reactions

The black colonies are presumed to be produced by bacteria reducing sulfite to sulfide, which reacts with the ferrous iron to form black ferrous sulfide

$$Na_2SO_3 \xrightarrow[\text{reduction}]{\text{bacterial}} H_2S$$

$$H_2S + FeSO_4 = FeS + H_2SO_4$$

Possible interference :

$$\text{Sulfur-containing proteins} \xrightarrow[\text{degradation}]{\text{bacterial}} H_2S$$

VI. Reagents

Diluent as described in section 3.3.

Growth medium : Peptone-iron sulfite agar (PIS-agar) as described in section 5.6.10, prepared for the cultivation of anaerobic bacteria as described in section 3.5, III.

For membrane filter and pour plate techniques, also prepare cover agar as described in section 5.6.10.

VII. Apparatus

- For pour plate technique, as described in section 3.6, II.
- For membrane filter technique, as described in section 3.8, II.
- For standing tube technique, as described in section 3.5, II.
- A water bath (large container with water) suitable for pasteurization of the sample, see IX.
- Incubator at $44 \pm 0.5°C$.

VIII. Sampling and samples

The taking of laboratory samples is described in section 2.
The preparation of test samples is described in section 3.2, their dilution in section 3.3.

IX. Procedure

IX.1 *Test portion*

Any size of test portion may be used with the membrane filter technique as long as the restrictions for the use of this technique are observed (see section 3.8, I). For test portions smaller than 100 ml, a 2-fold decrease in volume is recommended.

If the membrane filter technique is not to be applied, the maximum volume of test sample to be analysed by the other techniques described is 50 ml. For smaller test portions, a 2-fold decrease in volume is recommended. This may be approximately performed by analysing test portions of 25, 10, 5, 2.5, 1, 0.5, 0.25 and 0.1 ml. For test portions larger than 2.5 ml, the tube technique should then be chosen. If large enough Petri dishes to allow complete mixing of the test portion and the agar medium are available, such dishes may also be employed.

If test portions of less than 0.1 ml are considered, dilute with sterile diluent in 10-fold dilutions as described in section 3.3 and use test portions of 1, 0.5 and 0.25 ml.

Select and record the volumes of test portion, V_i, to be analysed from each test sample. If dilution is applied, also record the dilution factor, F.

IX.2 *Preparation of colony count cultures*

IX.2.1 *Membrane filter technique*

Liquefy pre-prepared NA-base I (single strength) and cover agar base, and temper at 43–45°C. Prepare the ferrous sulfate and sodium sulfite solutions as described in section 5.6.10. Prepare as described in section 5.6.10, or bring out from storage, sulfuric acid or thioglycolate-solution for the cover agar.

If pasteurization is wanted, perform the pasteurization by placing all the laboratory samples or suspensions in suitable containers (e.g., the sampling bottles) in water at approximately 60°C. Slowly bring the temperature up to 80°C and keep at this temperature for 10–15 minutes (*50, 53*). Remove the containers from the water bath and allow to cool.

Remove one container of NA-base I from the tempering bath. Add the ferrous sulfate solution and mix carefully without getting air bubbles into the medium. Add the sulfite solution and mix carefully. The correct volumes of ferrous sulfate and sulfite solutions for different portions of NA-base are given in Table 13.

Table 13. Details of the final preparation of growth medium for membrane filter and plate count techniques

Reagent	Volume (ml) for use with dishes of diameter (mm) :	
	50–60	90–95
NA-base I	100	200
Ferrous sulfate	1.0	2.0
Sodium sulfite	1.0	2.0

Pour plates of thickness 2–4 mm in 50–60-mm or 90–95-mm diameter dishes. The volumes of medium required are 6–11 ml or 13–26 ml respectively, and one portion should be enough for 7–8 plates.

Then filter the first test portion through a membrane filter as usual for this technique (see section 3.8, IV). Place the filter *grid side down* on a solidified agar plate.

Proceed with the next test portions until all the prepared plates have been used.

Remove enough cover agar base from the tempering bath to suffice for the prepared plates, and prepare the final cover agar as described in Table 14.

Table 14. Details of the final preparation of cover agar

Reagent	Volume (ml) for Petri dishes with lower dish of diameter (mm) :	
	50–60	90–95
Cover agar for 5–6 mm depth	15	30
Cover agar base	150	300
Sodium thioglycolate solution	1.5	3.0
or		
Sodium sulfite solution	3.0	6.0
Sulfuric acid [a]	3.0	6.0

[a] Enough to bring the pH-value of the final cover agar within 7.2–7.5.

Pour the cover agar over the membrane filter to a layer of thickness 5–6 mm ; about 15 ml are required for 50–60-mm dishes and about 30 ml for 90–95-mm dishes. Allow to solidify and place in the incubator as soon as possible. Then proceed with another set of 7–8 test portions until all test samples have been analysed.

IX.2.2 *Pour plate technique*

Liquefy pre-prepared 200-ml portions of NA-base I (single strength) and 300-ml portions of cover agar base and temper at 43–45°C. Prepare the ferrous sulfate and sodium sulfite solutions as described in section 5.6.10. Prepare as described in section 5.6.10, or bring out from storage, sulfuric acid or thioglycolate solution for the cover agar.

If pasteurization is wanted, perform the pasteurization by placing suitable containers with laboratory samples or suspensions in water at approximately 60°C. Slowly bring the temperature up to 80°C and keep at this temperature for 10–15 minutes (*50, 53*). Remove the containers from the water bath and allow to cool.

Pipette the chosen test portions into Petri dishes. If dilution is wanted, dilute the (pasteurized) laboratory sample or suspension and choose test portions as described in IX.1. Proceed with the next sample, and continue until 7–8 Petri dishes have been prepared. Then, remove one bottle of NA-base from the tempering bath. Add 2 ml of ferrous sulfate solution. Mix carefully without getting air bubbles into the medium. Add 2 ml of sodium sulfite solution. Mix carefully. Pour this final growth medium into the Petri dishes to a depth of 2–4 mm (13–26 ml per dish). Mix and allow to cool.

Remove one bottle of cover agar base from the tempering bath. Add 3 ml of sodium thioglycolate solution and mix carefully, or 6 ml of sodium sulfite solution and mix carefully, then 6 ml of sulfuric acid and mix again. Pour layers of thickness 5–6 mm of this cover agar on the prepared, solidified agar plates. Place in the incubator as soon as possible after solidification. Proceed with another set of 7–8 test portions until all test samples have been analysed.

IX.2.3 *Standing tube technique*

Liquefy suitable portions of NA-base I and II, depending on the volumes of test sample to be analysed. Temper NA-base I at 43–45°C, NA-base II preferably at 45–55°C to avoid unwanted solidification. Prepare the ferrous sulfate and sodium sulfite solutions as described in section 5.6.10.

Pipette the chosen test portions into the tubes. If necessary add diluent as described in Table 15.

If pasteurization is wanted, place the tubes in water at 60°C. Slowly bring the temperature up to 80°C and keep at this temperature for 10–15 minutes (*50, 53*).

Remove the tubes from the water bath and allow to cool to a minimum of 45–43°C.

If pasteurization is not wanted, prewarm small and large tubes containing volumes larger than 1 and 10 ml respectively, by tempering in a water bath at 43–45°C.

Table 15. Details of the tube count procedure for anaerobic, sulfite-reducing spore-formers

Test portions or medium	Quantity required for:	
	Normal size test tubes: 18×180 mm or 16×160 mm	Large size test tubes: 25×250 mm
Test portions	0.1–1 ml	0.1–10 ml
Growth medium I	fill up	fill up
Test portions	2.5 and 5 ml	25 ml
Sterile diluent	up to 10 ml	up to 50 ml
Growth medium II	10 ml	50 ml
Growth medium I	fill up	fill up
Test portions	10 ml	50 ml
Growth medium II	10 ml	50 ml
Growth medium I	fill up	fill up

Remove enough NA-base from the tempering bath to suffice for 5–8 tubes. Prepare the final single or double strength medium as described in Table 16. Mix carefully without introducing air bubbles after each addition.

Table 16. Details of the final preparation of growth medium for the standing tube technique

Reagent	Quantity (ml) required for tubes of size:			
	16×160 mm or 18×180 mm		25×250 mm	
NA-base I	200		350	
NA-base II		10		50
Ferrous sulfate solution	2	0.2	3.5	1.0
Sodium sulfite solution	2	0.2	3.5	1.0

The portions of single-strength medium are sufficient for 5–8 of the smaller-size and 3 of the larger-size tubes and may also be used for topping up tubes to which double strength medium has been added.

Add the growth medium to the tubes as described in Table 15 and mix carefully without introducing air bubbles. Quickly solidify the medium by placing the tubes in cold water.

Proceed with a new portion of growth medium and sample tubes until all the test samples have been analysed.

When completely solidified, but as quickly as possible, place the tubes in the incubator.

IX.3 *Incubation*

Incubate at $44 \pm 0.5°C$ for 24 ± 2 hours in an aerobic incubator. Large standing tubes can be given optimum incubation conditions by placing in a water bath, because the temperature inside the culture then rises more quickly than in an air incubator, and thus gives rise to fewer " false positive " colonies.

Anaerobic incubation of plates is not recommended with this growth medium, since this may enhance growth of interfering, anaerobic sulfide-producers.

IX.4 *Counting*

Count and record the number of black colonies per tube, plate or filter.

Sulfite reducers produce black colonies with black halos. The size of the halos will govern the upper limit of counts per filter, plate, or tube. As a rule, the counts may be accepted as long as separate colonies are discernible, otherwise report : " confluent halos ". Sometimes no black but only greyish to white colonies appear on plates. This is a sign of faulty technique—too much atmospheric oxygen has been absorbed in the medium or cover agar (cf. section 5.6.10, formula No. 13).

Colonies of sulfite-reducers on a membrane filter and on agar plates are shown in Plates 15 and 16.

X. EXPRESSION OF RESULTS

Express the bacterial density of the test sample, BDT, as described for each technique in section 3.

The formula for tubes, plates, and membranes with optimal counts is :

$$\text{BDT} = \frac{\Sigma C_i}{\Sigma V_i} \times V_s$$

The standard volume, V_s, is 100 ml.

Calculate the bacterial density of the laboratory sample, BDL, as described in section 3.10.

XI. SCHEMATIC REPRESENTATION OF THE PROCEDURE

XI.1 *Membrane filter technique*

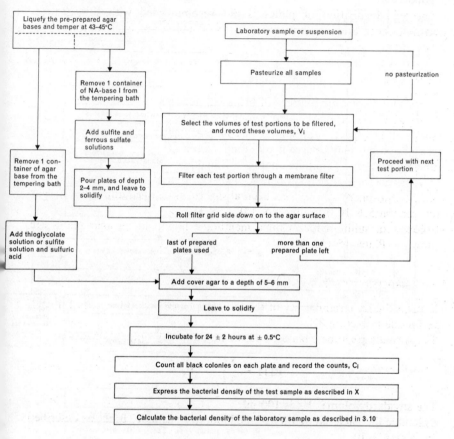

XI.2 *Pour plate technique*

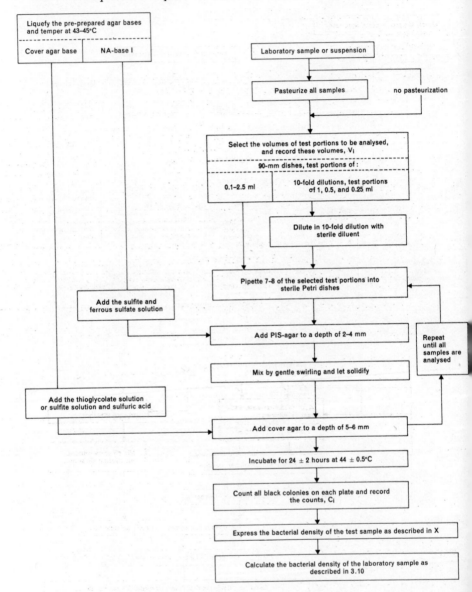

Liquefy the pre-prepared agar bases and temper at 43–45°C

Cover agar base | NA-base I

Laboratory sample or suspension

Pasteurize all samples | no pasteurization

Select the volumes of test portions to be analysed, and record these volumes, V_i

90-mm dishes, test portions of :

0.1–2.5 ml | 10-fold dilutions, test portions of 1, 0.5, and 0.25 ml

Dilute in 10-fold dilution with sterile diluent

Add the sulfite and ferrous sulfate solution

Pipette 7–8 of the selected test portions into sterile Petri dishes

Add PIS-agar to a depth of 2–4 mm

Repeat until all samples are analysed

Mix by gentle swirling and let solidify

Add the thioglycolate solution or sulfite solution and sulfuric acid

Add cover agar to a depth of 5–6 mm

Incubate for 24 ± 2 hours at 44 ± 0.5°C

Count all black colonies on each plate and record the counts, C_i

Express the bacterial density of the test sample as described in X

Calculate the bacterial density of the laboratory sample as described in 3.10

XI.3 *Tube technique*

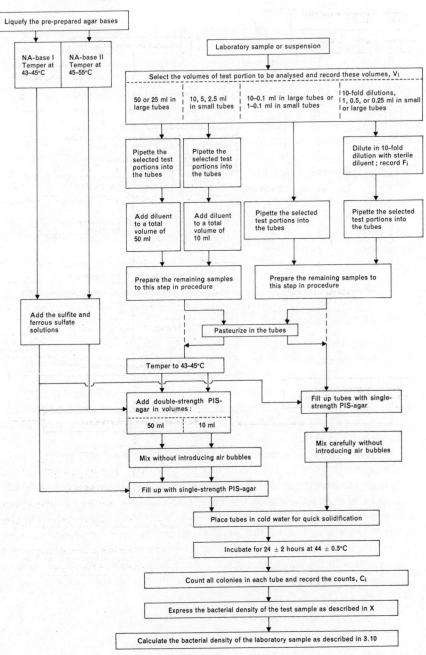

XII. SPECIAL CASES

Notes on field performance

No special field technique has been developed for anaerobic sulfite-reducing spore-formers, but the laboratory procedures may be performed without modification. The growth medium must be freshly prepared; thus melting of the agar bases and tempering to 45°C will have to be performed in the field. The possible need for pasteurization also adds extra work and equipment.

Thus, the analysis of anaerobic sulfite-reducing spore-formers is not well suited for field performance.

Spores are expected to be neither activated nor inactivated during transport; hence, if spore counts are wanted, the transportation time should not be as critical as for non-spore-forming bacteria, so that field techniques are not required. The sample may, however, also contain vegetative cells, and little is known about the ability of vegetative cells to form spores during long transports. Thus, no departure from the general rules of transportation can be allowed.

5.5 Reference method for enumeration of heterotrophic microorganisms

5.5.1 *General considerations*

Natural water contains a variety of microorganisms having different optimum temperatures for growth. Most microorganisms natural to water and capable of growth in laboratory media, produce better growth at 10–25°C than at higher temperatures. Organisms that grow best at 35–37°C usually grow less readily in natural water; if present, therefore, they are more likely to have gained access from external sources, except in countries with tropical climates.

In order to select the bacteria most likely to multiply in the water, temperature is used as a selective agent, and $20 \pm 1°C$ is chosen as the incubation temperature. None of the incubation conditions used in different countries will give the maximum counts of colonies on the medium used nor the maximum counts of heterotrophic organisms obtainable from the water. Therefore, one of the simplest media in use was chosen for the heterotrophic plate count and 3 days as incubation time. The method is performed with the traditional pour plate technique because many countries already have water quality criteria based on data from this method.

5.5.2 *Heterotrophic plate count*

I. SCOPE

This analysis is intended to detect the presence of easily degradable organic matter in water, with the aim of identifying possible problems associated with different uses of the water (see section 5.1.2).

II. FIELD OF APPLICATION

This pour plate method may be used for all types of fresh water samples, observing the normal restrictions on the use of this technique (see section 3.6, p. 312).

III. DEFINITIONS

All microorganisms capable of growing into visible colonies in the growth medium in 72 ± 3 hours at $20 \pm 1°C$ are considered to be heterotrophic microorganisms.

IV. PRINCIPLE

The principle of the pour plate count is fully described in section 3.6. In short, the water sample is mixed with the growth medium in a Petri dish, left to solidify, incubated, and at the end of the incubation time the visible colonies are counted.

V. REAGENTS

Diluent as described in section 3.3.
Use the peptone-yeast extract agar described in section 5.6.10. The medium may be pre-prepared in 13–15-ml portions ready for use and stored at 5–10°C. This medium is designed for microorganisms natural to fresh water; therefore, addition of sodium chloride is not recommended.

VI. APPARATUS

- In general as described for the pour plate technique in section 3.6.II.
- Pipettes suitable for 5, 1 or 0.1 ml of sample, and 1-ml and 10-ml pipettes for dilution if necessary.
- Incubator at $20 \pm 1°C$.

VII. SAMPLING AND SAMPLES

The taking of the laboratory sample is described in section 2. Dilution of the laboratory sample is described in section 3.3.

VIII. PROCEDURE

VIII.1 *Test portion*

Use test portions of 5–0.1 ml of the laboratory sample, or dilute the laboratory sample in 10-fold dilutions and use 1 ml of the selected dilutions as test portion. The optimum number of bacteria per test portion is, as usual for pour plates of diameter 90–95 mm, 100–300 bacteria capable of growing into visible colonies in the pour plate. Guidance for withdrawing suitable test portion volumes is given in section 3.6, Table 5 (p. 314).

VIII.2 *Check test*

When the laboratory sample is to be diluted, also analyse a test portion of 1 ml from each container of diluent to check for contamination.

VIII.3 *Preparation of the colony count cultures*

Liquefy and temper the medium as described in section 3.6, III. Shake the test sample (section 3.2), immediately withdraw the test portion and add to the Petri dish. Record the volume of test portion, V, and the dilution factor F if the sample is diluted.

Repeat this procedure for a suitable number of test samples, observing that no more than 20 minutes elapse between withdrawing the test portion and addition of growth medium.

Then, remove the medium containers from the tempering bath, wipe off any water on the outside, and pour the plates. Mix and allow to solidify. Proceed with next samples until all have been analysed. Invert the plates and incubate at $20 \pm 1°C$ for 72 ± 3 hours.

VIII.4 *Counting*

Select plates for counting, as described in section 3.6.V, p. 315. Count all colonies developing in the plate, fungi included. Record the result as described in section 3.6.V.

IX. EXPRESSION OF RESULTS

Express the bacterial density of the test sample, BDT, as described in section 3.6. The formula for plates with colony numbers below 300 is :

$$\text{BDT} = \frac{\Sigma C_i}{\Sigma V_i} \times V_s$$

By tradition the standard volume, V_s, for heterotrophic plate counts is 1 ml. Calculate the bacterial density of the laboratory sample, BDL, as described in section 3.10.

X. SCHEMATIC REPRESENTATION OF THE PROCEDURE

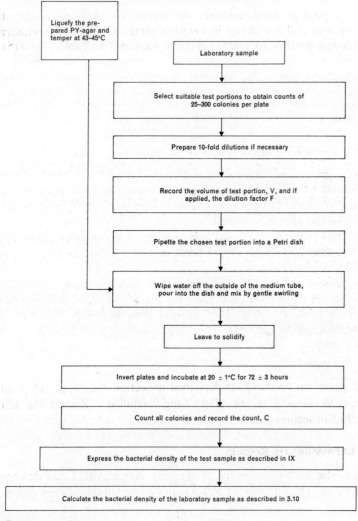

Liquefy the prepared PY-agar and temper at 43–45°C

Laboratory sample

Select suitable test portions to obtain counts of 25–300 colonies per plate

Prepare 10-fold dilutions if necessary

Record the volume of test portion, V, and if applied, the dilution factor F

Pipette the chosen test portion into a Petri dish

Wipe water off the outside of the medium tube, pour into the dish and mix by gentle swirling

Leave to solidify

Invert plates and incubate at 20 ± 1°C for 72 ± 3 hours

Count all colonies and record the count, C

Express the bacterial density of the test sample as described in IX

Calculate the bacterial density of the laboratory sample as described in 3.10

XI. SPECIAL CASES

Notes on field performance

Pour plate count is not a suitable technique for field use. The spread plate technique with the same growth medium may be used if the water to be analysed contains, per ml, at least 250 bacetria capable of growing on the medium.

To obtain the maximum range of bacterial density with a minimum number of plates, an MPN multiple-spot technique similar to the MPN multiple-tube technique may be used (*84*). Make two 10-fold dilutions of the water to be analysed. Then add 5 separated drops of the water, each of 0.1 ml or 0.01 ml, to the well dried surface of one agar plate ; to the second plate add 5 drops of identical volume (0.1 or 0.01 ml) of the first dilution, and finally to a third plate 5 drops of identical volume of the last dilution. Mark the plates with the appropriate dilution factor and record the volumes and dilution factors used. Do not invert the plates for incubation. If water condenses on the inside of the lid, the plates may be inverted after the sample has been absorbed.

Incubate as usual.

After incubation, check for the presence or absence of growth in each of the 5 spots on the 3 plates. To ease the locating of each spot, each plate may be marked beforehand with 5 circles by the use of a suitable flame-sterilized cork borer.

Record the number of positive spots (with growth) in each series of 5 circles. Find and record the corresponding MPN-value from Table 1.

Calculate as follows :

$$\text{BDL} = \frac{\text{MPN-value}}{10 \times V_u} \text{ bacteria per ml.}$$

V_u is the volume of undiluted water sample, which is recommended to be 0.1 ml or 0.01 ml. With $V_u = 0.1$ ml, the method covers the region 2 to > 1600 bacteria per ml, with $V_u = 0.01$ the region is 20 to > 16 000 bacteria per ml.

5.6 Culture media

5.6.1 *Quality criteria for water used in the preparation of culture media*

Only distilled or demineralized water free from traces of dissolved metals and bactericidal or inhibitory compounds may be used for the preparation of culture media and reagents.

Toxicity in distilled water may be derived from fluoridated water high in silica. Other sources of toxicity are silver, lead, and various unidentified organic complexes. Where condensate return is used as feed for a still, toxic amines or other boiler compounds may be present in the distilled water. Residual chlorine or chloramines may also be found in distilled water prepared from chlorinated water supplies. If chlorine compounds are found in the distilled water, they should be neutralized by the addition of an equivalent amount of sodium thiosulfate or sodium sulfite.

Distilled water should also be free from contaminating nutrients. Such contamination may be derived from flashover of organics during distillation ; continued use of exhausted carbon filter beds ; deionizing columns in need of recharging ; solder flux residues in new piping ; dust and chemical fumes ; and storage of water in unclean bottles. Distilled water should preferably be stored out of direct sunlight to prevent growth of algae. Feedwater to a still is often passed through a deionizing column and a carbon filter. If these columns are well maintained, most inorganic and organic contaminants will be removed. If maintenance is poor, the input water may be degraded to a quality lower than that of the raw tap water.

The best distillation system is made of stainless steel. Quartz and borosilicate glass, in that order of preference, are also acceptable (*23*). Tin-lined hardware is least desirable because maintenance is difficult. All connecting plumbing should be of stainless steel or borosilicate glass. Storage reservoirs should preferably be of stainless steel and should be protected from dust.

Tests for bactericidal properties or presence of growth-stimulating substances should be performed if there is any doubt about the quality of the distilled water. The test may be designed to compare the growth velocities of a known bacterium (*Enterobacter aerogenes*, *Pseudomonas fluorescens* or others) in a chemically defined medium with distilled water of known, good quality and the same medium prepared with the doubtful distilled water. One such test is described in detail in reference *23*. In that test, a ratio exceeding 1.2 for the two growth velocities is assumed to indicate the presence of growth-stimulating substances, and a ratio below 0.8 to indicate that the water contains toxic substances.

Taking copper as one relative measurement of distilled water toxicity, the maximum sensitivity of this test will be 0.05 mg of copper per litre in a distilled water sample.

5.6.2 *Reagents for adjusting pH value in culture media*

Use 1 mol·l^{-1} NaOH and 1 mol·l^{-1} HCl for adjustment of reaction unless otherwise stated.

5.6.3 *Dyes and indicators (23, 63, 80, 85, 86, 87)*

Dyes and indicators are essential to the preparation of most differential culture media. In such media the dyes may act as bacteriostatic agents, as inhibitors of growth, or as indicators of changes in the degree of acidity or alkalinity of the substrate. It is obvious, therefore, that only dyes of known purity and known dye content should be used in the preparation of media.

Great care is necessary in the preparation of differential or selective media, even with dyes standardized by the most modern methods. Therefore, as far as possible, only dyes and indicators of a brand certified for use in culture media should be used.

The characteristics of dyes and indicators used in bacteriological media are summarized in Table 17.

5.6.4 *Bile salts (61, 62, 63)*

When "bile salts" are specified in a formula, standardized mixtures with a minimum effective concentration of 0.25–0.5% should be used. When

Table 17. Characteristics of indicators and dyes used in bacteriological media

Name used in this chapter	Synonyms, chemical name and formula	Colour Index Number	
		Rowe's 1924	1956/1971
Rosolic acid	Pararosolic acid, aurin, aurine, corallin. 4-[bis(4-hydroxyphenyl)methylene]-2,5-cyclohexadien-1-one	—	—
Rose bengal [a]	rose bengal 2B, CI acid red 94 disodium or dipotassium salt of 4,5,6,7-tetrachloro-3',6'-dihydroxy-2',4',5',7'-tetraiodospiro[isobenzofuran-1(3H),9'-(9H)xanthen]3-one	—	45 440
Brom(o)cresol purple	4,4'-(3H)-2,1-benzoxothiol-3-ylidene)bis[2-bromo-6-methylphenol]S,S-dioxide	—	—
Ethyl violet	N-[4-[bis[4-(diethylamino)phenyl]methylene]-2,5-cyclohexadiene-1-ylidene]-N-ethyl-ethanaminium chloride	—	42 600
Methyl blue	Aniline blue (water soluble), CI acid blue 93 disodium [[4-[bis[4-[(sulfophenyl)amino]phenyl]methylene]-2,5-cyclohexadiene-1-ylidene]amino]benzenesulfonate	707	42 755

[a] The name rose bengal is also sometimes applied to compounds other than the disodium and dipotassium salts shown in column 2.

Table 17 *(continued)*

Name used in this chapter	Synonyms, chemical name and formula	Colour Index Number	
		Rowe's 1924	1956/1971
Malachite green	Aniline green, China green, diamond green B, Bx, fast green, CI basic green 4 and other names N-[4-[[4-(dimethylamino)phenyl]phenyl-methylene]-2,5-cyclohexadien-1-ylidene]-N-methylmethaniminium chloride	657	42 000
Esculin	Esculoside, bicolorin, enallachrome, poly-chrome, ecosyl; in leaves and bark of horse chestnut *(Aesculus hippocastanum)* 6-(β-D-glucopyranosyloxy)-7-hydroxy-2H-1-benzopyran-2-one	—	
TTC	2,3,5-triphenyl-2H-tetrazolium chloride	—	—

" bile salts No. 3 " are specified, a specially modified fraction of bile salts with a minimum effective concentration of 0.1–0.2% should be used.

5.6.5 *Antibiotics*

Some selective media for microorganisms contain antibiotics (Tables 6 and 7). During media preparation, these antibiotics must be handled with great care. Some are more toxic than others, and the toxicity of certain compounds, such as streptomycin, requires that any unnecessary handling should be avoided; the use of such compounds should be restricted to selected cases of treatment. It is recommended that, whenever possible, such antibiotics should be replaced by less toxic compounds, such as chloramphenicol.

Chloramphenicol (bacteriostatic agent) and cycloheximide (fungicide) are heat stable and may be autoclaved in the medium (*88*). Cycloheximide (actidione) inhibits many but not all saprophytic fungi and also a few pathogenic fungi, including some *Candida* species and *Trichosporon cutaneum*.

5.6.6 *Agar*

The various types of agar available have changed considerably in recent years. A satisfactory gel strength can now be obtained with a concentration of 0.8–2% depending on the quality. For the agar media in this chapter, a satisfactory gel strength with a concentration of 1.5% has been assumed, but this should be varied according to the quality of the agar available.

If necessary, the concentration of agar may be raised to make the medium solidify in countries with hot climates.

Variation may also occur in the clarity of agar solutions and in the degree to which after-precipitation occurs, particularly on mixing with other ingredients, on sterilization, or when maintained in a molten state. Agars are, however, available that remain clear enough for filtration to be unnecessary for most media, and in the following instructions the use of agars of this quality has been assumed. If other agars are used, filtration through cellulose pulp will be required.

5.6.7 *Peptones (23, 61, 62, 63, 89)*

Where peptone is mentioned in any of the following formulae, any standard bacteriological peptone will be satisfactory unless a particular grade is specified. Most peptones form clear solutions, which remain clear when the pH is adjusted. Some peptones, however, form a precipitate when alkali is added. Media containing these peptones therefore require to be filtered. In the media specifications given in this chapter the use of peptones that remain clear has been assumed.

The following are notes on peptones used in media preparation.

Tryptone (*63*) Trypticase (*89*)	Tryptone and trypticase are peptones rich in the amino acid tryptophane. This is of importance in tests for indole production (coliform bacteria). The name tryptone is used as the product name for both the European and American products. Therefore this name is also kept here.
Casitone (*63*) Peptone C (*23*)	Casitone is stated by the producer to be a " pancreatic (tryptic) digest of casein ". Peptone C (Sheffield manufacture : NZ-amine-AS) is also reported to be a pancreatic digest of casein. When these product names are used in the original formulae, the specifications in this chapter will state : " peptone from pancreatic digestion of casein ".
Thiotone (*89*) Thiopeptone (*63*) Peptone B (*23*)	These peptones are made by peptic digestion of animal tissues and are characterized by a high sulfur content. Peptone B (Wilson manufacture : " thiopeptone ") is made by enzymatic digestion of animal tissue. When specified in the original formulae, the specifications in this chapter will state " peptone from peptic digestion of animal tissue ".

Tryptose (*61, 62, 63*)	Tryptose is a mixed peptone produced under this name both in Europe and in America, and the name is kept here as "tryptose peptone" (since the suffix -ose is reserved for sugars in chemical nomenclature, " peptone " is added to the product name to prevent misinterpretation).
Biosate (*89*)	This peptone is described as a hydrolysate of both plant and animal proteins, being composed of and combining the attributes of yeast autolysate and pancreatic digest of casein. It is specified in the American formulae as interchangeable with tryptose.
Proteose peptone (*61, 62, 63*)	Proteose peptone is a mixed peptone produced under this name both in Europe and in America and the name is kept here.
Polypeptone (*89*)	Polypeptone is described by the producer as made up of equal parts of trypticase and thiotone, i.e., equal parts of " peptic digest of animal tissue " and " pancreatic digest of casein ".

5.6.8 *Sterilization of culture media and reagents (23, 75)*

All culture media, except those containing sugars (lactose, glucose), should be sterilized in an autoclave for 15 minutes after the temperature has reached 121°C, or at 114°C for 20 minutes, unless otherwise stated.

Sugar media may be sterilized as above if the following precautions are taken : The maximum elapsed time for exposure of sugar media to any heat (from time of closing the loaded autoclave to unloading) is 45 minutes. Preheating the autoclave before loading can reduce the total needed heating time to within the 45 minutes limit. To permit uniform heating and rapid cooling, materials should be packed loosely and in small containers. When the pressure reaches zero, the medium must be removed from the autoclave and cooled quickly to avoid decomposition of sugars by prolonged exposure to heat. An alternative sterilization procedure for sugar media is to autoclave at 114°C for 10 minutes, followed by control of sterility by incubation at 37°C for 24 hours.

Heat-sensitive reagents or media constituents may be sterilized by aseptic filtering through membrane filters of pore size 0.2–0.3 μm.

Borosilicate or similar glassware is recommended for use in bacteriological work. Material dissolved from glass bottles of poor quality during autoclaving may cause marked changes in the reaction and in the mineral salt content of the water or nutrient medium.

5.6.9 *Storage of culture media (23, 29)*

Dehydrated media (powders) should be stored in tightly closed bottles in the dark at less than 30°C in an atmosphere of low humidity and should not be used if they discolour or become caked so as to lose their free-flowing power. It is advisable to purchase dehydrated media in small quantities that will be used within 6 months after opening.

Liquid media in fermentation tubes, if stored in a refrigerator or even at moderately low temperatures, may dissolve sufficient air to produce, upon incubation at 35–37°C, a bubble of air in the tube. It is therefore imperative that fermentation tubes that have been stored at a low temperature be incubated overnight before use and that those tubes containing air be discarded.

Fermentation tubes may be stored at approximately 25°C, but because evaporation may proceed rapidly under these conditions—resulting in marked changes in concentration of the ingredients—storage at this temperature should not exceed a period of 1 week.

All other types of sterile media should be stored under refrigeration to prevent evaporation, except when stored in tightly closed containers, which may be kept in the dark at room temperature.

Storage in a conventional refrigerator is indicated : " Stored at 2–10°C. "

5.6.10 *Specifications for the preparation of media*

The names of the culture media used in the methods included in section 5 of this chapter have been changed from those of the original descriptions and made consistent. The new names are based on the active ingredients in each medium. The original names used in the research literature and the names used in some commercial product manuals are given under " Synonyms " in Table 18.

Table 18. Names of culture media

Page	Medium no.	Abbreviation	Full name	Synonyms and references
414	1	PY-agar	Peptone-yeast extract agar	—
414	2	—	Lactose agar	—
414	3	LL-broth	Lactose-lauryl sulfate broth	Lauryl tryptose broth *(61, 63, 89, 90)*
415	4	LB-broth	Lactose-bile broth	EC medium *(63, 89, 91)*
415	5	LBR-medium	Lactose-bile-rosolic acid medium	M-FC broth *(63, 72, 89)*
416	6	VFH-medium	Vitamin-free peptone holding medium	M-VFC holding medium *(23, 74)*
416	7	LFG-medium	Lactose-formate-glutamate medium	MM-glutamate medium, Modified Gray's medium *(24, 62, 71)*
417	8	GA-TTC-agar	Glucose-azide-TTC agar	Slanetz & Bartley's medium *(61, 92)* M-Enterococcus agar *(62, 63, 89)*
418	9	GA-broth	Glucose-azide broth	Azide dextrose broth *(61, 63, 89, 93)*
418	10	GAE-broth	Glucose-azide-ethyl violet broth	Ethyl violet azide broth *(64, 89, 94)*
419	11	CABE-agar	Citrate-azide-bile-esculin agar	PSE-agar, Pfizer selective enterococcus agar *(23, 29, 95)*
419	12	PIS-agar	Peptone-iron sulfite agar	Iron sulfite agar *(40, 50)*
421	13	—	Cover agar	—

Each laboratory is strongly urged to compare the specifications given in this section with the specifications of the commercial products to be considered. The exact name of an acceptable and easily available commercial product should then be noted in the box reserved for this purpose in each specification.

No. 1 PEPTONE-YEAST EXTRACT AGAR

PY-agar, for heterotrophic plate count (*77*).

Dehydrated product name :

Peptone [a]	6 g
Yeast extract	3 g
Agar	15 g
Distilled water	1 litre

Dissolve by heating in boiling water. If necessary, adjust the reaction so that the pH-value of the sterilized medium remains within the region 7.0 ± 0.1. Dispense the dissolved medium in amounts of 13–15 ml into test tubes with metal or plastic caps, and sterilize by autoclaving.

No. 2 LACTOSE AGAR

For colony counts, special cases, coliform bacteria (*29, 73*)

Dehydrated product name :

Peptone	5 g
Meat extract	3 g
Lactose	5 g
Agar	15 g
Distilled water	1 litre

Dissolve by heating in boiling water. Adjust the reaction so that the pH-value of the sterilized medium remains within the region 7.0–7.4. (Note : See sterilization restrictions for sugar media, section 5.6.8.)

No. 3 LACTOSE-LAURYL SULFATE BROTH

LL-broth, for MPN-presumptive test, coliform bacteria (*23, 61, 63, 89, 90*)

Dehydrated product name :

Tryptose peptone	20 g
Lactose	5.0 g
Dipotassium hydrogen phosphate, K_2HPO_4	2.75 g
Potassium dihydrogen phosphate, KH_2PO_4	2.75 g
Sodium chloride, NaCl	5.0 g
Sodium lauryl sulfate	0.10 g
Distilled water	1 litre

The pH should be 6.8 ± 0.1 after sterilization. Prior to sterilization, dispense in 10-ml volumes to test tubes provided with inverted vials (Durham tubes). The Durham tubes should be of such dimensions that the inverted vial will be at least partially covered after sterilization when some of the medium has filled the tube. If 10-ml test portions are to be used, the medium should be made double strength (use 500 ml instead of 1 litre of distilled water). (Note : See sterilization restrictions for sugar media, section 5.6.8.)

---

[a] Pancreatic digest of casein.

No. 4 LACTOSE-BILE BROTH

LB-broth, for MPN-confirmative
test, coliform bacteria
(*23, 63, 89, 91*)

Dehydrated product name :	

Tryptose peptone or peptone from
pancreatic digestion of casein 20 g
Lactose 5.0 g
Bile salts mixture or bile salts No. 3 (see
section 5.6.4) 1.5 g
Dipotassium hydrogen phosphate, K_2HPO_4 4.0 g
Potassium dihydrogen phosphate, KH_2PO_4 1.5 g
Sodium chloride, NaCl 5.0 g
Distilled water 1 litre

The pH should be 6.9 ± 0.1 after sterilization. Prior to sterilization, dispenst
in fermentation tubes with sufficient medium to cover the inverted vial at lease
partially after sterilization. (Note : See sterilization restrictions for sugar
media, section 5.6.8.)

No. 5 LACTOSE-BILE-ROSOLIC ACID MEDIUM

LBR-medium, faecal coliform
membrane filter medium
(*23, 63, 72, 89*)

Dehydrated product name :	

Tryptose peptone [a] 10 g
Peptone from pancreatic digest of casein [a] 2.5 g
Peptone from peptic digest of animal tissue [a] 2.5 g
Yeast extract 3.0 g
Lactose 13 g
Sodium chloride, NaCl 5.0 g
Bile salts No. 3 or bile salts mixture (see section 5.6.4) 1.5 g
Methyl blue 0.10 g
Distilled water 1 litre

Dissolve the ingredients—or rehydrate the commercial product—in the distilled
water containing 10 ml of 1% rosolic acid in 0.2 mol·l^{-1} NaOH. Heat the
medium to the boiling point, promptly remove from heat and cool to below
45°C. Do not sterilize by autoclaving. The final pH should be 7.4. The finished
medium may be stored at 2–10°C, but any unused medium should be discarded
after 96 hours (4 days). The rosolic acid reagent will decompose if sterilized
by autoclaving. The stock solution should be stored in the dark at 2–10°C
and discarded after 2 weeks, or sooner if its colour changes from dark red to
muddy brown.
A solid medium may be prepared by the addition of 15 g of agar per litre.

---

[a] Original formula :
Tryptose or biosate 10.0 g
Proteose peptone No. 3 or polypeptone 5.0 g

No. 6 VITAMIN-FREE PEPTONE HOLDING MEDIUM

VFH-medium, holding medium for
delayed incubation method for
faecal coliforms on membrane filters
(*23, 29, 74*)

Dehydrated product name :

Vitamin-free peptone [a] from pancreatic digestion of casein (or 20 ml of a 1% solution)	0.2 g
Sodium benzoate	4.0 g
Sulfanilamide	0.5 g
Ethanol (96%)	10 ml
Distilled water to a volume of	1 litre
Final pH	6.7 ± 0.1

Warm to dissolve the ingredients, then sterilize by filtration through a 0.2-μm membrane filter.

No. 7 LACTOSE-FORMATE-GLUTAMATE MEDIUM

LFG-medium, alternative presumptive test medium, coliform MPN-
method (*24, 62, 71*)

Dehydrated product name :

Lactose	10	g
Sodium formate	0.25	g
Sodium-L-glutamate	6.4	g
Dipotassium hydrogen phosphate, K_2HPO_4	0.90	g
Magnesium sulfate, $MgSO_4 \cdot 7\ H_2O$	0.10	g
Calcium chloride, $CaCl_2 \cdot 2\ H_2O$	0.010	g
Ferric ammonium citrate	0.010	g
L(−)-cystine	0.020	g
L(−)-aspartic acid	0.024	g
L(+)-arginine hydrochloride	0.020	g
Thiamine	0.0010	g
Nicotinic acid	0.0010	g
Pantothenic acid	0.0010	g
Bromcresol purple	0.010	g
Ammonium chloride, NH_4Cl	2.5	g
Distilled water	1 litre	
Final pH	6.7 ± 0.1	

Dissolve the ingredients—or the dehydrated product—in the distilled water. Add ammonium chloride if the dehydrated product does not contain this salt. Distribute in volumes of 10 ml into fermentation tubes and sterilize by auto-claving. (Note : See sterilization restrictions for sugar media, section 5.6.8.) For test portions of 10 ml, make double-strength medium by dissolving the ingredients in 500 ml of distilled water and distribute in volumes of 10 ml into fermentation tubes.

---

[a] Original formula : Vitamin-free casitone.

No. 8   GLUCOSE-AZIDE-TTC AGAR

GA-TTC-agar, for faecal streptococci, colony counts (*61, 62, 64,*
89, 92)

> Dehydrated product name :

Tryptose peptone	20	g
Yeast extract	5.0	g
Glucose	2.0	g
Dipotassium hydrogen phosphate, K_2HPO_4	4.0	g
Sodium azide, NaN_3	0.40	g
Agar	10	g
2,3,5-triphenyltetrazolium chloride (TTC)	0.10	g
Distilled water	1	litre

Suspend the ingredients (except the TTC)—or rehydrate the commercial product —in the distilled water.

CAUTION : Sodium azide, NaN_3, is a hypotensive agent. Any contact with mucous membranes (nose, mouth) should be avoided, since this may bring about unconsciousness. Avoid draughts when weighing and do not pipette solutions containing NaN_3 using mouth suction. Antidote : Levarteernol bitartrate (80).

Place in a boiling water bath until the agar is completely dissolved, and leave in the boiling water for 5 minutes more. The pH should be 7.2 after heating and no adjustment should be necessary. Immediately before use, add a 1% aqueous, filter-sterilized solution of TTC, 10 ml per litre of medium or 2 ml per 200 ml of medium.

For the membrane filter technique, pour directly into sterile Petri dishes and store in the dark. The plates may be stored at 2–10°C for up to 30 days, or when placed in a sealed container to prevent drying, for at least 6 months at 4°C.

For the pour plate technique, dispense in volumes of 200 ml into sterile, suitable containers without addition of TTC-solution. These containers may be held at 43–45°C for a maximum period of 4 hours before pouring the plates. Do not remelt solidified medium. Add the TTC-solution shortly before use.

Additional comments : Poor differential colony colour on glucose-azide-TTC agar can result from either an unsatisfactory grade of tetrazolium indicator or from its exposure to excessive sterilization temperatures. Laboratory experience indicates that a 5-minute exposure in a boiling water bath after the agar has melted and addition of filter-sterilized tetrazolium after cooling will eliminate many of the irregularities observed. Sodium azide deteriorates with age in dehydrated media held for two years or more prior to reconstitution. Steriliz-ation in autoclaves with long time cycles or contact with a chemically contami-nated boiler steam source can cause decomposition of sodium azide to form toxic acid products. Addition of a sodium carbonate buffer is sometimes necessary to prevent undesirable shifts in pH during sterilization.

No. 9   GLUCOSE-AZIDE BROTH

GA-broth, faecal streptococci
presumptive MPN-medium (*23, 61,*
63, 89, 93)

Dehydrated product name :

Tryptone or polypeptone	15	g
Meat extract	4.5	g
Glucose	7.5	g
Sodium chloride, NaCl	7.5	g
Sodium azide, NaN_3 [a]	0.20	g
Distilled water	1 litre	

Dissolve the ingredients—or rehydrate the commercial product—in the distilled
water. Distribute in test tubes in 10-ml volumes and sterilize by autoclaving

(Note : See sterilization restrictions for sugar media, section 5.6.8.) The pH
should be 7.2 after sterilization.

For double-strength medium, use 500 ml instead of 1 litre of distilled water.

No. 10   GLUCOSE-AZIDE-ETHYL VIOLET BROTH

GAE-broth, faecal streptococci
confirmative MPN-medium (*23,*
64, 89, 94)

Dehydrated product name :

Tryptone	20 g
Glucose	5.0 g
Sodium chloride, NaCl	5.0 g
Dipotassium hydrogen phosphate, K_2HPO_4	2.7 g
Potassium dihydrogen phosphate, KH_2PO_4	2.7 g
Sodium azide, NaN_3 [a]	0.40 g
Ethyl violet	0.80 g
Distilled water	1 litre

Dissolve the ingredients—or rehydrate the commercial product—in the distilled
water, and adjust the reaction with 1 mol·l⁻¹ NaOH so that the pH-value after
sterilization will be 7.0 ± 0.1. Dispense in 10-ml volumes in test tubes and
sterilize by autoclaving. (Note : See sterilization restrictions for sugar media,
section 5.6.8.)

---

[a] See *Caution* under Medium No. 8.

No. 11   CITRATE-AZIDE-BILE-ESCULIN AGAR

CABE-agar, alternative plate count medium for faecal streptococci
(*23, 29, 95*)

Dehydrated product name :

Peptone from pancreatic digest of casein [a]	17 g
Peptone from enzymatic digest of animal tissue [b]	3.0 g
Yeast extract	5.0 g
Bile salts (bacteriological bile)	10 g
Sodium chloride, NaCl	5.0 g
Sodium citrate	1.0 g
Esculin	1.0 g
Ferric ammonium citrate	0.50 g
Sodium azide, NaN_3 [c]	0.25 g
Agar	15 g
Distilled water	1 litre

Dissolve the ingredients—or rehydrate the commercial product—in the distilled water by heating in boiling water

Dispense in volumes of 13–15 ml into test tubes and sterilize by autoclaving. The pH-value should be 7.0–7.2 after sterilizing. Temper to 43–45°C. The medium may be held at this temperature for a maximum of 4 hours before preparing pour plates.

No. 12   PEPTONE-IRON SULFITE AGAR

PIS-agar, for anaerobic, sulfite-reducing spore-formers (*40, 50*)

Dehydrated product name :

Complete formula :

Peptone	5.0 g
Meat extract	5.0 g
Ferrous sulfate, $FeSO_4 \cdot 7 H_2O$ [d]	0.80 g
Sodium sulfite, Na_2SO_3 [e]	1.3 g
Agar	15 g
Distilled water + test portion	1000–1100 ml
pH-value	7.2–7.5

Prepare as follows :

A. *Nutrient agar base, NA-base :*

	Single strength I	Double strength II
Peptone	5.0 g	10 g
Meat extract	5.0 g	10 g
Distilled water	1 litre	1 litre
Agar	15 g	30 g

[a] Original recipe : Peptone C (*95*)

[b] Original recipe : Peptone B (*95*)

[c] See *Caution* under Medium No. 8.

[d] WILSON & BLAIR (*96*) prescribed : "8% solution of ferric chloride, 1 ml/l". If $FeCl_3 \cdot 6 H_2O$ was what they intended for use, 0.8 g of ferrous sulfate per litre is in accordance with the original formula, the mole weights of this salt and of ferric chloride being almost identical.

[e] The concentration of Na_2SO_3 in the final medium should be 0.12–0.13%.

Dissolve the peptone and beef extract in the distilled water. Adjust the reaction to pH 7.2–7.4. Add the agar and dissolve by heating in boiling water. Autoclave in suitable portions for the technique to be employed :

Membrane filter technique : Distribute NA-base I in 100-ml portions for dishes of 50–60 mm diameter, or in 200-ml portions for dishes of 90–95 mm, in screw-cap bottles or other bottles with tight-fitting stoppers. These volumes will be enough for pouring 7–8 plates.

Pour plate technique : 200-ml amounts in screw-cap bottles or other bottles with tight-fitting stoppers. This amount will be sufficient for pouring 7–8 plates of diameter 90–95 mm.

Tube technique :

    (*a*) Large tubes :

            Test portions up to 10 ml : 350 ml NA-base I in screw-cap bottles.
            Test portions between 10 and 50 ml, including the latter : 50 ± 2 ml
            NA-base II in screw-cap tubes or bottles.

    (*b*) Small tubes (16×160 mm or 18×180 mm) :

            Test portions up to 1 ml : 200 ml NA-base I in screw-cap bottles.
            Test portions between 1 and 10 ml, including the latter : 10 ± 1 ml
            NA-base II in screw-cap tubes.

All the medium containers will have to be fitted with screw-caps or stoppers in order to allow mixing the ferrosulfate and sodium sulfite solutions prior to pouring.

B. *Sodium sulfite solution*

Na_2SO_3	13 g
or $Na_2SO_3 \cdot 7H_2O$	26 g
Distilled water	100 ml

There is no great risk of infection with sulfite reducers if this solution is used without being sterilized. However, if sterilization is preferred, sterilize by filtration to avoid a change in concentration by evaporation.

C. *Ferrosulfate solution*

$FeSO_4 \cdot 7\ H_2O$	8 g
$0.01\ mol \cdot l^{-1}\ H_2SO_4$	100 ml

Dissolve the ferrosulfate in the diluted sulfuric acid without heating. Heating above approximately 50°C will cause precipitation of ferric oxides, while dissolving without heating leads to a relatively stable solution. Sterilization should not be necessary, but if preferred, sterilize by filtration. The solution should be discarded as soon as precipitate of ferric hydroxides is visible.

The ferrous sulfate is dissolved in $0.01\ mol \cdot l^{-1}$ sulfuric acid for two purposes:

    1. To prevent precipitation of ferric hydroxides.

    2. To neutralize the effect on the pH-value when sodium sulfite is added to the NA-base. The final pH-value should be 7.2–7.5, and the pH-value of the NA-base is regulated so that the final medium, after addition of ferrous sulfate and sodium sulfite, has a pH-value within the given limits.

No. 13 COVER AGAR

To be used with the pour plate and membrane filter techniques for anaerobic, sulfite-reducing spore-formers. This is a modification of the cover agar formula given in referece *14*.

Peptone	10 g
Sodium sulfite, Na_2SO_3	1.3–2.6 g
or Sodium thioglycolate, $HS \cdot CH_2 \cdot CO \cdot ONa$	1.0 g
Agar	15 g
Distilled water	1 litre
pH-value	7.2–7.5

Preparation :

Dissolve the peptone in distilled water and adjust the reaction to pH 7.2–7.4. Distribute this peptone solution and the agar into screw-cap bottles in volumes in accordance with later use :

	Agar	Peptone soln.
For plates of diameter 50–60 mm :	2.3 g	150 ml
For plates of diameter 90–95 mm :	4.5 g	300 ml

Sterilize by autoclaving. This is the cover agar base, which may be stored.

Solutions to be prepared shortly before each use :

Either :   Sodium thioglycolate, 5 g in 50 ml distilled water.
Or :   Sodium sulfite solution as in specification No. 12.

These solutions need not be sterilized, but if preferred, sterilize by filtration. If sodium thioglycolate is preferred, regulate the reaction of the cover agar base to near the upper limit, pH 7.5, the thioglycolate-solution being slightly acidic.
The sodium thioglycolate solution may be stored for a short time, but should be discarded as soon as it becomes oxidized (showing discoloration).
If sodium sulfite is preferred, also have in stock 0.01 mol·l^{-1} H_2SO_4 for adjustment of the reaction of the cover agar base after addition of the sodium sulfite. A concentration of 2.6 g sulfite per litre in the cover agar is recommended to ensure anaerobic conditions in pour plates throughout the incubation period. A sulfite concentration of 1.3 g·l^{-1} usually works well with membrane filters, but for pour plates, double this concentration has been found optimum for consistent results with identical volumes of test portion.

6. PATHOGENIC AGENTS

6.1 Introduction

Domestic wastewater and wastewater from abattoirs and dairies contain infectious agents from the animal-human reservoir. Sick animals and human beings as well as symptomless carriers excrete pathogens, which may later appear in wastewater, sludge, and surface water. Such pathogens include viruses, rickettsias, parasites, fungi, and bacteria.

The most important pathogenic parasites are *Taenia*, *Diphyllobothrium*, *Ancylostoma*, *Ascaris*, *Trichuris*, *Enterobius* and *Schistosoma*, all of which are transmitted in the form of their eggs.

Some important pathogenic protozoa are present in sludge, sewage, and surface water. Such protozoa include *Entamoeba* and *Giardia*. Some potentially pathogenic protozoa often present in such materials include *Trichomonas, Hartmanella, Naegleria* and *Balantidium*.

Whether sludge and sewage water take part in the spreading of *Toxoplasma gondii* is unknown at the present time.

Some pathogenic fungi, such as *Cryptococcus, Histoplasma, Candida* and *Trichophyton* may be present in sludge, sewage, and surface water.

Coxiella burnetii is a rickettsia, which may be present in sludge, sewage, and surface water, especially water polluted from slaughter houses and dairies.

The most important pathogenic bacteria in this connexion are *Salmonella, Vibrio, Leptospira, Shigella*, enteropathogenic coli, *Yersinia, Franciscella, Brucella, Pseudomonas, Aeromonas, Listeria, Staphylococcus*, Group B *Streptococcus, Mycobacteria, Clostridium botulinum, Clostridium perfringens* and *Bacillus anthracis*.

Shigella may be transmitted by contaminated drinking water, but the isolation from sludge, sewage water, and surface water seems problematic. Therefore, the methods described in the following include only some bacteria, such as *Salmonella, Vibrio* and *Leptospira*, all of which may cause epidemiological problems.

The methods described for the demonstration of *Salmonella, Vibrio cholerae* (including NAG-*Vibrio*), *Vibrio parahaemolyticus* and pathogenic *Leptospira* have been selected and modified so that they may be used as screening tests in a non-specialized laboratory. The final typing may then be carried out in a reference laboratory with the necessary specialization and expertise. A primary screening in the local laboratory may ensure the necessary fast transport from the sampling location to the laboratory and increase the chance of obtaining relevant information collected by a bacteriologist with a knowledge of local conditions.

A precise procedure must be prescribed for work in such non-specialized local laboratories, so that the recorded findings may be comparable and reliable.

While this section concentrates on pathogenic bacteria in water, it will not be complete from the public health point of view unless non-bacterial pathogenic and potentially pathogenic agents are also mentioned. These agents, which are often transmitted by water, are constantly gaining in importance owing to the ever-growing demand for water and the decreasing supply, which leads to increased reuse (*151*). A list of these agents and a short description of the related diseases, habitat, and modes of transmission are given. However, no methods for the examination of non-bacterial agents are provided here, although such methods may be available and practised in various countries.

6.2 Pathogenic agents transmitted by water

VIRUSES

Adenoviruses (56)

Disease : Fever, acute upper and lower respiratory tract infections, inflammation of the eyes; symptoms of enteritis or central nervous system involvement less common.

Victims : Humans.

Habitat of agent : Human body as mentioned under " disease "; also multiplies in the intestinal tract and excreted with the faeces.

Route of transmission : Transmission by water reported from swimming pools with inadequately chlorinated water.

Enteroviruses (1, 56)

Polioviruses, coxsackieviruses, echoviruses.

Disease : Fever, headaches, nausea, diarrhoea, muscular pains, meningitis, paralysis (infrequent with infections other than those caused by polioviruses). Some strains of the latter two viruses may cause hepatitis.

Habitat of agent : Human body; multiplies in the intestinal tract and excreted with the faeces.

Route of transmission : Transmission by faecal pollution of drinking and bathing water suspected but not yet proved.

Reoviruses

Disease : Demonstrated in connexion with the common cold, and other upper and lower respiratory tract infections, with diarrhoea, exanthema, and heptatitis, especially in children.

Virus(es) of infectious hepatitis (1, 56)

Disease : Fever, nausea, anorexia, diarrhoea, hepatitis (acute or chronic).

Victims : Humans.

Habitat of agent : Human body; multiplies in the intestinal tract and excreted with the faeces.

Route of transmission : Person-to-person contact; faecal pollution of drinking and swimming water (epidemiological evidence). May be concentrated and transmitted by shellfish living in polluted water if the shellfish are eaten by humans.

BACTERIA

Aeromonas (97, 98)

Diseases : Septicaemia in immunosuppressed host, diarrhoea, pneumonia, abscesses, wound infections. Cause epizootic septicaemia in cold-blooded animals (frogs, salamanders, snakes, fish) and give wound infections in fish.

Victims : Humans, cold-blooded animals.
Habitat of organism : Surface water, especially surface water with high content of organic compounds, wells, and cold-blooded animals.
Route of transmission : Contact with surface water, ingestion of surface water, aspiration of surface water or consumption of foodstuffs produced in aquatic environments.

Bacillus anthracis (99, 100)

Disease : Anthrax.
Victims : Cattle, sheep, pigs, humans.
Habitat of organism : In pustules of the victim, soil and sewage water, especially sewage water from industries employed in the treatment of hair, skin, and intestines. Spores persist for long periods in contaminated materials, such as soil, dust, water, or infected animal tissue.
Route of transmission : The organisms most commonly gain entrance to the body of the victim through a cut in the skin, where they form an inflamed pustule which, when developed, is covered with a black crust. They may also gain entrance through the intestine and respiratory system.

Campylobacter jejuni, Campylobacter coli

Diseases : Diarrhoea, fever.
Victims : Humans, animals.
Habitat of organisms : Swine, birds, dogs, humans. Isolated from water.
Route of transmission : Food, water, pet animals.

Clostridium botulinum (56)

Disease : Botulism.
Victims : Humans, cattle, horse, furred animals, birds, fish.
Habitat of organism : Soil and marine and fresh-water bottom sediments, especially in the northern hemisphere and in waters receiving drainage from large areas of land.
Route of transmission : In nature the bacteria may produce toxins during anaerobic decomposition of animal tissue. Fish from polluted waters are often contaminated with *C. botulinum*. Toxin is produced in contaminated foodstuff under suitable temperatures : above 6°C for type E and above 12°C for other serotypes (A, B, C, D, and F). Victims become ill from eating contaminated and toxin-containing foodstuff. Toxin is destroyed by boiling and frying.

Clostridium perfringens (56)

Diseases : *C. perfringens* type A causes gas gangrene in humans. *C. perfringens* type A causes mild enteritis, and type C a severe form of necrotic enteritis in man and animals.

C. perfringens types A, C, D, and E cause struck, braxy, etc. in animals.
Habitat of organism : Faecal origin ; also present in soil and mud exposed to sewage or manure. Present in wounds complicated by gas gangrene.
Route of transmission : Grows in food contaminated by faecally polluted water ; produces toxins that cause gastroenteritis in relation to sporulation.

Coliform bacteria with R-factors (*101, 102, 103, 104, 105*)

Disease : Health risk to swimmers suspected, but not yet established.
Victims : Humans, domestic animals.
Habitat of organism : Human faeces.
Route of transmission : Faecal pollution of water with these bacteria may lead to the transfer of R-factors to antibiotic-sensitive enteropathogens like *E. coli*, *Salmonella*, *Shigella*. As a result, humans and animals may become infected with antibiotic-resistant pathogens.

Enteropathogenic Escherichia coli (56)

Disease : Gastroenteritis.
Victims : Humans, domestic animals, esp. infants.
Habitat of organism : Human and animal excreta.
Route of transmission : Faecal pollution of drinking water.

Francisella tularensis (56, 66, 99)

(*Pasteurella tularensis*)
Disease : Tularaemia.
Victims : Man and other warm-blooded animals, highly infectious for rodents.
Habitat of organism : In the body of victims. Also found in natural waters.
Route of transmission : Bacteria transmitted by blood-sucking arthropods, inhalation, ingestion, and contact. The organisms penetrate unbroken skin and mucous membranes to cause infection. Water-borne infections have been reported from the USSR ; Montana, USA ; Alberta, Canada ; and Turkey ; in the case reported from the USSR (*56*) an artesian well supply used for drinking water was contaminated by river water, and the riverside was found to be infested with rats from which the infection probably came.

Klebsiella spp. (66, 68)

Disease (potential pathogen) : infections in the respiratory and the urinary tract ; inflammation of the lungs (*K. pneumoniae*).
Victims : Humans and animals.
Habitat of organism : Widely distributed in nature—in soil, water, grain,

etc.—and normally found in the intestinal canal of man and animals. May also reproduce in process water of the pulp and paper industry, and the effluent from a single modern paper machine may contain *Klebsiella* strains, detectable as total and even faecal coliforms, in numbers of the same order of magnitude as the sewage of a town.

Route of transmission : Possible health hazard from different uses of polluted water, either from the bacteria as such or from transference of antibiotic resistance to other pathogens of the same family. *Klebsiella* strains are resistant to penicillin in standard doses, but may be sensitive to high concentrations. The sensitivity to other drugs is variable, but the proportion of resistant strains is increasing steadily. Resistance to antibiotics is transmissible by R-factors to other members of the *Enterobacteriaceae* and vice-versa.

Leptospira (56, 99, 106)

Disease : Fever, renal insufficiency, conjunctivitis, leptospiral jaundice.
Victims : Humans, animals.
Habitat of organism : Urine of infected wild and domestic animals (rats, pigs, cattle).
Route of transmission : Water infected with excreta of domestic and wild animals. The spirochaete is capable of penetrating the skin ; thus infection may be contracted by wading or swimming in such waters. Pathogenic leptospires will only survive for a few hours in marine water.

Listeria spp. (L. monocytogenes) (66, 107, 108).

Disease : Meningitis, encephalitis, septicaemia, endocarditis, abortion, abscesses and local purulent lesions.
Victims : Humans, domestic and wild animals, and fowls.
Habitat of organism : Found in faeces of domestic and wild animals, fowls and man, on vegetation and in silage, and in sewage water.
Route of transmission : Food-borne and venereal transmission, transmission by water through food infected by faecally polluted water.

Mycobacteria (including *Mycobacterium tuberculosis, Mycobacterium bovis, Mycobacterium avium, Mycobacterium marinum* and other pathogenic mycobacteria)

Disease : Tuberculosis.
Victims : Humans and animals, including fish.
Habitat of organism : Sputum and faeces of man and animals ; consequently, mycobacteria may be present in sewage water and sludge, especially from hospitals.
Route of transmission : Aspiration of polluted water during bathing can cause infection. Cattle and other animals may acquire infection from sewage-contaminated water used for agricultural purposes and, in the

case of cattle, for drinking water. Mycobacteria survive for long periods in nature.

Pseudomonas aeruginosa (66, 101, 102)

Disease : Ear and eye infections ; wound, burn, and urinary tract infections ; enteritis.
Victims : Humans, animals, and occasionally plants.
Habitat of organism : Soil and water. Commonly isolated from clinical specimens.
Route of transmission : Infected swimming waters (swimming pools). Densities greater than 100 organisms per 100 ml may expose swimmers to an infective dose. Infected drinking water.

Salmonella typhi (56, 66, 99, 102)

Disease : Typhoid fever.
Victims : Humans only.
Habitat of organism : Multiplies in the intestines of victims and also in healthy carriers. Excreted in the faeces and/or urine.
Route of transmission : Faecally polluted drinking water is a relatively common vehicle of infection ; also transmitted by food. May be concentrated in shellfish living in polluted water and transmitted by consumption of raw shellfish. A few organisms may be sufficient for an infectious dose.

Salmonella paratyphi A and B (2, 56, 66, 99, 102)

Disease : Paratyphoid fever (usually milder than typhoid).
Victims : Humans only (*S. paratyphi* B also, but very rarely, in animals).
Habitat of organism : Multiplies in the intestines of victims and symptomless carriers and also in foodstuffs.
Route of transmission : Disease more often results from infected foodstuffs than from water. The original source of infection is human faeces. May be concentrated and transmitted by shellfish living in polluted waters.

Salmonella spp. (56, 99)

Diseases : Enteric infections and gastroenteritis.
Victims : Humans and animals.
Habitat of organism : Multiplies in the intestines of victims but symptomless excretors are common. Also multiplies in food.
Route of transmission : As for *S. paratyphi* A and B. One of the most frequent agents of food-borne infections in man. In water, relatively massive doses are necessary to produce symptoms.

Shigella spp. (S. flexneri, S. dysenteriae, S. sonnei, S. boydii) (2, 56, 99).

Disease : Bacterial dysentery. Common in the tropics.

Victims : Man and higher monkeys.

Habitat of organism : The intestinal tract of man and higher monkeys, both victims and healthy carriers ; infected foodstuffs.

Route of transmission : Food infected by faecally polluted water or by flies, less commonly drinking water. Water-borne outbreaks occur in association with gross faecal contamination. The infectivity of some *Shigella* is very great (*S. dysenteriae*).

Staphylococci (S. aureus, S. epidermidis) (*2, 66, 101, 109, 110*)

Diseases : A wide range of infections and intoxications ; boils, abscesses, meningitis, furunculosis, pyaemia, osteomyelitis, otitis, suppuration of wounds, and food poisoning.

Victims : Host range very wide.

Habitat of organism : Potential pathogens associated with skin, skin glands, and mucous membranes of warm-blooded animals, including man. Found in swimming pools and natural bathing waters.

Route of transmission : Transmission of skin, throat and nasal infections by bathing water suspected, but not yet established. Ear infections due to *S. aureus* are suspected of being transmitted by bathing water.

Streptococci, haemolytic, Lancefield's group A and C (*66, 100*)

Diseases : Skin, throat and nasal infections in man.

Victims : Man and animals.

Habitat of organism : Respiratory tract, various lesions and inflammatory exudates. Found in swimming pools and natural bathing waters.

Route of transmission : Transmission by bathing water suspected but not yet established.

Streptococci, haemolytic, Lancefield's group B (*66, 111*)

Diseases : Mastitis in cattle and arthritis, osteomyelitis, pneumonia and conjunctivitis in humans, especially infants. Neonatal septicaemia and meningitis are also known.

Victims : Cattle, humans.

Habitat of organism : Milk and udder tissues of cows with mastitis ; found in water polluted by sewage.

Route of transmission : Milk ; transmission by water thought possible, but not yet established. Human infections caused by streptococci group B are still a growing problem.

Streptococci, Lancefield's group D (including *S. faecalis, S. faecium, S. bovis,* and *S. equinus*)

Diseases : These organisms have been incriminated in outbreaks of food-borne diseases, such as diarrhoea, vomiting, nausea, and colic, but tests with human volunteers have given conflicting results.

Victims : Humans.
Habitat of organism : Intestinal tracts of man and animals, food, and water polluted by sewage.
Route of transmission : Food contaminated by faecally polluted water or directly by faecal contact.

Vibrio alginolyticus (112)

Diseases : Otitis, sore throat, wound infections.
Victims : Humans.
Habitat of organism : Marine coastal areas and marine foodstuffs.
Route of transmission : Contact with sea water and sediments.

Vibrio cholerae (56, 99, 113)

Disease : Cholera (endemic in Lower Bengal and spreads to other parts of the globe from time to time).
Victims : Humans.
Habitat of organism : Cholera vibrios infect the intestines of man and are excreted in the faeces of victims and healthy carriers.
Route of transmission : Drinking water is the most important vehicle, but may also be spread by infected food. The original source of infection is human faeces, and food may be infected by polluted water or flies.

Non-agglutinable (NAG) vibrios (V. cholerae other than cholera vibrio) (113, 114)

Disease : Gastroenteritis.
Victims : Humans.
Habitat of organism : Sewage, surface water and foodstuffs from aquatic environments, especially mussels and oysters.
Route of transmission : Contaminated food and water, shellfish from polluted water. Birds may also play a role in the spreading of these organisms.

Vibrio parahaemolyticus (115, 116, 117)

Diseases : Gastroenteritis, wound infections.
Victims : Humans.
Habitat of organisms : Marine coastal areas and marine foodstuffs.
Route of transmission : Marine foodstuffs. Wound infection by contact with sea water.

Yersinia enterocolitica, Yersinia pseudotuberculosis (118, 119, 120)

Diseases : Diarrhoea, fever, acute and chronic arthritis, erythema nodosum, abdominal symptoms, glamerunephrisis.

Victims : Humans, rodents.

Habitat of organisms : Swine, humans, rodents. Isolated from surface water, wells, fish, frogs, and snails.

Route of transmission : Direct transmission from man to man possible, transmission by infected food suspected. *Yersinia* have been found in water and fish, indicating that water may be of importance.

CYANOBACTERIA (66)

Formerly known as Cyanophyceae or blue-green algae (*121, 122*). Some strains of certain species of these organisms have been found to produce toxins, which may be transmitted to humans and animals by water. Species reported to include toxin-producing strains are :

Microcystis spp., *Nodularia spumigena, Anabaena flos-aquae, Aphanizomenon flos-aquae, Coelosphaerium kuetzingianum, Gleotrichia echinulata.*

Disease : Toxin disease. Large doses cause general paralysis without unconsciousness and have a high mortality in animals. Small doses cause reduction of milk production in cows, development of photosensitivity, general fatigue, salivation, and headache ; both diarrhoea and constipation have been reported. Longer exposure may affect the liver (jaundice). May cause allergic reactions in humans bathing in affected water. Reported from Australia, Canada, Denmark, Federal Republic of Germany, Israel, South Africa, USA and USSR.

Victims : Humans, domestic and wild animals, fish and birds.

Habitat of organism : Brackish water and eutrophic lakes.

Route of transmission : Toxin-producing cyanobacteria in high concentration may affect the animals living in the water (food chain) or drinking the water. Such water may be a potential risk for probable water supplies. The cyanobacteria may accumulate along the shore through the effect of wind. Living cells may excrete enough toxin to make the water poisonous for animals drinking near the shore. Sudden death of *Microcystis* populations has been reported to be accompanied by the release of toxins into the water. The toxicity decreases during decomposition of dead populations. Some toxins are reported to be unaffected by aluminium flocculation, filtration, chlorination, or boiling the water, and some are reported to be decomposed by chlorination.

FUNGI

Candida albicans (44, 53)

Disease : Thrush and skin infections.

Victims : Humans.

Habitat of organism : Mucous membranes and alimentary tract of humans and animals ; may multiply in the intestines. Found in sewage, in swimming pools, and frequently isolated in high numbers from industrial waters used in metal industries (oil-water emulsions, etc.).

Route of transmission : Generally by direct contact with mucous membranes or excreta from infected membranes. Transmission by bathing water suspected.

PROTOZOA

Balantidium coli (123)

Disease : May cause diarrhoea, colic, nausea and vomiting.
Victims : Humans.
Habitat of organism : Man and swine.
Route of transmission : Faecally polluted food and water.

Entamoeba histolytica (56, 99)

Disease : Amoebic dysentery. Common in Africa, India, other tropical countries, and America.
Victims : Humans.
Habitat of organism : Intestines of victims and carriers. Discharged with faeces and may thus be present in sewage water and sludge.
Route of transmission : Spread by contaminated waters and sludge used as fertilizer ; also by contaminated food. Flies may convey the infection to food. Cysts survive for more than a month in waters below 10°C, but for 3 days only at 30°C. Cysts are more resistant to chlorination than coliform bacteria, but the dose needed to destroy them is well within the range of practical superchlorination. Sand filters are effective in preventing water-borne infections.

Giardia lamblia (Giardia enteritis) (124, 125, 126)

Diseases : Chronic diarrhoea, abdominal cramp, anaemia.
Victims : Humans.
Habitat of organism : Worldwide distribution. Present in faeces and contaminated materials (soil, sewage, surface water, swimming pools).
Route of transmission : Not totally known, but faecal contamination of food and water seems important. Transmission directly from person to person possible.

Naegleria and Hartmanella (127)

Diseases : Primary amoebic meningoencephalitis (PAME) is known to be caused by *Naegleria* and possibly by other soil amoeba such as *Hartmanella*.
Victims : Humans.
Habitat of organism : Soil and water.

Route of transmission : May perhaps be spread as a result of bathing and swimming in warm swimming pools, warm lakes, etc.

HELMINTHS

Nematodes (56, 99)

Oxyuris (Enterobius) vermicularis, Trichuris trichiura, Ascaris lumbricoides.

Disease : In most cases, only symptom is irritation of the anus. Heavy infections result in intermittent diarrhoea and anaemia.

Victims : Humans, mostly children.

Habitat of organisms : Intestines of infected persons.

Route of transmission : The nematode is discharged with the faeces. Danger to man from sewage effluents and dried sludge used as fertilizer. Also reported to be transmitted through local well water supply. Transmission by swimming water also possible.

Ancylostoma, Necator (56)

Disease : Severe anaemia.

Victims : Humans ; common in tropical countries ; occurs among miners in Europe.

Habitat of organisms : The organisms are blood-sucking parasites in the small intestine. Eggs discharged in the faeces. Where conditions are favourable, eggs develop into free-swimming larvae which thrive in damp ground or in water.

Route of transmission : Infects man in the larval stage, usually through the skin, but occasionally by the mouth, if infected water or vegetables are consumed.

Dracunculus medinensis (56)

Disease : Guinea-worm disease, dracontiasis. Occurs in Africa, India and other tropical countries.

Victims : Humans ; intermediate host : cyclops.

Habitat of organism : Worm embryos develop in the human intestine to males and females. After impregnation, the female penetrates the intestine and migrates to the subcutaneous tissues, where it attains its full development and may reach 0.3–1 m in length. When mature, almost the whole of the worm is occupied by the uterus, which is full of coiled-up embryos. Finally, it bores through the skin, often at the foot or ankle, to discharge the embryos into water. Newly discharged embryos seek an intermediate host, which is generally a cyclops. If the cyclops is swallowed by man in drinking water, it is digested by the gastric juice, and the worm embryos liberated.

Route of transmission : Infected drinking water. Prophylaxis consists in preventing infected persons from coming into contact with water supplies ; and in the destruction of the intermediate host. Cyclops are removed by sand filtration, by excess lime treatment, and by boiling the water (or heating to 65°C). Cyclops are resistant to comparatively large doses of chlorine.

Flatworms (56, 99)

Taenia solium (*pork tapeworm*).   Common in Germany and elsewhere in continental Europe, Africa, Asia and South America.

Disease : Cysticerci cause very serious disease in man.

Victims : Man and pig.

Habitat of organism : Adult tapeworm lives in the intestine of man. Proglottides (mature segments) containing many ova are shed and discharged in the faeces.   Further development of eggs takes place in pig, where the egg casing is digested and the embryos liberated to develop in various parts of the body, such as the muscles, liver and brain, into cysticerci.

Route of transmission : The normal route of transmission to man is by digestion of inadequately cooked pork containing cysticerci. Direct hand-to-mouth transfer of eggs is possible, and polluted water may play a minor part in spreading this disease via irrigation or use of sludge as fertilizer.

Taenia saginata (*cattle tapeworm*).   Worldwide distribution, found with highest frequency in East Africa.

Disease : Serious disease caused by cysterci.

Victims : Man and cattle.

Habitat of organism : The adult tapeworm lives in the intestine of man. Mature segments discharged in faeces as for *T. solium*.   Transmitted to cattle where eggs develop to cysticerci.

Route of transmission : Cattle become infected by drinking water contaminated with human faeces and from grazing on sewage-irrigated land or land manured with sewage sludge. Man contracts the parasite by eating infected inadequately cooked beef.

Taenia echinococcus

Disease : Hydatid disease or echinococcosis, common in Australia, Argentina, Europe, North Africa and the United States.

Victims : Dogs, sheep, cattle and man.

Habitat of organism : Adult form in dogs, larval stage in sheep, cattle or man.

Route of transmission : Dogs contract the parasite by eating infected meat from sheep or cattle. Man, sheep, and cattle become infected by contact with infected dogs, or by eating food or drinking water contaminated by the excreta of dogs.

Dibothriocephalus latus (Diphyllobothrium latum)

Disease, victims : Parasitic to man and animals. The countries mainly affected are USSR, Finland, USA, Canada, Japan, Philippines, Chile and Africa.

Habitat of organism : Adult form in man and dog. Eggs are passed in the faeces. Water may become contaminated by sewage or directly by dogs. In water the eggs develop into embryos within a fortnight and then find their first intermediate host : a crustacean *(Cyclops, Diaptomus)*. Infected crustaceans are ingested by fish (pike, perch, salmon, trout, etc.) and the larvae develop into the plerocercoid form.

Route of transmission : Man and dog are infected by eating fish raw or insufficiently cooked. Fish are infected by living in faecally polluted waters.

Trematodes (flukes) (56, 99)

Diseases : Fluke diseases, such as schistosomiasis, are very common in Egypt, other parts of Africa, the Middle East, India, China, Laos, Thailand, the Philippines, and South America. Only a few cases have been reported in Europe, although liver flukes are not uncommon in ruminants. At present increasing in some areas of the world with the spread of irrigation farming.

Schistosoma haematobium

Victims : Humans. Eggs excreted in the urine, rarely in the faeces. Common in Egypt and other parts of Africa.

Schistosoma mansoni

Victims : Humans. Eggs excreted in the faeces, rarely in the urine. Common in South America and Africa.

Schistosoma japonicum

Victims : Humans, domestic animals. Common in Asia.

Habitat of organisms : In the flukes the sexes are separate. They inhabit the portal vein and its branches, and mesenteric veins. The eggs reach water by pollution with urine or faeces and hatch into ciliated embryos (miracidia). These die after approximately 24 hours unless they reach a suitable host—a freshwater snail. Here the larva becomes a sporocyst, which gives off many daughter sporocysts. These produce large numbers of cercariae, which leave the snail and swim about in the water. They die after approximately 48 hours unless they gain access to a human body. Access is obtained by piercing the skin, or the mucous membrane of the mouth if the water is swallowed. They then enter the blood stream, are carried to the liver and portal veins, and develop into adult males and females in about two months.

Route of transmission : External contact with water containing cercariae, as in washing, wading, and swimming, is the commonest mode of infection.

6.3 Factors influencing the number and types of pathogens present

Among the factors determining the number and types of pathogens in polluted waters are :

(*a*) The epidemiological situation in the area ;

(*b*) The methods employed in wastewater treatment ;

(*c*) Tourism ;

(*d*) Abiotic and biotic factors that result in reduction of the number of viable organisms ;

(*e*) Possibilities for propagation.

In wastewaters and recipient waters pathogenic bacteria will be present intermittently and sporadically. Pathogenic bacteria are generally outnumbered by non-pathogens, and the demonstration of the pathogens will depend largely on the selective capacity of the substrates employed. It may be necessary to employ sample volumes larger than those used for conventional water examination in order to demonstrate the presence of pathogenic bacteria. The special difficulties characterizing such examinations underline the importance of international standardization of growth media, solid media, membrane filters, and the biochemical and serological methods employed. Furthermore standardization of sampling, volumes of water, transportation of the samples, etc., is highly desirable and is, in fact, a decisive condition for the comparability of results.

6.4 Methods for demonstration of salmonella

6.4.1 *Introduction*

Quantitative and/or qualitative determination of salmonella in recipient waters may be relevant when evaluating the hygienic quality of the water.

Salmonellosis other than infection with *Salmonella typhi* and *Salmonella paratyphi* is a common zoonosis. Reservoirs include man, mammalians, birds, and reptiles. These animals may, directly or indirectly, contaminate the aquatic environment as well as aquatic animals and plants. Normally the continued presence of salmonella in water depends on their continued excretion by the infected hosts.

6.4.2 *Definition*

The genus *Salmonella* belongs to the Enterobacteriaceae and comprises motile (few exceptions) oxidase-negative, catalase-positive, facultatively anaerobic, Gram-negative rods. Salmonella attack sugars by fermentation with gas production—an important exception is *S. typhi*, reduce sulfite to sulfide, and decarboxylate lysine (few exceptions).

6.4.3 *Qualitative examination*

6.4.3.1 *Principles.* The examination comprises the following steps :

(*a*) Inoculation of a selective enrichment broth with the desired sample volume, membrane filter, or gauze pad.

Pre-enrichment in a non-selective medium before incubation in a selective enrichment medium may preferably be used as an optimum procedure. A certain amount of the pre-enrichment culture is then transferred into a selective enrichment medium.

(*b*) Streaking from the enrichment medium on to selective primary indicator plates, and preferably also transfer to a second selective enrichment broth.

(*c*) Streaking suspect colonies from the primary plate on to secondary plates. Here salmonella and non-salmonella colonies may be differentiated, so that the following time-consuming identification may be facilitated.

(*d*) Biochemical and serological examination of the suspected salmonella colonies from secondary plates.

Substances that may be added to obtain the necessary selectivity of the growth media include : brilliant green, crystal violet, sodium desoxycholate, potassium tetrathionate, sodium hydrogen selenite, magnesium chloride, strontium chloride, strontium hydrogen selenite, and alkylbenzene sulfonate.

6.4.3.2 *Equipment employed*

Sterile containers
Gauze pads (*128*)
Filter equipment, vacuum pump and receiving flask
Sterile membrane filters (0.45 μ)

Flasks for the enrichment cultivation from the pads or the filter membranes

Incubators at 35–37°C and 42°C ± 0.5°C, preferably water bath incubators

Petri dishes

Test tubes for biochemical reactions

Microscope slides for agglutinations

Agglutinating sera

6.4.3.3 *Non-selective (preenrichment) medium (133)*

Peptone	10 g
NaCl	5 g
Na_2HPO_4, 12 H_2O	9 g
KH_2PO_4	1.5 g
Distilled water	1000 ml

Dissolve the ingredients in the water by heating.
Adjust the pH to 7.2 ± 1.

6.4.3.4 *Selective culture media*

A. Liquid enrichment media

1. *Potassium tetrathionate broth according to Preuss (134)*

Peptone	8.6 g
NaCl	6.4 g
Potassium tetrathionate	20.0 g
Crystal violet	0.005 g
Distilled water	1000 ml

The pH is adjusted to 6.5 ± 0.1.
Sterile substrate powders are dissolved in water without heating.

2. *Strontium selenite broth (135)*

Bacto tryptone	5 g
NaCl	8 g
Strontium hydrogen selenite	2 g
Na_2HPO_4	0.5 g
Distilled water	1000 ml

Strontium hydrogen selenite dissolved in water without heating
The pH is adjusted to 6.8 ± 0.1.

B. Solid selective substrates for primary plates

1. *Brilliant green-lactose-saccharose agar (136)*

Meat extract	5 g

Peptone	10.0 g
Lactose	10.0 g
Sucrose	10.0 g
NaCl	3.0 g
Na_2HPO_4	2.0 g
Phenol red	0.08 g
Brilliant green	0.0125 g
Agar	12.0 g
Distilled water	1000 ml

Adjust pH to 6.9. Autoclave at 121°C for 15 minutes.

Before pouring plates, 8 mg sodium sulfadiazine or 0.3 ml alkylbenzene sulfonate (Teepol) per 100 ml of medium substrate may be added to prevent swarming of *Proteus* species. The plates must be dried until there is no more condensation water left.

2. *Bismuth sulfite agar (136)*

Peptone	10 g
Meat extract	5 g
D(+)-glucose	5 g
Ferrous sulfate	0.3 g
Na_2HPO_4	4 g
Brilliant green	0.025 g
Bismuth sulfite	8 g
Agar	15 g
Distilled water	1000 ml

The pH is adjusted to 7.6 ± 0.1
Rather thick plates must be prepared, using about 20 ml substrate per plate. The plates must be dried free from condensation water before use.

3. *Desoxycholate-citrate agar (136)*

Meat extract	5.0 g
Peptone	5.0 g
Lactose	10.0 g
Sodium citrate	6.0 g
Sodium thiosulfate	5.4 g
Ferric ammonium citrate	1.0 g
Sodium desoxycholate	3.0 g
Neutral red	0.02 g
Agar	12.0 g
Distilled water	1000 ml

The pH is adjusted to 7.5 ± 0.1

Avoid autoclaving.

C. SOLID INDICATOR SUBSTRATE FOR SECONDARY PLATES

Mannitol-phenol red agar (134)

Beef extract	1 g
Proteose peptone No. 3	10 g
Sodium chloride	5 g
Agar	15 g
Phenol red	0.025 g
Mannitol	10 g
Distilled water	1000 ml

The pH is adjusted to 7.4.
Autoclave at 121°C for not more than 10 minutes.

6.4.3.5 *Sampling*

Sampling for salmonella may be carried out by means of gauze pads (according to Moore) suspended at the sampling site for 1–4 days or by means of grab samples, which are filtered so that the sample is concentrated on the filter membrane. The gauze pad represents an unknown volume of water, the volume being dependent on water current, time of exposure, etc.

6.4.3.6 *Growth*

The bacteria collected by the gauze pad or on the membrane filters are preferably cultivated first in non-selective media before cultivation in selective media. For gauze pads use 300 ml of pre-enrichment broth and for membrane filters use 100 ml of pre-enrichment broth. The non-selective medium is incubated for 16–18 hours at 37°C. Then transfer 10 ml of pre-enrichment broth to 200 ml of selective media (see section 6.4.3.4, A.1 or A.2).

If the demonstration of *Salmonella typhi* is especially desired, the strontium selenite broth medium (section 6.4.3.4, A.2) at 37°C seems well suited. For more general examinations for the *Salmonella* group, potassium ʒetrathionate broth (section 6.4.3.4, A.1) is recommended.

6.4.3.7 *Cultivation on primary plates*

The media for cultivation on primary plates are given in section 6.4.3.4, B. Cultures from the liquid enrichment medium (6.4.3.4, A.1 and/or A.2) are streaked on solid selective substrate (6.4.3.4, B.1 and/or B.2 and/or B.3) after 18–24 hours and after 48 hours. The primary plates are incubated for 24 hours at 35–37°C. Further enrichment may also be used. Medium B.2 is preferred for isolation of *Salmonella typhi*.

Colonies corresponding to one of the following descriptions are suspected of being salmonella :

(*a*) red colonies on brilliant green-lactose-saccharose agar (medium B.1) (Plate 17) ;

(*b*) flat black-centred colonies showing a metallic lustre (so-called rabbit's eye) on bismuth sulfite agar (medium B.2) (Plate 18) (some salmonella may appear as green colonies without blackening and metallic lustre) ;

(*c*) pale pink to colourless colonies on desoxycholate-citrate agar (medium B.3) (Plate 19).

6.4.3.8 *Cultivation on secondary plates*

Solid indicator substrate for cultivation on secondary plates is given in section 6.4.3.4, C. Suspicious colonies from cultivation on primary plates (section 6.4.3.7) are transferred to this substrate. Colonies that appear yellow (mannitol positive) are examined by means of biochemical and serological tests.

The minimum requirements for screening include the use of lysine broth, ONPG broth,[a] urea broth, and indole broth, and stab cultures in TSI-agar [b] and iron sulfite agar. Suspicious colonies are tested by agglutination with Salmonella O-antiserum A-I. It must be emphasized that O-antiserum A-I will not react against all *Salmonella* serotypes but only against somatic antigens 0.1–0.16 ; it may be supplemented with other antisera reacting against somatic antigens higher than 0.16. Agglutination must be carried out using colonies from non-inhibitory media.

Final typing and phage typing, if desired, must take place in a reference laboratory. Differential diagnostic problems are mainly due to *Citrobacter*, lactose-negative *E. coli*, *Edwardsiella*, *Providencia*, *Shigella*, *Yersinia*, and *Proteus*.

6.4.4 *Quantitative examination*

Quantification may be desirable and semiquantitative or quantitative examinations may be carried out as most probable number (MPN) estimations, using a membrane filter corresponding to the often very large volume of water necessary. The volume of water to be examined depends on the degree of pollution, i.e., on whether it is sewage water or slightly polluted surface water.

The filter membrane is preferably first cultivated in non-selective media (see section 6.4.3.6). Each of the pre-enrichment cultures is then inoculated in selective broth (see section 6.4.3.6). Each of the selective cultures is examined as described for qualitative examinations. MPN tables such as those employed for *E. coli* I water examinations may be used to determine the MPN of *Salmonella* per 100 ml by correcting for the water volume employed.

---

[a] Orthonitrophenyl-β-D-galactopyranoside broth.
[b] Triple sugar iron agar.

6.5 Methods for the demonstration of *Vibrio cholerae* and NAG vibrios

6.5.1 *Introduction*

Examinations for the presence of *Vibrio cholerae* and NAG vibrios in surface water may be desired in connexion with recognized epidemics and in order to evaluate the hygienic standard.

Cholera is a human disease. The infectious agent enters the recipient water directly from the infected host or indirectly in wastewater from areas with clinical cases, persons in the incubation period or healthy carriers. The importance of the healthy carriers is increasingly recognized. The presence in the recipient water of cholera bacteria and NAG vibrios depends on a continuous supply. The production of shellfish in areas where cholera occurs epidemically or endemically has attracted the attention of epidemiologists and should be taken into account in connexion with increased tourism when the possibility of spreading these bacteria is investigated. The survival time in the receiving water varies according to the biotype and the physicochemical conditions of the water.

6.5.2 *Definition*

Cholera bacteria are facultatively anaerobic, motile, catalase positive, oxidase positive, Gram negative, often curved rods, which have a single polar flagellum. *Vibrio cholerae* does not hydrolyse arginine, but decarboxylate lysine and ornithine. Sugars are decomposed fermentatively without gas production.

NAG vibrios resemble *Vibrio cholerae* morphologically and biochemically but may usually be distinguished serologically (*137*).

6.5.3 *Examination procedure*

6.5.3.1 *Principles*. The examination comprises the following steps :

(*a*) Cultivation in selective fluid enrichment broth of gauze pads or membrane filters corresponding to the desired volume of water.

The use of concentrated selective fluid enrichment broth may be useful. Such concentrated broths revert to normal strength upon the addition of the appropriate volume of a sample of water or sewage to be examined, depending on the concentration of the selective broth.

(*b*) Plating from selective fluid growth medium on to selective primary indicator plates.

(*c*) Isolation of pure cultures from suspect colonies using non-selective substrates.

(*d*) Screening of suspect colonies by means of serological tests and selected biochemical tests.

(*e*) Mailing of suspect cultures to a specialized laboratory for final biochemical-serological typing and phage typing to distinguish between classical *Vibrio cholerae*, eltor biotypes, and NAG vibrios. Chemicals that may be added to the media to obtain the desired selectivity may include : taurocholate, tellurite, citrate, alkyl-aryl-sulfonate, thiosulfate. A selective effect in solid and fluid substrates may also be obtained by keeping the substrates alkaline (max. pH 9.2).

6.5.3.2 *Equipment and supplies*

Sterile containers
Filtering equipment, vacuum pump and receiving flask
Sterile membrane filters of 0.45 μm pore size
Flasks for the selective cultivation of filters
37°C incubator, preferably a water bath incubator
Petri dishes
Tests tubes for biochemical tests
Microscope slides for agglutination
Agglutinating sera

6.5.3.3 *Culture media*

A. SELECTIVE FLUID GROWTH MEDIA

1. *Alkaline peptone water (138)*

Peptone	10 g
NaCl	10 g
Distilled water	1000 ml

The pH is adjusted to 8.6 ± 0.1

2. *Taurocholate-tellurite-peptone water (129)*

Trypticase	10 g
NaCl	10 g
Sodium taurocholate	5 g
Na_2CO_3	1 g
Distilled water	1000 ml

The pH is adjusted to 9.2 ± 0.1
Autoclave at 121°C for 15 minutes.
Before use 1 ml of filter-sterilized 1% potassium tellurite in water is added.

B. SOLID SELECTIVE SUBSTRATES FOR PRIMARY PLATES

1. *Thiosulfate-citrate-bile salt-sucrose agar (TCBS agar) (138)*

Peptone	10 g
Yeast extract	5 g
Sodium citrate	10 g
Sodium thiosulfate	10 g
Ox bile (dried)	5 g
Sodium cholate	3 g
Sucrose	20 g
NaCl	10 g
Ferric citrate	1 g
Thymol blue	0.04 g
Bromothymol blue	0.04 g
Agar	14 g
Distilled water	1000 ml

The pH is adjusted to 8.6 ± 0.1
Sterilize by boiling, but avoid autoclaving.

2. *Taurocholate-tellurite-gelatine agar (TTGA) (129)*

Trypticase	10 g
NaCl	10 g
Sodium cholate	5 g
Na_2CO_3	1 g
Gelatine	30 g
Agar	15 g
Distilled water	1000 ml

The pH is adjusted to 8.5 ± 0.1
Autoclave at 121°C for 15 minutes.
1 ml of 1% filter-sterilized potassium tellurite solution is added to the medium before pouring the plates.

C. SOLID NON-SELECTIVE MEDIA FOR PREPARATION OF PURE CULTURES

1. *Blood agar*

Tryptose	10 g
Beef extract	3 g
NaCl	5 g
Agar	5 g

5% of sheep or cattle blood is added to the melted and cooled substrate before pouring the plates.

6.5.3.4 *Typing sera employed*

Vibrio cholerae antiserum 0–1.

6.5.3.5 *Sampling*

The examination of water for *Vibrio cholerae*, including NAG vibrios, may be carried out by means of gauze pads suspended at the sampling site for 1–2 days, or by means of grab samples. The gauze pads represent an unknown volume of water, the volume being dependent on water current and time of exposure. Grab samples may be concentrated on membrane filters, allowing the filters to represent the often large volume of water necessary for demonstration of *Vibrio cholerae*. Examination of grab samples by means of concentrated selective enrichment broth may be used (*114*) (see section 6.5.3.1(*a*)).

6.5.3.6 *Growth*

The membrane filters are incubated in selective fluid growth medium (section 6.5.3.3, A.1 and/or A.2) for 6–20 hours at 35–37°C and then plated on the selective media (section 6.5.3.3, B.1 and/or B.2). Alternatively, inoculations from medium A.1 or A.2 may be carried out using new selective growth broth and then plating on medium B.1 and/or B.2.

6.5.3.7 *Cultivation on solid selective substrates*

Inoculated plates are incubated for 24 hours at 35–37°C.

Colonies suspected of being *Vibrio cholerae* or NAG vibrios are either :

(*a*) flat yellow colonies with a diameter of 2–3 mm on TCBS agar (medium B.1) (Plate 20), or

(*b*) grey black-centred colonies surrounded by a halo and 1.5–4 mm in size after 48 hours' incubation on TTGA (medium B.2) (Plate 21). After 48 hours, a colony of *V. cholerae* may reach 2–4 mm in diameter ; a black centre appears and zonal changes occur (development of a halo around the colony).

Suspect colonies are transferred to non-selective solid substrates for the preparation of pure cultures and screened by means of biochemical and serological tests. The minimum requirements for screening (*139*) include the following tests :

Motility
Oxidase
Hugh/Leifson
Lactose
Sucrose

Arabinose
ONPG broth
Inositol
Voges-Proskauer broth
Lysine *(132)*
Ornithine *(132)*
Arginine *(132)*
Growth in 1% tryptone broth without NaCl
Growth in 1% tryptone broth with 4% NaCl
Growth in 1% tryptone broth with 8% NaCl
Slant culture in TSI agar
Resistance against antibiotics (pteridine)
Slide agglutination (*Vibrio cholerae* antiserum 0–1)

The oxidase test must not be carried out using colonies from selective media and the agglutination test must not be carried out on colonies from media with high sugar content.

Haemolysis of blood agar (sheep blood) may give an indication as to the biotype.

Cultures that appear to be *Vibrio cholerae* on the basis of the biochemical and agglutination tests are sent to the reference laboratory. All strains that biochemically resemble *Vibrio cholerae* but do not agglutinate 0–1 antiserum must also be sent to the specialized laboratory.

The differential diagnostic problems connected with the examination of water samples for *Vibrio cholerae* are due mainly to sucrose-positive bacteria growing on the selective primary plates. Such bacteria include *Vibrio anguillarum*, *Vibrio alginolyticus*, some *Vibrio parahaemolyticus*, other vibrios and some *Proteus*. NAG vibrios may easily be taken for *Vibrio cholerae* or vice versa ; therefore, agglutination with 0–1 antiserum must also be carried out with boiled cultures if the normal agglutination test is negative.

6.6 Methods for the demonstration of *Vibrio parahaemolyticus*

6.6.1 *Introduction*

Quantitative and/or qualitative determination of *Vibrio parahaemolyticus* in receiving waters may be relevant when it is desired to evaluate the hygienic quality of the water.

Vibrio parahaemolyticus is regarded as potentially a human pathogen. The continued presence of this organism in the marine environment is not dependent on contamination from the human host, since it reproduces in the bottom sediments. Thus, fish, crustaceans and molluscs play a role in the spread of infection.

6.6.2 *Definition*

Vibrio parahaemolyticus is a facultatively anaerobic, facultatively halo-philic, often curved Gram negative rod, which possesses a single polar flagellum. The bacteria are indole positive (few exceptions), catalase positive, and oxidase positive. *Vibro parahaemolyticus* attacks sugars by fermentation without gas production. *V. parahaemolyticus* does not hydrolyse arginine but decarboxylates lysine.

6.6.3 *Examination procedure*

6.6.3.1 *Principles*. The examination comprises the following steps :

(*a*) Culturing of membrane filters representing the desired volume of the water sample in selective fluid media.

The use of concentrated fluid selective enrichment broth makes it possible to obtain the normal concentration of nutrients and selective compounds upon the addition of the necessary volume of the surface water or sewage to be examined, depending upon the concentration of the selective broth.

(*b*) Plating from the selective growth medium on to selective primary indicator plates.

(*c*) Preparation of pure cultures of suspect colonies from the primary plates on non-selective plates.

(*d*) Screening of suspect strains by means of serological and selected biochemical tests.

Chemicals that may be added to media to make them selective comprise : sodium chloride, colistin, tylosin, citrate, thiosulfate, taurocholate and alkylbenzene sulfonate. A selective effect in solid and fluid media may be obtained by adjusting the pH to 8.6–9.2.

6.6.3.2 *Equipment and supplies*

Sterile containers
Filter equipment, vacuum pump and receiving flask
Sterile membrane filters with a pore size of 0.45 μm
Erlenmeyer flasks for the cultivation of the filter membranes
35–37°C and 42°C ± 0.5° incubators, preferably water bath incubators
Petri dishes
Test tubes for biochemical tests
Microscope slides for agglutination
Agglutinating sera

6.6.3.3 *Culture media*

A. SELECTIVE FLUID GROWTH MEDIA

1. *Meat broth to which is added NaCl, soluble starch and alkylbenzene sulfonate (115)*

Meat broth	1000 ml
Yeast extract	3 g
Peptone	10 g
NaCl	60 g

5 g of soluble starch, dissolved in boiling water, is added to the medium after sterilization. The substrate may be employed with or without the addition of 0.2% alkylbenzene sulfonate. The pH is adjusted to 7.4 ± 0.1.

2. *Salt colistin broth*

Yeast extract	3.0 g
Tryptone	10.0 g
NaCl	20.0 g
Colistin methane sulfonate	500 000 IU
Sterile water	1 000 ml

Dissolve in the cold. Adjust the pH to 7.4, then add colistin (final concentration 500 IU per ml). Keep at 4°C.

B. SOLID SELECTIVE SUBSTRATE FOR PRIMARY INDICATOR PLATES

1. *Thiosulfate-citrate-bile salt-sucrose agar (TCBS-agar)*

Peptone	10 g
Yeast extract	5 g
Sodium citrate	10 g
Sodium thiosulfate	10 g
Ox bile (dried)	5 g
Sodium cholate	3 g
Sucrose	20 g
NaCl	10 g
Ferric citrate	1 g
Thymol blue	0.04 g
Bromothymol blue	0.04 g
Agar	14 g
Distilled water	1000 ml

The pH is adjusted to 8.6 ± 0.1
Avoid autoclaving

2. *Bromothymol blue-Teepol-salt agar (BTB agar)*

Beef extract	3 g
Peptone	10 g
Sucrose	10 g
Teepol (610)	2 ml
NaCl	30 g
Bromothymol blue	0.08 g
Agar	15 g
Distilled water	1000 ml

The pH is adjusted to 7.8 ± 0.1
Autoclave at 121°C for 15 minutes

6.6.3.4 *Sera employed*

Vibrio parahaemolyticus O-antisera 1–11
Pooled K antisera I–VIII

6.6.3.5 *Sampling*

Grab samples are taken on the selected locations. The samples are refrigerated and transported as fast as possible to the laboratory. The desired volume of water of the sample is filtered through a sterile membrane filter (pore size 0.45 μm) and the membrane filters are placed in growth broth (section 6.6.3.3, A.1 or A.2). Examination of grab samples by means of concentrated selective fluid enrichment broth may be useful (see section 6.6.3.1).

6.6.3.6 *Growth*

The filter membranes are cultivated in selective fluid growth medium (section 6.6.3.3, A.1 and/or A.2) for 18 hours at 35–37°C or 42°C $\pm$ 0.5°C followed by plating on primary plates (section 6.6.3.3, B.1 and/or B.2).

6.6.3.7 *Cultivation on selective primary indicator plates*

The inoculated selective primary indicator plates are incubated for 24–48 hours at 37°C.

Colonies suspected of being *Vibrio parahaemolyticus* are either:

(*a*) flat greenish colonies with a bluish-green centre and a diameter of 2–4 mm after 24 hours' incubation on TCBS (medium B.1) (Plate 22) (after 48 hours a colony may reach 5 mm in diameter); or

(*b*) bluish-green colonies with a diameter of 2–4 mm after 24 hours incubation on bromothymol blue-Teepol-salt agar (medium B.2) (Plate 23).

Suspect colonies are streaked on blood agar plates for pure culture preparation. Motile, oxidase-positive strains are subjected to minimum screening (*139*) using the following tests :

Motility
Hugh/Leifson with 2% NaCl
Anaerobic starch salt agar with 5% NaCl (*130*)
Voges-Proskauer broth with 2% NaCl
Ornithine broth with 2% NaCl (*132*)
Arginine broth with 2% NaCl (*132*)
Lysine broth with 2% NaCl (*132*)
Growth in tryptone broth with 8% NaCl
Growth in tryptone broth with 10% NaCl
Growth in tryptone broth without NaCl
Arabinose with 2% NaCl
Resistance against antibiotics (pteridine)
Growth at $42°C \pm 0.5°C$

Agglutination may be of importance because some marine vibrios seem very similar to *Vibrio parahaemolyticus* from a biochemical point of view. Suspect strains are sent to a reference laboratory.

The differential diagnostic problem will be due mainly to sucrose-negative bacteria growing on the selective primary plates used. Such bacteria include other marine vibrios and some *Proteus* (*140*). Certain *Vibrio parahaemolyticus* strains are sucrose-positive and could easily be mistaken for *Vibrio cholerae*, including NAG-vibrio, *Vibrio alginolyticus*, *Vibrio anguillarum* and other sucrose-positive vibrios.

6.6.4 *Semiquantitative and quantitative examinations*

Semiquantitative as well as quantitative examinations may be desirable because *Vibrio parahaemolyticus* are often present in considerable numbers in water and bottom sediments. Quantitative examinations may be carried out, in principle, as MPN estimations, as for salmonella (section 6.4.4) or by direct plating of, for example, 0.5 ml of water on each of 10 large Petri dishes (diameter 13 cm). Thus 5 ml of water are examined from each water sample.

6.7 Demonstration of leptospires

6.7.1 *Introduction*

Leptospirosis is a zoonosis in which fresh water plays a central role in spreading the disease to man and animals. Examinations for leptospires may therefore be desirable when it is necessary to determine the suitability of water for bathing or for irrigation. The infectious agent of leptospirosis may be excreted in the urine of many different species of mammals, birds, and reptiles. The leptospires may enter the recipient water directly via the urine or indirectly via wastewater or run-off from adjacent land. The continued presence of leptospires appears to be dependent on continued contamination from the man-animal reservoir.

6.7.2 Definition

Leptospires are aerobic, flexible, motile bacteria without external flagella; they have a helical form, with axial filaments inserted in the cytoplasmic body subterminally at opposite ends (*141*). Length 6–20 μm, breadth 0.1 μm, wavelength 0.5-0.6 μm and amplitude 0.1 μm. Leptospires should preferably be cultivated in media containing antibody-free serum or bovine albumin.

6.7.3 Examination procedure

6.7.3.1 Principles

Young guinea-pigs (leptospire-antibody free) weighing < 200 g are inoculated intraperitoneally with a known amount (max. 3 ml) of water. After 4 weeks, examination is conducted on

(*a*) serum,
(*b*) aseptically removed kidney samples.

The guinea-pig blood is tested for antibodies by means of known strains of leptospires using microscopic agglutination-lysis tests (*142*). The kidney samples are cultivated in fluid or semisolid, selective and non-selective substrates. Inoculated tubes are examined every week using dark field microscopy. Positive tubes may be tested against known antisera.

6.7.3.2 Equipment

Filtering equipment including receiving flasks and filter membranes of 0.45μm pore size
Sterile syrings (5 ml)
Small test tubes for cultivation
Microscope slides for agglutination-lysis tests
Microscope with dark-field condensor.

6.7.3.3 Culture media

1. *Stuart's medium* (*143*)

Asparagine	0.13 g
Thiamine	0.020 g
NH_4Cl	0.27 g

$MgCl_2$	0.19 g
NaCl	1.93 g
Na_2HPO_4	0.66 g
KH_2PO_4	0.09 g
Distilled water	900 ml

The pH is adjusted to 7.3 ± 0.1
Add fresh antibody-free rabbit serum corresponding to 1–10 ml per 100 ml.

2. *Korthof's medium (143)*

Peptone	0.8 g
NaCl	1.4 g
$NaHCO_3$	0.02 g
KCl	0.04 g
$CaCl_2$	0.04 g
KH_2PO_4	0.24 g
Na_2HPO_4	0.88 g
Distilled water	1000 ml

The pH is adjusted to 7.3 ± 0.1
Add fresh antibody-free rabbit serum corresponding to 1–10 ml per 100 ml.

3. *Tween 80 albumin medium*, modified by Johnson & Harris (*131*)

(*a*) *Stock solutions :*

Ten stock solutions are prepared using the following quantities per 100 ml of distilled water :

$ZnSO_4, 7H_2O$	0.4 g
NH_4Cl	25.0 g
$CaCl_2, 2H_2O$	1.0 g
$MgCl_2, 6H_2O$	1.0 g
$FeSO_4, 7H_2O$	0.5 g
$CuSO_4, 5H_2O$	0.3 g
Glycerol	10.0 g
Tween 80	10.0 g
Thiamine	0.5 g
Cyanocobalamin (vitamin B_{12})	0.02 g

The pH of the stock solutions does not require adjustment.

(b) *Basal mixture (A)* :

Na_2HPO_4	1.0 g
KH_2PO_4	0.3 g
NaCl	1.0 g
Distilled water	997 ml

When these salts have dissolved add 1 ml of the following stock solutions : NH_4Cl, thiamine and glycerol. Adjust pH to 7.4 and sterilize by auto-claving.

(c) *Albumin supplement (B)* is prepared by adding 20.0 g of bovine albumin, fraction V, to 100 ml of distilled water. When this has dissolved add the following stock solutions slowly while the albumin solution is being stirred :

$CaCl_2, 2H_2O$	2.0 ml
$MgCl_2, 6H_2O$	2.0 ml
$ZnSO_4, 7H_2O$	2.0 ml
$CuSO_4, 5H_2O$	0.2 ml
$FeSO_4, 7H_2O$	20.0 ml
Cyanocobalamin	2.0 ml
Tween 80	25.0 ml

The pH is adjusted to 7.4 and the total volume is brought to 200 ml. Sterilize by filtration.

(d) The *complete medium* consists of 1 volume of B and 9 volumes of A. The substrate may be used with or without the addition of sodium pyruvate (100 $\mu g.l^{-1}$) (*144*).

The addition of 5-fluorouracil (100 $\mu g.ml^{-1}$) is reported to give the substrate a certain degree of selectivity (*145*).

6.7.3.4 *Sera*

Pooled and single antigens and antisera are commercially available.

6.7.3.5 *Animals*

Guinea-pigs 3–4 weeks old are employed.

6.7.3.6 *Sampling*

The water samples are preferably taken at a depth of 0.3–0.5 m. They are refrigerated and promptly transported to the laboratory protected against sunlight. Just before use, the samples are thoroughly mixed by shaking vigorously.

6.7.3.7   *Injection of guinea-pigs*

Five guinea-pigs are inoculated intraperitoneally for each water sample, using a dose of max. 3 ml of unfiltered water. Preferably guinea-pigs are also inoculated with water filtered through membrane filters (pore size 0.45 μm). Repeatedly filtered water may be used for the inoculation of culture media (section 6.7.3.3, media 1, 2 and 3) (*146*).

The filtration is employed to remove other possible pathogenic bacteria that may interfere with the examination. The diameter and amplitude of *Leptospira* are less than the corresponding values for *Borrelia*, *Treponema* and *Spirochaeta*, of which the last named are often present in water.

After 4 weeks the blood of the guinea-pigs is tested for antibodies and the kidneys are examined for the presence of pathogenic *Leptospira*.

(*a*)   *The antibody test.* The aseptically drawn blood is tested for antibodies using 4–14-day old cultures of known strains of *Leptospira* cultivated in fluid media (section 6.7.3.3, media 1, 2 or 3). The antigen concentration should be of an order of magnitude around 50 million per ml.

Serum dilutions $1 \to 10$, $1 \to 30$, $1 \to 100$, $1 \to 300$, $1 \to 1000$ and $1 \to 3000$ are made in saline. The ratio of antigen to antibody employed is given in the following table, where the numbers of drops are indicated :

Saline (drops)	8	9	9
Serum (drops)	2	1	1
Serum dilution	$1 \to 5$	$1 \to 50$	$1 \to 500$

Antigen-antibody mixtures for the agglutination-lysis test are prepared as shown in the following tables :

Antigen (drops)	3	3	3
Serum dilution (drops) [a]	3 ($1 \to 5$)	3 ($1 \to 50$)	3 ($1 \to 500$)
Final serum dilution	$1 \to 10$	$1 \to 100$	$1 \to 1000$

Antigen (drops)	3	3	3
Saline drops	2	2	2
Serum dilution (drops) [a]	1 ($1 \to 5$)	1 ($1 \to 50$)	1 ($1 \to 500$)
Final serum dilution	$1 \to 30$	$1 \to 300$	$1 \to 3000$

---

[a] The first 3 drops of serum dilution are taken from the $1 \to 5$ serum dilution, the second 3 drops are taken from the $1 \to 50$ serum dilution, and the third 3 drops are taken from the $1 \to 500$ serum dilution.

The antigen-antibody mixtures are incubated for 3 hours in the tubes at 30°C ± 0.5°C, and for 1 hour at room temperature. They are then examined microscopically. The titre is expressed as the highest serum dilution that, after reaction with the antigen, may cause agglutination of more than 50% of the cells. Controls must be included in the test.

For screening the test may be simplified by using only the 1 → 100 serum dilution in the agglutination test. If a positive reaction is obtained, other serum dilutions may be tested.

(*b*) *Examination of aseptically removed kidney samples.* The aseptically removed kidney tissue is ground in a mortar together with medium 1 (section 6.7.3.3). Tissue suspensions 10^{-1} to 10^{-5} are made.

From each suspension 3 drops are inoculated into tubes containing 7–9 ml fluid medium (section 6.7.3.3, media 1, 2 and/or 3).

The tubes are incubated in the dark at 30°C ± 0.5°C for 2 months. The cultures are examined every second week using dark field microscopy. If growth is observed, the culture is inoculated into tubes of medium containing 8-azoguanine (100 µg·ml^{-1}) (*147*) or copper sulfate (10 µg·ml^{-1}) (*148*). Saphophytic leptospires are relatively resistant to these two compounds.

The best method for distinguishing between pathogenic and non-pathogenic leptospires is inoculation into experimental animals or into fluid substrates without serum. Only saprophytic strains grow in media without serum.

Suspect, isolated leptospires in fluid substrates may be tested against known antisera by the microscopic agglutination-lysis test, as mentioned under (*a*) above.

Water samples are suspected of being positive for leptospires if:

(*a*) the inoculated guinea-pigs possess serum antibody titres ⩾ 100, or

(*b*) pathogenic leptospires are demonstrated in fluid media inoculated with tissue from the inoculated guinea-pigs.

Isolated *Leptospira* strains are sent to a reference laboratory for further serological examination and confirmation.

REFERENCES

1. McCoy, J. H. Sewage pollution of natural waters. *In :* Sykes, G. & Skinner, F. A., ed. Microbial aspects of pollution. London & New York, Academic Press, 1971 (Society for Applied Bacteriology, Symposium Series, No. 1).

2. Moore, B. The health hazards of pollution. *In :* Sykes, G. & Skinner, F. A., ed. Microbial aspects of pollution. London & New York, Academic Press, 1971 (Society for Applied Bacteriology, Symposium Series, No. 1).

3. VAN DONSEL, D. J. & GELDREICH, E. E. Relationships of Salmonella to fecal coliforms in bottom sediments. *Water Res.*, **5** : 1079–1087 (1971).

4. BONDE, G. J. Pollution of a marine environment. *J. Water Pollut. Contr. Fed.*, **39** : R45–R63 (1967).

5. KOHL, W. Bakteriologische Untersuchung von Wasserpflanzen aus der Donau und von Nebenflüssen. Wissenschaftliche Kurzreferate, 1. Teil, XVIII. Arbeitstagung, Internationale Arbeitsgemeinschaft Donauforschung der Societas Internationalis Limnologiae, Regensburg, BRD, Sept. 1975.

6. WORLD HEALTH ORGANIZATION. International Standards for Drinking Water, 3rd ed. Geneva, 1971.

7. ORMEROD, K. S. Review and comparison of methods used in different countries for the analysis of total coliform bacteria, fecal coliform bacteria, fecal streptococci and *Clostridium perfringens*. Oslo, Norwegian Institute for Water Research, 1974 (Report NIVA XB-01).

8. ORMEROD, K. S. Methods for indicator bacteria selected for inclusion in the chapter on bacteriology in a " Manual on Analysis for Water Pollution Control " in preparation by the World Health Organization. *In :* Daubner, I., ed. II. Internationales Hydromikrobiologisches Symposium, Smolenice, 2.-4. Juni 1975, Bratislava, Veda, 1977.

9. COLLINS, V. G. ET AL. Sampling and estimation of bacterial populations in the aquatic environment. *In :* Board, R. G. & Lovelock, D. W., ed. Sampling-microbiological monitoring of environments. London & New York, Academic Press, 1973. (Society for Applied Bacteriology, Technical Series, No. 7).

10. KRISS, A. E. Suitability of Nansen water-sampler for microbiological investigations in seas and oceans. *Microbiology*, **31** : 865 (1963).

11. KRISS, A. E. Marine microbiology (deep sea). Edinburgh & London, Oliver & Boyd, 1963 (Translated by J. M. Shewan and Z. Kabata).

12. KRISS, A. E., LEBEDEVA, M. N. & TSIBAN, A. V. Comparative estimate of a Nansen and microbiological water bottle for sterile collection of water samples from depths of seas and oceans. *Deep-Sea Res.*, **13** : 205 (1966).

13. KRISS, A. E. ET AL. Microbial population of oceans and seas, London, Arnold, 1967.

14. RODINA, A. G. Methods in aquatic microbiology, Baltimore, University Park Press & London, Butterworths. (Translated, edited and revised by R. R. Colwell and M. S. Zambruski. Originally published in Russian in 1965 as *Metody vodnoi mikrobiologij*).

15. WILLIAMS, E. D. F. A submerged membrane filter apparatus for microbiological sampling. *Marine Biol.*, **3** : 78 (1969).

16. EDMONDSON, W. T. & WINBERG, G. G. A manual on methods for the assessment of secondary productivity in fresh waters. Oxford & Edinburgh, Blackwell Scientific Publications (IBP Handbook No. 17).

17. EMERY, K. O. Bacterial bottom sampler. *Limnol. Oceanogr.*, **3** : 109–111 (1958).

18. VAN DONSEL, D. J. & GELDREICH, E. E. Bacterial bottom sampler for water sediments. The aquatic environment : Microbial transformations and water management implications. Washington, DC, US Government Printing Office, 1972 (EPA 430/G-73-008).

19. CRAIB, J. S. A sampler for taking short undisturbed marine cores. *J. Cons. perm. int. Explor. Mer.*, **30** : 34 (1965).

20. BRINKHURST, R. O., CHUA, K. E. & BATOOSINGH, E. Modifications in sampling procedures as applied to studies on the bacteria and tubificid oligochaetes inhabiting aquatic sediments. *J. Fish. Res. Bd Canada*, **26** : 2581–2593 (1969).

21. CLEEMPOEL, S. D. M. & BARBETTE, J. The effect of small concentrations of sodium thiosulphate on the flora of samples of water for bacteriological analysis. *Trib. CEBEDEAU*, **20** : 27–32 (1967).

22. WORLD HEALTH ORGANIZATION. European Standards for Drinking-Water, 2nd ed., Geneva, 1970.

23. AMERICAN PUBLIC HEALTH ASSOCIATION, AMERICAN WATER WORKS ASSOCIATION, WATER POLLUTION CONTROL FEDERATION. Standard methods for the examination of water and wastewater, 14th ed., Washington DC, APHA-AWWA-WPCF, 1976.

24. GREAT BRITAN, DEPARTMENT OF HEALTH AND SOCIAL SECURITY, WELSH OFFICE, MINISTRY OF HOUSING AND LOCAL GOVERNMENT. The bacteriological examination of water supplies, 4th ed., London, H. M. Stationery Office, 1969 (Reports on Public Health and Medical Subjects No. 71 : referred to in text as " UK report No. 71 ").

25. HALVORSON, H. O. & ZIEGLER, N. R. Application of statistics to problems in bacteriology : III. A consideration of the accuracy of dilution data obtained by using several dilutions. *J. Bact.*, **26** : 559–567 (1933).

26. BADGER, E. H. M. & PANKHURST, E. S. Experiments on the accuracy of surface drop bacterial counts. *J. appl. Bact.*, **23** : 28–36 (1960).

27. NIEMELÄ, S. The quantitative estimation of bacterial colonies on membrane filters. *Ann. Acad. Sci. Fenn.*, *Ser. A IV*, vol. 90 (1965).

28. DAVEY, K. W. & RICHARDS, J. P. The use of an homogenization technique to investigate changes in the heterotrophic bacteria population of activated sludge. *Water Wastes Treat.*, **13** : 44–48 (1970).

29. GELDREICH, E. E. Handbook for evaluating water bacteriological laboratories, Cincinnati, US Environmental Protection Agency (1975) (EPA-670/9–75–006 : Available to the public through the National Technical Information Service, Springfield, Virginia 22151, USA).

30. MELCHIORRI-SANTOLINI, U. Enumeration of microbial concentration in dilution series (MPN). *In :* Sorokin, Y. I. & Kadota, H., ed. Techniques for the assessment of microbial production and decomposition in fresh waters, London, Blackwell Scientific Publications, 1972 (IBP Handbook No. 23).

31. SWEDEN, ROYAL MEDICAL OFFICE. Bacteriological examinations of water, Stockholm, 1966 (Meddelanden från Kungliga Medicinalstyrelsen Nr. 112) (in Swedish).

32. PRESSWOOD, W. G. & BROWN, L. R. Comparison of Gelman and Millipore membrane filters for enumerating fecal coliform bacteria. *Appl. Microbiol.*, **26** : 332–336 (1973).

33. DUTKA, B. J., JACKSON, M. J. & BELL, J. B. Comparison of autoclave and ethylene oxide-sterilized membrane filters used in water quality studies. *Appl. Microbiol.*, **28** : 474–480 (1974).

34. GREEN, B. L., CLAUSEN, E. & LITSKY, W. Comparison of the New Millipore HC with conventional membrane filters for the enumeration of fecal coliform bacteria. *Appl. Microbiol.*, **30** : 697–699 (1975).

35. TAYLOR, E. W. & BURMAN, N. P. The application of membrane filtration techniques to the bacteriological examination of water. *J. appl. Bact.*, **27** (2): 294–303 (1964).

36. BURMAN, N. P. Recent advances in the bacteriological examination of water. *In :* Collins, C. H., ed., Progress in microbiological techniques, London, Butter. worths, 1967.

37. DAUBNER, I. Mikrobiologie des Wassers. Berlin, Akademie Verlag, 1972.

38. SWAROOP, S. Estimation of bacterial density of water samples : methods of attaining international comparability. *Bull. World Health Organ.*, **14** : 1089–1107 (1956).

39. HALVORSON, H. O. Some elements of statistics for microbiologists. Trondheim, The Technical University of Norway, 1958 (Fulbright Lectures 1957–58).

40. BONDE, G. J. Bacterial indicators of water pollution—A study of quantitative estimation, Copenhagen, Teknisk Forlag, 1963.

41. HALD, A. Statistical theory with engineering applications, 5th ed., New York, Wiley, 1962.

42. HALD, A. Statistical tables and formulas, 5th ed., New York, Wiley, 1965.

43. SIEGEL, S. Nonparametric statistics for the behavioral sciences : International Student Edition, New York, McGraw-Hill, 1956.

44. ENGELBRECHT, R. S. ET AL. New microbiological indicators of wastewater chlorination efficiency. Washington DC, US Environmental Protection Agency, 1974 (EPA-670/2–73–082).

45. GELDREICH, E. E. & KENNER, B. A. Concepts of fecal streptococci in stream pollution. *J. Water Pollut. Contr. Fed.*, **41**, R336–R352 (1969).

46. GELDREICH, E. E. The use and abuse of fecal streptococci in water quality measurements. *In :* Proceedings of the First Microbiology Seminar on Standardization of Methods, San Francisco, CA, January 1973, Washington DC, US Environmental Protection Agency, 1973 (EPA-R4–73–022).

47. SUTTON, R. G. A., GHOSH, A. C. & HOBBS, B. C. Isolation and enumeration of *Clostridium welchii* from food and faeces. *In :* Shapton, D. A. & Board, R. G., ed. Isolation of anaerobes, London & New York, Academic Press, 1971.

48. ORMEROD, J. G. A simple method for the detection of manganese in particles on membrane filters. *Limnol. Oceanogr.*, **11** (4) : 635–636 (1966).

49. ORMEROD, K. S. [Problems with sludge and animals in water distribution systems], Oslo, Norwegian Institute for Water Research, 1974 (Temarapport 2 : in Norwegian).

50. DANSK STANDARDISERINGSRÅD. [Advanced bacteriological drinking-water examination (Method A) : Danish Standard DS-265.1], 1st ed., Copenhagen, 1974 (in Danish).

51. DANSK STANDARDISERINGSRÅD. [Simplified bacteriological drinking-water examination (Method B) : Danish Standard DS-265.2], 1st ed., Copenhagen, 1974 (in Danish).

52. NORGES STANDARDISERINGSFORBUND. [Methods for bacteriological examination of potable water : Norwegian Standard NS 4751], 1st ed., Oslo, 1976 (in Norwegian).

53. CZECHOSLOVAKIA, MINISTRY OF FORESTRY AND WATER MANAGEMENT IN COOPERATION WITH THE HYDRAULIC RESEARCH INSTITUTE. Standard methods for the water quality examination for the member countries of the council for mutual economic assistance, Prague, 1968.

54. MINISTERSTVO LESNÍHO A VODNIHO HOSPODÁŘSTVÍ ČSR. Metody mikrobiologického rozboru vody, 2, Prague, 1971 (in Czech.).

55. CROSS, T. & ROWBOTHAM, T. J. The isolation, enumeration and identification of

nocardioform bacteria in clean and polluted streams, and in lake waters and mud. *In :* Brownell, G. H., ed. Proceedings of the First International Conference on the Biology of the Nocardiae, Merida, Venezuela—Augusta, GA, McGowen, 1974.

56. HOLDEN, W. S., ed. Water treatment and examination, London, Churchill, 1970.

57. ENGELBRECHT, R. S. ET AL. Detection of new microbial indicators of chlorination efficiency. *In :* Proceedings of the AWWA Water Quality Technology Conference, Dallas, Texas, December 2 and 3, 1974, pp. X1–X10.

58. ENGELBRECHT, R. S. ET AL. New microbial indicators of disinfection efficiency, Cincinatti, US Environmental Protection Agency, 1977 (EPA-600/2–77–052).

59. WILLIAMS, S. T. & CROSS, T. Actinomycetes. *In :* Booth, C., ed. Methods in microbiology, vol. 4, London & New York, Academic Press, 1971.

60. BOOTH, C. Fungal culture media. *In :* Booth, C., ed. Methods in microbiology, vol. 4, London & New York, Academic Press, 1971.

61. MERCK, E. Mikrobiologisches Handbuch. Trockennährböden, Nährbodengrundlagen und sonstige Präparate für die Mikrobiologie, Darmstadt.

62. OXOID LTD. The Oxoid Manual of Culture Media, Ingredients and other Laboratory Services, 3rd ed., 1973, and separate supplement : Three new media for water testing as described in Report No. 71 (1969) : The bacteriological examination of water supplies.

63. DIFCO LABORATORIES INC. Difco Manual of Dehydrated Culture Media and Reagents for Microbiological and Clinical Laboratory Procedures, 9th ed., Detroit, 1953 (reprinted 1969).

64. DIFCO LABORATORIES INC. Difco supplementary literature, Detroit, 1972.

65. BREED, R. S. ET AL., ED. Bergey's Manual of Determinative Bacteriology, 7th ed., Baltimore, Williams & Wilkins, 1957.

66. BUCHANAN, R. E. & GIBBONS, N. E., ED. Bergey's Manual of Determinative Bacteriology, 8th ed., Baltimore, Williams & Wilkins, 1974.

67. GELDREICH, E. E. Sanitary significance of fecal coliforms in the environment, Cincinnati, US Department of the Interior, 1966 (Publication WP-20–3).

68. GELDREICH, E. E. Fecal coliforms. *In :* Proceedings of the First Microbiology Seminar on Standardization of Methods, San Francisco, California, January 1973, Washington DC, United States Environmental Protection Agency, 1973, pp. 25–42 (Document No. EPA-R4–73–022).

69. STANIER, R. Y., DOUDOROFF, M. & ADELBERG, E. A. The microbial world, Englewood Cliffs, Prentice-Hall, 1957.

70. GELDREICH, E. E. ET AL. The coliform group. II. Reactions in EC medium at 45°C. *Appl. Microbiol.*, **6** : 347 (1958).

71. THE PUBLIC HEALTH LABORATORY SERVICE STANDING COMMITTEE. Bacteriological examination of water supplies : A minerals-modified glutamate medium for the enumeration of coliform organisms in water. *J. Hyg. (Camb.)*, **67** : 367–374 (1969).

72. GELDREICH, E. E. ET AL. A fecal coliform medium for the membrane filter technique. *J. Amer. Water Works Ass.*, **57** : 208 (1965).

73. ROSE, R. E., GELDREICH, E. E. & LITSKY, W. Improved membrane filter method for fecal coliform analysis. *Appl. Microbiol.*, **29** : 532–536 (1975).

74. TAYLOR, R. H., BORDNER, R. H. & SCARPINO, P. V. Delayed-incubation membrane-filter test for fecal coliforms. *Appl. Microbiol.*, **25**, 363–368 (1973).

75. MEYNELL, G. G. & MEYNELL, E. Theory and practice in experimental bacteriology, Cambridge, University Press, 1965.

76. CAMPBELL, L. M. & ROTH, I. L. Methyl violet : a selective agent for differentiation of *Klebsiella pneumoniae* from *Aerobacter aerogenes* and other Gram-negative organisms. *Appl. Microbiol.*, **30**, 258–261 (1975).

77. Eaux d'alimentation. Méthodes d'analyse bactériologique. *J. off. Répub. française*, March 1960, pp. 11–14.

78. BUTTIAUX, R., MUCHEMBLE, G. & LEURS, Th. La colimétrie de l'eau sur membranes filtrantes. *Ann. Inst. Pasteur*, **84** : 1010–1025 (1953).

79. DAUBNER, I. & MAYER, J. Die Anwendung des Oxydase-Testes bei der hygienisch-bakteriologischen Wasseranalyse. *Arch. Hyg. (Berl.)*, **152** : 302–305 (1968).

80. MERCK & CO., INC. The Merck Index of Chemicals and Drugs, 7th ed., Rahway, 1960.

81. MARSHALL, R. S., STEENBERGEN, J. F. & McCLUNG, L. S. Rapid technique for the enumeration of *Clostridium perfringens*. *Appl. Microbiol.*, **13**, 559–563 (1965).

82. HAUSCHILD, A. H. W. & HILSHEIMER, R. Evaluation and modification of media for enumeration of *Clostridium perfringens*. *Appl. Microbiol.*, **27** : 78–82 (1974).

83. HAUSCHILD, A. H. W. & HILSHEIMER, R. Enumeration of food-borne *Clostridium perfringens* in egg yolk-free tryptose sulfite cycloserine agar. *Appl. Microbiol.*, **27**, 521–526 (1974).

84. HARRIS, R. R. & SOMMERS, L. E. Plate-dilution frequency technique for assay of microbial ecology. *Appl. Microbiol.*, **16**, 330–334 (1968).

85. BDH Laboratory Chemicals 1975/76, export edition. Obtainable from BDH Chemicals Ltd., Broom Road, Pool BH12 4NN, England.

86. Eastman Organic Chemicals List No. 44, 44th ed., 1966. Obtainable from Distillation Products Industries, Eastman Organic Chemicals department, Rochester, New York, USA.

87. Gurr Biological Stains and Reagents, 3rd ed., 1971. Obtainable from Searle Diagnostic, Gurr Products, High Wycombe, Bucks, England.

88. STOCKDALE, Ph. M. Fungi pathogenic for man and animals : 1. Diseases of the keratinized tissues. *In :* Booth C., ed. Methods in microbiology, vol. 4, London & New York, Academic Press, 1971.

89. BBL Manual of Products and Laboratory Procedures, 5th ed., 1968, 2nd reprint 1969. Obtainable from Baltimore Biological Laboratory, Division of BioQuest, Cockeysville, MD, USA.

90. MALLMAN, W. L. & DARBY, C. W. Uses of lauryl sulphate tryptose broth for the detection of coliform organisms. *Amer. J. publ. Health*, **31** : 127 (1941).

91. PERRY, C. A. & HAJNA, A. A. Further evaluation of EC medium for the isolation of coliform bacteria and *Escherichia coli*. *Amer. J. publ. Health*, **34** : 735 (1944).

92. SLANETZ, L. W. & BARTLEY, C. H. Numbers of enterococci in water, sewage and feces determined by the membrane filter technique with an improved medium. *J. Bact.*, **74** : 591–595 (1957).

93. MALLMAN, W. L. & SELIGMAN, E. B. A comparative study of media for the detection of streptococci in water and sewage. *Amer. J. publ. Health*, **40** : 286 (1950).

94. LITSKY, W., MALLMAN, W. L. & FIFIELD, C. W. Comparison of the most probable numbers of *Escherichia coli* and enterococci in river waters. *Amer. J. publ. Health*, **45** : 1049 (1955).

95. PFIZER DIAGNOSTICS DIVISION. Pfizer Selective Enterococcus (PSE) Agar. *In :* Pfizer Diagnostics Technical Bulletin, obtainable from Pfizer Diagnostics Division, 235 E. 42nd Street, New York, NY, USA.

96. WILSON, W. J. & BLAIR, E. M. McV. The application of a sulphite-glucose-iron agar medium to the quantitative estimation of *B. welchii* and other reducing bacteria in water supplies. *J. path. Bact.*, **27** : 119–121 (1924).

97. SIMON, G. & VON GRAVENITZ, A. Intestinal and water-borne infection due to *Aeromonas hydrophila*. *Publ. Health Lab.*, **27** : 159–162 (1969).

98. SCHUBERT, R. H. W. Das Schicksal der Aeromonaden in Kläranlagen, Faultürmen und in der Erde. *Arch. Hyg. (Berl.)*, **151** : 243–287 (1967).

99. HAWKES, H. A. Disposal by dilution ? An ecologist's viewpoint. *In :* Sykes, G. & Skinner, F. A., ed. Microbial aspects of pollution, London & New York, Academic Press, 1971 (Society for Applied Bacteriology, Symposium Series No. 1).

100. FROBISHER, M. Fundamentals of microbiology, 6th ed., Philadelphia & London, Saunders, 1957.

101. GELDREICH, E. E. Bacterial criteria for specific water needs. Paper presented at the American Society for Microbiology Seminar " Microbial Pollution Indicators " during the annual meeting May 12–17, 1974.

102. GELDREICH, E. E. Microbiological criteria concepts for coastal bathing waters. *Ocean Management*, **3** : 225–248 (1974–1975).

103. GRABOW, W. O. K., PROZESKY, O. W. & SMITH, L. S. Drug resistant coliforms call for review of water quality standards. *Water Res.*, **8** : 1–9 (1974).

104. GRABOW, W. O. K., PROZESKY, O. W. & BURGER, J. S. Behaviour in a river and dam of coliform bacteria with transferable or non-transferable drug resistance. *Water Res.*, **9** : 777–782 (1975).

105. GRABOW, W. O. K., VAN ZYL, M. & PROZESKY, O. W. Behaviour in conventional sewage purification processes of coliform bacteria with transferable or non-transferable drug resistance. *Water Res.*, **10** : 717–723 (1976).

106. CRAWFORD, R. P., HEINEMANN, J. H., McCULLOCH, W. F., DRESCH, S. L. Human infections associated with waterborne leptospirosis and survival studies on serotype pomona. *Amer. vet. med. Ass.*, **159** : 1477–1484 (1971).

107. KRISTENSEN, K. K. [Water hygiene, present knowledge and research needs], Copenhagen, Danish Water Quality Research Institute, 1974 (in Danish).

108. BALACESCU C. & GRÜN, L. Bakteriologisch-parasitologische Untersuchungen in öffentlichen Hallenbädern. *Zbl. Bakt., I. Abt. Orig. B*, **160** : 292–296 (1975).

109. SEELIGER, H. P. R. ET AL. Die Isolierung von Listeria monocytogenes aus Stuhl-klärschlamm und Erdproben. *Path. Microbiol.*, **28** : 590–601 (1965).

110. CRONE, P. B. & TEE, G. H. Staphylococci in swimming pool water. *J. Hyg. (Camb.)*, **73** : 213–220 (1974).

111. HOWARD, J. B. & McCRACKEN, G. H. The spectrum of Group B streptococcal infections in infancy. *Amer. J. Dis. Childh.*, **128** : 815–818 (1974).

112. RUBIN, I. S. & TILTON, R. C. Isolation of *Vibrio alginolyticus* from wound infections. *J. clin. Microbiol.*, **2** : 556–558 (1975).

113. DUTT, A. K., ALVI, S. & VELAUTHON, T. A shellfish-borne cholera outbreak in Malaysia. *Trans. roy. Soc. trop. Med. Hyg.*, **65** : 815–818 (1971).

114. BISGAARD, M. & KRISTENSEN, K. K. Isolation, characterization and public health aspects of *Vibrio cholerae* NAG isolated from a Danish duck farm. *Avian Path.* **4** : 271–276 (1975).

115. KRISTENSEN, K. K. The occurrence of *V. alginolyticus* and *V. parahaemolyticus* in the Sound. *Nord. Vet Med.*, **26** : 188–196 (1974).

116. SAKAZAKI, R. Halophilic vibrio infections. *In* : Riemann, H., ed., Food-borne infections and intoxications. New York, Academic Press, 1969.

117. RAYMOND, C. F. & PANKEY, G. A. Tissue invasion by unnamed marine vibrios. *J. Amer. med. Ass.*, **15** : 1173–1176 (1975).

118. BOTTLER, R. G., WETZLER, T. F. & COWAN, A. B. *Yersinia enterocolitica* and yersinia-like organisms isolated from frogs and snails. *Bull. Wildlife Dis. Ass.*, **4** : 110–115 (1968).

119. KAPPERUD, G. & JONSSON, B. *Yersinia enterocolitica* in brown trout from Norway. *Acta path. microbiol. scand. Sect. B*, **84** : 66–68 (1976).

120. LASSEN, J. *Yersinia enterocolitica* in drinking water. *Scand. J. infect. Dis.*, **4** : 125–127 (1972).

121. SKULBERG, O. [Water-bloom with blue-green algae—causative agent of poisoning in man and animals]. *In : Fauna*, **9** (1) : 19–26 (1956) (in Norwegian).

122. SCHWIMMER, D. & SCHWIMMER, M. Algae and medicine. *In* : Jackson, D. F., ed., Algae and man, New York, Plenum Press, 1964.

123. BENENSON, A. S., ED. Control of communicable diseases in man, 11th ed., Washington DC, American Public Health Association, 1970.

124. UNITED STATES, CENTER FOR DISEASE CONTROL. Annual summary 1974. Food borne and water borne diseases, US Department of Health, Education and Welfare, 1976, p. 79.

125. JOKIPII, L. & JOKIPII, A. M. M. Giardiasis in travelers : A prospective study. *J. infect. Dis.*, **130** : 295–299 (1974).

126. THOMPSON, R. G., KARANDIKAR, D. S. & LEEK, J. Giardiasis, an unusual cause of epidemic diarrhoea. *Lancet*, **1** : 615–616 (1974).

127. VAN DIJCK, J. P. & VAN DE VOORDE, H. The effect of thermal pollution on the distribution of *Naegleria fowleri. J. Hyg. (Camb.)*, **75** : 7–13 (1975).

128. MOORE, B. The detection of paratyphoid carriers in town by means of sewage examination. *Monthly Bull. Minst. Health (Lond.)*, **7** : 241–248 (1948).

129. MONSUR, K. A. A highly selective gelatine—taurocholate—tellurite medium for the isolation of *Vibrio cholerae. Trans. roy. Soc. Med. Hyg.*, **55** : 81–88 (1964).

130. BAROSS, J. & LISTON, J. Isolation of *Vibrio parahaemolyticus* from the Northwest Pacific. *Nature (Lond.)*, **217** : 1263–1264 (1968).

131. JOHNSON, R. C. & HARRIS, W. G. Differentiation of pathogenic and saprophytic leptospires. I. Growth at low temperatures. *J. Bact.*, **94** : 27–31 (1967).

132. MØLLER, V. Simplified tests for some amino acid decarboxylases and for the arginine dihydrolase system. *Acta path. microbiol. scand.*, **36** : 158–172 (1955).

133. EDEL, W. & KAMPELMACHER, E. H. Comparative studies on *Salmonella* isolations from feeds in ten laboratories. *Bull. World Health Org.*, **50** : 421–426 (1974).

134. KRISTENSEN, K. K. Undersøgelser over forekomst af salmonella-bakterier i spildevand og forurenet havvand. *Nord. vet. Med.*, *I. Metodik*, **21** : 353–369 (1969).

135. IVESON, J. B. & MACKAY-SCOLLAY, E. M. An evaluation of strontium chloride, Rappaport and strontium selenite enrichment for the isolation of Salmonellas from man, animals, meat products and abattoir effluents. *J. Hyg. (Camb.)*, **70** : 367–385 (1972).

136. DUNN, C. & MARTIN, W. I. Comparison of media for isolation of *Salmonella* and *Shigella* from fecal specimens. *Appl. Microbiol.*, **22** : 17–22 (1971).

137. SAKAZAKI, R., GOMEZ, G. Z. & SEBALD, M. Taxonomical studies of the so-called NAG-Vibrios. *Jap. J. med. Sci.*, **20** : 265–280 (1967).

138. BOCKEMÜHL, J. Isolierung und Identifizierung von Cholera-Vibrionen. *Zbl. Bakt. Hyg.*, *I. Abt. Orig. A*, **218** : 251–271 (1971).

139. HUGH, R. & SAKAZAKI, R. Minimal number of characters for the identification of *Vibrio* species, *Vibrio cholerae* and *Vibrio parahaemolyticus*. *Publ. Health Lab.*, **30** : 133–137 (1972).

140. SAKAZAKI, R. The present status of studies on *Vibrio parahaemolyticus* in Japan, Washington DC, Food and Drug Administration, 1971, pp. 1–21 (Seminar lecture).

141. BIRCH-ANDERSEN, A., HOVIND HOUGEN, K. & BORG-PETERSEN, C. Electron microscopy of leptospira. I. Leptospira strain pomona. *Acta path. microbiol. scand.*, *Sect. B*, **81** : 665–676 (1973).

142. TURNER, L. H. Leptospirosis. II. Serology. *Trans. roy. Soc. trop. Med. Hyg.*, **62** : 880–899 (1968).

143. TURNER, L. H. Leptospirosis. III. Maintenance, isolation and demonstration of leptospires. *Trans. roy. Soc. trop. Med. Hyg.*, **64** : 623–646 (1970).

144. JOHNSON, R. C. ET AL. Cultivation of parasitic Leptospires. Effect of pyruvate. *Appl. Microbiol.*, **26** : 118–119 (1973).

145. JOHNSON, R. C. & ROGERS, P. 5-fluorouracil as selective agent for growth of Leptospirae. *J. Bact.*, **87** : 422–426 (1964).

146. BRAUN, J. L., DIESCH, S. L. & MC CULLOCH, W. F. A method for isolating leptospires from natural surface waters. *Canad. J. Microbiology*, **14** : 1011–1012 (1968).

147. BRAUN, J. L. & MC CULLOCH, W. F. Use of 8-azoguanine to differentiate leptospires isolated from Iowa surface waters. *Appl. Microbiol.*, **16** : 174–175 (1968).

148. IVANOV, I. & BABUDIERI, B. Isolation and systematic study of the first Bulgarian strains of saprophytic Leptospiras. *Ann. Ist. Super. Sanità*, **7** : 91–94 (1971).

149. ROWBOTHAM, T. J. & CROSS, T. Ecology of *Rhodococcus coprophilus* and associated actinomycetes in fresh water and agricultural habitats. *J. gen. Microbiol.*, **100** : 231–240 (1977).

150. AL-DIWANY, L. J. & CROSS, T. Ecological studies on nocardioforms and other actinomycetes in aquatic habitats. *In :* Mordarski, M., Kurłyowicz, W. & Jeljaszewicz, J., ed. Nocardia and streptomyces, Stuttgart & New York, Fischer, 1978.

151. WHO MEETING OF EXPERTS. Reuse of effluents : Methods of wastewater treatment and health safeguards, Geneva, World Health Organization, 1973 (WHO Technical Report Series, No. 517).

VIROLOGICAL EXAMINATION

E. Lund[a]

CONTENTS

[a] Professor and Head, Department of Veterinary Virology and Immunology, Royal Veterinary and Agricultural University, Copenhagen, Denmark.

1. GENERAL CONSIDERATIONS

The designation of reference methods for virological examinations of water is not yet possible for reasons that will be discussed later in this chapter. However, in view of the need for parallel virological, bacteriological, and epidemiological research on the transmission of water-borne diseases, virological examinations should be encouraged ; this chapter has been written to help water laboratories to gain experience by offering them what seems the best available information at the present time.

The virus concentration methods described in this chapter may be used for either raw or partially treated wastewater, as well as for very highly treated waters. Efficient and reliable concentration methods for detecting small quantities of viruses in large volumes of turbid natural waters, such as river, lake and coastal waters, have not yet been fully evaluated. Despite the fact that a number of comparative studies on virus detection methods have been made, additional, quantitative studies are needed to evaluate systematically the more promising methods.

The chapter includes methods for the concentration and preparation of water samples for subsequent analysis in a specialized laboratory. Such activities should be undertaken, or at least supervised, by a person trained in bacteriological techniques with full understanding of the limitations of the methods and the types of sample to be processed. The sample should be taken only after discussion with the specialized laboratory. If the "average laboratory"[a] is undertaking concentration of samples, it must be understood that careful handling and disposal of materials are required because of the special risks associated with concentrated samples, which might possibly contain a large number of pathogens.

Tissue culture technique would be difficult for the "average laboratory", and should be carried out by a specialized laboratory.

---

[a] See volume 1, chapter 7.

Bacteriology undoubtedly offers the most practical and sensitive tests for the detection of recent faecal pollution. Pathogens present in polluted waters are usually outnumbered by the normal intestinal organisms, and the pathogenic bacteria often die out more rapidly than indicator bacteria, such as *Escherichia coli*. The water bacteriologist therefore operates under the assumption that the search for normal faecal organisms provides a much wider margin of safety than a search for the specific pathogens and that the recent faecal pollution indicated by normal faecal organisms does cover the potentially dangerous situation.

The isolation of viruses requires more highly specialized and time-consuming procedures than those used for routine bacteriological examinations. Therefore, it is highly desirable that virological examinations be avoided and that bacterial indicators be used. It has often been assumed that pathogens, including viruses, tend to die out more rapidly than the bacterial indicators. This assumption is not correct for enteric viruses. Domestic sewage contains large numbers of human enteric viruses even in nonepidemic periods and, although sewage treatment processes may remove important quantities of viruses, no conventional treatment is capable of totally removing them. In addition, chlorination as practised in conventional sewage treatment plant does not produce substantial inactivation, even when bacteria are killed extensively.

1.1 *E. coli* as indicator of enteric viruses in polluted waters

For *untreated sewage* as well as for *surface waters* containing recent sewage pollution it is reasonable to assume that viruses may be present if *E. coli* is present. Although *E. coli* is often present in sewage in relatively constant amounts, the enteric virus concentrations vary seasonally in the temperate climates of Europe with a maximum around September, and during this peak period there may be about 10^3 infectious units per 100 ml of raw sewage or even more. Poliomyelitis vaccinations may mask the naturally occurring seasonal variations of enteric virus concentrations in sewage by producing a preponderance of vaccine strain viruses.

Although enteroviruses and adenoviruses seem to be present throughout the year in urban sewage from larger cities, the serotypes of enteric viruses present in sewage may vary from year to year.

The die-off rates of *E. coli* in fresh water, and especially in sea water, are much faster than the rates of virus inactivation. Biological sewage treatment and chlorination remove and kill *E. coli* more efficiently than viruses. Thus, treated wastewaters that are free from *E. coli* may contain demonstrable amounts of viruses.

Because it is easier, faster, and cheaper to detect bacteriophages (e.g., coliphages) than to detect viruses in sewage and polluted waters, it is often proposed that they be employed as indicators of enteric virus pollution.

Such reasoning is not warranted, because all that is shown by demonstrating coliphages is the presence of coliform bacteria, which could be done in a more direct way.

In summary, it may be concluded, that if *E. coli* are present in a sample, then enteric viruses may be present, but the ratio between the two cannot be reliably predicted from bacteriological data only. Absence of *E. coli* does not ensure absence of enteric viruses from a sample.

1.2 The different types of virus that may be detected in polluted waters

Viruses multiply only inside a living cell. The virus–host-cell relation may be very specific. Viruses contain one nucleic acid, which is either RNA or DNA in a single- or double-stranded form. Their size is between 20 and 300 nm. All virus particles contain a protein layer (the capsid). In some viruses the capsid is the outer layer, but other types have an additional lipid-containing envelope. Each animal species, including man, may be host, usually transiently, for many different viruses.

" Selective substrates " for virus growth do not exist to the same extent that they do in bacteriology. However, this does not imply that all known human viruses can be found by using one type of host cell. The viruses commonly encountered in polluted waters are mainly non-enveloped, acid-stable, and relatively resistant to chemical and physical degradation. They are enteric viruses, because they are transient inhabitants of the intestinal tract and are shed with the faeces in large quantities by infected individuals.

Although priority must be given to factors affecting the health of man, those affecting agriculture, the conservation of wild life and fishery resources must also be recognized, and therefore the presence of non-human viruses should also be studied along with their possible dissemination by water. This would involve the use of tissue-cell cultures from non-primate animals, including fish, and from plants.

The animal viruses commonly found in water are *enteroviruses, reoviruses, rotaviruses* (orbiviruses), *adenoviruses*, the *virus of hepatitis A* (infectious hepatitis), and certain parvo-like viruses, such as the Norwalk agent (*8, 25, 42, 95*). Methods for the cultivation of the hepatitis A virus, the rotaviruses, and the parvo-like gastroenteritis viruses are not yet routinely available. An immunoelectronmicroscopic method (*23*) has made possible the demonstration of aggregates of virus-like particles in suspected faecal extracts, but evidence for waterborne spread of the hepatitis A virus is still epidemiological, because the virus cannot be cultivated.

It is very likely that once the proper cultivation methods are available, an additional number of human viruses will be demonstrated in faecally polluted waters.

The human enteric viruses and some of their characteristics are given in Table 1. By enteric viruses is meant a group of dissimilar viruses, including not only enteroviruses but also other viruses that, because they are produced in the human intestinal tract, may also be spread through faecal pollution.

The number of subclinical or inapparent enteric virus infections is perhaps a hundredfold greater than the number of infections displaying overt disease symptoms. Therefore, epidemiological evidence based on the occurrence of disease may be an inadequate basis for evaluating the spread of enteric viruses. In addition, one type of virus may give rise to diseases of quite different character and dissimilar viruses may cause the same clinical symptoms. It is only by demonstration and identification of the virus itself or by suitable serological examinations of blood samples that the actual cause of disease can be determined. In Table 2 the most common symptoms caused by enteric viruses are listed.

The demonstration of a certain virus type by means of cell cultures or experimental animals does not furnish any information about the virulence of a particular strain. Such information may in principle only be obtained by experiments using the natural host or by knowledge about certain genetic markers that are characteristic of the virulent or non-virulent strains. Such markers are not available for more than a few of the enteric viruses. Any virus isolated must be assumed to be virulent unless a special investigation of genetic markers has been carried out.

1.3 Factors influencing the numbers and the types of virus that may be demonstrated using a certain method of isolation

In a mixture of different viruses, such as may be expected in samples of urban sewage, the ones that grow fastest and give the most pronounced cell destruction (cytopathic effects, CPE) or appear in the highest concentration will be the ones most easily demonstrated. If an intensive study of all of the viruses in a sewage sample is desired, the sample should be divided into aliquots for inoculation into a series of cell cultures or animals. Each time a specific virus is demonstrated in a culture or animal a sufficient amount of antiserum should be added to this material to neutralize the virus already identified. When this neutralized material is reinoculated into a host, it is possible for additional virus types to appear. Because such a procedure is too impractical for routine use, it must be accepted that the presence of some virus types will be masked by others that are faster growing or present in relatively higher concentrations.

In order to detect the fullest range of known enteric viruses, inoculations should be made in both newborn mice and cell cultures. Only the coxsackie-viruses among the enteric viruses are pathogenic for newborn mice, but some type B coxsackieviruses may be easily detected in cell cultures. Inoculation of mice is often omitted in examinations of polluted waters and

Table 1. Human enteric viruses and some of their characteristics

Virus group	Size and chemical composition	Virus types	Host range for natural infection	Principal cultivation methods
Enterovirus	About 25 nm in diam., containing a single-stranded RNA molecule in a protein shell	Poliovirus No. 1–3	Man	In cultures of human and simian cells
		Coxsackievirus type A 1–24	Man	In newborn mice and certain human cell cultures
		Coxsackievirus type B 1–6	Man	In newborn mice and cultures of human and simian cells
		Echovirus [a] No. 1–33 [b]	Man	In cultures of human and simian cells
Adenovirus	About 70–80 nm in diam., containing a double-stranded DNA molecule in a protein shell provided with fibres	Human adeno-virus No. 1–33	Man	In cultures of human cells
Reovirus	About 75 nm in diam. with a double-stranded RNA molecule in a double protein shell	Reovirus No. 1–33	Man and a number of domestic and wild animals	In cultured cells of simian and human origin
		Rotavirus (orbivirus, reovirus-like)	Man	Human fetal intestinal organ cultures
Virus of infectious hepatitis	Possibly a par-vovirus or an enterovirus	Not known, possibly only one type	Man	No known method except possibly in marmosets and chimpanzees
Virus of acute gastroenteritis	Possibly members of the parvovirus group		Man	No method available

[a] Enteric cytopathogenic human orphan virus, i.e., virus other than poliovirus or coxsackie-viruses demonstrated through the cell destruction they cause in cell cultures that have been inoculated with faecal material; when first discovered they could not be related to disease and hence were called orphan viruses. Many are now known to be the cause of disease (see Table 2).

[b] There are not 33 types of echoviruses. Some have been combined into one type (e.g., echovirus Nos. 1 and 8) or removed from the group (e.g., echovirus No. 10, which became the first reovirus, and echovirus 28, which is accepted as a rhinovirus). Coxsackievirus type A 23 is identical with echovirus 9.

Table 2.   Diseases that may occur after an infection with a human
enteric virus [a]

Virus type	Symptoms of disease [b]
Poliovirus 1–3 Coxsackievirus A 1–24 Coxsackievirus B 1–6 Echovirus 1–33	Fever, headaches, nausea, diarrhoea, muscular pains, meningitis, paralytic poliomyelitis (infrequent with viruses other than poliovirus). Some coxsackie- and echo-strains have caused hepatitis. Some enteroviruses cause exanthema.
Adenovirus 1–28	Fever, acute upper and lower respiratory tract infections, inflammation of the conjunctiva, more rarely symptoms of enteritis or central nervous system involvement.
Reovirus 1–3	Virus has been demonstrated in connexion with the common cold and other upper and lower respiratory tract infections, with diarrhoea, exanthema, and hepatitis, especially in children.
Rotavirus	Infantile gastroenteritis
Hepatitis virus	Fever, nausea, anorexia, diarrhoea, hepatitis (acute or chronic).
Virus of acute gastroenteritis	Acute gastroenteritis ; " winter vomiting disease ".

[a] In most cases infections are inapparent, even with the highly pathogenic viruses. In addition, the disease symptoms for each virus are variable, depending on such host factors as immunity, age, and general resistance, and on the initial dose of virus.

[b] For each virus type there may be a considerable number of virus strains, which may vary in pathogenicity. Routine cultivation procedures for the isolation of viruses provide no information on the pathogenicity of the viruses.

thus group A coxsackieviruses may be overlooked. However, a number of strains of coxsackievirus A have been isolated either in primary or continuous line monkey kidney cultures, human fetal diploid kidney, primary human embryonic kidney, or human continuous cell lines.

1.3.1 *Detection of viruses by inoculation in cell cultures*

Except for the group A coxsackieviruses, the known enteric viruses are generally cytopathogenic for human and/or simian cells.

1.3.2 *Inoculations into cultures of human cells*

Primary cultures of embryonic cells, human amnion cells, human diploid cell strains, or continuous cell lines can be used. Using selected human cells, polioviruses, coxsackieviruses group B, adenoviruses, most echoviruses, and some group A coxsackieviruses may be detected. Adenoviruses will rarely be detected unless blind passage to new cultures is carried out. Reoviruses may be demonstrated in cell cultures of human or simian origin. Prolonged incubation in roller tubes may promote production of haemagglutinins in high titre thus permitting the demonstration of virus even in the absence of cytopathic changes.

1.3.3 *Inoculations in cell cultures of primate origin*

Monkey cells may be used as primary cell cultures of kidneys from rhesus, cynomolgus, or African green monkeys, or as continuous lines of monkey kidney cells, line Vero or BGM. Using monkey cells, polioviruses, group B coxsackievirus, reoviruses, and a broad spectrum of echoviruses may be demonstrated, but only rarely will adenoviruses be detected. If it is possible to have a regular supply of primary, secondary, or tertiary human embryonic kidney cells, this single cell culture type could be expected to cover nearly the whole range of viruses. If this is not possible, the inoculation of the samples in two kinds of cells is recommended (one human and one simian cell type) in order to pick up as many echoviruses and adenoviruses as possible. For specific purposes, a single type of cell may be sufficient, but the limitation in the spectrum of detectable virus must be realized.

Blind passages are often necessary for detecting viruses in cell-toxic samples, for detecting adenoviruses, or if it is desired to demonstrate viruses masked by the presence of other viruses. The number of virus-positive samples can be expected to increase slightly upon blind passage even for polio-, coxsackie-, and echoviruses. For the demonstration of reoviruses, prolonged incubation of the initial cultures may be more helpful.

In general, the preparation and inoculation of cell cultures for virus detection cannot be recommended for the average laboratory engaged in bacteriological testing because of the special skill and high costs involved. However, in special situations it might be possible to attempt an examination for viruses after consultation with a specialized laboratory by using commercially produced cells and ready-for-use commercial media and reagents. The costs will be considerable. Those engaged in planning such work should consult detailed publications such as *Diagnostic procedures for viral and rickettsial infections (46)*.

1.4 Quantification of viruses

Two methods are available for titration of viruses based upon the ability of viruses to cause observable destruction in cultured cells:

1.4.1 *Quantal assays by 50% end point titrations*

These assays usually involve determination of the 50% tissue culture infective dose ($TCID_{50}$). Serial tenfold dilutions of the virus-containing material are made, a small volume of each dilution is inoculated into a number of tube cultures and the cells are incubated at 37°C. A $TCID_{50}$ is defined as the dilution giving microscopically observable cytopathological changes in half the inoculated cultures after an appropriate incubation period. This value may be estimated by methods described by Reed &

Muench (71) or Kärber (44). The titration error using 5 tubes per dilution is around $10^{\pm 0.3}$. This end point titration could also be applied to titrations in laboratory animals such as mice, in which case the titration unit would be a correspondingly obtained 50% infective dose (ID_{50}) or lethal dose (LD_{50}). For titrations employing 6 mice per tenfold dilution the titration error is usually somewhat larger than that for cell cultures and is probably at least $10^{\pm 0.5}$. Quantal assays can also be performed by determination of the most probable number of cytopathogenic units (MPNCU). Chang et al. (9) have suggested that the MPNCU method might be employed rather than the $TCID_{50}$ method. In fact it seems the only method that will yield a valid result if the sample is assumed to contain such a small number of virus units that the whole of it must be inoculated and the viruses do not form plaques. The problems involved in applying statistical methods to samples that do not have even distributions are treated in chapter 2, section 4.2.

1.4.2 Determinations of plaque-forming units (PFU)

Many of the viruses in waste water may be titrated by the plaque technique. This is essentially equivalent to the bacterial colony count on a solid substrate. A monolayer of cells is exposed to a small volume of virus-containing fluid allowing sufficient time for the viruses to adsorb to the cells. The fluid is then usually removed and a nutrient agar overlayer is placed over the cell monolayer. The virus produced in the primary infected cells is thus kept from spreading except to the neighbouring cells, and the focus of infected and destroyed cells gradually becomes big enough to be observed by the naked eye if the remaining viable cells are stained with a vital stain. The number of plaques produced thus corresponds to the number of infectious virus particles or clumps of such particles in the suspension. Plaque titrations give the most precise enumeration of virus provided the work is carried out with a homogeneous suspension of free virus particles. However, the sensitivity of the plaque titrations and the accuracy of the plaque counts will be affected if the suspension contains aggregates of virus particles or viruses bound to other particles. Substances in the suspension that are toxic to the cells may also influence the results so that the plaque titrations may become erroneous or even impossible and quantal assays may be necessary.

Natural samples usually contain mixtures of viruses. It would be ideal to identify each type of virus but this is impractical, unless the number of isolates is relatively small. Because mixtures of viruses are generally present in wastewater, the viral titre may be underestimated by the plaque technique because it allows rapidly replicating viruses of high plaquing efficiency to overgrow or preclude other viruses that may be present in the sample. The use of selective culture conditions in the plaque technique may not even be suitable for detection of some viruses, even when they are the only ones present. Reoviruses, adenoviruses, and many echoviruses, all of which may be present in wastewater, require somewhat different conditions for plaquing in relation to such factors as cell type, optimum dilution of viral suspension to preclude crowding of plaques, composition of overlay medium, and period of observation. Selection of culture cell type is also an important factor in quantal titrations, but composition of maintenance medium is not critical, and serial dilutions, together with adequate observation periods, prevent failure to detect slowly replicating viruses that may actually predominate in numbers.

Conclusion regarding selection of method for quantification. Ideally, both plaque titrations and end point titrations should be used in field studies, and the highest concentration found should be taken as the best estimate of the virus concentration. Virus mixtures and slow-growing viruses may be more easily identified by quantal assays in monolayer cultures with subsequent subcultures from the primary cultures.

1.5 The significance of the presence of virus in polluted water

Virological examinations are laborious and expensive to carry out and only a few laboratories are equipped to do them. It is important to realize that there have been only a few documented outbreaks of waterborne viral disease. Most of these were hepatitis outbreaks that were caused by direct or indirect contamination of the water as a result of obvious neglect of established practices, as might have been demonstrated through bacteriological examination. Endemic water-borne type A hepatitis other than indirect transmission through shellfish has not been documented. The most prevalent documented water-borne disease is gastroenteritis, but the viral etiology of these outbreaks has not been established.

It appears possible to infect man with as little as a single cell culture infective dose of virus. However, it seems more likely that a larger dose is usually required. Only a small proportion of infected persons become clinically ill, even when infected with a virulent strain of virus. For this reason, lack of epidemiological evidence of water-borne disease does not necessarily mean that there is no such spread. The relative degree of viral pollution of waters compared to food and drink and direct contact will determine if a certain degree of viral pollution in water is significant. The amount of disease spread will depend as much on such population factors as socioeconomic conditions, immunological status, age distribution, and general level of disease resistance as on the quantity of particular viruses present.

1.6 Virus standards

The setting of virus standards for different kinds of water has been only tentatively attempted, and the levels suggested are arbitrary and not based on considerations of risk of infection or disease. It is generally agreed that potable waters should contain no viruses, but at present there is no agreement as to how this can be defined in terms of sample volumes and the sensitivity and accuracy of the methods employed for virus detection. WHO drinking water standards suggest less than 1 infectious virus unit per litre on the basis of examination of 10-litre samples. Standards of less than 1 infectious virus unit per 10 gallons of recreational water and less than 1 unit per 100 gallons of drinking water have been suggested by some scientists in the USA. These are apparently somewhat more stringent standards, but the methods employed in virological examinations have not been intercalibrated, so this is not necessarily a correct interpretation. The important question is how much virus does it take to infect man so that infection may be transmitted and/or cause disease in the infected person? This information is needed to establish " acceptable-level-of-risk " criteria for water-borne viruses.

If viruses are present in finished waters they probably occur at levels as low as one virus particle per 500–1000 l of water. The success of many methods for concentrating viruses depends upon those physicochemical attributes of the viruses that enable them to adsorb to various substances and then to be recovered by elution. When dealing with low multiplicities of viruses in large volumes of water, the efficiency of the virus concentration system is of prime importance. Because there is no virus detection technique available today that is 100% efficient, negative findings may be misleading. In addition, there is no guarantee that the virus cultivation systems employed will reveal all the virus types present in the water.

The rational way of assuring a virus-free potable water and other waters of acceptable quality seems to be protection of the raw water sources from faecal pollution by controlling the discharge of insufficiently treated effluent into surface waters and other precautions, rather than by establishing standards that cannot be achieved or enforced.

1.7 Research needs

The detection of small amounts of viruses in large volumes of water is possible, but the efficiencies of virus recoveries will probably vary depending upon the method employed, the water quality, and the particular laboratory. Much work is still needed before it will be possible to select a single method that ensures reliable quantitative virus recovery. Intercalibration programmes would be desirable and could possibly be carried out once a method is agreed upon because field samples could possibly be made sufficiently homogeneous and stable to make such an evaluation possible.

Less laborious and more rapid ways of detecting viruses in water and wastewater than by cultivation and identification are needed, but no candidate method of sufficient ease, sensitivity, and economy is at present available.

2. SAMPLING

Samples for virological examination should be taken by, or under the guidance of, a trained bacteriologist using accepted bacteriological techniques. It would be most desirable to concentrate samples on site or at least locally. The concentrated samples should then be examined by the specialized laboratory.

2.1 Sample size

The size of the sample will depend upon the extent of virus contamination of the water. A number of studies in which viruses have been detected in sewage treatment plant effluents have utilized samples as small as 200 ml. To obtain more representative samples it may be advantageous to collect samples several times larger than the volume to be examined and then remove an aliquot. It is possible to demonstrate small amounts of viruses in hundreds of litres of water, but the costs involved in transportation, concentration, equipment, etc. may be prohibitive for routine use, even in major public health laboratories.

2.2 Frequency of sampling

The sampling frequency depends on the purpose of the work. Virological examination of water is especially useful in certain critical situations, such as for estuarines used for commercial shellfishing, studies of sewage treatment plants of new or unique design, surveillance of wastewater reclamation systems to be used as sources of potable water, and special epidemiological studies. With the increasing pollution of water resources and the growing need for reuse and recycling of water, virological examinations are becoming more and more important.

2.3 Dip or grab samples

These may be collected in plastic or glass containers. Dip samples may be used for the study of any kind of water. Although the ideal procedure would be to employ sterile containers, it may be sufficient in many cases —except for drinking water supplies—to use clean plastic containers. If water quality is highly variable it may be advisable to take 24-hour composite samples using a suitable sampling device.

2.4 Swab samples

In spite of certain limitations, swab sampling may still be useful for some studies. Melnick et al. (*54*) were the first to point out that swab samples from wastewaters give a higher yield of virus-positive samples than dip samples, and several authors have confirmed this. On the other hand, it is impossible to quantitate the findings obtained using swabs ; they should therefore be used only when the emphasis is on obtaining the highest possible number of positive samples rather than an estimate of the actual virus concentration.

Sampling by means of swabs is especially useful for raw and treated wastewaters. The usefulness of swabs for sampling from surface waters and sea waters is questionable and there is general agreement that they are definitely not suitable for sampling drinking water. Swabs are useful in situations where the pollution is moderate and a substantial proportion of the virus content of the water is bound to particles that can be trapped in the swab. Swab sampling should be regarded only as *a primitive concentration method*.

Swab samples may be obtained by hanging cotton wrapped in several layers of gauze (*54*), or polyethylene sponges (*50*), at the sample collection point. The pads should be clean, but need not be sterilized. After 24–48 hours' exposure, the swabs are placed in a plastic bag and transported to the laboratory in a suitable sealed container. In the laboratory, the fluid in the swab is squeezed out through a hole cut in the plastic bag. Some workers adjust the swab fluid to pH 8.0 by means of sodium hydroxide and/or add beef extract ($30 \text{ g} \cdot \text{l}^{-1}$) or calf serum ($20 \text{ g} \cdot \text{l}^{-1}$) prior to extraction from the swab.

2.5 Transportation of samples

If the samples reach the laboratory within two hours and the temperature does not exceed 25°C, there is no need for refrigeration as the viruses that might be detected are fairly stable. Whenever possible the samples should be concentrated *in situ* to avoid the transportation of large fluid volumes. For transportation lasting longer than 2 hours or at higher temperatures, refrigeration is advisable. A loss in viral titre may result from freezing and thawing, but it may still be preferable to the transportation of samples at ambient temperatures above 25°C.

In the laboratory the samples must be kept in the cold before examination, and they should be processed as soon as possible. If the samples are kept for more than 2 days prior to processing they should be frozen. However, every effort should be made to avoid freezing as a loss in titre may result.

If the sample contains chlorine residuals, the chlorine should be neutralized with sodium thiosulfate, as inactivation of viruses can occur during transportation. A concentration of 100 mg of sodium thiosulfate per litre of sample could be added to the sample bottle before the sample is collected. A surplus of thiosulfate is not harmful because it does not adversely affect viruses. Chloroform may also be used to inhibit growth of microorganisms during transportation.

3. CONCENTRATION METHODS

3.1 Limitations

It is strongly recommended that all laboratories undertaking the concentration of viruses from waters do so with a full appreciation of the limitations and pitfalls of the methods; personnel using concentration methods should therefore be instructed in a specialized laboratory familiar with these techniques.

A number of different methods are employed for the concentration of viruses in water. The methods described should be used only after the following reservations have been carefully considered :

(*a*) The methods described are experimental and several are still evolving.

(*b*) The efficiency of each method described varies widely, especially with changes in the quality of the water sampled.

(*c*) Although some methods give good quantitative recovery of known amounts of added viruses, it is most difficult to evaluate whether they are quantitative when employed on field samples.

(*d*) None of the methods described is yet supported by large amounts of data. None has been studied with more than a few virus types. Few studies are available that compare the efficiency of one method with that of another under the same conditions.

(*e*) Some of the techniques described require expensive equipment. In a methodology so rapidly evolving, there is a risk of obsolescence.

3.2 Selection of the most suitable method

Waters should be classified with regard to their expected virus load. For the selected virus concentration methods described in this chapter an indication of the water volume that they are capable of processing is given and this will indicate the type of water to which the method can be applied.

Because organics of unknown nature and turbidity influence the efficiency of virus concentration methods, these factors should be considered in the choice of the method.

In addition to its efficiency, a virus concentration method should be simple and require as little expensive equipment as possible. In the following, different methods are tentatively suggested and evaluated including alternative methods in which expensive equipment is not utilized. Simple and flow-through filter adsorption-elution, ultrafiltration, two-phase polymer separation, and chemical adsorption-precipitation methods are described in detail and other methods are mentioned.

Raw domestic wastewater from urban areas may contain up to 10^5 TCID$_{50}$ per litre. If at least 10^4 TICD$_{50}$ or 10^4PFU are present per litre one may *demonstrate virus by direct inoculation without any further concentration*. With most samples, however, a concentration procedure is necessary. Virus purification may be necessary if quantitation by PFU is wanted because toxic components of wastewater may otherwise make plaque assays impossible by destroying the cell sheets.

3.3 Methods for sample volumes of 200–5000 ml

3.3.1 *Simple filter adsorption-elution systems*

The samples may be of 200–5000 ml, taken as dip or swab samples. The expected virus load should be more than one infectious unit per litre.

The advantages of the membrane techniques are their simplicity and speed. The problems encountered are the possible removal of viruses associated with particulate matter, if the sample is clarified prior to virus adsorption, loss of viruses due to interference with virus adsorption by soluble substances in the water, and incomplete elution of viruses adsorbed to filters.

Certain filters made from cellulose derivatives of fibreglass are commonly used to concentrate viruses. The filter adsorption-elution technique is based on the adsorption of viruses to the filters followed by their elution from the filters in a small volume of fluid. The concentration efficiencies obtained with artificially contaminated samples are reported to be satisfactory. However, variable field samples are more difficult to handle, and wastewater samples often require prefiltering. If a prefilter is used to remove particulate matter, it must be eluted in order to obtain quantitative virus recovery.

Addition of salts such as $MgCl_2$ or $AlCl_3$ and a lowering of the pH to 3.0 or 3.5 improve adsorption to the filter. Because low pH may be deleterious to some viruses, time is an important factor in the procedure. Moreover, some viruses may behave differently from those used in the development and testing of the method.

3.3.2 *Adsorption and precipitation methods employing polyvalent cation salts*

Viruses may be adsorbed on preformed alum, aluminium hydroxide, ferric chloride, or lime flocs. Instead of adsorption on preformed flocs addition of salts to the wastewater to form a floc addition *in situ* may be used to precipitate viruses. A method employing alum precipitation and elution with pH 9.0 trisbuffer has been reported as being efficient, but has not been adequately evaluated for different viruses. The size of the sample is limited by the bulk of the precipitate, which readily clogs ordinary filters. Moreover, collection of flocs by centrifugation is not practical for large samples. The method of adsorption to and elution from aluminum hydroxide as developed by England (*19*) is given in detail in Annex 1.

3.3.3 *Precipitation by protamine sulfate*

Negatively charged proteins can be precipitated by positively charged protamine sulfate in aqueous solution. The precipitate may be dissolved in 1 M NaCl. Reoviruses and adenoviruses are concentrated efficiently but some enteroviruses are not precipitated. The reason for this difference in virus precipitation efficiency remains unknown. The use of alum precipitation and protamine precipitation in tandem has been suggested as a means of maximizing the recovery of a variety of enteric viruses. The protamine precipitation technique (*17, 18*) is described in Annex 2.

3.3.4 *Hydroextraction and aqueous polymer two-phase separation techniques*

Hydroextraction using polyethylene glycol (*11, 75*) has been used (*92*) to concentrate viruses in 500-ml wastewater samples to a final volume of 5 ml in dialysis tubing. Instead of separation by dialysis, the Albertsson two-phase separation system for purification and concentration of viruses, as described by Philipson et al. (*64*), may be employed. The method has been reported to work in wastewater samples (*49*), but the efficiency is reported to vary from 5–100% (*21, 72*). The method seems best suited for 0.2–2.0-litre samples. If the expected virus load is less than 10 infectious units per litre of sample, then additional steps should be used, such as adding another two-phase separation step and thereby increasing the degree of concentration an additional tenfold. The method is useful for moderately or grossly polluted water, but may work erratically when used on sludge samples. It may be added as a final step to concentrate eluates from precipitates or filters. The method is simple and requires little technical equipment. The virus recovery efficiency varies with this technique, unless the pH, ionic strength and salt concentration of the samples are carefully controlled. It has been reported that strains of coxsackievirus type B2 and echovirus 6 are inhibited by dextran sulfate 2000 (*31*), and that phase separation is not always obtained (*32*). If the proper conditions cannot be obtained, it is advisable to use hydroextraction (*4, 75*) instead of polymer two-phase separation. In the hydroextraction procedure a dialysis bag containing the water sample is placed in a polyethylene glycol (PEG) solution or in a bed of dry PEG. Water and microsolutes pass out of the dialysis bag into the PEG but viruses and other macrosolutes are retained and thereby concentrated. The two-phase separation technique may also be employed as a secondary step in a concentration procedure from large volumes of water.

The two-phase method is described in Annex 3.

3.3.5 *Soluble alginate filters*

These filters were described by Gärtner (*34*) and have been employed by several workers (e.g., *7, 63, 66, 74*).

An alginate filter may be made in the laboratory and cast on a filter-paper support. Following filtration of the sample to remove viruses, sodium citrate is used to dissolve the alginate filter and recover the retained viruses. A sample of up to 1 litre may be passed through a 47-mm diameter filter with good virus retention. Virus losses on or in the filter do not occur because the filter is dissolved. The dissolved filter is inoculated into cell cultures. Prefiltering of the sample is nearly always necessary in this method because alginate filters clog more easily than the usual microporous filters used to concentrate viruses by adsorption.

The filters are not suitable for samples larger than 1 litre because the filtration rate is too slow. The sample should contain a minimum of colloid material in order to avoid filter clogging. The filter is adversely affected by high ionic strengths.

Neither small volumes of unclarified raw waters nor large volumes of highly treated waters have been conveniently processed by soluble alginate filters.

3.4 Methods for large amounts of water (5–400 litres or more)

Examinations of large samples of water are possible only in a few special laboratories and such examinations require special techniques and equipment.

3.4.1 *Tangential fluid flow ultrafiltration systems*

Ultrafiltration is a process of selective molecular separation. Different membrane configurations, such as hollow fibres, flat discs, and cartridges of rolled sheets, are available, but little experience with these configurations has been reported. Only a flat membrane method has so far found general application (*62, 63*). A flat membrane method is described in Annex 4.

3.4.2 *Flow-through filter adsorption-elution systems*

Filter adsorption-elution (FAE) procedures are employed for concentrating viruses from water, wastewater and other aqueous fluids (*35, 79*). These methods are based upon the ability of viruses to become reversibly adsorbed to reactive surfaces as a result of electrochemical interactions. A number of filter materials and configurations have been employed as virus adsorbents, including : (*a*) cellulose nitrate membranes, 0.45 µm porosity, (*b*) cellulose acetate, cellulose nitrate or fibreglass cartridge-type depth filters, 0.45–8.0 µm porosity, and (*c*) fibreglass-asbestos-epoxy filter discs, 0.45–0.65 µm porosity. In some cases, the water being processed has first been clarified to prevent clogging of the virus adsorbent by suspended matter in the water. In order to enhance virus adsorption, the water is acidified and in some cases a polyvalent cation salt, such as calcium, magnesium, or aluminium chloride, is added prior to filtering through the virus adsorbent. As the water is passed through the filter, the viruses are adsorbed to the filter surface. Trivalent aluminium ions may be more efficient than divalent magnesium or calcium ions for increasing virus adsorption.

Adsorbed viruses may be eluted from the filters with a small volume of eluent, usually a slightly to moderately alkaline proteinaceous fluid— such as serum, beef extract, or nutrient broth—or a highly alkaline buffer consisting of 0.05 M glycine buffered to pH 11.5 with NaOH.

Mix (*60*) has suggested that virus adsorption to filter surfaces may occur by a number of possible mechanisms, such as : (*a*) hydrophobic bonding between nonpolar aliphatic and aromatic groups on the surfaces of both the viruses and the filters, (*b*) hydrogen bonding between polar groups on the surfaces of the viruses and the filters, and (*c*) salt bridging between negatively charged groups on the surfaces of the viruses and the filters by adsorbed cations obtained from the bulk solution. Because the pore size of the filter is considerably larger than the diameter of the virus particles, filtration or physical entrapment is not considered to be a significant mechanism for removal of viruses by the filter, unless the viruses are present as large aggregates.

Both single-stage and multistage FAE procedures have been developed for concentrating enteric viruses from water and wastewater. In the single-stage procedures, the viruses are adsorbed to and then eluted from a filter or filter series only once, while in the multistage procedures, the viruses are adsorbed to and then eluted from a filter two or more times in succession. In the first adsorption stage of the multistage procedure, the water is often processed on a continuous flow-through basis. This makes it possible to process larger volumes of water than could be processed by a single-stage, batch procedure. In addition, at each successive stage of the multistage procedure, smaller filters and hence smaller eluate volumes are employed, thereby making it possible to achieve greater degrees of virus concentration than could be achieved in a single-stage procedure.

In general, single-stage FAE procedures can be conveniently used for fluid volumes of up to about 20 litres, which makes them suitable for waters that are likely to contain relatively large amounts of viruses, such as sewage, treated sewage effluents, and highly polluted waters. Multistage procedures were developed primarily for processing large volumes of water containing relatively small quantities of viruses, such as groundwater, less polluted surface water, and highly treated water.

In Annex 5 procedures employing single-stage and multistage FAE procedures are described.

3.5 Methods for sludge samples

From the point of view of cell toxicity, sludge samples present extreme problems. On the other hand, viruses may be detected from primary sediments and flocs by chemical treatment without any concentration step. The method of precipitation with polyvalent cation salts seems useful, but passing to new cell cultures from the original ones is often necessary because of cell toxicity. This is true even when eluates are inoculated. Methods for virus detection in sludge samples are not sufficiently developed for inclusion in this chapter.

4. DECONTAMINATION OF SAMPLES

The immediate decontamination of specimens upon receipt in the laboratory is recommended. As a general rule, samples concentrated before they are shipped to the specialized laboratory should be decontaminated before shipment to control the growth of contaminating microorganisms. Except for cases where the concentrated sample to be examined has been ultra-filtered or otherwise rendered sterile, the samples must be decontaminated prior to virus examination. Some workers do this by centrifugation at around 13 000 g for 10–30 minutes or filtering through 0.45-µm pore size membranes. These procedures are not recommended because viruses adsorbed to particles may be removed in this way. Treatment with concentrations of antibiotics 10 times greater than those normally in the culture media may be successfully employed if allowed to act for some hours prior to inoculation. This procedure is applicable to samples where the inocula will be about one tenth of the total volume of fluid in a cell culture. Higher antibiotic concentrations may be toxic to the cells. For some types of waters the antibiotic mixture routinely employed in tissue culture media could be employed : 100 units of penicillin and 100 mg of streptomycin per ml. For the decontamination of samples of sewage effluents, wastewater, polluted river water, and stored river water, the addition of three further antibiotics (neomycin, fungizone, and polymyxin B) has been successfully employed (*66*). The antibiotics are added so that the final concentrations in cell cultures are 70 units of neomycin, 2–5 units of fungizone (or 70 units of nystatin) and 100 units of polymyxin B per ml.

Because all the enteric viruses are non-enveloped, they are resistant to treatment with lipid solvents such as ether and chloroform. Consequently, a simple decontamination procedure is treatment with ether or chloroform. Although efficient, ether is not recommended because of the fire risk. Residuals of lipid solvents must be carefully removed from the samples, as they are very harmful to the cell cultures. The following technique may be employed : Around 30% of the sample volume of chloroform is added, and the sample is shaken occasionally during a 1-hour period. The water phase is separated by pipetting, and the water sample is treated by bubbling air through for around 10 minutes. Before inoculation, the sample is left open to the atmosphere to remove remaining traces of the chloroform.

5. TRANSPORTATION OF CONCENTRATED SAMPLES

For shipping of the concentrated, decontaminated samples to the specialized laboratory, cooling to 4°C is recommended. If this is not possible, the samples should be dispatched frozen on dry ice.

Annex 1

CONCENTRATION OF VIRUS BY ADSORPTION TO AND ELUTION FROM Al(OH)$_3$

1. Summary

When added to sewage or other waters at pH 6, aluminium hydroxide adsorbs virus, which may be recovered by filtration or centrifugation. The viruses are eluted from the complex with beef extract or some other suitable eluant.

2. Scope and Application

The quality of virus adsorbed by Al(OH)$_3$ bears a direct relationship to the quantity of salt employed. However, ease of recovery of salt-virus complex diminishes with increasing volume of salt, so a compromise must be reached between adsorption efficiency and technical feasibility.

The method is best suited to raw sewage, highly polluted water, or partially treated effluents, because with such samples a relatively small sample of a few litres or less suffices.

2.1 *Advantages*

1. The method concentrates enteroviruses, reoviruses, and adenoviruses.

2. The method requires only equipment commonly found in a water or microbiology laboratory.

2.2 *Limitations*

1. Sample size is limited to a few litres or less for convenient collection of the $Al(OH)_3$-virus complex.

2. The desorption procedure may not elute all adsorbed virus.

3. Apparatus and Materials

Filter holders
Prefilters (such as Millipore Corp. No. AP 20), 47 mm (or 90 mm) and 124 mm diameter
Filter flasks
Rubber or plastic tubing for filter equipment
pH meter or alternative method for pH determination
Magnetic stirrer (or other means of mixing reagents)
Low-speed centrifuge (to be used at 2000 g or less)
Mechanical shaker, mixer, or alternative method for mixing reagents

4. Reagents

Deionized or distilled water
Tween 80, 1.0 ml$\cdot$l^{-1} in water
1 M HCl solution
$Al(OH)_3$ (for preparation see section 5.2)
2 M Na_2CO_3 solution
0.025 M $AlCl_3$ solution
0.15 M NaCl solution
30 g$\cdot$l^{-1} beef extract, pH 7.0 (for elution)

5. Procedure

5.1 *Pretreatment of filter discs*

To prevent adsorption of virus to the discs pretreat filter discs as follows: Stack 3 or 4 prefilter discs in a filter holder and pass through them by negative or positive pressure a 1 ml·l⁻¹ solution of Tween 80 in quantity sufficient to wet the discs completely (about 200 ml), followed by distilled water for thorough rinsing (about 2 litres). Sterilize treated disc by autoclaving.

5.2 *Preparation of insoluble Al(OH)₃*

Prepare the insoluble salt according to the method of Wallis & Melnick (*92*) but make the stock suspension twice as concentrated : Add 3 ml of 2 M Na₂CO₃ to 100 ml of 0.025 M AlCl₃ and place the flask on a magnetic stirrer at room temperature for 15 minutes. Centrifuge the suspension at 1100 g for 15 minutes and discard the supernatant fluid. Wash the sediment once with 0.15 M NaCl, resuspend it on 0.15 M NaCl, and autoclave it at 120°C for 15 minutes. Cool the suspension, sediment the precipitate by centrifugation, and resuspend it in 50 ml of sterile 0.15 M NaCl. Store the stock suspension at 4°C.

5.3 *Prefiltration of sample*

To remove gross particulate matter, filter sample through 2 layers of prefilters, 124 mm in diameter, treated with Tween 80. Adjust pH of sample to 6.0 with 1 M HCl. Add stock Al(OH)₃ suspension to give a 1 : 100 dilution of the stock suspension in the sample. Place the flask of reactants on a magnetic stirrer for 2 hours at room temperature.

Collect the salt-virus complex either by filtration or centrifugation.

(*a*) **By filtration.** Filter the sample through a prefilter disc (such as Millipore Corp. No. AP 20) treated with Tween 80. Often only a few hundred ml can be filtered through a 47-mm diameter disc before it becomes clogged. A clogged disc may be set aside and replaced by a fresh disc. Use of a larger diameter filter disc may give better results. After filtration is completed, remove the disc(s) to a Petri dish and cut it (or them) into pieces that can be transferred to a wide-mouthed screw-capped test tube. Add eluent (30 g·l⁻¹ beef extract, pH 7) in quantity sufficient to cover the pieces of prefilter, and either strap the tube to a mechanical shaker for 5–15 minutes or place it in a vortex mixer for several minutes for vigorous mixing.

(*b*) **By centrifugation.** Centrifuge the Al(OH)₃-treated sample at 1700 g for 15–20 minutes. Discard the supernatant fluid and add 5–10 ml or other selected volume of eluent (30 g·l⁻¹) beef extract, pH 7.0) to the sediment. Mix thoroughly for several minutes.

Centrifuge the mixture at 1700 g for 30 minutes to sediment the Al(OH)₃ and bacteria. After decontamination the supernatant is ready for inoculation.

Annex 2

CONCENTRATION OF VIRUS WITH PROTAMINE SULFATE

1. Summary

Negatively charged proteins can be precipitated by positively charged protamine sulfate in aqueous solution. Following protamine sulfate treatment of protein-supplemented samples of raw sewage or partially treated effluents, certain viruses are present in the precipitate, which can be dissolved in 1 M NaCl.

2. Scope and Application

Reoviruses and adenoviruses are concentrated and recovered more efficiently than by many other methods. Some enteroviruses are precipitated and others not ; the explanation of this remains unknown.

2.1 *Advantages*

(1) Reoviruses and adenoviruses are more efficiently concentrated and recovered than by many other methods.

(2) Inasmuch as the precipitate that contains the virus is dissolved, recovery of the contained virus is complete.

(3) The procedure requires only equipment that is generally found in a water or microbiology laboratory.

2.2 *Limitations*

(1) The method is not optimal for concentrating enteroviruses ; some enteroviruses are concentrated, others are not. For this reason it may be advantageous to combine this method with that given in Annex 1 for a more complete recovery.

(2) The procedure is not applicable to highly treated effluents or natural waters, because (*a*) sample size is limited to a few litres or less, and (*b*) the proportions of reagents would have to be restandardized because the protamine reaction is greatly influenced by the ionic strength of the sample as well as by the pH and protein content.

(3) Different batches of protamine sulfate may vary somewhat in reactivity.

3. Apparatus and Materials

Filter holders for prefiltration and for collecting precipitates
Prefilters (such as Millipore Corp. No. AP20), 47 and 124 mm diameter
Side-arm filter flasks
Rubber or plastic tubing for filter equipment
pH meter or alternative method for determining pH
Magnetic stirrer or other means of mixing reagents
Centrifuge

4. Reagents

Deionized or distilled water
Tween 80, 1.0 ml·l^{-1} in water
Bovine albumin, fraction V, 50 g·l^{-1} in water
Protamine sulfate, 10 g·l^{-1} in water
Fetal bovine serum, inactivated for 30 min at 56°C
1 M HCl and 1 M NaOH for adjustment of sample pH
The bovine albumin, protamine sulfate, and fetal bovine serum may be sterilized by filtration and stored at 4°C

5. Procedure

5.1 *Preparation of prefilters*

To prevent adsorption of virus to the discs pretreat filter discs as follows : Stack 3 or 4 discs in a filter holder and pass through them by negative or positive pressure about 200 ml of 1 ml·l^{-1} Tween 80. Follow this with about 2 litres of deionized or distilled water for thorough rinsing of the discs. Sterilize the treated discs by autoclaving them for 15 min at 120°C.

5.2 *Filtration of sample*

To remove gross particulate matter, filter the sample through 2 layers of prefilters, 124 mm in diameter, treated with Tween 80. Supplement the sample with bovine albumin to a final concentration of 2.5 g·l^{-1}. Adjust the pH to 7.5–7.8 with 1 M HCl or 1 M NaOH. Add protamine sulfate (stock 10 g·l^{-1} solution) to give an optimal concentration in the region of 0.25 g·l^{-1} or 0.5 g·l^{-1} (to be determined for each lot by prior titration with a known quantity of virus, determining the recovery efficiency). Place the flask of reactants on a magnetic stirrer for 30 minutes at room temperature. Precipitate may not be grossly apparent.

Collect precipitate by vacuum filtration of the sample through a prefilter disc (47 mm in diameter) *that has been pretreated with Tween 80 to prevent viral adsorption.* If the filter disc becomes clogged, replace it by a fresh disc, saving the clogged one. Later, stack the used discs in the filter holder before passage of 1 M NaCl through them to dissolve the precipitate.

After vacuum filtration of the sample, turn off the vacuum and supply a small sterile vessel or test tube for collection of concentrated viral filtrate. (Millipore Corp. stainless-steel hydrosol filter is provided with a 15-ml conical glass tube that is convenient). Dissolve the precipitate on the upper surface of the prefilter disc(s) by adding (with the vacuum off) a small volume (e.g., 0.5 ml) of 1 M NaCl, ensuring that it completely covers the disc surface. Wait 5 minutes and then draw the fluid under vacuum into the receiving vessel. To the upper surface of the prefilter disc, add a quantity of water 6 times the volume of the 1 M NaCl and draw it through, rinsing the disc and making sure that the filtrate is isotonic.

Add fetal bovine serum (approximately 10% by volume) to the filtrate to stabilize the virus.

5.3 *Alternative method for collecting and dissolving the precipitate*

After the 30-minute mixing period described in the above procedure, centrifuge the sample at 1700 *g* for 15 minutes. Discard the supernatant fraction. Add 0.5 ml of 1 M NaCl to the sediment and mix well. Add 3.0 ml of water to effect an isotonic solution, followed by 0.5 ml of fetal bovine serum to stabilize the virus.

Annex 3

CONCENTRATION BY TWO-PHASE POLYMER SEPARATION

1. Summary

Viruses can be concentrated by an aqueous polymer two-phase separation. Polyethylene glycol and dextran are added to the sample under proper physicochemical conditions so that the water separates in two phases. The polyethylene glycol will form an upper layer consisting of about 99% of the water and most of the impurities. The lower layer will contain about 1% of the water, the dextran and the virus. The maximum concentration factor is 100. This method is best suited to samples of high densities of virus because of the limited sample volume that can be handled.

2. Scope and Application

The aqueous polymer two-phase system was first developed as a method for the concentration and purification of virus suspensions (*64*). Because of its simplicity and economy it has been employed for the detection of virus in raw sewage and treated effluents. Only if the ionic strength and the pH are correct for the specific virus will the separation and concentration be successful.

Enteroviruses and adenoviruses (*50, 51*) have been recovered by this technique.

2.1 *Advantages*

(1) The method offers the advantages of simplicity and economy because minimum equipment and labour are needed.

(2) The method is applicable to field use.

(3) The method may recover large numbers of many kinds of viruses from naturally polluted samples.

2.2 *Limitations*

(1) Only limited volumes can be processed. Although it is possible to add additional two-phase separation steps, this becomes rather complicated because of necessary adjustments of ionic conditions. For field samples, the methods is best suited to a one-step procedure and consequently a maximum concentration factor of 100. The sample volume could be in the range of 200 ml to 10 litres, but the range 200 ml to 1 litre is the most convenient. The method is therefore most suitable for moderately to grossly polluted waters.

(2) Unsuitability of PFU determinations. Virological assay by PFU determinations is not recommended because the samples to be inoculated may be cytotoxic or contain particulate matter. The method is unsuitable for sludges and other particulate samples because it yields erratic results (*52*).

(3) Varied recovery efficiency. In some reports (*51*) virus recovery from sewage samples was good when employing $TCID_{50}$ assays, but in other reports (*21*) the recovery rate was poor when PFU assays were used.

(4) Only a *limited number of viruses* have been tested, and it has not been established that viruses of naturally polluted waters behave like the ones of the artificially contaminated samples. It is possible that the physical and chemical conditions for optimum virus recovery vary among the enteric viruses; the conditions for maximum virus recovery have not yet been established.

(5) Virus inactivation. It has been reported that coxsackievirus B_2 and echovirus type 6 become rapidly inactivated by dextran sulfate (*31*), and that replacing the dextran sulfate 2000 by dextran T-500 minimizes virus losses (*32*).

3. Apparatus and Materials

Sample bottles with caps or rubber stoppers, such as 1-litre glass bottles with plastic screw caps
pH meter
Magnetic stirrer or shaking machine ; shaking by hand can also be used
Conductivity meter (this is necessary for controlling the ionic strength of some types of water ; a simple meter is adequate)
Pear-shaped separating funnels (funnels with burette-shaped bottoms are very useful, but may have to be made specially).

4. Reagents

Sodium dextran sulfate 2000 (DS) *a* in a 200 g·l⁻¹ solution.

Sodium dextran sulfate 2000 (DS) [a] in a 200 $g \cdot l^{-1}$ solution.

Polyethylene glycol (PEG) [b] in a 300 $g \cdot l^{-1}$ solution. Phosphate buffer (0.01 M), pH 7.2. Sodium chloride solution (5M).

Remark on dextran : In the original work dextran sulfate 2000 was employed but two enteric viruses have been reported (*31*) to lose infectivity through the effects of the dextran sulfate. Dextran sulfate 2000 and 500 may be employed for the separation, but dextran T-500 may also be used (*32*). Dextrans with lower molecular weights and DEAE-dextran are ineffective.

5. Procedure

(1) In the following description a sample size of 200 ml is employed. To this sample in a 500 ml bottle is added 20 g of 5 M NaCl, 58 g of 300 $g \cdot l^{-1}$ PEG solution and 2.7 g of 200 $g \cdot l^{-1}$ DS solution. For raw urban sewage, treated effluent, and brackish waters the sample ionic strength is so low that it may be disregarded when determining the total ionic strength, which then depends essentially on the added NaCl.

(2) It is essential that the pH be adjusted to 7.20 ± 0.05. For this purpose 0.01 M phosphate buffer is employed. If the buffer volume required would significantly increase the sample volume, adjust with 1 M HCl or 1 M NaOH.

(3) Shake the sample vigorously for about 1 hour ; with less efficient shaking the concentration of the virus in the DS-bottom-phase may become less efficient. After the shaking, the sample is placed in a separating funnel of suitable size.

---

[a] Pharmacia, Uppsala, Sweden.
[b] Carbowax 6000.

(4) The funnel is stored at 2–6°C for 24 hours; the fluid should then be separated in two phases consisting of a DS phase of about 2.0–2.5 ml and the remainder. In a number of cases, especially raw sewage, a lot of particulate matter will have collected at the interphase. It has been found very useful to test separately the first bottom sample, i.e., the DS-phase, as well as the " interphase " (i.e., the next 2-ml sample) (*51*). Different viruses and mixtures of viruses may be found in these two sub-samples (*50*).

No further treatment apart from decontamination is required. The concentrated samples should be tested on tube cultures making blind-passages, for maximum recovery.

Annex 4

CONCENTRATION BY ULTRAFILTRATION

1. Summary

Ultrafiltration (UF) is employed when testing for virus in large quantities (100 l or more) of water. Ultrafiltration is a process of selective molecular separation. It employs membranes that pass solvent and solute of low molecular weight, retaining solutes and colloidal matter of larger molecular dimensions than the porosity of the membrane.

The water sample, in a stirred (UF) acrylic cell, is filtered under positive pressure through a supported membrane. The membrane combines selectivity, high throughput, and resistance to clogging. Retention of viruses can be maximized by choosing a membrane that retains particles well below the size of the viruses.

2. Scope and Application

In a suitably sized apparatus large volumes of relatively unpolluted waters may be tested.

2.1 *Advantages*

(1) Ultrafiltration is a simple and practical physical separation process in which the viruses are not subjected to chemical treatment or variations in pH levels.

(2) The recovery rate has been consistent and high.

(3) Although the method is suitable for all types of waters it is especially useful in testing large volumes of relatively unpolluted waters.

2.2 *Limitations*

(1) Filtration rates are relatively slow (approximately $3\ \mathrm{l\cdot hr^{-1}}$), but the process can be run during the night.

(2) When highly polluted waters are processed by this method other macromolecules than viruses will be concentrated also. These substances may be toxic to the tissue cultures used for virus evaluation. This toxicity, however, may be a useful screening test for organic toxicants in polluted waters.

3. Apparatus and Material

3·1 Virus concentration apparatus (like the Amicon Model 2000 High Output UF cell, 2 litre, with power supply) comprising :
   Stainless steel reservoir with tube fittings
   Concentration unit : Base, acrylic sleeve, membrane support disc, stirrer, fill port plug, top cap assembly, knurled locking knobs, motor housing assembly
   Power supply box
   Stirring control unit
3.2 Nitrogen gas tube
3.3 Boiling dish large enough for the virus concentrator
3.4 Flask (filtrate receptacle)
3.5 Sterile gloves
3.6 Sterile evaporating dishes (190 mm in diameter) with cover
3.7 Sterile rubber policeman (boot) attached to 15-cm glass rod
3.8 Sterile forceps
3.9 Two 5-litre beakers

4. Reagents

4.1 Sterile distilled or deionized water
4.2 Eluent : Hanks' salt solution with 0.5% lactalbumin hydrolysate (H-La) (available as dry powder)
4.3 Solutions for disinfection :
   Calcium hypochlorite solution containing a concentration of free chlorine of $12\text{--}15\ \mathrm{mg\cdot l^{-1}}$
   Formaldehyde, $20\ \mathrm{g\cdot l^{-1}}$ solution

4.4 Sodium thiosulfate ($Na_2S_2O_3$) solution (5 g·l^{-1}), for neutralization of residuals of chlorine

5. Procedure

5.1 *Sterilization of equipment*

Disconnect the apparatus placing all tubes, knobs, screws, stirrer assembly, membrane support disc, etc., in the boiling dish. The membrane support disc must be placed flat in the boiling dish. Water is added and the contents boiled for 30 min. The stainless steel reservoir, base holder, top cap assembly, and the filtrate receptacle (flask) are wrapped and autoclaved on a dry cycle for 15 min at 120°C. Soak the acrylic sleeve in 4 l of sterile water to which is added 400 ml of the stock calcium hypochlorite solution so that the concentration of free chlorine is 10–13 mg·l^{-1}. Allow to remain for a minimum period of 30 min. Rinse the sleeve in sterile $Na_2S_2O_3$ and then in sterile distilled water and cover with sterile cloth. The membrane is decontaminated and resterilized by adding a 20 g·l^{-1} formaldehyde solution to the container and leaving for a minimum of 30 min. The membrane is rinsed well in sterile water.

5.2 *Assembly of filtration unit*

The unit is assembled with aseptic precautions:

(1) Arrange the sterile stainless steel reservoir, the power supply box, stirring control unit, boiling dish (containing sterile knurled locking knobs, screws, stirrer assembly, port plug, spatula, tubing and tube fittings, and the membrane support disc) and the filtrate receptacle (flask) etc., to suit the worker. (It is found to be most convenient and efficient if arranged from left to right in the above order).

(2) Remove wrappings from the sterile reservoir, cell base, and the top cap assembly, taking care not to touch any of the sterile parts. (The undersurface of the top cap assembly is covered with aluminium foil prior to wrapping. This foil covering is only removed at a later stage in the assembling).

(3) Place the membrane support disc in the cell base and place the membrane on this disc. Insert rubber " O " ring and place acrylic sleeve in position.

(4) Remove the aluminium foil from the top cap assembly and invert to insert " O " ring. Secure the stirrer assembly by means of the two small screws, using a sterile spatula. Fit the top cap assembly to the sleeve and loosely fasten the six knurled locking knobs. Screw the port plug into the top cap assembly.

(5) Attach the fitting on the liquid withdrawal tube (ferrules and hexagonal nut) to the top cap assembly and the other fitting to the liquid " outlet " fitting on the reservoir. Fix the black rubber ring into the lid of the reservoir.

(6) Attach one end of the fitting on the gas tube to the gas " inlet " fitting on the reservoir and the other end to the power supply box at " gas out ".

(7) Fasten the 3 screws connecting the stirring motor to the top cap assembly.

(8) Attach the outflow pipe (red) leading from the cell base exit and insert the other end into the filtrate receptacle (flask), if an endpoint controller is used.

An endpoint controller may be used to shut the system off automatically when the desired amount of ultrafiltrate has been collected. The probes of the endpoint controller must be in the filtrate flask and secured to a retort stand at the required height. The contacts must be inserted at the power supply box in order to complete the circuit.

The membrane is tested by pressing the " power " button and ensuring that the set pressure builds up. The unit should maintain the pressure even if the gas inflow from the gas cylinder is temporarily interrupted.

(9) Release the pressure by pressing the " power " button and remove the lid of the reservoir, placing it on a sterile Petri dish. The apparatus is now ready for use.

5.3 *Operation of unit*

(1) Fill the reservoir with the water sample and fix the lid firmly.

(2) Turn on the power and allow the cell to fill three-quarters with the water sample before adjusting the stirrer at a suitable speed (usually a setting of 5.5 is sufficient).

(3) Ensure that filtrate is passing through at a steady speed. Reduce the stirrer speed as the level of water drops in the cell. When all the water to be tested has passed through the membrane, remove the end of the tube leading to the filtrate receptacle (flask) and lower the end to a level below that of the membrane to prevent a backflow of water. Turn the power off.

(4) After the pressure has dropped, remove the six knurled locking knobs and place them in the boiling dish. Remove the top cap assembly and place the acrylic sleeve in a 5-l beaker.

Aseptically remove the " O " ring and place it in the boiling dish. Then carefully remove the membrane and place it in a sterile evaporating dish, immediately replacing the cover.

5.4 *Elution of virus from membrane*

Using a sterile syringe, an aliquot of 5 ml of eluent (H-La) is introduced carefully onto the membrane and gently spread evenly over the surface of the membrane using a sterile rubber policeman, thus removing and collecting all visible signs of any sediment or residue on the membrane. The H-La on the membrane is withdrawn with a sterile syringe and put into a sterile bottle. This procedure is repeated 4 times, thus employing 20 ml of eluent. The specimen is then decontaminated and centrifuged at 1700 g for 30 min. The supernatant is withdrawn with a sterile syringe, put into a sterile bottle and suitably labelled. The concentrated sample is now ready for virus evaluation.

Annex 5

FILTER ADSORPTION-ELUTION SYSTEMS FOR CONCENTRATING VIRUSES

1. Summary

The filter adsorption-elution (FAE) procedures are based upon the ability of viruses to adsorb reversibly to reactive surfaces. Cellulose nitrate membranes, cellulose acetate, cellulose nitrate or fibreglass cartridge type depth filters, and fibreglass-asbestos-epoxy filter discs have been used as adsorbent filters. The water is usually acidified and polyvalent cations added before filtration to increase virus adsorption. The adsorbed virus is eluted from the filter with a small volume of alkaline proteinaceous fluid or glycine buffer, pH 11.5. Single-stage FAE procedures are convenient for fluid volumes of up to about 20 litres. Multistage procedures have been developed for processing large volumes of water that contain relatively small quantities of virus. A two-stage FAE procedure is summarized in Fig. 1.

2. Scope and Application

Many variations in both single-stage and multistage FAE procedures have been reported in the literature. However, relatively little work has yet been done to determine if any of these variations are superior to others. For this reason, single-stage and multistage procedures are described here only in general terms. These procedures are intended only as guidelines; more detailed information concerning equipment, materials, and particular operations may be obtained from the references.

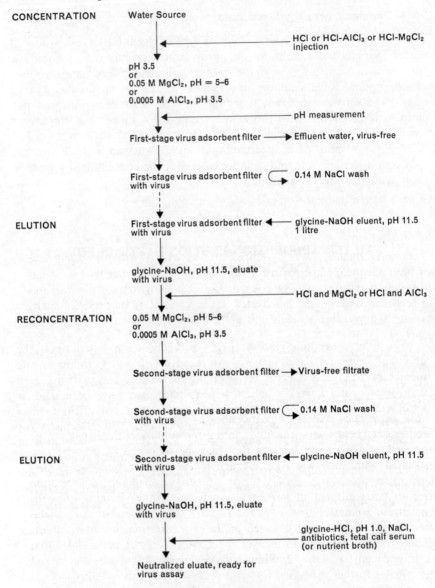

Fig. 1. Two-stage filter adsorption-elution procedure for concentrating
viruses from water

FAE methods were developed primarily for enteroviruses. The choice of pH and ionic conditions for virus adsorption depends, in part, upon water quality.

2.1 *Advantages*

(1) Large volumes of drinking water and other very clean waters can be processed and enteroviruses have been efficiently adsorbed from such waters using a variety of pH levels and ionic conditions.

(2) Enteroviruses have been adsorbed to filters from a variety of water and waste-water samples by adjusting the samples to pH 3.5 and adding $AlCl_3$ to a final concentration of 0.0005 M (*39, 61, 70, 80*).

2.2 *Limitations*

(1) FAE methods were developed primarily for enteroviruses and have not been adequately evaluated for their ability to recover reoviruses, rota-viruses, parvoviruses, hepatitis A virus, and adenoviruses. Adenoviruses are reported to be rapidly inactivated at pH levels of 10.0 or more, thereby making it impossible to elute adsorbed adenoviruses with glycine-NaOH at pH 11.5 (*24*).

(2) A number of different pH levels and ionic conditions have been successfully used for adsorbing viruses in water and wastewater to filter surfaces. Not all of the adsorption conditions can be successfully used for all types of water and wastewater.

(3) Suspended matter or particulates in water or wastewater tend to clog the adsorbent filters, thereby limiting the volume of fluid that can be processed. Furthermore, viruses that may be adsorbed to or otherwise associated with such water-borne particulates may be removed in any clarification procedures applied prior to virus adsorption. Clarification prior to virus adsorption has been widely used in FAE techniques for concentrating enteric viruses (*2, 10, 12, 20, 39, 57, 80*), but particulate-associated viruses are not detected in the concentration procedure unless special methods are used to recover the viruses from the particulates that are trapped on the clarifying filters. Clarifying filters must be eluted and their eluates further processed for virus recovery if quantitative recovery is desired.

Prefiltration is not included in the procedure here described. Information on its use may be found in the references cited.

(4) Certain types of soluble or colloidal organic matter in some waters and wastewaters, collectively referred to as membrane-coating components (MCC), can interfere with virus adsorption to filter surfaces, presumably by occupying the sites to which viruses adsorb. As water is processed

through an adsorbent filter, these MCCs can accumulate to such an extent that viruses will no longer be able to adsorb. In some waters this situation may occur long before the filters become physically clogged. Because there is no convenient way to predict the concentrations of MCCs in a given water, it may be necessary to determine its MCC concentration experimentally using water samples that have been deliberately contaminated with known quantities of specific enteric viruses (*90, 91*).

3. Single-stage Filter Adsorption-elution Procedure

3.1 *Apparatus and materials*

Membrane filter holder equipped with a pressure relief valve
Pressure vessel, 4, 12, or 20 litres, depending upon sample size
pH-meter
Positive pressure source equipped with a pressure gauge—positive pressure air pump or cylinder of compressed air or nitrogen equipped with a regulator valve
Hoses and fittings for connecting positive pressure source, pressure vessel, and membrane filter holder in series
Virus adsorbent filters—cellulose nitrate/acetate (*90, 91*) or fibreglass-asbestos-epoxy (*80, 81*)

3.2 *Reagents*

Virus eluent—0.05 M glycine adjusted to pH 11.5 with 1 M NaOH (*84, 88*), 30 g·l^{-1} beef extract (*2, 68*) or nutrient broth concentrate, 5 times, at pH 9.0 (*37*)
Hydrochloric acid—0.1 M and 1.0 M. Eluate neutralizer when using pH 11.5 glycine—NaOH as eluent is 0.05 M glycine adjusted to pH 1.0–1.5 with M HCl (*84, 88*)
Sodium hydroxide—0.1 and 1.0 M
Sodium thiosulfate—concentrated stock solution (100 ×) containing 10 g per litre
Sodium chloride—2.8 M (160 g·l^{-1}) and 0.14 M (8 g·l^{-1})
Nutrient broth concentrate, 10 times, or heat-inactivated fetal calf serum.
Aluminium chloride—0.05 or 0.5 M stock solution *or* magnesium chloride—1.0 M stock solution. (Either AlCl$_3$ cr MgCl$_2$ is required for all samples except very clean waters that are low in turbidity and dissolved organic matter; use for such waters is optional).

3.3 *Procedure*

(1) The sample of water or wastewater is adjusted to pH and ionic conditions suitable for virus adsorption. One of 3 adsorption conditions is

commonly used, depending mainly upon water quality : (*a*) pH 3.5, which is used only for very clean waters that are low in turbidity and dissolved organic matter, (*b*) pH 3.5 and 0.0005 M $AlCl_3$, or (*c*) pH 3.5 to 6.0 and 0.05 M $MgCl_2$. The chemical additions are made while the sample is being mixed rapidly. Rapid mixing of the sample is especially important when adding acid or base, because inadequate mixing may result in virus inactivation owing to local pH extremes within portions of the sample. When using $AlCl_3$ or $MgCl_2$, pH adjustments are made before the $AlCl_3$ or $MgCl_2$ is added. After $AlCl_3$ addition, the pH of the sample may have to be readjusted to 3.5.

(2) The pressure vessel containing the sample is connected to the source of positive pressure and the filter holder. The sample is forced through the adsorbent filter at a flux of about 25 ml per minute per cm^2 of filter surface area and the filtrate is discarded.

(3) If $AlCl_3$ or $MgCl_2$ has been used to enhance virus adsorption, the filters are washed with 0.14 M NaCl in order to remove excess Al or Mg ions. The volume of NaCl wash depends upon the surface area of the filter. One ml of NaCl solution is used per cm^2 of filter surface area. The NaCl wash procedure is omitted if the sample being filtered had no polyvalent cations added.

(4) Adsorbed viruses are eluted from the filter(s) with one of the eluents recommended above. The eluent volume depends upon the surface area of the filter. The minimum elution volume is about 0.5 ml per cm^2 of filter surface area. In order to obtain efficient virus elution, the eluent is added to the filter holder in a manner that will cause it to cover the filter surface completely with a layer of eluent. This can be done by opening the pressure relief valve on the filter holder, disconnecting the positive pressure source from the filter holder inlet and then pouring or pipetting the eluent into the filter holder inlet. When eluent begins to discharge from the pressure relief valve, the valve is quickly closed. The positive pressure source is reconnected to the filter holder inlet, and the pressure is *slowly* increased until eluate begins to flow from the outlet of the filter holder. This eluate is collected in a sterile container. When all the eluate has been collected, the pressure is slowly increased in order to force retained fluid from the filters and thereby obtain maximum eluate recovery.

If the eluent is glycine-NaOH, pH 11.5, the collected eluate should have pH 11.0 or more. If the eluate pH is less than 11.0, then the elution procedure is repeated with another volume of glycine-NaOH, pH 11.5. Immediately after pH measurement, the collected eluate is adjusted to pH 7.0 to 7.5 with glycine-HCl, pH 1.0–1.5. The entire elution procedure should be completed within 5 minutes in order to avoid virus inactivation due to high pH.

If the eluent is beef extract or nutrient broth, it may be necessary to : (a) expose the membrane to the eluent for an extended time period (37), or (b) sonicate the membrane (3), or (c) triturate the membrane by grinding it with alundum in a mortar and pestle (91) in order to achieve efficient virus elution.

(5)   After decontamination the eluate is ready for virus evaluation.

4. Multistage Filter Adsorption-elution Procedures

Multistage FAE procedures have been developed primarily for concentrating enteroviruses from large volumes of drinking water and other very clean waters that are low in turbidity and dissolved organic matter and are likely to contain only very small quantities of viruses.

4.1   *Apparatus and materials*

(1)   Virus concentration apparatus :

Water pump (required when the water being processed is not under adequate pressure)

First-stage virus adsorbent filter holder

Second-stage virus adsorbent membrane holder (47 mm diameter plastic or stainless steel membrane filter holder)

Source of positive pressure equipped with a pressure gauge

Hoses with fittings for connecting the various components of the virus concentration apparatus

Pressure vessel, 4 l capacity (for the 0.14 M NaCl rinse water and the pH 11.5 glycine-NaOH eluent that are used in the first stage of the virus concentration procedure)

Two-way valve, mounted in-line between the point of chemical addition and the first-stage virus adsorbent filter

pH-meter with combination pH electrode mounted in-line between the point of chemical addition and the two-way valve

Water meter (located in-line between the two-way valve and the first-stage virus adsorbent filter)

Flow meter located in-line after the pump

Pressure gauge located in-line between the flow meter and the pH electrode

Chemical feed system consisting of a 20-l pressure vessel with an in-line pressure gauge on the inlet side and a check valve and a precision metering valve on the outlet side. The outlet is connected to the water line via a " tee ". In order to aid the mixing of the chemicals into the flowing water, some type of diffuser can be placed on the outlet of the chemical feed line where it enters the flowing water inside the " tee ".

(2) Virus adsorbent filters, for first and second stages of the concentration procedure.

4.2 *Reagents*

Chemical feed solution for the first concentration stage is made up either with HCl alone or with HCl mixed with $AlCl_3 \cdot 6H_2O$ or with $MgCl_2 \cdot 6H_2O$ as concentrates. The composition of the concentrate depends upon water quality, but the final concentration in the water should be 0.0005 M $AlCl_3$ or 0.05 M $MgCl_2$.

Sodium chloride solutions (2.8 M and 0.14 M).

Aluminium chloride or magnesium chloride concentrated stock solution.

Glycine-NaOH, pH 11.5—adjust 0.05 M glycine containing 0.005 $g \cdot l^{-1}$ phenol red to pH 11.5 with 1 M NaOH. This solution should not be stored for more than a few hours because the pH may decrease.

Glycine-HCl, pH 1.0—adjust 0.05 M glycine containing 0.005 $g \cdot l^{-1}$ phenol red to pH 1.0 with 1 M HCl.

Nutrient broth concentrate, 10 times, or heat-inactivated fetal calf serum.

Sodium thiosulfate—a stock solution containing 10 $g \cdot l^{-1}$. For use it is diluted 1 : 100.

4.3 *Procedure*

4.3.1 *General description.* The most promising multistage FAE procedures for very clean waters consist of two-stages. In some experimental trials small quantities of enteroviruses in 400-l volumes of tapwater were concentrated to a volume of about 10 ml with a virus recovery efficiency of about 50%.

The general two-stage procedure for highly treated waters is as follows : Water flowing at a rate of about 4–10 litres per minute is adjusted to a pH level and ionic conditions that will promote virus adsorption by adding hydrochloric acid and possibly aluminium or magnesium chloride. The water then passes through a large-capacity, cellulose ester or fibreglass virus adsorbent filter or filter series. After the desired volume has been processed, the adsorbed viruses that have accumulated on the filter surfaces are eluted with about 1 litre of glycine-NaOH buffer, pH 11.5. The eluate obtained is readjusted by the addition of hydrochloric acid and aluminium chloride to pH and ionic conditions that enhance virus adsorption. The sample is press-ure filtered on a batch basis through a second, smaller filter series consisting of fibreglass-asbestos-epoxy filter discs. After washing the filters with a small volume of 0.14 M NaCl to remove excess aluminium ions, the adsorbed viruses are eluted from the filters with several ml of glycine-NaOH buffer, pH 11.5. The eluate is adjusted to pH 7. The two-stage FAE procedure is shown diagrammatically in Fig. 1.

Two similar types of equipment have been developed for performing the two-stage FAE procedure. The two types of equipment differ primarily in the way chemicals are added to the water in the first stage of the procedure. In one method the chemicals are added to the flowing water from a pressur-ized reservoir. Chemical addition is controlled manually with a precision metering valve, and it is monitored down-stream from the point of addition by in-line pH measurement. In the other method, chemical addition is made with a fluid proportioning pump that is activated by the flowing water. The chemical feed rate is controlled by presetting syringe-type feed pumps that are part of the fluid proportioner. With both feed systems, a small sample of the water to be processed is first titrated to the desired adsorption pH with a standardized solution of hydrochloric acid in order to predetermine the required volume ratio of water to chemical feed solution. Either procedure may be used for chemical addition in the first processing stage. Because the operating procedures for the fluid proportioner have recently been described in detail elsewhere (*36, 84*), the use of the other chemical feed system will be described here.

4.3.2 *Preparation of virus concentration apparatus.* Assemble the virus concentrator. All components that contact the water should be sterilized by autoclaving, ethylene oxide, or some other appropriate method. Alterna-tively, the apparatus may be disinfected by treating for 30 minutes with a solution containing 25 mg·l^{-1} of free chlorine. Chlorine treatment is followed by treatment with sterile sodium thiosulfate solution in order to neutralize the chlorine. Certain sterilizing or disinfecting methods may be unsuitable for certain components of the virus concentration apparatus. The component manufacturer should be consulted for instructions on sterilizing or disin-fecting. All virus concentration operations, including equipment assembly and sample processing, should be done with aseptic technique.

4.3.3 *Preparation of chemical feed solution for first stage processing*

(1) The choice of which chemical feed solution to use is based largely on water quality. Viruses can be efficiently concentrated from large volumes of

very clean water that is low in turbidity and dissolved organic matter by adjusting to pH 3.5 with HCl. Waters of poorer quality may in addition require aluminium or magnesium chloride to enhance virus adsorption.

The concentration of the chemical feed solution is determined immediately prior to processing the water through the virus concentration apparatus. Although the chemical feed system is capable of operating over a wide range of feed rates, a ratio of chemical feed solution to water volume of 1 : 50 is both practical and convenient. A 1 : 50 ratio requires that the chemical feed solution is 50 times more concentrated than the concentration desired in the water. The $AlCl_3$ and $MgCl_2$ concentrations usually employed to enhance virus adsorption are 0.0005 M and 0.05 M, respectively. Therefore, the concentrations of $AlCl_3$ and $MgCl_2$ would have to be 0.025 M and 2.5 M, respectively.

(2) The concentration of HCl required to reduce the pH of the water to some specific value and, hence, the concentration in the chemical feed solution depends upon the alkalinity of the water. This is determined by titrating a sample of the water to the pH required for virus adsorption with an HCl solution of known concentration. The concentration of HCl in the titrated water is determined and the HCl concentration in the chemical feed solution is made 50 times greater than this value. When $AlCl_3$ and HCl are used together in a single chemical feed solution, the concentration of the HCl may have to be lowered somewhat from the value calculated on the basis of the titration in order to compensate for the acidity of the $AlCl_3$.

A problem may arise when either HCl plus $AlCl_3$ or HCl plus $MgCl_2$ is used as the chemical feed solution if there is a change in the alkalinity of the water during processing. This may result in having to change the ratio of chemical feed solution to water volume in order to maintain the desired pH in the water. If the feed solution contains $AlCl_3$ or $MgCl_2$, this could result in a change in the concentration of Al or Mg ions in the water. While an increase in Al or Mg ions will not adversely affect virus adsorption, a large decrease in the concentration of these ions could result in decreased virus adsorption efficiency. In order to avoid this risk, the feed solution may be prepared with higher $AlCl_3$ or $MgCl_2$ concentrations. This would compensate for a reduced ratio of chemical feed solution to water volume caused by a decrease in alkalinity. For example, if it is believed that the alkalinity of the water may decrease to such an extent that the ratio of acidified $AlCl_3$ solution to water volume has to be decreased from 1 : 50 to 1 : 100, then the $AlCl_3$ concentration in the feed solution could be reduced to 0.05 M. Thus, at ratios of 1 : 50 and 1 : 100, the $AlCl_3$ concentrations in the water would be 0.001 M and 0.0005 M, respectively.

Alternatively, the HCl and the $AlCl_3$ (or $MgCl_2$) may be added to the water separately, using two independent chemical feed systems. This would eliminate the problem associated with a combined chemical feed solution and changes in the alkalinity of the water. However, the feed system for the $MgCl_2$ or $AlCl_3$ would require an in-line flow meter or some other flow measuring or controlling system that would make it possible to achieve the desired final $MgCl_2$ or $AlCl_3$ concentration in the flowing water.

(3) When the chemical feed solution has been prepared, it is placed in the 20-litre capacity pressure vessel. The vessel is closed, the reservoir outlet is connected to the water line and the metering valve is closed. The pressure vessel inlet is connected to a source of positive pressure, but pressure is not applied until the water is to be processed.

4.3.4 *First stage processing*

(1) The virus concentration apparatus is assembled. The two-way valve is set so that the flow of water is diverted *away* from the first-stage virus adsorbent filter. The chemical feed solution metering valve is in the closed position and the pressure vessel containing the chemical feed solution is not pressurized.

(2) The water pump is turned on or the water line is opened so that the flow rate through the apparatus is between 4 and 10 litres per minute.

(3) The pressure in the water line is noted, and with the metering valve still closed, the chemical feed system is pressurized to $3-7 \times 10^4$ Pa·cm^{-2} above the water line pressure.

(4) The pH of the flowing water is noted and the chemical feed metering valve slowly opened until the pH of the water reaches the desired value.

(5) With the two-way valve, the water flow is directed towards the first-stage virus adsorbent filter, and the water meter is read. Water is allowed to flow through the filter until the desired volume has been processed. During the course of processing, the pH of the water should be kept within ± 0.5 pH units of the desired value by adjusting the metering valve, if necessary. The pressure in the chemical feed system should also be kept at $3-7 \times 10^4$ Pa·cm^{-2} above the pressure in the water line. Increasing the pressure in the chemical feed system must be done slowly in order to avoid an excess flow of chemicals into the water. It may even be necessary concurrently to decrease the flow of chemicals by adjusting the metering valve.

(6) When the desired volume has been processed, the water flow is directed away from the virus adsorbent filter by means of the two-way valve. The metering valve on the chemical feed system is closed, and the chemical feed system is depressurized. The water pump or water supply line is shut off.

(7) If $AlCl_3$ or $MgCl_2$ has been used to enhance virus adsorption, then 0.14 M NaCl is used to wash excess Al or Mg ions from the filter. If only HCl had been used to enhance virus adsorption, then this wash procedure

may be omitted. Generally, 1–4 litres of 0.14 NaCl is an adequate wash volume, depending upon the size of the virus sorbent filter. The NaCl solution is placed in a 4-litre pressure vessel, an the pressure vessel outlet is connected to the inlet of the filter holder. The pressure vessel inlet is connected to a positive pressure source, the NaCl solution is forced through the filter, and the filtrate is discarded.

(8) The virus adsorbent filter is purged of excess fluid by connecting the positive pressure source to the filter holder inlet and turning on the pressure. The purged fluid is discarded.

(9) One litre of glycine-NaOH, pH 11.5, eluent is placed in the 4-litre pressure vessel that was used for the NaCl wash. The pressure vessel outlet is connected to the filter holder inlet and the filter holder bleed valve is opened. The positive pressure source is connected the pressure vessel inlet and the pressure is applied slowly, so that eluent begins to fill the void space in the filter holder. When eluent just begins to flow from the bleed valve, the valve is quickly closed. The eluent is slowly passed through the virus adsorbent filter, and the resulting filtrate (the eluate) is collected in a sterile container. When all the eluent has been filtered, the pressure is slowly increased in order to force additional fluid from the filter.

(10) The pH of the collected eluate is checked, and the eluate is immediately neutralized by adding glycine-HCl, pH 1.0. During neutralization, the eluate is continuously and vigorously mixed in order to prevent virus inactivation due to low pH conditions within portions of the eluate solution. If the eluate pH was less than 11.0 before neutralization, then this elution procedure should be repeated with another 1 litre of eluent. The two eluates would then be combined for further processing.

4.3.5 *Second-stage processing*

(1) The viruses in the eluate are further concentrated (reconcentrated) by a second-stage FAE procedure. The eluate from the first stage of processing is adjusted to the pH and the ionic conditions that will enhance virus adsorption. (These conditions are usually either pH 3.5 and 0.0005 M $AlCl_3$ or pH 5.0 to 6.0 and 0.05 M $MgCl_2$, the former set of conditions being more widely used (*39, 40, 80, 84, 87*).) The eluate is adjusted to the desired pH level with glycine-HCl, pH 1.0. Aluminium or magnesium chloride is then added from a concentrated stock solution to give the desired final concentration. While the chemical additions are being made, the sample is continuously and rapidly mixed.

(2) The sample is placed in a 4-litre pressure vessel, the pressure vessel outlet is connected to the inlet of the second-stage, 47-mm diameter virus

adsorbent filter, and the pressure vessel inlet is connected to a positive pressure source. The pressure is slowly turned on so that the sample passes through the filter at a flow rate of not more than 400 ml/minute. The filtrate is discarded.

(3) In the reconcentration procedure, a precipitate often forms in the sample upon pH adjustment and AlCl$_3$ or MgCl$_2$ addition. The precipitate may clog the virus adsorbent filter before the entire sample volume can be processed. Viruses in the eluate often become associated with this precipitate so that removal of the precipitate prior to filtration results in virus losses. At the present time, there are no reliable and proven methods for second-stage processing when precipitation occurs. Aluminium hydroxide precipitation (20), aqueous polymer phase separation (87), and hydroextraction by dialysis against polyethyleneglycol (94) have been suggested as alternative reconcentration procedes, but there are at present insufficient data on the use of these methods for reconcentration purposes to recommend their use. However, one possible way to reduce or eliminate precipitation is to process a small volume of water the first stage of the virus concentration procedure.

(4) After passing the entire sample through the virus adsorbent filter, the filter is washed with 2 ml of 0.14 M NaCl in order to remove excess Al or Mg ions. The NaCl solution is pipetted directly into the inlet of the virus adsorbent filter or, alternatively, it is placed in a small pressure vessel connected to the filter inlet. Positive pressure is used to pass the NaCl solution through the filter, and the filtrate is discarded.

(5) Adsorbed viruses are eluted from the filter with a 7-ml volume of glycine-NaOH buffer, pH 11.5. The eluent is pipetted directly into the filter holder inlet, the inlet is connected to a positive pressure source and the pressure is carefully turned on so that the eluate flows slowly from the filter outlet into a sterile container. When all the fluid has been collected, the pressure is slowly increased in order to force retained fluid from the filter and obtain maximum eluate recovery.

(6) The eluate pH is measured, and the eluate is immediately adjusted to pH 7.0–7.5 with glycine-HCl, pH 1.0. If the eluate pH was less than 11.0 before pH adjustment, the elution procedure is repeated with additional 7-ml volumes of glycine-NaOH, pH 11.5, until the eluate pH is at least 11.0. The entire elution procedure should be completed within 5 minutes.

(7) After decontamination the eluate is ready for virus evaluation.

REFERENCES

1. BERG, G. Transmission of viruses by the water route. New York, Interscience, 1967.

2. BERG, G. Integrated approach to the problem of viruses in water. *J. san. Engng Div. Amer. Soc. Civ. Engrs*, **97** : 867–882 (1971).

3. BERG, G., DAHLING, D. R. & BERMAN, D. Recovery of small quantities of viruses from clean water on cellulose nitrate membrane filters. *Appl. Microbiol.*, **22** : 608–614 (1971).

4. BERG, G. Removal of viruses from sewage, effluents, and waters. — 1. A review. *Bull. Wld Hlth Org.*, **49** : 451–460 (1973).

5. BERG, G. Removal of viruses from sewage, effluents, and waters. — 2. Present and future trends. *Bull. Wld Hlth Org.*, **49** : 461–469 (1973).

6. BELFORT, G., ROTEM, Y. & KATZENELSON, E. Virus concentration using hollow fiber membranes. *Water Res.*, **9** : 79–85 (1974).

7. BISHOP, R. F. et al. Virus particles in epithelial cells of duodenal mucosa from children with acute nonbacterial gastroenteritis. *Lancet*, **2** : 1281–1283 (1973).

8. CHANG, S. L. Waterborne viral infections and their prevention. *Bull. Wld Hlth Org.*, **78** : 401–414 (1968).

9. CHANG, S. L. et al. Application of the " most probable number " method for estimating concentrations of animal viruses by the tissue culture technique. *Virology*, **6** : 27–42 (1958).

10. CLIVER, D. O. Factors in the membrane filtration of enteroviruses. *Appl. Microbiol.*, **13** : 417–425 (1965).

11. CLIVER, D. O. Detection of enteric viruses by concentration with polyethylene glycol. *In :* BERG, G. Transmission of viruses by the water route. New York, Interscience, 1967, pp. 109–120.

12. CLIVER, D. O. Enterovirus detection by membrane chromatography. *In :* BERG, G. ed. Transmission of viruses by the water route. New York, Interscience, 1967, pp. 139–141.

13. CLIVER, D. O. Virus interactions with membrane filters. *Biotechnol. Bioengng.*, **10** : 877–889 (1968).

14. COULON, G. & NETTER, R. La recherche des virus dans l'eau potable. Etude critique des méthodes et résultats. *Bull. Inst. nat. Santé Rech. méd.*, **22** : 941–956 (1967).

15. DONCŒUR, F. Contribution à l'étude de l'élimination des enterovirus au cours du traitement des eaux d'alimentation. Thesis, Nancy, 1972.

16. ELLENDER, R. D. & SWEET, B. H. Newer membrane concentration processes and their application to detection of virus pollution of waters. *Water Res.*, **6** : 741–746 (1972).

17. ENGLAND, B. Protamine sulfate precipitation of reovirus and adenovirus for their assay on sewage and effluents. *Bact. Proc.*, page 194 (1970).

18. ENGLAND, B. (1972) : Concentration of reovirus and adenovirus from sewage and effluent by protamine sulfate (salmine treatment). *Appl. Microbiol.*, **24** : 510–512 (1972).

19. ENGLAND, B. Recovery of viruses from waste and other waters by chemical methods. *In :* BERG, G. Symposium : Detection of viruses in waste and other waters. *Devel. industr. Microbiol.*, **15** : 174–183 (1974).

20. FARRAH, S. R. et al. Concentration of viruses from large volumes of tap water using pleated membrane filters. *Appl. Microbiol.*, **31** : 221–226 (1976).

21. FATTAL, B., KATZENELSON, E. & SHUVAL, H. I. Comparison of methods for isolation of viruses in water. *In :* MOLINA, J. F., jr & SAGIK, R. P. Virus survival in water and wastewater systems. Austin, Center for Research in Water Resources, University of Texas, 1974, pp. 19–30.

22. FEINSTONE, S. M. et al. Buoyant density of the hepatitis. A virus-like particle in cesium chloride. *J. Virol.*, **13** : 1412–1414 (1974).

23. FEINSTONE, S. M., KAPIKIAN, A. Z. & PURCELL, R. H. Hepatitis A : Detection by immune electron microscopy of a virus-like antigen associated with acute illness. *Science*, **182** : 1026–1028 (1973).

24. FIELDS, H. A. & METCALF, T. G. Concentration of adenovirus from seawater. *Water Res.*, **9** : 357–364 (1975).

25. FLEWETT, T. H., BRYDEN, A. S. & DAVIES, H. Virus particles in gastroenteritis. *Lancet*, **2** : 1497 (1973).

26. FOLIGUET, J.-M. & DONCŒUR, F. Inactivation assay of enteroviruses and salmonella in fresh and digested wastewater sludge by pasteurization. *Water Res.*, **6** : 1399–1407 (1972).

27. FOLIGUET, J.-M. & DONCŒUR, F. Elimination des virus au cours du traitement de l'eau, prechloration au " break-point ". *Water Res.*, **8** : 651–657 (1975).

28. FOLIGUET, J.-M., LAVILLAUREIX, J. & SCHWARTZBROD, L. Virus et eaux. II. Mise en évidence des virus dans le milieu hydrique. *Rev. épidém., Méd. soc. et Santé publ.*, **21** : 185–259 (1973).

29. FOLIGUET, J.-M., SCHWARTZBROD, L. & GAUDIN, O. G. La pollution virale des eaux usées, de surface et d'alimentation. Etude effectuée dans le département français de Meurthe-et-Moselle. *Bull. Wld Hlth Org.*, **35** : 737–749 (1966).

30. GRABOW, W. O. K. The virology of waste water treatment. *Water Res.*, **2** : 675–701 (1968).

31. GRINDROD, J. & CLIVER, D. O. Limitations of the polymer two-phase system for detection of viruses. *Arch. Virusforsch.*, **28** : 337–347 (1969).

32. GRINDROD, J. & CLIVER, D. O. A polymer two phase system adapted to virus detection. *Arch. Virusforsch.*, **31** : 365–372 (1970).

33. GRINSTEIN, S., MELNICK, J. L. & WALLIS, C. Virus isolations from sewage and from a stream receiving effluents of sewage treatment plants. *Bull. Wld Hlth Org.*, **42** : 291–296.

34. GÄRTNER, H. Retention and recovery of poliovirus on a soluble ultrafilter. *In .* BERG, G., ed. Transmission of viruses by the water route. New York, Interscience, 1967, pp. 121–127.

35. HILL, W. F. jr, AKIN, E. W. & BENTON, W. H. Detection of viruses in water. A review of methods and application. Proceedings of the 13th Water Quality Conference. *Water Res.*, **5** : 967–995 (1971).

36. HILL, W. F. jr et al. Apparatus for conditioning unlimited quantities of finished waters for enteric virus detection. *Appl. Microbiol.*, **27** : 1177–1178 (1974).

37. HILL, W. F. jr et al. Virus in water. II. Evaluation of membrane cartridge filters for recovering low multiplicities of poliovirus from water. *Appl. Microbiol.*, **23** : 880–888 (1972).

38. HILL, W. F. jr et al. Recovery of polioviruses from turbide estuarine water on microporous filters by the use of celite. *Appl. Microbiol.*, **27** : 506–512 (1974).

39. HOMMA, A. et al. Virus concentration from sewage. *Water Res.*, **7** : 945–950 (1973).

40. JAKUBOWSKI, W., HILL, W. F., jr & CLARKE, N. A. Comparative study of four microporous filters for concentrating viruses from drinking water. *Appl. Microbiol.*, **30** : 58–65 (1975).

41. JAKUBOWSKI, W. et al. Epoxy-fiberglass adsorbent for concentrating viruses from large volumes of potable water. *Appl. Microbiol.*, **28** : 501–502 (1974).

42. KAPIKIAN, A. Z. et al. Visualization by immune electron microscopy of a 27-nm particle associated with acute infectious nonbacterial gastroenteritis. *J. Virol.*, **10** : 1075–1081 (1972).

43. KAPIKIAN, A. Z. et al. New C-F. test for the human reovirus-like agent of infantile gastroenteritis. *Lancet*, **1** : 1056–1060 (1975).

44. KÄRBER, G. Beitrag zur kollektiven Behandlung pharmakologischer Reihenversuche. *Arch. exper. pathol. Pharmakol.*, **162** : 480–491 (1931).

45. KOTT, Y. et al. Bacteriophages as viral pollution indicators. *Water Res.*, **8** : 165–171 (1974).

46. LENNETTE, E. H. & SCHMIDT, N. J. Diagnostic procedures for viral and rickettsial infections, 4th ed., New York, American Public Health Association Inc., 1969.

47. LIU, O. C. et al. Virus in water. — I. A preliminary study on a flow-through gauze sampler for recovering virus from waters. *Appl. Microbiol.*, **21** : 405–410 (1971).

48. LUND, E. The effect of pretreatments on the virus contents of sewage samples. *Water Res.*, **7** : 873–879 (1973).

49. LUND, E. & HEDSTRÖM, C.-E. The use of an aqueous polymer phase system for enterovirus isolations from sewage. *Amer. J. Epid.*, **84** : 287–291 (1966).

50. LUND, E. & HEDSTRÖM, C.-E. A study on sampling and isolation methods for the detection of virus in sewage. *Water Res.*, **3** : 823–832 (1969).

51. LUND, E., HEDSTRÖM, C.-E. & JANTZEN, N. Occurrence of enteric viruses in wastewater after activated sludge treatment. *J. Water Pollut. Contr. Fed.*, **41** : 169–174 (1969).

52. LUND, E. & RØNNE, V. On the isolation of virus from sewage treatment plant sludges. *Water Res.*, **7** : 863–871 (1973).

53. MASCOLI, C. C. et al. Recovery of hepatitis agents in the marmoset from human cases occurring in Costa Rica. *Proc. Soc. exp. Biol. (N.Y.)*, **142** : 276–282 (1973).

54. MELNICK, J. L. et al. Coxsackie viruses from sewage : Methodology including an evaluation of the grab sample and gauze pad collection procedures. *Amer. J. Hyg.*, **59** : 185–195 (1954).

55. MELNICK, J. L. & WENNER, H. A. Enteroviruses. *In :* Lennette, E. H. & Schmidt, N. J., ed. Diagnostic procedures for viral and rickettsial infections, 4th ed., New York, American Public Health Association Inc., 1969, pp. 529-602.

56. METCALF, T. G., SLANETZ, L. W. & BARTLEY, H. Enteric pathogens in estuary waters and shellfish. *In :* Chichester, C. O. & Graham, H. D., ed. Microbiological safety of fishery products, New York, Academic Press, 1973, pp. 215–233.

57. METCALF, T. G., WALLIS, C. & MELNICK, J. L. Concentration of viruses from seawater. *In :* Advances in water pollution research (Proceedings of the 6th International Conference on Water Pollution Research, Jerusalem, June 18–23, 1972). Oxford, Pergamon Press, 1973, pp. 109–115.

58. METCALF, T., WALLIS, C. & MELNICK, J. L. Environmental factors influencing isolation of enteroviruses from polluted surface waters. *Appl. Microbiol.*, **27** : 920–926 (1974).

59. METCALF, T., WALLIS, C. & MELNICK, J. L. Virus enumeration and public health assessments in polluted surface water contributing to transmission of virus in nature. *In :* Malina, J. F., jr & Sagik, B. P., ed. Virus survival in water and wastewater systems, Water Resources Symposium Number Seven. Austin, Center for Research in Water Resources, University of Texas, 1974.

60. MIX, T. The physical chemistry of membrane interaction. *Develop. industr. Microbiol.*, **15** : 136–142 (1974).

61. MOORE, M. L., LUDOVICI, P. P. & JETER, W. S. Quantitative methods for the concentration of viruses in wastewater. *J. Water Pollut. Contr. Fed.*, **42** : R21–R28 (1970).

62. NUPEN, E. M. Virus studies on the Windhoek wastewater reclamation plant (South-West Afrika). *Water Res.*, **4** : 661–672 (1970).

63. NUPEN, E. M. & STANDER, G. J. The virus problem in the Windhoek wastewater reclamation plant. Paper presented at the 6th International Conference on Water Pollution Research, Jerusalem, 1972.

64. PHILIPSON, L., ALBERTSSON, P.-Å. & FRICK, G. The purification and concentration of viruses by aqueous polymer phase systems. *Virology*, **11** : 553–561 (1960).

65. POYNTER, S. F. B., JONES, H. H. & SLADE, J. S. Virus concentration by means of soluble ultrafilters. *In :* Board, R. G. & Lovelock, D. W., ed. Some methods for microbiological assay, London, Academic Press, 1975, pp. 65–74 (Society for Applied Bacteriology, Technical Series No. 8).

66. POYNTER, S. F. B., personal communication.

67. PROVOST, P. J. et al. Physical, chemical and morphologic dimensions of human hepatitis A virus strain CR 326. *Proc. Soc. exp. Biol. (N.Y.)*, **148** : 532–539 (1975).

68. RAO, N. U. & LABZOFFSKY, N. A. A simple method for the detection of low concentrations of viruses in large volumes of water by the membrane filter technique. *Canad. J. Microbiol.*, **15** : 399–403 (1969).

69. RAO, V. C. Detection of viruses in water. A report of project USA–3100. Washington, Pan American Health Organization, WHO Regional Office for the Americas, 1970.

70. RAO, V. C. et al. A simple method for concentrating and detecting viruses in wastewater. *Water Res.*, **6** : 1565–1576 (1972).

71. REED, L. J. & MÜNCH, H. A simple method of estimating fifty percent end points. *Amer. J. Hyg.*, **27** : 493–498 (1938).

72. SCHWARTZBROD, L. et al. Utilisation du système des polymères à 2 phases pour la concentration des virus dans le milieu hydrique : Modifications techniques et évaluation de la sensibilité de la méthode. *Microbia*, **1** : No. 2 (1975).

73. SCHÄFER, E. Quantitative recovery of poliovirus 2 in surface waters. *Sewage*, **112** : 109–113 (1971).

74. SHUVAL, H. J. Detection and control of enteroviruses in the water environment. *In :* Developments in water quality research. Proceedings of the Jerusalem International Conference on Water Quality and Pollution Research. Ann Arbor. Ann Arbor-Humphrey Science Publications, 1969, pp. 47–71.

75. SHUVAL, H. J. et al. Concentration of enteric viruses in water by hydroextraction and two-phase separation. *In :* Berg, G., ed. Transmission of viruses by the water route. New York, Interscience, 1967, pp. 45–55.

76. SHUVAL, H. J. et al. The phase-separation method for the concentration and detection of viruses in water. *Water Res.*, **3** : 225–240 (1969).

77. SHUVAL, H. I. & KATZENELSON, E. The detection of enteric viruses in the water environment. *In :* Mitchell, R., ed. Water pollution microbiology, New York, Wiley-Interscience, 1971.

78. SIMKOVÁ, A. & WALLNEROVÁ, Z. Isolations of coxsackieviruses from Danube river water. *Acta virol.*, **17** : 363 (1973).

79. SOBSEY, M. D. Detection methods for enteric viruses in water and wastewater. *In :* BERG, G. et al., ed. Viruses in water, Washington DC, American Public Health Association, 1976, pp. 89–127.

80. SOBSEY, M. D. et al. Concentration of enteroviruses from large volumes of water. *Appl. Microbiol.*, **26** : 529–534 (1973).

81. SOBSEY, M. D. et al. Virus removal and inactivation by physical-chemical waste treatment, *J. environm. Engng Div. Amer. Soc. Civ. Engrs*, **99** : 245–252 (1973).

82. SOBSEY, M. D., WALLIS, C. & MELNICK, J. L. Development of a simple method for concentrating enteroviruses from oysters. *Appl. Microbiol.*, **29** : 21–26 (1975).

83. SORBER, C. A., MALINA, J. F. jr & SAGIK, B. P. Virus rejection by the reverse osmosis-ultrafiltration processes. *Water Res.*, **6** : 1377–1388 (1972).

84. Standard Methods for the Examination of Water and Wastewater, 14th Edition, Washington, DC, American Public Health Association, 1976.

85. SWEET, B. H. & ELLENDER, R. D. Electro-osmosis : A new technique for concentrating viruses from water. *Water Res.*, **6** : 775–779 (1972).

86. SWEET, B. H., ELLENDER, R. D. & LEONG, J. K. I. Recovery and removal of viruses from water-utilizing membrane techniques. *In :* Berg, G., ed. Symposium : Detection of viruses in waste and other waters. *Develop. industr. Microbiol.*, **15** : 143–159 (1974).

87. WALLIS, C., HENDERSON, M. & MELNICK, J. L. Enterovirus concentration on cellulose membranes. *Appl. Microbiol.*, **23** : 462–480 (1972).

88. WALLIS, C., HOMMA, A. & MELNICK, J. L. A portable virus concentrator for testing water in the field. *Water Res.*, **6** : 1249–1256 (1972).

89. WALLIS, C., HOMMA, A. & MELNICK, J. L. Apparatus for concentrating viruses from large volumes. *J. Amer. Water Works Ass.*, **64** : 189–196 (1972).

90. WALLIS, C. & MELNICK, J. L. Concentration of enteroviruses on membrane filters. *J. Virol.*, **1** : 472–477 (1967).

91. WALLIS, C. & MELNICK, J. L. Concentration of viruses from sewage by adsorption on Millipore membranes. *Bull. Wld Hlth Org.*, **36** : 219–225 (1967).

92. WALLIS, C. & MELNICK, J. L. Concentration of viruses on aluminum and calcium salts. *Amer. J. Epidem.*, **85** : 449–468 (1967).

93. WELLINGS, F. M., LEWIS, A. L. & MOUNTAIN, C. W. Virus survival following wastewater spray irrigation of sandy soils. *In :* Malina, J. F. jr & SAGIK, B. P., ed. Proceedings of the Center for Research in Water Resources Symposium No. 7. Austin, University of Texas, 1974, pp. 253–260.

94. WELLINGS, F. M. et al. Demonstration of virus in groundwater after effluent discharge onto soil. *Appl. Microbiol.*, **29** : 751–757 (1975).

95. WYATT, R. G. et al. Comparison of three agents of acute infectious nonbacterial gastroenteritis. *J. infect. Dis.*, **129** : 709–714 (1974).

ANNEX 1
SPECIAL
ACKNOWLEDGEMENTS

The World Health Organization is grateful to the specialists below who collaborated in the preparation of this book. Their comments on various chapters were taken into consideration during the revision of those chapters and the finalization of the manuscript.[a]

Alabaster, Mr J. S., Retired Head, Pollution Division, Stevenage Laboratory, Water Research Centre, Stevenage, Herts, United Kingdom

Albrecht, Dr, Chief Medical Director, Public Health Laboratory, Trier, Federal Republic of Germany

Anagnostidis, Dr. K., Director and Professor, Institute of Systematic Botany, University of Athens, Athens, Greece

Barbette, Mr J., Institute of Hygiene and Epidemiology, Brussels, Belgium

Barrow, Dr G. I., Director, Environmental Hygiene Reference Laboratory, Public Health Laboratory Service, Centre for Microbiology and Research, Porton Down, Wilts, United Kingdom

Benson-Evans, Dr Kathryn, Senior Lecturer, Botany Department, University College, Cardiff, United Kingdom

Berg, Dr G., Chief, Biological Methods Branch, Environmental Monitoring and Support Laboratory, US Environmental Protection Agency, Cincinnati, OH, USA

Bernatova, Dr V., Centre of General and Environmental Hygiene, Institute of Hygiene and Epidemiology, Prague, Czechoslovakia

Besch, Mr W. K., Institute of Water and Water Management, State Office of Environmental Protection, Baden-Württemberg, Karlsruhe, Federal Republic of Germany

Bonde, Dr G. J., Professor, Institute of Hygiene, University of Aarhus, Aarhus, Denmark

Bonini, Mr A., Health Protection Directorate, Commission of the European Communities (CEC), Luxembourg, Luxembourg

Borneff, Dr J., Professor and Director, Institute of Hygiene, University of Mainz, Mainz, Federal Republic of Germany

Borowski, Dr J., Professor and Director, Department of Microbiology, Institute of Biostructure, Bialystok, Poland

[a]The specialists listed here, unless also chapter authors and/or participants in one or more working groups (see Annex 2), are reviewers by correspondence of one or more draft chapters.

An effort has been made to update the professional titles and positions held by the specialists listed in this Annex in order to reflect the situation valid in 1980 and 1981 during the compilation of this acknowledgement list and its submission to the printer.

510

Breitig, Dr G., Institute of Water Economy, Berlin, German Democratic Republic

Brisou, Dr J., Professor, Ch. Nicolle Laboratory, University Hospital Centre, Poitiers, France

Cabridenc, Mr R., National Institute for Research in Applied Chemistry (IRCHA), Vert-le-Petit, France

Clarke, Dr N. A., Laboratory Studies Division, Health Effects Research Laboratory, National Environmental Research Center, US Environmental Protection Agency, Cincinnati, OH, USA

Cliver, Dr D. O., Associate Professor, Food Research Institute, University of Wisconsin, Madison, WI, USA

Coin, Dr L., Chairman, Department of Waterworks and Sanitation, French Council of Public Hygiene, Charenton-le-Pont, France

Cook, Mr D. G., Canada Centre for Inland Waters, Burlington, ON, Canada

Cross, Dr T., University of Bradford, Yorks, United Kingdom

Čuta, Dr J., Institute of Hygiene, Prague, Czechoslovakia

Daubner, Dr I., Chief, Limnology Section, Institute of Experimental Biology and Ecology, Bratislava, Czechoslovakia

Davoli, Dr R., Professor and Director, Institute of Microbiology, University of Florence, Florence, Italy

Deàk, Dr Susanne, Chief, Department of Water Hygiene, State Institute of Hygiene, Budapest, Hungary

Dehavay, Mr P., Ecologist, Institute of Hygiene and Epidemiology, Brussels, Belgium

Djukič, Mr M., Water and Wastewater Engineering and Water Pollution Research Department, Jaroslav Černi Institute for Development of Water Resources, Belgrade, Yugoslavia

Dumont, Dr H. J., Laboratory of Morphology and Taxonomy, Museum of Zoology, State University, Gent, Belgium

Dussart, Mr B., Senior Research Officer, Biological Station, National Centre for Scientific Research, University of Paris, Les Eyzies, France

Dutka, Mr B. J., Head, Microbiology Laboratories, Scientific Operations Division, Canada Centre for Inland Waters, Burlington, ON, Canada

Eichenberger, Mr E., Biological Department, Swiss Federal Institute of Water Resources and Water Pollution Control (EAWAG), Dübendorf, Switzerland

Ekedahl, Dr G., Head, Analytical Laboratory, National Swedish Environment Protection Board, Solna, Sweden

Engelbrecht, Dr R. S., Professor, Environmental Engineering, University of Illinois, Urbana, IL, USA

England, Mrs B., Virologist, Department of Public Health, County of San Diego, CA, USA

Evison, Mrs L. M., Lecturer in Public Health Engineering, Department of Civil Engineering, University of Newcastle upon Tyne, Newcastle, United Kingdom

Felföldy, Dr L. J. M., Senior Advisor on Biology, Research Institute of Water Resources Development (VITUKI), Budapest, Hungary

Ferreira, Dr P. S., Chief Laboratory, Institute of Marine Biology, Faro, Portugal

Festy, Mr B., Laboratory of Hygiene, City of Paris, Paris, France

Finichiu, Dr M., Institute of Hygiene, Iasi, Romania

Fjerdingstad, Mr E., Retired Head, Water Laboratory, Institute of Hygiene, University of Copenhagen, Copenhagen, Denmark

Foliguet, Dr J. M., Professor and Director, Hygiene Laboratory and Research of Public Health, University of Nancy 1, Nancy, France

Foschini, Mrs V., Administrator, Commission of the European Communities (CEC), Brussels, Belgium

Fry, Dr F. E. J., Professor Emeritus, Department of Zoology, University of Toronto, Toronto, ON, Canada

Gärtner, Dr G., Hygiene Institute, University of Kiel, Federal Republic of Germany

Geldreich, Mr E. E., Chief, Microbiological Treatment Branch, Water Supply Research Division, National Environmental Research Center, US Environmental Protection Agency, Cincinnati, OH, USA

Gerletti, Dr M., Professor, Department for Applied Hydrobiology, Water Research Institute, National Research Council, Milan, Italy

512 *Annex 1. Special Acknowledgements*

Glooschenko, Mr W. A., Applied Limnology and Physical Processes Section, Canada Centre for Inland Waters, Burlington, ON, Canada

Golowin, Dr S., Biologist, Institute of Meteorology and Water Economy, Wroclaw, Poland

Grabow, Dr W. O. K., National Institute for Water Research, Council for Scientific and Industrial Research, Pretoria, South Africa

Graham, Mr C. R., Hydrobiologist, Water Directorate, Department of the Environment, London, United Kingdom

Greenberg, Mr A., Chief, Bioenvironmental Laboratories Section, California Department of Health, Berkeley, CA, USA

Grunnet, Dr K., Institute of Hygiene, University of Aarhus, Denmark

Hasselrot, Dr T. B., Research Laboratory, The National Swedish Environment Protection Board, Solna, Sweden

Häusler, Dr J., Water Research Institute, Prague, Czechoslovakia

Hawkes, Mr H. A., Reader, Applied Hydrobiology Section, Department of Biological Sciences, University of Aston, Birmingham, United Kingdom

Henau, Mr H. de, Head, Environmental Research Laboratory, Procter and Gamble ETC (European Technical Centre), Strombeck-Bever, Belgium

Hill, Dr W. F., Senior Research Virologist, Health Effects Research Laboratory, US Environmental Protection Agency, Cincinnati, OH, USA

Hooren, Mr G. van, Hydrobiologist, Institute of Hygiene and Epidemiology, Brussels, Belgium

Husmann, Dr, Chief Medical Director, Public Health Laboratory, Koblenz, Federal Republic of Germany

Hutchinson, Mr M., Medmenham Laboratory, Water Research Centre, Medmenham, Bucks, United Kingdom

Jakubowski, Dr W., Virologist, Water Supply Research Division, National Environmental Research Center, US Environmental Protection Agency, Cincinnati, OH, USA

Jebb, Dr W. H. H., Retired Director, Public Health Laboratory, Oxford, (deceased), Anglesey, United Kingdom

Kampelmacher, Dr E. H., Professor and Director, National Institute of Public Health, Bilthoven, Netherlands

Katzenelson, Dr E., Public Health Laboratories (Abu Kabir), Ministry of Health, Tel-Aviv, Israel

Kečkeš, Dr S., Consultant, Environmental Pollution, Environmental Health Division, World Health Organization (WHO), Geneva, Switzerland

Kisselinov, Dr C., Hygienic-Epidemiological Inspectorate, Russe, Bulgaria

Kohonen, Dr T., Microbiologist, Water Research Institute, National Board of Waters, Helsinki, Finland

Kool, Mr H. J., Head, Laboratory of Microbiology, Chemical-Biological Division, National Institute of Drinking-Water Supply, Voorburg, Netherlands

Koppe, Dr P., Chief, Chemistry and Biology Laboratory, Ruhrverband, Essen, Federal Republic of Germany

Kovachev, Mr S., Zoological Institute, Bulgarian Academy of Sciences, Sofia, Bulgaria

Krech, Dr U., Professor of Microbiology, Institute of Medical Microbiology of the Canton St Gallen, St Gallen, Switzerland

Kristensen, Mr K. K., Lecturer, Veterinary Faculty for FAO Fellows and Scholars, Copenhagen, Denmark

Krogh, Mr O., Deputy Director, Danish Institute for Water Quality, Hørsholm, Denmark

Kumpf, Mr J., Retired Chief, Environmental Health, World Health Organization Regional Office for Europe, Copenhagen, Denmark

Lafontaine, Dr A., Professor and Director, Institute of Hygiene and Epidemiology, Brussels, Belgium

Landner, Dr L., Head, Section on Biological Effects, Swedish Institute for Water and Air Pollution Research (IVL), Stockholm, Sweden

Lane, Mr D. J., Chief Chemist, Engineering and Water Supply Department, State Water Laboratories, Salisbury, SA, Australia

Leentvaar, Mr P., Head, Department of Hydrobiology, Institute of Nature Conservation, State Forestry Conservation, Ministry of Agriculture and Fisheries, Leersum, Netherlands

Leynaud, Dr G., Chief, Division of Water Quality, Fishing and Fish Breeding, and Chief Engineer, Technical Centre of Rural Water Engineering and Forests, Ministry of Agriculture and Rural Development, Paris, France

Liperovskaja, Mrs E. S., Water and Sewerage Operations Board, Moscow, USSR

Lund, Dr Ebba, Professor and Head, Department of Veterinary Virology and Immunology, Royal Veterinary and Agricultural University, Copenhagen, Denmark

Maděra, Dr V., Professor and Retired Director, Department of Water Technology, Institute of Chemical Technology, Prague, Czechoslovakia

Mancy, Dr K. H., Professor, Department of Environmental and Industrial Health, School of Public Health, University of Michigan, Ann Arbor, MI, USA

Margalef, Dr R. M., Professor, Department of Ecology, Institute of Applied Biology, University of Barcelona, Barcelona, Spain

Mark, Dr H. van der, Head, Hydrobiological Laboratory, National Institute of Sewage Purification, Ladystad, Netherlands

Mašinova, Dr L., Centre of General and Environmental Hygiene, Institute of Hygiene and Epidemiology, Prague, Czechoslovakia

Matoničkin, Dr I., Professor, Zoological Department, University of Zagreb, Zagreb, Yugoslavia

Mazzetti, Dr G., Professor and Dean, University of Florence Medical School, Florence, Italy

Megay, Dr K. Director, Federal Research Institute for Bacteriological Serology, Linz, Austria

Melnick, Dr J. L., Collaborating Center for Virus Reference and Research, Department of Virology and Epidemiology, Baylor College of Medicine, Houston, TX, USA

Metcalf, Dr T. G., Chairman and Professor, Department of Microbiology, University of New Hampshire, Durham, NH, USA

Mitrovic-Tutundzic, Dr Vera, Assistant Professor of Biology, Jaroslav Černi Institute for Development of Water Resources, Belgrade, Yugoslavia

Montgomery, Dr H. A. C., Manager, Data and Research, Southern Water, Worthing, Sussex, United Kingdom

Müller, Mr D., Federal Centre of Water Resources, Koblenz, Federal Republic of Germany

Müller, Dr Gertrud, Professor and Director, Water Bacteriology Laboratory, Institute of Water, Soil and Air Hygiene, Federal Health Office, Berlin (West) (deceased).

Netter, Dr R., Acting Director-General, Ministry of Health and Social Security, Paris, France

Nöthlich, Dr I., Biologist, Federal Centre of Water Resources, Koblenz, Federal Republic of Germany

Nunes, Dr M. C., Institute of Marine Biology, Lisbon, Portugal

Nupen, Mrs E. M., Virologist, National Institute for Water Research, South African Council for Industrial and Scientific Research, Pretoria, South Africa

Nusch, Dr E. A., Hydrobiologist, Ruhrverband, Essen, Federal Republic of Germany

Omland, Dr T., Norwegian Defence Microbiological Laboratory, National Institute of Public Health, Oslo, Norway

Ormerod, Mrs K., Head, Biological Laboratory Section, Norwegian Institute of Water Research, Oslo, Norway

Pattée, Mr E., Professor of Animal Biology, Claude Bernard University, Villeurbanne, France

Persoone, Dr G., Professor, Laboratory for Biological Research of Environmental Pollution, State University, Gent, Belgium

Pétursson, Dr S., Department of Bacteriology, Icelandic Fisheries Laboratories, Reykjavik, Iceland

Pike, Dr E., Stevenage Laboratory, Water Research Centre, Stevenage, Herts, United Kingdom

Pittwell, Mr L. R., Secretary, Standing Committee of Analysts, Department of the Environment, London, United Kingdom

Pokorny, Dr J., Centre of General and Environmental Hygiene, Institute of Hygiene and Epidemiology, Prague, Czechoslovakia

Poynter, Dr S. F. B., Retired Chief Microbiologist, Scientific Services Department, New River Head Laboratories, Thames Water, London; at present, Berkhamsted, Herts, United Kingdom

Praszkiewicz, Dr A., Institute for Meteorology and Water Economy, Warsaw, Poland

Price, Mr D. R. H., Chief Quality Officer, Anglian Water Authority, Huntingdon, Cambs, United Kingdom

Rao, Dr N. U., Deputy Director and Head, Microbiology Division, Central Public Health Engineering Research Institute, Nagpur, India

Rogovskaya, Dr C. I., Senior Scientific Worker, All-Union Scientific Research Institute of Water Supply, Canalization, Hydrotechnical Construction and Engineering Hydrogeology (VODGEO), Moscow, USSR

Rosén, Mr G., Research Laboratory, The National Swedish Environment Protection Board, Solna, Sweden

Russev, Dr B., Zoological Institute, Bulgarian Academy of Sciences, Sofia, Bulgaria

Schaeffer, Dr C. O., Retired Ministry of Public Health and Environmental Hygiene, Leidschendam, Netherlands

Schäfer, Dr E., Department of Virology, Ernst-Rodenwaldt Institute, Koblenz, Federal Republic of Germany

Schmitz, Dr W., Director, Department of Water Quality, State Centre for Water Resources, Karlsruhe, Federal Republic of Germany

Schubert, Dr R., Chief, Department of General and Environmental Hygiene, Centre of Hygiene, Frankfurt/M, Federal Republic of Germany

Seeliger, Dr H. P. R., Institute of Hygiene and Microbiology, Würzburg, Federal Republic of Germany

Signorini, Dr G. F., Professor and Director, Institute of Hygiene, University of Florence, Florence, Italy

Šimkovà, Dr Adriena, Senior Research Worker and Head, Enterovirus Laboratory, Research Institute of Epidemiology and Microbiology, Bratislava, Czechoslovakia

Simonsgaard, Mrs V., Retired Chief Engineer, Danish Standards Association, Hellerup, Denmark

Sladeček, Dr V., Associate Professor of Hydrobiology, Department of Water and Environmental Technology, Institute of Chemical Technology, Prague, Czechoslovakia

Sobsey, Dr M. D., Assistant Professor of Environmental Microbiology, Department of Environmental Sciences and Engineering, School of Public Health, University of North Carolina, Chapel Hill, NC, USA

Solbé, Mr J. F. de L. G., Manager, Fish, Toxicity and Biodegradability, Environmental Protection, Stevenage Laboratory, Water Research Centre, Stevenage, Herts, United Kingdom

Sparell, Dr L., Retired Project Manager, Microbiology, Swedish Institute for Water and Air Pollution Research (IVL), Stockholm, Sweden

Steel, Mr J. A. P., Chief Biologist, Reservoir Laboratory, Thames Water, West Molesey, Surrey, United Kingdom

Straub, Dr C. P., Professor and Director, Environmental Health, School of Public Health, University of Minnesota, Minneapolis, MN, USA

Stroganov, Dr N. S., Professor, Chair of Hydrobiology, Faculty of Soil Biology, Moscow State University, Moscow, USSR

Symon, Dr K., Professor and Head, Chair of General and Environmental Hygiene, Medical Faculty of Hygiene, Prague, Czechoslovakia

Szebellédy, Dr Joza, Retired Consultant, Institute of Water Pollution Control, Research Centre of Water Resources Development (VITUKI), Budapest, Hungary (deceased)

Tamplin, Dr B. R., Bioenvironmental Laboratories Section, California Department of Health, Berkeley, CA, USA

Taylor, Dr E. W., Retired Director of Water Examination, Metropolitan Water Board; at present private consultant, London, United Kingdom

Tullander, Dr V., Head, Bacteriological Laboratory, Research Laboratory, The National Swedish Environment Protection Board, Solna, Sweden

Tümpling, Dr W. von, Institute of Water Economy, Erfurt, German Democratic Republic

Uhlmann, Dr D., Professor and Head, Chair of Hydrobiology, Water Section, Technical University, Dresden, German Democratic Republic

Vaccarezza, Mr J., Principal Administrator, Department of the Environment and Consumers' Protection, Commission of the European Communities (CEC), Brussels, Belgium

Vial, Dr J., Assistant Director and Chief, Environmental Health Laboratory, Pasteur Institute, Lyons, France

Vinberg, Dr G. G., Head, Laboratory of Fresh Water and Experimental Hydrobiology, Zoological Institute of the Academy of Sciences of the USSR, Leningrad, USSR

Vollenweider, Dr R. A., Senior Scientist, National Water Research Institute, Canada Centre for Inland Waters, Burlington, ON, Canada

Wahba, Dr A. H. W., Regional Officer for Appropriate Technology for Health, World Health Organization Regional Office for Europe, Copenhagen, Denmark

Wallnerova, Dr Zleta, Department of Virology, Research Institute of Epidemiology and Microbiology, Bratislava, Czechoslovakia

Weber, Dr C., Chief, Aquatic Biology Methods Research, Environmental Monitoring and Support Laboratory, US Environmental Protection Agency, Cincinnati, OH, USA

Williams, Mr P. F., Research Fellow, Botany Department, University College, Cardiff, United Kingdom

Woodiwiss, Mr P., Chief Biologist, Nottingham Region Laboratory, Severn-Trent Water Authority, Nottingham, United Kingdom

Zon, Dr J. C. J. van, Senior Scientist, Institute of Biological and Chemical Research on Field Crops and Herbage, Wageningen, Netherlands

ANNEX 2
LIST OF WORKING GROUPS

WORKING GROUP ON ANALYTICAL METHODS IN WATER POLLUTION
CONTROL, COPENHAGEN, 7–10 NOVEMBER 1972

Temporary Advisers

Dr J. Čuta
Dr G. Ekedahl
Mr E. Fjerdingstad
Mr H. A. Hawkes
Dr P. Koppe
Dr Ebba Lund (Chairman)
Dr V. Maděra
Dr K. H. Mancy (Rapporteur)
Dr H. A. C. Montgomery (Vice-Chairman)
Mrs K. Ormerod
Dr V. Sladeček
Dr Jozsa Szebellédy
Dr J. Vial

Representatives of Other Organizations

International Organization for Standardization (ISO)
    Mrs V. Simonsgaard
International Association on Water Pollution Research (IAWPR)
    Mr O. Krogh

World Health Organization Secretariat

Dr S. Kečkeš
Mr J. Kumpf
Dr M. J. Suess (Secretary)
Dr A. H. W. Wahba

WORKING GROUP ON BACTERIOLOGICAL AND VIROLOGICAL EXAMINATION
OF WATER, MAINZ, 21–25 APRIL 1975

Temporary Advisers

Dr Albrecht
Dr G. I. Barrow
Dr G. Berg
Dr G. J. Bonde

Dr J. Borneff
Dr J. Borowski
Dr L. Coin
Dr Susanne Deàk
Mr B. J. Dutka
Dr J. M. Foliguet
Mr E. E. Geldreich (Co-Rapporteur)
Mr A. Greenberg (Rapporteur)
Dr Husmann
Dr E. Katzenelson
Mr K. K. Kristensen
Dr A. Lafontaine (Chairman)
Dr Ebba Lund
Dr Gertrud Müller
Mrs E. M. Nupen (Co-Rapporteur)
Mrs K. Ormerod
Dr S. F. B. Poynter
Dr C. O. Schaeffer
Dr E. Schäfer (Vice-Chairman)
Dr R. Schubert
Dr Adriena Šimkovà
Dr M. D. Sobsey
Dr K. Symon (Vice-Chairman)
Dr V. Tullander
Dr J. Vial

Representatives of Other Organizations

Commission of the European Communities (CEC)
  Mr A. Bonini
  Mrs V. Foschini
International Organization for Standardization (ISO)
  Dr J. Vial
International Association of Microbiological Societies (IAMS)
  Dr H. P. R. Seeliger
International Association on Water Pollution Research (IAWPR)
  Dr Ebba Lund

World Health Organization Secretariat

Dr M. J. Suess (Secretary)
Dr A. H. W. Wahba

WORKING GROUP ON BIOLOGICAL EXAMINATION AND EURTROPHICATION,
BRUSSELS, 17–20 JUNE 1975

Temporary Advisers

Mr J. S. Alabaster
Mr J. Barbette
Mr R. Cabridenc
Dr I. Daubner

Mr P. Dehavay
Mr E. Fjerdingstad
Dr M. Gerletti
Dr S. Golowin
Mr H. A. Hawkes
Mr G. van Hooren
Dr L. Landner
Dr H. van der Mark
Dr I. Nöthlich
Dr E. A. Nusch
Mr E. Pattée
Dr G. Persoone (Vice-Chairman)
Dr W. Schmitz
Dr V. Sladeček
Mr J. A. P. Steel (Rapporteur)
Dr D. Uhlmann (Chairman)
Dr R. A. Vollenweider
Dr C. Weber
Dr J. C. J. van Zon

Representatives of Other Organizations

Commission of the European Communities (CEC)
    Mrs V. Foschini
    Mr J. Vaccarezza
International Organization for Standardization (ISO)
    Mr R. Cabridenc
European Council of Chemical Manufacturers' Federations (ECCMF)
    Mr H. de Henau

World Health Organization Secretariat

Dr M. J. Suess (Secretary)

INDEX